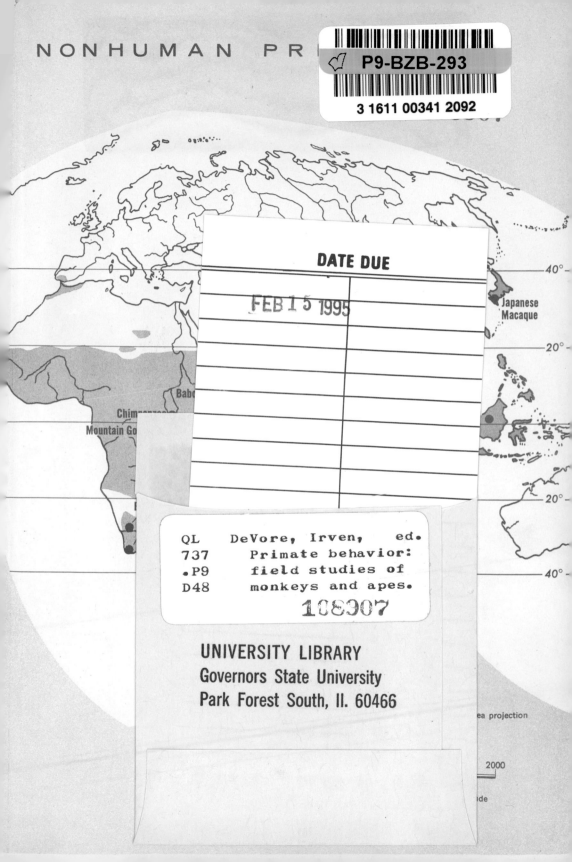

NONHUMAN PR

P9-BZB-293

3 1611 00341 2092

DATE DUE

FEB 1 5 1995

Japanese
Macaque

40°

20°

20°

40°

ea projection

2000

# Primate Behavior
## FIELD STUDIES OF MONKEYS AND APES

# CONTRIBUTORS

JARVIS R. BASTIAN
   University of California, Davis
MIRZA AZHAR BEG
   Aligarh Muslim University, India
CLARENCE RAY CARPENTER
   University of North Carolina
IRVEN DeVORE
   Harvard University
JANE GOODALL
   Cambridge University
K. R. L. HALL
   University of Bristol
DAVID A. HAMBURG
   Stanford University
PHYLLIS JAY
   University of California, Davis
CARL B. KOFORD
   National Institute of Neurological
   Diseases and Blindness
JANE B. LANCASTER
   University of California, Berkeley
RICHARD B. LEE
   University of California, Berkeley
PETER MARLER
   University of California, Berkeley
WILLIAM A. MASON
   Delta Regional Primate Center,
   Covington, Louisiana
JEAN JACQUES PETTER
   Muséum Nationale d'Histoire
   Naturelle, Paris
VERNON and FRANCES REYNOLDS
   London, England
GEORGE B. SCHALLER
   The Johns Hopkins University
M. RAFIQ SIDDIQI
   Aligarh Muslim University, India
PAUL E. SIMONDS
   University of Oregon
CHARLES H. SOUTHWICK
   The Johns Hopkins University
SHERWOOD L. WASHBURN
   University of California, Berkeley

# ◆ Primate Behavior

## FIELD STUDIES OF MONKEYS AND APES

Edited by IRVEN DeVORE

*Harvard University*

HOLT, RINEHART AND WINSTON

*New York · Chicago · San Francisco · Toronto · London*

To Clarence Ray Carpenter

# Preface

Man's acquaintance with the monkeys and apes is as ancient as man himself. In the Orient and the Near East monkeys were included among the gods to be worshipped. Tribes living in the same forests as the great apes claim kinship to them, accommodating the apes in their cosmologies as special forms of human beings. In early Pleistocene Africa, a million-and-a-half or more years ago, protoman must have competed with the other primates for his very existence. The interest of Europeans, and Western science, is far more recent. Aristotle, and more particularly Galenus, dissected monkeys and remarked upon the close correspondence of monkey and human internal organs. But it was not until the middle of the nineteenth century, in the early days of modern anatomy and the development of evolutionary theory, that such spokesmen as Huxley and Darwin firmly confronted the Western world with the extraordinary pertinence of the apes for understanding man's own biological history.

Anatomical knowledge of the monkeys and apes has accumulated at a steady rate during the last century, and most people would assume that knowledge of their behavior in the wild has increased at the same pace. However, this has not been true. Brief attempts were made to study the African apes, for example, as early as 1856; but, except for incidental observations by explorers and naturalists, virtually nothing systematic was known about the natural behavior of a single monkey or ape until Clarence Ray Carpenter began his study of the howler monkeys of Panama in 1931. And, except for Carpenter's pioneering studies of the howler, gibbon, and rhesus, and those of Bingham on the gorilla and of Nissen on the chimpanzee, the entire subject of primate field studies lay dormant for nearly twenty years. Although a number of excellent brief field studies were made in the intervening years, the modern period of primate studies, with its emphasis on long-term, careful observation, did not begin until the middle 1950s, when the Japan Monkey Center was established at Kyoto University and when Stuart A. Altmann undertook a two-year restudy of the rhesus monkey colony on Cayo Santiago.

In less than a decade field studies of nonhuman primates have multiplied at an almost unbelievable rate, and today there are well over 50 individuals from at least nine countries engaged in such studies. Equally remarkable has been the multidisciplinary background of the field investigators, including people with training as different as physical and social anthropology, experimental and comparative psychology, and zoology.

This book is one result of a nine-month "Primate Project" held at the Center for Advanced Study in the Behavioral Sciences, Stanford, California, during 1962–1963. Organized by Sherwood L. Washburn and David A. Hamburg, and supported by a grant (No. M–5502) from the National Institutes of Health, the Center study group sought to bring together people of diverse backgrounds whose common interest was the study of free-ranging primates. Those who held Center fellowships throughout the period were: Irven DeVore, K. R. L. Hall, Phyllis Jay, Hiroki Mizuhara, Vernon Reynolds, and George B. Schaller. They, together with Hamburg, Frances Reynolds, and Washburn, constituted the continuing study group.

In order to involve a wider circle of investigators in the planning of the Primate Project, a conference was held at the Center from September 5 to 12, 1962. The purpose of this conference was to evaluate the present position and future possibilities of primate field studies, to discuss the relationship between field and laboratory studies, to explore the implications of primate behavior data for problems in psychology and psychiatry, and to plan the contents of the present volume. In addition to the Center study group, this conference was attended by:

| | |
|---|---|
| Stuart A. Altmann | Jane B. Lancaster |
| Jarvis R. Bastian | Richard B. Lee |
| Frank A. Beach | William A. Mason |
| John B. Calhoun* | Benjamin D. Paul* |
| Clarence Ray Carpenter | Arthur J. Riopelle |
| Preston Cutler | Carl Rogers* |
| John D. Ellefson | Donald S. Sade |
| Harry F. Harlow | Paul E. Simonds |
| John Kaufmann | Charles H. Southwick |

Contributors to the volume who were able to join the study group for short periods during the year included Bastian, Carpenter, Marler, Mason, and Southwick. The group was also able to take advantage of the comments and criticism of visitors to the Center, such as Adriaan Kortlandt and John Paul Scott. Finally, most of the authors met together again at the Center for a working conference in May 1963 to discuss the results of the study group and the progress and final organization of the present volume.

---

* Other Fellows at the Center

The purpose of the Center Primate Project was to bring together a group of people who had just completed long-term field studies of monkeys and apes, and by providing them with sufficient opportunities for discussion over many months, to arrive at mutual understandings concerning the description and interpretation of primate behavior. This was felt to be especially necessary in a field that had grown out of not one but a wide variety of scientific disciplines, each with its own emphasis and conceptual framework. The chapters of this volume became the focus of these group discussions. As each draft appeared, copies were circulated among the members of the Center group and other scientists participating in the project, and revised drafts were prepared from the resulting comments and criticism. The group was determined that this volume should not be a collection of symposium papers, tenuously held together by a broad theme, but a volume that would systematically survey the results of recent field studies and present its conclusions in a uniform manner.

Ideally, each of the chapters that describes a field study of a single species would follow the same format, presenting the data gathered on ecology and behavior in an outline which remained the same throughout all the chapters. Wherever possible this has been done, but the different studies had not been originally undertaken with the same goals in mind, nor were opportunities in the field the same for any two investigators, and each chapter necessarily reflects these diverse goals and opportunities. But the study group was able to agree upon broad objectives and was able to insure that concepts and terminology were used uniformly throughout the book. For example, the Center personnel repeatedly discussed the problems of comparing the social organization of different primate species. A number of the discussants felt that enough was now known about the social organization of a variety of monkeys and apes to justify the clearly defined use of the word "troop" to designate a particular kind of group organization. A "troop" so defined consists of a discrete group of adults of both sexes, together with juveniles and infants, that maintains social identity and spatial unity over long periods. Such a troop is an easily recognizable unit with relatively impermeable social boundaries, although young males or groups of young males may live outside the troop. This definition of a "troop" would well describe the basic social unit of almost all of the monkey species studied so far—the olive, yellow, and chacma baboon; the rhesus, Japanese and bonnet macaque; langurs; colobus monkeys; and howler monkeys. With little qualification it would also describe the social organization of the gorilla (some gorilla groups have a rather high turnover in membership), but it is clearly not a description of chimpanzee social organization, nor does it apply, apparently, to gibbons, orangutans, or hamadryas baboons. In the interests of objective terminology and because we were aware that the social organization of very few primate species has been studied, the members of the project decided to call all social units in the book simply "group." It was through such discussions that the Center participants were able to agree on the implications of common terms and to use these terms in a consistent manner throughout the book.

Courses and seminars on the social behavior and ecology of the primates are now being taught in a number of universities, and one purpose of this book is to provide a text for use in such courses. But primate behavior data are relevant to a wide variety of subjects in the social and biological sciences, and this book was also planned with this wider audience in mind; it assumes no prior technical knowledge in science. The contents of this book do not represent a single point of view, but what the authors hope are a distillation of many points of view brought to bear on a common subject.

I.D.

Cambridge, Mass.
January 1965

# Acknowledgments

The support of the National Institutes of Health, whose grant made the Primate Project possible, is gratefully acknowledged, as is the support of the executive staff of the Center for Advanced Study in the Behavioral Sciences — Ralph Tyler, Preston Cutler, and Jane Kielsmeier, who were our gracious hosts during the Center year.

This book is the result of the cooperation of many persons, over many months, who gave so unstintingly of their time to the preparation of the manuscript that the editor's role became incidental. Prominent among these are Anne Brower, who piloted all of the drafts through the difficult shoals of English grammar and scientific obscurantism; Jean Savage, who was in charge of typing and proofreading; and Richard Lee, who served as research assistant to the project.

Frances Reynolds began and Jane Lancaster completed the bibliography, and Jane Lancaster and Nancy DeVore helped collate illustrations and text. Suzanne A. Chevalier edited the translation of Chapter 9 from the French, augmenting it with selections from Petter's earlier publications. Hildegarde Teilhet and Alice Davis aided in typing the manuscripts, Miriam Gallaher proofread them, and Chris Dodds was in charge of duplicating them. In their capacities as Center librarians Betty Callaway and Claire Christman located source materials for the authors. The figures were prepared at the Medical Illustration Department of Stanford University by Margaret L. Muller and Louise Follett, except for Figs. 3–10 and 15–5, and the drawings in Chapter 16 which were done by Derry Bogert. Contributors of photographs other than those taken by the authors are acknowledged in the accompanying captions. Nancy DeVore prepared the index.

It is a pleasure to acknowledge the enthusiastic aid of all these, as well as those who saw the book through the final production process at Holt, Rinehart and Winston.

I.D.

# Contents

SHERWOOD L. WASHBURN
and DAVID A. HAMBURG

1

◆ The Study of Primate Behavior

Animal behavior may be investigated in the laboratory, in artificial colonies, or under natural conditions. The kinds of knowledge gained from these different approaches supplement each other, and all are necessary if the complex roots of behavior are to be understood.

The study of the clinging reflex offers an example of this interrelationship of approaches. Harlow has shown that a baby monkey will cling to a piece of cloth; if the monkey is placed on a smooth surface it will attempt to stand, but if the cloth touches the monkey it will cling instead of trying to stand. The clinging reflex thus takes precedence over the righting reflex. This isolated fact has little meaning in the laboratory, but when free-ranging monkeys are observed the infants are seen to cling to their mothers when the group moves. In all the kinds of monkeys studied so far the clinging reflex is present at birth, and the infant monkey's survival depends on this ability to cling while its mother feeds, walks, and runs. The existence of the reflex and the infant's response to various textures can be investigated only in the laboratory, but the adaptive significance of the behavior can be appreciated only in the field. Mammals have adapted to meet the problem of the care of the newborn in many different ways: by the construction of nests, burrows, and lairs in which the young may stay; by rapid maturation so the young may keep up; by births taking place in protected locations. Most primates have adapted by the ability of the young to cling.

This behavior adaptation, reflex clinging, is essential for the survival of the species, and it must be observed to be appreciated. A newborn gibbon does not cling to a calm and sitting mother, but to one which feeds at the ends of branches that are swaying in the wind. Far above the ground, the mother may suddenly run along a branch, drop below it, taking a few violent swings, and then plunge out into the air, dropping many feet to a lower branch in a neighboring tree, landing on swaying branches or with more swings. The infant clings through these violent acrobatics, and in the flight

1

of gibbons through giant trees the infant-mother problem is shown to be very different from the way it appears in a small cage. The strength of the clinging is essential to survival, for the mother cannot be inactive and live. The mother's hands and feet are completely involved in locomotion, and in her swings and leaps she cannot help the infant and survive herself.

The behavior of mother and infant gibbon is an adaptation to the arboreal way of life. It depends on the behavior of both mother and infant, on the grasping hands and feet of the infant, on reflexes, and, probably, on behavior the adult female has learned. Monkeys brought up in isolation do not know how to take care of their infants (Harlow 1962; Mason, Chap. 15, this volume). Here again the interrelation of the field and the laboratory are shown. The field study shows the nature and importance of the infant's and the mother's behavior, but which parts of the behavior are reflex and which learned cannot be told from the field work any more than the actual problems and hazards of the relation of mother and infant can be seen in the laboratory.

The natural situation may be further complicated because the mother may be helped by other members of the group. For example, a mother baboon was seen with a newborn infant, probably only a few hours old. The infant still could not cling adequately, and its mother repeatedly helped it with one hand. The three-legged walking was difficult for the mother and she lagged behind the main body of the group of baboons and sat down every few yards. Right beside her walked an adult male. When she sat, he sat; when she started up, he started up. His actions were timed to hers, and she was never left without protection during this awkward period.

Mothers with young are centers of interest for other females, adult males, and juvenile females. It is not just the mother-infant relation that is important; this essential diadic relation is imbedded in a matrix of social interaction. The infant monkey is born into an intensely social group, and the survival of the infant depends on the adaptation and survival of the whole group. The size and composition of this group depend on the species of primate. Its patterned behavior differs depending on the structure, physiology, and ecology of the particular species and group, but in all the monkeys and apes adaptation is by group life, and survival is only possible for a member of a group. In nature the observer sees evidence of this vital sociability in the functioning of the group, and in the laboratory Butler (1954) has shown that monkeys will work hard when the only reward is the sight of another monkey.

The behavior of the mother and of the infant monkey, and the associated behavior of the other monkeys in the group, make possible the survival of the species. Reproduction depends on breeding seasons, mating patterns, developmental physiology, and on the social structures of the group. The young are conceived, carried and born, and reared only through the coordination of a wide range of structural, physiological, and behavioral mechanisms. Behavior is an essential part of the adaptive mechanisms as seen in field studies, but much of the important adaptive behavior does not appear under normal laboratory conditions. Field studies are particularly important in discovering the actual way the adaptive behavior functions.

The relations of structure and function and behavior are so important in understanding the importance of field studies that two further examples will be given here.

1. Sleep is a major behavioral problem. Old-World monkeys sleep at night, frequently on small limbs high off the ground. By sleeping at night in positions of difficult access, the monkeys avoid most of the carnivores, since the latter are active only after dark. But since the monkeys are social, large numbers of animals must sleep in small numbers of trees, and preferably away from the trunk and large limbs where carnivores can easily climb. The monkeys have evolved specialized sitting pads, ischial callosities, that permit them to sleep sitting upright in comfort. This is the usual position in the trees, but monkeys will nap lying on their sides if comfortable protected places are available. In a zoo the same monkey that slept sitting up in the wild will sleep on its side. The structure of callosities and their distribution in the primates had been studied, but it was only in the field studies that their importance became apparent. Among the apes, the gibbons have callosities and probably sleep in a sitting position (more study is needed here). The great apes have lost their callosities and only traces are left in some individuals (Miller 1945; Schultz 1956). But they build nests and sleep in them, the nests performing the same function as the callosities, both are structures letting the animals sleep in trees. It has been shown that nest building is learned (Bernstein 1962), so a learned behavior pattern has replaced the function of the ischial callosity and has led to its evolutionary loss.

2. Fear provides a second example of structure-function. Structure need not be hard and obvious like callosities; emotional responses also are rooted in the animal's physiology and are essential adaptations. Such responses will be considered particularly in the last chapter in their relation to human evolution, but they are important in the context of structure-function as well. The primate actors in their social groups are highly emotional, and no deep understanding of primate social life is possible unless the emotions are considered. For example, it has been shown in conditioning experiments with several mammalian species that fear is hard to extinguish; fear lingers on while learned responses of a rewarding nature drop out more readily, when the responses are no longer rewarded. This experimental finding becomes particularly interesting in relation to some recent field observations.

In Nairobi Park DeVore had begun to study a large group of more than 80 baboons, which could easily be approached in a car. A local parasitologist shot two of these baboons with a .22 rifle, and eight months later this group was still "wild" and could not be approached, even though the animals must have seen cars almost daily in the interval. The adaptive function of such behavior is striking: danger is learned in one trial and this kind of learning will not extinguish for a long time. It takes many, many neutral experiences, probably over years, to extinguish one violent experience. It should be especially noted in the baboon incident described above that it is very unlikely all the animals in the group saw the shooting; the experience of some of the animals became part of the whole group's adaptive behavior. In contrast to this, it has been found by the Japanese, who not only have provisioned monkeys but also have deliberately introduced new foods and studied their adoption, that it may take months for a new, pleasant food habit to spread to all the members of the group. In the case of fear, survival is at stake and a minimum experience produces a maximum result. In the case of a new eating habit, it is probably even advantageous that a new food be tried slowly. Adaptation under natural conditions shows clearly why it is essential for fear to be quickly learned and hard to extinguish.

The social group itself is an adaptation of supreme importance. For instance, as the preceding example of the baboon group illustrates, the members of a group do not necessarily learn fearful response to a particular situation from their individual experiences. Among baboons, when dominant animals give a warning cry and run, the others flee without looking for the source of the danger. As will be described repeatedly in later chapters reporting field observations, the majority of primates live their whole lives in close association with others. The social group occupies a range, shares knowledge of local foods, paths, and dangers, and offers opportunity for play, grooming, and close association. In the group the young and females are protected, and dominance gives an order to society. For monkeys the reproductive success that is necessary for evolutionary success occurs only within the group. Field studies are particularly important to these findings because it is only under natural conditions that the functioning group may be observed.

Under natural conditions an individual animal often cannot respond promptly to motivational pressures, even when basic physiological needs are involved. For example, a thirsty baboon cannot safely leave the group and go away seeking water. When baboons are living in country where water is restricted, the whole group moves to water, and the individual can satisfy its needs only as the whole pattern of the group's activity makes this possible.

If baboons are drinking water from many small sources (such as the puddles from the spray at Victoria Falls), any animal can drink when it wants to and drinking is frequent. But the same animals when drinking from the Zambesi River, where there are crocodiles, monitor lizards, and pythons, drink rapidly and with extreme care. At the end of the dry season a group approaching a water hole moves with caution, frequently pausing and watching other animals to assess the safety of the area. Thirst is satisfied within the complex patterned activity of the group, and the nature of this activity shows that the animals of the group know the local problems and are prepared to meet crises.

Neither individual monkeys nor the social group can wait until confronted by needs and situations (danger, thirst, hunger, sex) to respond to them; the social system must be *adapted to anticipate* both daily needs and occasional crises. A system that could meet only day-to-day problems would not survive for long, and evolution, through natural selection, builds a substantial margin of safety into the individual animals and into their way of life. The group moves more, is more exploratory, is more playful than there is any need for on the average day, but by so doing it is preparing for crises. The individual animals appear stronger and more intelligent than is necessary for normal activity, but survival requires coping with the rare event.

In field studies the primary data are the observations of the behavior of the animals. Daily activities are recorded, and, with time and luck, encounters with carnivores, diseased animals, injuries, fights, and other crises are observed. The size of a range or the number of individuals in a group may be objectively recorded, but the comparison and interpretation of the data necessarily involve subjective evaluations. Is the number of individuals in a group determined by species-specific biology, ecological factors, social factors, or by a combination of all of these? When data on the behavior of nonhuman primates are presented, the question arises whether the behavior is instinctive or learned. Behavior may, of course, be recorded without regard to this question, but it cannot be interpreted without consideration of this issue. Recent experimental work (Mason, Chap. 15, this volume) has shown that learning is far more important in the development of social behavior than anyone had imagined; monkeys reared in isolation even fail to mate normally, an activity that many thought to be purely instinctive. Actually the relative roles of inherited and environmental factors may be very different for different items of behavior. Infant clinging may be an almost purely inbuilt reflex, and adequate sexual performance may require only a minimum of childhood play, whereas food habits may be largely learned. There is much room for further experimentation and field work.

In summary, from an evolutionary point of view selection is for successful behavior. Structure, physiology, social life, all these are the result of selection, and the structure-physiology-behavior of populations of primates are adapted to each other and to a way of life. Parts of this complex are almost entirely the result of heredity with a minimum dependence on environment, whereas others are heavily influenced by learning. It is advantageous for behavior to be adaptable, to adjust to a wide variety of circumstances. What is inherited is ease of learning, rather than fixed instinctive patterns. The species easily, almost inevitably, learns the essential behaviors for its survival. So, although it is true that monkeys learn to be social, they are so constructed that under normal circumstances this learning always takes place. Similarly, human beings learn to talk, but they inherit structures that make this inevitable, except under the most peculiar circumstances. Although great efforts have been expended, chimpanzees simply do not learn to communicate verbally. The genetically determined neural substrate is not sufficient to support speech behavior.

# CLASSIFICATION

The primates whose behavior is described in the subsequent chapters are a very small sampling of a large and highly diversified group of mammals. There are 50 genera, nearly 200 well-defined species, and some 600 described varieties of living primates, and there are reliable field studies of the behavior of less than one dozen. Of the usually recognized families of primates, that of the apes, the Pongidae (gibbon, orangutan, chimpanzee, and gorilla) is the only one in which a majority of the genera have been the subject of systematic, continued observation under natural conditions. In planning further field work and in assessing the studies now available it is essential to see what is known relative to the broad pattern of the evolution of the whole order of the primates. The following discussion of classification is for those who are interested in behavior, and this naturally leads to a less complicated classification than is usually found in the literature. (For the most useful treatments of primate classification see Simpson 1945, 1949 Chap. 7, 1962, and 1963; Piveteau 1957; Fiedler 1956; and Clark 1960.)

The primates differ from other mammals in the structure of their hands and feet. Whether one examines the hand of a man or that of a lemur (either a recent lemur or the Eocene *Notharctus*), the digits are long with flattened terminal phalanges. The flattened bones show that the fossil form had nails, rather than claws. This primate hand, or foot, is adapted to grasp and to hold on by the skin on the ends of the fingers rather than to dig in with a claw (Clark 1936; Bishop 1962). Climbing by grasping has proved a highly successful locomotor adaptation, and, in my opinion, lies behind many other primate characters of the teeth, skull, vertebrae, and viscera.

In a primitive mammal each digit ends in a claw that is firmly attached to the last finger bone (terminal phalanx). A pad of specialized, weight-bearing, nonmovable skin is at the base of the claw. Then the digits are covered with hairy skin, and there are more pads on the palm. The transformation from the primitive paw into a primate hand or foot involves the thinning of the claw, flattening of the terminal phalanx, lengthening of all phalanges, and the loss of the discrete pads. Thickened skin, specialized for weight-bearing, becomes continuous over all the ventral surface of the palms, soles, and digits. This is a complex adaptation that is not paralleled in any other group of mammals.

As weight increases, climbing with claws becomes increasingly precarious, and probably much of the success of the primates as a group lies in the climbing ability of moderate-sized animals (from 5 to 40 pounds). It should be remembered that much of the food in a forest is at the ends of the branches. The herbivores of the forest canopy must climb to the ends of branches, and it may be that the fundamental primate advantage is in the ability to grasp small twigs and feed securely. The detail of the use of hands and feet should be investigated experimentally in primates and arboreal nonprimates of comparable body size.

Naturally, the adaptation of any order of mammals is complex, and primates share many other features besides the adaptations of the hands and feet. However, in relation to behavior these locomotor adaptations may be the most fundamental; grasping hands and feet make possible an efficient harvest of the vast food supply high in the tropical and subtropical forest. The abundance of food and the importance of the arboreal adaptive zone are shown by the population density of the howler monkeys, which may be more than 100 per square mile, on Barro Colorado (Carpenter, Chap. 8, this volume). There are other kinds of monkeys on the island, and I believe that densities of over 200 per square mile are by no means uncommon for monkeys, particularly when more than one species is present.

## CERCOPITHECIDAE, OLD-WORLD MONKEYS

The majority of field studies available to us are of the Old-World monkeys, and the members of the family Cercopithecidae are the most common laboratory primates. It is in part for these reasons and in part to avoid a pseudo-evolutionary order that the data on the behavior of baboons, macaques, and langurs will be presented first.

Old-World monkeys separated from other primates some 30 million years ago in the Oligocene period. They are all quadrupedal animals, adapted to climbing by grasping hands and feet. The trunk is long, narrow, and deep (Schultz 1956), and a long lumbar region and flexion of the trunk are important in locomotion. In the general form of the trunk and arrangement of the viscera, these monkeys do not differ from some prosimians or even nonprimates. The hands and feet are the primary locomotor specialization.

The teeth are remarkably similar in all the Old-World monkeys; the cusp pattern on the molar teeth sharply distinguishes the whole family from prosimians or apes (Remane 1956). In the skull, the braincase is large, the interorbital region narrow, and the orbits directed forward with bony lateral walls. These cranial features reflect the large brain, the reduced sense of smell, and the importance of vision. Stereoscopic, color vision is characteristic of the whole group, and this appears to correlate well with features of the skull (Simons 1962; Noback 1962).

Within the family Cercopithecidae there are two subfamilies, Cercopithecinae and Colobinae; the latter have been distinct since at least Miocene times. The primary difference is in the viscera. The Colobinae have greatly enlarged stomachs, so large that one-fourth of an animal's weight may be stomach and stomach contents. The huge stomach displaces the other abdominal viscera. For example, the liver has no contact with the diaphragm and the right kidney is very low. The teeth are highcusped and tend to be smaller than in the Cercopithecinae.

The large, specialized stomach is an adaptation to digesting large quantities of leaves, and this dietary adaptation has made the Colobinae more arboreal than the Cercopithecinae. All have long tails, and only one species (*Presbytis entellus*) spends much time on the ground. The Colobinae are particularly abundant in Asia, and there are many species in southeast Asia alone. *Presbytis entellus* (sacred langur, Hanuman monkey) lives in the drier parts of India and Ceylon. In southeast Asia there are two species groups of *Presbytis* (called *Trachypithecus* and *Presbytis* by Pocock 1934). In addition there are three genera, *Nasalis, Pygathrix,* and *Rhinopithecus*, which are probably only species of a single genus all the members of which have limbs of equal length and odd noses and live under very wet conditions. (It should be remembered that the South China Sea was land during the time of the last glacial advance, and the ranges of these forms would then have been adjacent.)

In Africa the subfamily is represented by a single genus, *Colobus*, which over all the African forests is divided into far fewer species than is *Presbytis* in southeast Asia. Today, just as the Colobinae are primarily Asiatic, the Cercopithecinae are primarily African. The situation is shown in the following tabulation:

|  |  | AFRICA | ASIA |
|---|---|---|---|
| Ground monkeys | Cercopithecinae | *Papio* *Theropithecus* *Erythrocebus* *Cercopithecus* *Cercocebus* | *Macaca* |
| Tree monkeys | Colobinae | *Colobus* | *Presbytis* (with 4 groups of species) *Nasalis,* (*Pygathrix, Rhinopithecus*) |

The baboons (including in *Papio*, the desert baboon *P. hamadryas*, or *Comopithecus*, and the forest baboons, drill and mandrill) are so similar to macaques that these two genera might well be united, except for the confusion in nomenclature that would result. It is interesting that the only forms that are closely similar in Asia and Africa are monkeys that move freely on the ground, often far from trees, and eat a very varied diet. *Theropithecus*, the gelada, is structurally very distinct from the baboons. *Erythrocebus* appears to be a close relative of *Cercopithecus* which has adapted to ground life by high-speed locomotion, a most interesting adaptation that is unique to the patas monkeys.

*Cercocebus*, the mangabeys, is an arboreal group that is characterized by a very long trunk and tail and a linear build. The mangabeys are active jumpers.

*Cercopithecus* (including *Miopithecus* and *Allenopithecus*) is a large and complex genus with at least three species groups and occupying many adaptive niches. It has the same sort of variety and complexity seen in the langurs (Colobinae) of southeast Asia.

Extensive field studies of social behavior are limited to a very small number of species. The largely ground-living macaques and baboons are the easiest to see, the most widely distributed, and the hardiest in the laboratory, and it is thus no accident that these are the most studied (this volume). By contrast there is only one extensive account of the social behavior of a langur (*Presbytis entellus*, Jay, Chap. 7, this volume).

It is obvious that substantial studies (of a year's duration and under good observational conditions) are needed for many genera of monkeys. Conclusions in science are not "truth" but are subject to revision, and in the present state of our knowledge generalizations about monkey behavior are guides to ordering the data and very tentative hypotheses rather than conclusions.

## PONGIDAE, THE APES

The apes (gibbon, orangutan, chimpanzee, gorilla) differ from monkeys primarily in their locomotor adaptations. They have lost the primitive quadrupedalism of the early primates and have adapted to life in the trees by relative elongation of the arms and profound changes in the trunk (Schultz 1956). In apes the trunk is short, wide, and shallow, compared to that of monkeys. The lumbar region is short, back muscles reduced, and flexion of the trunk is not important in locomotion. In the arm the clavicle is long, and the scapula lies on the back of the thorax. The shoulder and arm muscles are especially adapted to abduction, flexion, and rotation. The basic adaptation is for feeding in small branches. It is so successful that orangutans or chimpanzees, weighing more than 150 pounds, can climb out to the ends of branches and eat the fruit and buds. Controlled study shows that the apes can do this easily. This feeding-climbing adaptation has led to the loss of the structures making monkey quadrupedalism possible and to the occasional practice of swinging under the branches as a mode of locomotion. This mode of locomotion has been called "brachiation" and the subject has been reviewed experimentally (Avis 1962).

In the short, wide trunk of the apes the viscera are arranged much as in man, and necessarily differently from the disposition in long, deep-trunked monkeys. Emphasis on behavior and its structural consequences leads one to see a very broad pattern of similarity that is lost if only isolated structures are compared.

In the ape the complex climbing-feeding adaptation of arms and trunk involves a wide variety of actions in which one arm, or leg, moves independently and slowly. Because of this and because of the emphasis on flexion and arm elongation, locomotion on the ground is varied and should be viewed as secondary to the arboreal adaptation and loss of primitive quadrupedalism.

In gibbons the arms are so long that bipedalism is the only possible gait on the ground, but balance is maintained by a wide variety of positions and motions of the arms. In orangutans the hands and feet are partially flexed, and weight is carried on the sides of the feet and the posterior part of the palms. The animals rarely come to the ground (Schaller 1961) and there is no secondary adaptation. In chimpanzee and gorilla terrestrial locomotion is important, and a unique development of thickened skin on the dorsal surface of the second phalanges of hand digits two to five carries weight.

In summary: When apes come to the ground, gibbons move the same way they do on the top of large branches, orangutans move clumsily with no special adaptation, and chimpanzees and gorillas show the unique adaptation of knuckle walking. When monkeys come to the ground, they continue the same locomotion pattern as that in the trees and there is minimum locomotion adaptation even in the most ground-living species.

Locomotion has been stressed because this seems to have been the basic adaptation that divided the Pongidae from the Cercopithecidae. Since fossil limb bones are rare, it is fortunate that the molar teeth are different in the two groups and show that the two families have been distinct since the Oligocene. Probably the simplest generic classification is as follows.

*Hylobates:* The gibbons of southeast Asia, including at least 5 well-defined species of small gibbons and the large siamang.

*Pongo:* The orangutan.

*Pan:* The gorilla and the chimpanzee (Simpson 1963). Placing gorilla and chimpanzee in *Pan* is supported by the detailed similarity in chromosome form (Klinger 1963) and in biochemical similarity (Goodman 1962, 1963; Zuckerkandl 1963).

*Hominidae:* Man is a primate and, according to both traditional structural (Huxley 1863) and recent biochemical (Goodman 1962, 1963) classification, is most similar to the Pongidae. As the evidence stands today, bipedalism as shown by foot and pelvis (Leakey 1963; Napier 1963) and tool use are equally old and characteristic of the earliest hominids. All recent forms belong to a single group, *Homo sapiens*. The psychological differences that so clearly separate the behavior of contemporary apes and that of man appear to have evolved long after the separation of the hominid line. The earliest bipedal toolmakers (genus *Australopithecus*) had brains no larger than those of contemporary apes, and it is probable that distinctively human mental abilities (speech, skill, degree of intelligence) evolved only in the last 4 to 6 hundred thousand years.

If the three families (Cercopithecidae, Pongidae, Hominidae) that have been considered so far are viewed from an evolutionary point of view, the Hominidae are derived from the Pongidae, perhaps some 2 to 4 million years ago. The separation of Pongidae and Cercopithecidae is much more ancient, probably more than 30 million years ago. In interpreting comparative studies or in selecting laboratory animals, it is important to remember that these families have been separate for these long periods of time and that evolution has continued in all the lines. The apes and monkeys of today are not the ancestral ones, and there are not enough primate fossils so that the relations of the major groups can be directly determined in any detail.

In spite of the long separation and subsequent evolution, Cercopithecidae, Pongidae, and Hominidae share a great deal in basic structure. They are remarkably similar in special senses and in the basic plan of the brain, viscera, and reproductive system. A very considerable gap separates these forms from the other primates.

## CEBOIDEA, NEW-WORLD MONKEYS

The ancestors of the Cercopithecidae were prosimians, and the prosimians were an extraordinarily diversified group. Apparently the "monkeys" of the New World evolved independently from New-World prosimians, and the similarities of New-World and Old-World monkeys are due to parallel evolution. Obviously, the existence of parallel lines gives many opportunities to test hypotheses, and the great diversity in New-World forms is of great interest. But the choice of a New-World monkey for study should be based on zoological considerations and not on the idea that the Ceboidea are in any way ancestral to the Cercopithecidae.

Since only one New-World monkey is described in this book, this is not the place for an extended discussion of these animals, but it should be stressed that they are far less uniform than the Old-World monkeys. The marmosets (Callithricidae) are a numerous group with at least two genera and *many* species. The sakis are the only short-tailed New-World forms, and comprise a very distinctive group. *Aotes* is the only nocturnal primate in the New World. In general structure it seems similar to *Callicebus*. I believe that the remainder of the New-World forms will prove to be more similar than those mentioned so far. In structure *Saimiri, Cebus, Ateles*, and *Alouatta* form a series, and it will be interesting to see if detailed study of the chromosomes and biochemistry brings more order or confirms the apparent great diversity of forms.

Brachiation evolved independently in some New-World forms, and study of their behavior and anatomy is of the greatest help in interpreting the situation in the Pongidae, where there are no intermediate living forms. Also there is a wide range in the structure of the tail from short to long and from normal to specialized prehensile. This variety will allow a detailed correlation of structure and behavior when the field studies are available.

## PROSIMIANS

For the first half of the age of the mammals (Paleocene and Eocene) the primates were represented by a very large number of highly diversified prosimians. The greatest diversity of primates was at that time, and they occupied more of the world than at any subsequent time until the advent of man. The prosimians became extinct in all northern and temperate regions and in the New World. In the Old World they continued as small, nocturnal forms that never compete directly with monkeys; on the island of Madagascar a protected group of lemurs underwent a remarkable local radiation. The living lemurs are diversified and specialized in structure and behavior, and the following general remarks need qualification with regard to particular taxa, as given here. The living prosimians have the grasping hand and foot complex, but lemurs retain a claw on the second toe and in *Tarsius* claws are retained on the second and third toes. In the Aye Aye (*Daubentonia*) the digits are elongated, but the terminal phalanges are compressed and the "nails" have much of the histological structure of claws (Clark 1936).

The prosimians have adapted to arboreal life by climbing and by grasping but have retained much of the special sensory equipment of a primitive mammal. They have specialized tactile hairs, a highly developed sense of smell, numerous scent glands, and vision is neither color nor stereoscopic (although I believe that previous statements on prosimian vision will be modified to some extent). Many prosimians are nocturnal. This means that the human observer in attempting to analyze behavior does not perceive the world of the animal he is studying; he cannot touch, smell, or see in the same way. The prosimian's face does not show the kinds of expressions seen in monkeys and apes. To the observer the problems caused by these differences are profound.

The contemporary prosimians living in Asia and Africa are all completely nocturnal and are divided in three very distinct groups.

|  | ASIA | AFRICA |
|---|---|---|
| Rapid leapers | Tarsiidae | Galagidae |
| Very slow movers | Lorisidae | Lorisidae |
|  | (*Loris,* | (*Perodicticus*) |
|  | *Nycticebus*) |  |

*Tarsius* is the only living relic of a very large and varied group of prosimians. The living tarsier is a highly specialized leaper. The galagos are also nocturnal leapers and may occupy a similar adaptive niche.

The extremely slow-moving lorises are a highly specialized family (Straus and Wisloski 1932).

The Madagascar lemurs have evolved without competition from monkeys or modern carnivores. This has allowed a remarkable local adaptive radiation and many forms became extinct during the Pleistocene. The behavior of these forms is discussed in Chapter 9.

The tree shrews, family Tupaiidae, are remarkably primitive in their structure. They retain claws and the typical structure of the paws, and have not shared in the evolutionary trends of skull, teeth, and brain that characterize the primates considered so far. In this brief introduction I have found it convenient to follow traditional usage and leave the tree shrews in the Insectivora. This decision stems from considering the grasping hands and feet as the fundamental primate adaptation. There seems to be no doubt that, as Simpson has put it, "the tupaioids are either the most primatelike insectivores or the most insectivorelike primates" (1945, p. 183). There is no doubt that the study of the structure and behavior of the tree shrews will help in understanding the origin of the primates, regardless of whether they are classified as the most primitive members of the order or as the group from which the order arose.

To the student of behavior, classification is essential because it gives a framework based on the best available understanding of the animals being investigated. For example, it shows at once that the animals treated in this book are only a very small selection from the many genera of living primates. It shows that this selection has been biased by an interest in man, as all the genera of apes except the *Pongo* have been the object of at least one major field study whereas only a single genus of New-World monkeys has received comparable attention. Classification helps in the evaluation of the available field studies, and offers the best guide to the planning of future investigations. It is hoped that this book will be revised over the years so that, eventually, it may be worthy of its title, *Primate Behavior*. Hopefully, the next edition will contain chapters on man, tree shrews, and much more on the prosimians. And it must be remembered that the behavior of even the best studied form is not as well known as that of many other animals. As time passes, we hope that these chapters will be replaced by far more definitive revisions.

# PART I

## ◆Monkeys and Prosimians

M ONKEYS and prosimians have spread across all of the major tropical and subtropical forest areas of both the New World and the Old World. In most of the tropics there are not only huge numbers of monkeys, but these are divided also into a remarkable number of varieties—a diversity of forms found in no other group of mammals. The success of the monkey-prosimian way of life can be illustrated by their diversity in morphology and behavior. New-World monkeys include the small diurnal marmosets and the large, noisy howler monkeys (Chap. 8). They include the nocturnal monkey *Aotes* as well as the aptly named spider monkey, one of several South American species whose prehensile tails serve as a fifth appendage. In the Old World the monkeys and prosimians display an even greater range of diversity, from tiny, timid mouse lemurs to the aggressive adult male baboon, which may weigh as much as 100 pounds. There are slow-moving, nocturnal prosimians, and leapers like the tarsier that can easily jump more than ten times their body length. There are forms that live entirely in the trees, others that come frequently to the ground, and still others that spend the day on the ground, returning to trees only to sleep.

Almost nothing is known about the behavior of the vast majority of these primates in nature, and indeed, because many primates die soon after capture, very little has been learned from captive specimens either. The following eight chapters include reports on all of the major groups of monkeys that had been the subjects of long-term field studies at the time the primate study group met at the Center for Advanced Study in the Behavioral Sciences. It was necessary to omit two of the four major groups of Old-World monkeys, the mangabeys *(Cercocebus)* and the guenons *(Cercopithecus)*. Although species in each of these genera are now being studied, the only previous report on a member of either group is Haddow's on *Cercopithecus ascanius* (1952–1953), a brief behavior study incidental to his virology research.

That five of the following eight chapters are concerned with only two closely related genera, the baboons and macaques, is a result both of the fact that these monkeys are primarily ground dwellers who often live in open areas where observation is easy, and of the fact that their terrestrial adaptation has been so successful that they have not only spread throughout the forests and open woodlands of Africa and Asia, but beyond the forested zones as well. The baboon-macaques are very hardy, capable of surviving in hot, treeless savannas and at altitudes where winter snow is common. Thus it is no surprise that they have proved to be easy to feed and maintain in captivity in the northern hemisphere, and that until very recently they were the only monkeys kept in laboratory colonies. More observer hours have been and continue to be devoted to the study of this monkey group than to any other.

Chapters 2 and 3 summarize the results of several years of work on African baboons. Although the adaptive capabilities of the baboon have

16

yet to be studied, for example, in West Africa, or in deep forest, a great deal is now known about their behavior and ecology in regions ranging from semidesert to sea coast to montane forest.

The common rhesus macaque of India, long *the monkey* in laboratory tests, is the subject of Chapters 4 and 5. The population survey of the rhesus undertaken by Charles H. Southwick, M. A. Beg, and M. R. Siddiqi in 1959–1960 was the most extensive study ever undertaken of the ecology and population structure of a nonhuman primate. The results of this survey, as well as a study of the social behavior of monkeys in a temple area, are reported in Chapter 4.

The rhesus monkeys that were brought to Cayo Santiago from India by C. R. Carpenter in 1938 have been under constant study since 1956, first by Stuart Altmann, and since 1958 by a series of investigators under the direction of Carl B. Koford. The transplanted monkeys of Cayo Santiago do not represent a normal wild population. The population density on the 40-acre island is high, the monkeys must be fed artificially, they are not preyed upon, and they are subject to periodic trapping. On the other hand, there are enormous advantages in being able to trap and tatoo each individual monkey and keep records of its physical and social development. Donald Sade's study of the kinship-based structure of rhesus grooming groups (n.d.), and Koford's report concerning the succession to high rank of the sons of high-ranking mothers (1963) are two examples of studies that can be carried out only when the observer can positively identify large numbers of individuals over a period of years. Another advantage of continuous observation is the opportunity to plot reproductive cycles and population dynamics over the years, and this aspect of the Cayo Santiago program is the subject of Chapter 5.

Both the baboon and the rhesus macaque are large, robust ground dwellers with many aspects of behavior and social organization in common. But there are a variety of smaller, more gracile macaque species in Asia, and a field study of one of these, the bonnet macaque, is contained in Chapter 6. The name "bonnet macaque" refers to the fact that the hair on the head is "parted in the center, radiating outward from a central cowlick." As might be expected from observing their less powerful slender bodies, these long-tailed macaques do not spend as much time on the ground as do rhesus monkeys, and in their social behavior the adult males are more tolerant and less aggressive than are rhesus males.

The Japanese macaque, *Macaca fuscata*, is broadly similar to the rhesus in its powerful body build, but it has thicker hair, a shorter tail, and in distribution is confined to the southern islands of Japan. Japanese scientists at the Japan Monkey Center initiated the post-war period of primate studies by long-term observation of macaques at Takasakiyama (see Frisch 1959). In succeeding years workers from the Japan Center have gone out to study many primate species in Africa, Asia, and South America, and have es-

tablished an international journal, *Primates*. The study group was fortunate in having Hiroki Mizuhara as one of the members of the primate
project, who presented the results of the Japanese macaque studies for
comparison and discussion. An extensive bibliography of studies by members of the Japan Monkey Center is included in the general bibliography at
the end of this volume, and Mizuhara has also supplied hitherto unpublished
data for Chapters 13 and 15.

As described in Chapter 1, all of the Old-World monkeys fall into two
subfamilies, the Cercopithecinae and the Colobinae. The primary distinction of the Colobinae is that all of the members of this group have a gut that
is specialized to digest large quantities of mature leaves. Except for a brief
study of the black and white colobus monkey in Northern Tanganyika (Ullrich 1961), virtually nothing was known of the ecology and behavior of this
major group of Old-World monkeys until Phyllis Jay's observations on the
common Indian langur, reported in Chapter 7. This langur, *Presbytis entellus*, spends much of its time foraging in the ground, but it remains under
or relatively near trees, dashing back to them if danger threatens. Langur
monkeys give an entirely different impression from that given by the rhesus, which they are often near. The langur body is long-limbed and narrow,
about 25 inches in length, and the tail of an animal this size is even longer, as
long as 40 inches. Langurs leap gracefully through trees, taking long jumps
easily — very different from the stocky, rather clumsy locomotion of rhesus
and baboons when they are in trees. In addition, the tenor of langur life is
relaxed, less aggressive, less dominance-oriented than is social life among
rhesus and baboons. Jay was able to make many of these comparisons directly, since one of her langur groups contained a pair of resident rhesus
monkeys.

New-World and Old-World monkeys have apparently evolved out of
different prosimian ancestors and are separated by at least 30 million years
of evolutionary history. Under comparable selective pressures the New-
World monkeys remarkably parallel the Old-World monkeys in general body
form and way of life. The comparative morphology of the two groups —
the differences in dentition, the brain, and the blood — is much better known
than is their comparative behavior. As pointed out in Chapter 1, brachiation
evolved independently in some New-World forms (Erikson 1963), and some
of these developed a specialized, prehensile tail, with a naked, sensitive
patch of skin near the tip. But New-World monkeys live in dense jungles
where observation conditions are very poor, and this difficulty, combined
with the fact that they are less closely related to man, has meant that South
American monkeys have been studied very little in the field.

In 1931 C. R. Carpenter initiated the modern period of long-term primate field studies with his classic study of the howler monkeys of Barro
Colorado Island. In the intervening years Carpenter, as well as others, has
returned to Barro Colorado both to study changes in the population struc-

ture and to make additional behavior observations. Adult male howlers are the largest of the New-World monkeys, weighing up to 20 pounds, but they are even more remarkable for the specialized enlargment of the hyoid apparatus in the throat, providing a resonator which is capable of projecting their "howls" a mile through thick jungle foliage. The results of some 24 months of observations of the howlers spread over 27 years are summarized in Chapter 8.

More than half of the living genera of prosimians are grouped in the super-family Lemuroidea and are confined to the island of Madagascar. In the protection of this island refuge they are safe both from competition with monkeys and from predation, and as a result the Madagascar lemurs have radiated into a variety of ecological niches that are occupied on the mainland by a combination of prosimians, monkeys, and apes. Since the near extinction of many species of lemur means a potential loss of many of the most valuable clues to the behavior of the prosimian ancestors of the other primates, the field studies begun by J. J. Petter in 1956 are of the utmost importance. Chapter 9 surveys the major conclusions from these ongoing lemur studies, differing from other chapters in this section in that it collates observations on locomotion, diet, activity rhythms, and so forth on as many species as it was possible to locate and observe. Lemurs and monkeys live in different sensory worlds with different patterns of social behavior and these differences emerge clearly from Petter's observations. Although field studies of tree shrews and other prosimians are now in progress, the only substantial field study of another prosimian is on the African bushbaby, *Galago senegalensis* (Sauer and Sauer 1963).

# IRVEN DEVORE and K. R. L. HALL

# 2
# ◆ Baboon Ecology

Man and the baboon have shared the African scene for more than a million years. The fossil bones of *Australopithecus* and of an early type of baboon are found intermingled in the floors of caves in South Africa. The chacma baboon was often depicted in Bushmen rock paintings, and, as a representative of the god Thoth, the hamadryas or "sacred baboon" held a prominent position in the pantheon of the ancient Egyptians. Today baboons are among the most serious of all agricultural pests, and many thousands are killed annually in vermin-control operations.

Baboons are large, primarily ground-living monkeys of the Family *Cercopithecidae*, Subfamily *Cercopithecinae*. In the past baboons have been divided into several genera and many species, but judged by modern taxonomic criteria it may be unnecessary to recognize more than one genus (*Papio*) and four species. One of these, the subject of this and the following chapter, is the most widely distributed baboon group, occurring in savannas and forests from the Tibesti Plateau in the north to Cape Town in the south, and across Central Africa from Dakar to the east coast. This group is usually divided into several species, including "chacma," "yellow," and "olive," but it may be that these forms are no more than racial variations of a single, widespread, "savanna" species (DeVore and Washburn 1963; Jolly 1963). For convenience, the baboons described here will be referred to by their common names: the chacma baboon in South Africa and the olive baboon in Kenya. In current nomenclature, which gives these forms specific rather

The 1959 baboon study in Kenya was part of a study of the origin of human behavior supported by the Ford Foundation, and the 1963 study was financed by a National Science Foundation Grant (No. GS-205), "Studies in the evolution of human behavior." The 1960 baboon study in South and South-West Africa was supported by a Royal Society and Nuffield Foundation Commonwealth Scholarship, that of 1961, by a Royal Society grant. Data for the Cape baboons during 1958–1959 was obtained while Hall was at the University of Capetown. We wish to thank the foundations and the numerous persons who helped us in Africa.

than racial status, the chacma is designated *Papio ursinus* and the olive baboon is usually designated *P. anubis* (or *P. doguera*).

In addition to the widespread savanna group, there are two species of short-tailed baboons in the forests of West Africa—the drill and mandrill. In North Africa and Arabia the desert baboon, *P. hamadryas*, lives in areas that are probably too dry and open for the other forms. In summary, the genus *Papio* is divided into a number of races and at least four species, including a savanna species (with several races), two forest species, and a desert species. The gelada baboon, *Theropithecus gelada* is very distinct from *Papio*, and is confined to the mountains of Ethiopia (Starck and Frick 1958).

The African baboons are very similar in body form and behavior to the Asiatic macaques. Both groups have 42 chromosomes (Chu and Bender 1961), and their distribution does not overlap. These Old-World terrestrial monkeys can cross rivers and live in dry areas, foraging far from trees. Both groups eat an eclectic, varied diet and live in social groups protected by powerful adult males. Such characteristics have enabled the baboon-macaques to occupy almost all of the Old-World tropical and subtropical regions with very little speciation.

Although brief behavioral studies had been made in the past (see Chapter 3), no ecological studies of baboons were undertaken until the late 1950s. The field studies on which this chapter is based are those of Hall in southern Africa and Washburn and DeVore in Kenya. Hall began his study in the Cape of Good Hope Nature Reserve, South Africa, in April 1958, and intensive periods of study, as shown in Table 2–1, were carried out by one or two observers, working either separately on different groups or together on the same groups, up to the end of October 1961 (see Figs. 2–1, 2–2, and 2–3).

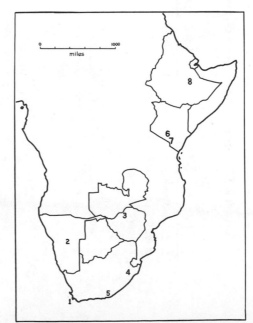

Fig. 2–1. Baboon study locations in eastern and southern Africa: (1) Cape Peninsula; (2) South-West Africa; (3) Southern Rhodesia; (4) Drakensberg Mountains, Natal; (5) Eastern Cape Province; (6) Nairobi Park, Kenya; (7) Amboseli Reserve, Kenya; (8) Eastern Ethiopia (hamadryas study by H. Kummer and F. Kurt).

TABLE 2–1. AREAS SAMPLED IN BABOON FIELD STUDIES, WITH LENGTH AND SEASON OF OBSERVATION PERIODS

| Area (Fig. 2–1) | Period of Study | Number of Observers | Days of Observation | Kinds of Observation |
|---|---|---|---|---|
| 1. *Cape Peninsula* chiefly Cape Nature Reserve | (1) April 1958–April 1959 | 1 | 61 | One day per week, with occasional successive day-series up to 14. Mainly ecological data on nonhabituated groups. Variable observation distances from 30 to 200 yards. |
| | (2) August–September 1960 (winter) | 1 | 42 | Continuous observation of one group, with occasional day on another group. Close-range observations (25 yards or less). Ecological and behavioral data. |
| | (3) August–September 1961 (winter) | 2 | 50 | Continuous observation of one group by both observers, then of this group and its neighbor group simultaneously by one observer. Close observations (25 yards or less). Ecological and behavioral data. |
| 2. *S.-W. Africa* Three main areas in radius of 80 miles of Windhoek. | July 1960 (winter) | 2 | 28 | Sampling of ecology in different regions, with some experimental observations on behavior. |
| 3. *S. Rhodesia* Kariba mainland, Kariba Island, and nonhunting areas along south bank of Zambesi. | June–July, October–November, 1961 (winter and spring) | 2 | 90 | Sampling of ecology in different regions; study of one flood-formed island population; close-range observations of one mainland group (30 days). |

| | | | | |
|---|---|---|---|---|
| 4. and 5. *Eastern South Africa* Drakensberg Mountains, East Cape Province. | August 1961 (winter) | 1 | 10 | Sampling of ecology. |
| 6. *Nairobi National Park* ("olive baboons") | (1) March 1959– January 1960 | 1–2 | 285 | Continuous, close-range observation on one group at a time. Three groups studied intensively; neighboring groups observed briefly. DeVore joined by S. L. Washburn in July. Behavioral and ecological data. |
| | (2) June–July 1963 | 2 | 45 | Restudy of population structure and changes in group organization by DeVore and Richard Lee. |
| 7. *Amboseli Reserve* ("yellow baboons") | September– November 1959 | 1–2 | 60 | Primarily ecological and census data, by Washburn and DeVore. Both Washburn and DeVore worked together for a while in each of the Kenya study areas, with more than 1200 hours of direct observations in all. |
| 8. *Eastern Ethiopia* (hamadryas) | November 1960– October 1961 | 2 | | Behavioral and ecological study by H. Kummer and F. Kurt. |

Fig. 2–2. Baboon study areas in southern Africa. *a. (Top)* East coast of the Cape Nature Reserve, Cape Peninsula. In the home range of S group; sleeping cliffs marked with arrows. *b. (Bottom)* Arid *Acacia* thornveld in South-West Africa.

c. (*Top*) Drakensberg Mountains in the Giant's Castle Reserve, Natal. Baboons range as high as the face of the escarpment; top of the escarpment is about 10,000 feet. d. (*Bottom*) A "kopie" in the eastern Cape Province where a group of baboons sleeps.

Fig. 2–3. Baboon study areas in East Africa. *a.* (*Top*) The SR group feeding in open grassland in Nairobi Park, Kenya. *b.* (*Bottom*) Baboons on an open pan at Amboseli Reserve, Kenya. Sleeping trees (*Acacia xanthophloea*) in background.

## STUDY METHODS

In general, the objective of the observers in both the Kenya and the southern Africa regions of study was to obtain data on the groups with minimum interference to their normal pattern of activity, either from observer presence or as a result of experimental changes of environment. Experiments in the field or on recently captured animals from a group have a limited usefulness in certain contexts (see diet section, and Chap. 3). The Japanese method of "provisionization" was never used, first because it was not necessary for our purposes, and second because it alters the ecological and behavioral patterns of the animals.

The methods used in obtaining ecological and behavioral data in the different regions of southern Africa had to be adapted to the local conditions and the time available for the study. With reference to the areas and observation periods of Table 2-1, observations were made in South-West Africa, Southern Rhodesia, and eastern South Africa, on groups that were not studied sufficiently long to become habituated to the observers, with the following exceptions:

Kariba mainland, group of 109, very close range (25 yards or less)
Kariba Island, whole population, close range (25–50 yards)
Drakensberg, group of 58, close range (25–50 yards)

These closer ranges were possible because the particular groups were to some extent habituated already, not to the observers, but to the proximity of human beings who did not harass them. All data were obtained by observers on foot, with the exception of (1) a few counts made of groups crossing vehicle tracks in the Mana Pools area that were made from a Land Rover, and (2) data obtained at sleeping cliffs in South-West Africa where the terrain made it feasible to construct blinds of rock and bush directly opposite the sleeping area. In the Cape Peninsula, one group only (S) became extremely tolerant (15 yards or less) as a result partly of familiarity with fishermen and other visitors to the area, partly of habituation to the regular all-day presence of the same one or two observers. Its neighbor, C group, habituated to being regularly observed by reducing tolerance distance from about 200 to 25 yards in 20 successive days. Such variations as these are of critical importance in assessing both ecological and behavioral findings from different study regions. Accurate group-size numerical data can be obtained at distances of 200 yards or more in very open habitat, such as South-West Africa or the foothills of the Drakensberg Mountains, but exact details of feeding or other behavior come only from close range.

The reaction of baboons to humans at Nairobi Park, the primary study site in Kenya, varied from one very tolerant group which climbed onto visitors' vehicles in search of food, to a wild group which would not allow a vehicle to approach closer than half a mile. The baboons at Amboseli were much less accustomed to the presence of tourists, and most groups would begin to move away if approached closer than about 40 yards. The most rewarding behavior observations were made on Nairobi Park groups which had become accustomed to the proximity of persons in automobiles, but which were not so tame that the presence of humans disrupted their usual cycle of activities. Most of the study was carried out while remaining inside a Land Rover, staying in the middle of a group or within a few yards of it and moving with it throughout the day. These conditions permit the observer to keep every animal in the group under close surveillance with a minimum of disturbance to normal activities. Although these baboons, after several weeks of habituation, would allow the observer to walk among them, the appearance of a person on foot made them obviously ill at ease. There was rarely any need to leave the vehicle except to follow the group into rocky areas or gorges, and the convenience of carrying many items of equipment in the vehicle, plus the possibility of encountering dangerous animals when on foot, all combined to make observations from a vehicle the most feasible course of action. When these observations were compared with observations made through binoculars it was apparent that the presence of human observers in an automobile altered the social behavior of these habituated groups very little. Additional comments on observation conditions and study techniques are reported in the following chapter. Pertinent information on field study equipment and procedures are included in the appendix ("Field Methods"). References to papers already published by the authors are contained in the bibliography, and in the following sections the southern Africa and Kenya studies will be cited by geographical reference rather than by author's names.

## STUDY AREAS

Because baboons are numerous in areas throughout subsaharan Africa and because no long-term field investigations had been carried out when the present studies were undertaken, initial study areas were chosen for convenience and good visibility. Although Hall was subsequently able to extend his observations to include regions with a variety of contrasting ecological conditions, a long-term study of baboons in a heavily forested area has not been carried out. Brief observations in semiopen forest regions such as Lake Manyara in Tanzania indicate that population density is higher in these areas and that the size of an average group may be appreciably larger in such forests than in more open, grassland-savanna habitats. Although much remains to be done, the present studies allow ecological comparisons over a larger and more varied series of habitats than can be made for any other nonhuman primate.

The six areas on which this report is based vary in altitude from sea level to 7000 feet, with wide variations in seasonal rainfall and vegetation.

## GROUP SIZE

Repeated counts of more than 2000 baboons in Kenya show a variation in group size from 9 to 185. In southern Africa a survey of baboons shows a range in group size from 8 to 109. Figure 2–4 summarizes group size for groups in Nairobi Park, Amboseli Reserve, and southern Africa.

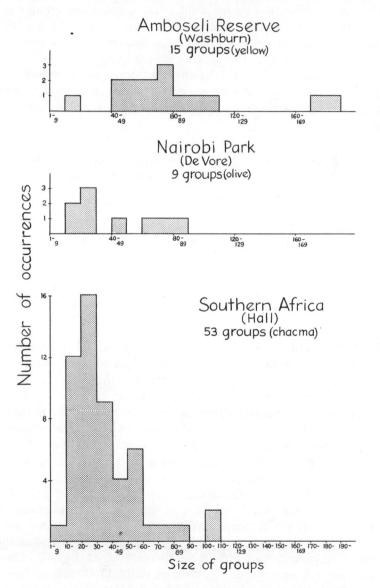

Fig. 2–4. Frequency of occurrence of baboon groups of different sizes in Amboseli Reserve, Nairobi Park, and southern Africa.

While all the present data indicate a central tendency (mean and median) in group size of 30 to 50, wide variation between areas, as well as within an area, is also obvious. For example, the smallest group in Nairobi Park is 12, the largest is 87, and the average size is 41; at Amboseli the range is from 12 to 185 with an average size of 80—twice the average at Nairobi. Population density is about 10 per square mile at Nairobi, and 25 or more per square mile at Amboseli. These data from Kenya, where the groups of 12 and 185, for example, shared the same area, indicate that group size in an area is related more to patterns of social behavior than to differences in the local environment. The only suggestion that local ecological conditions may influence group size comes from the single study area where differences in altitude were marked. In the Drakensberg Mountains of South Africa a brief sampling of the population showed a negative correlation between the height of a group's home range and the number of individuals in the group (Table 2–2).

TABLE 2–2. RELATIONSHIP OF GROUP SIZE TO HEIGHT OF HOME RANGE IN FIVE GROUPS, GIANT'S CASTLE RESERVE, DRAKENSBERG MOUNTAINS, NATAL

| Number of Groups | Number of Baboons in Group | Estimated Altitude, in Feet, of Home Range |
|---|---|---|
| 1 | 15 | 6000–7000 + |
| 2 | 21 | 5000–6000 |
|  | 21 or 22 |  |
| 1 | 37 | 4500–5500 |
| 1 | 58 | 4000–4500 |

Although this small sample can only suggest a trend that needs confirmation by samples taken in surrounding valleys, it is not unreasonable to suppose that group size in this area is dependent upon the food resources. While baboon foods are relatively plentiful at the lower elevations, they steadily decrease in the upper reaches. Because they move as a group as they forage for food, there may be an upper limit to group size in areas where food is scarce. Baboons usually travel about three miles a day, and a large group would have more difficulty accommodating the nutritional needs of all its members when food is hard to obtain.

While it is difficult to find distinct correlations between habitat, food supply, and group size within local areas, such correlations between widely separated areas should become more apparent as further studies are made. Hall found that the central tendency in group size was lowest in the arid, relatively inhospitable study area in South-West Africa, highest in Southern Rhodesia, and fell between these extremes in the Drakensberg, East Cape, and Cape Peninsula of South Africa (Table 2–3).

TABLE 2-3. REGIONAL DIFFERENCES IN NUMERICAL SIZES

| Area | Number of Troops | Mean | Range | Standard Deviation ± |
|---|---|---|---|---|
| South-West Africa* | 20 | 27 | 8–65 | 13.8 |
| South Africa (Drakensberg, East Cape and Cape Peninsula) | 15 | 31 | 15–58 | 13.6 |
| Southern Rhodesia | 18 | 46 | 12–109 | 28.5 |
| Whole region | 53 | 34 | 8–109 | |

* Some of the S.-W. African groups may have been subject to hunting.

It may be that the small "one-male-group" structure of hamadryas baboon groups (Kummer and Kurt 1963) is an advantageous foraging pattern for this species in the dry, open savanna of Ethiopia, although Kummer (personal communication) states that hamadryas group structure remains the same in areas with a rich food supply. In contrast to the average group size of 40 to 80 (with as many as 30 adult males in one group) found in chacma, olive, and yellow baboons, Kummer and Kurt found that hamadryas groups contained internal units consisting of only one adult male, together with one to four, rarely up to nine, females with their young offspring. These one-male units seldom move independently of each other, and the normal foraging group is more comparable to other baboon groups, that is, a group of 30 to 50 animals. The hamadryas also differ from the other baboons described in this and the following chapter in that they come together in large "sleeping parties." While all the other varieties of baboons described in this chapter sleep as a group, at sleeping sites which are used repeatedly and which are very rarely used by more than one group, various hamadryas groups come together in sleeping parties which may be as large as 750. It is tempting to regard this pattern as an adaptation to an area where food sources are sparse and scattered, and yet where suitable sleeping places are so rare that the groups must gather at night at the few sites available to them. Clearly we are only beginning to understand some of the ecological factors which influence group size and population density.

## GROUP MOVEMENT AND RANGE

### Day Range

Studies in southern Africa, Kenya, and on hamadryas in Ethiopia all indicate the average distance traveled by baboons during a day is three miles.

This measures the shortest distance from the sleeping place in the morning, along the route traveled during the day, and back to a sleeping place in the evening. The distance the group or any individual baboon actually walks is much greater, since feeding activity is meandering. There is also considerable latitude in the distance traveled on any particular day. This varies from only a few yards (when a Kenya group sleeps in a fig tree and feeds in and under the tree throughout the following day) to a maximum distance of 12 miles (observed once for a group of 65 in South-West Africa). The contrast in available food between a heavily laden fig tree and the sparse vegetation of the study area in South-West Africa suggests that available food is the single most important factor affecting length of day range. This is supported by observations at different seasons, which show that during the seasons when suitable vegetable foods are most plentiful average day ranges are shorter (Hall 1962a:193). A second reason for the longer average day range in the dry season (Kenya) or winter (Cape) is that a group is more likely to shift to a new core area (see below) during these seasons. It is likely that this shifting is also related to the available food supply, representing movement to a new locus of foraging activity after reduction of the available food in the former locus.

## Sleeping Sites

The most general statement it is possible to make about baboon sleeping sites is that they seem to choose the safest places available to them. In the past different varieties of baboons have been characterized as preferring a particular kind of sleeping place, such as cliffs instead of trees. While it seems likely that groups may develop traditional preferences in local areas, our data would not confirm any widespread correlation between species or race and choice of sleeping site. In Southern Rhodesia and Kenya baboons usually sleep in tall trees, such as fig trees or "fever trees" (*Acacia xanthophloea*) (Fig. 2–3). In the Cape, in South-West Africa, and in Ethiopia, (hamadryas) baboons usually sleep on steep cliff faces (Fig. 2–2). If there are no tall trees in an area, Kenya baboons also sleep on cliff faces, and some groups, in South Africa at least, may use a cave as a sleeping site.

The number of sleeping places used by a group varies widely. In the Cape and in Ethiopia, with few tall trees available and a limited number of sleeping cliffs, a group usually has very few sleeping sites. The number of sleeping sites used by a group seems to be a direct function of the number of suitably tall and spacious trees or of the extent of the steep cliffs available. In Kenya, one group, whose core area contained only one isolated grove of tall trees, slept in this spot on all but two evenings throughout ten months of almost daily records, while groups that ranged along the river might have as many as 14 sleeping sites. In South Africa, a group may use only a single available "kopie," (Fig. 2–2) or, where there is a continuous

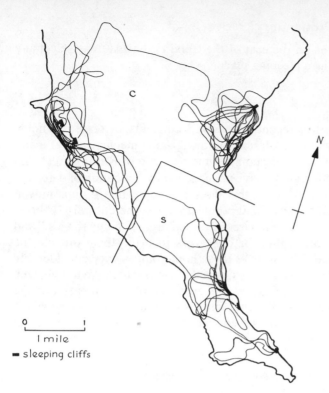

Fig. 2–5a. Ten day ranges for group S and 21 day ranges for group C, Cape Reserve. The sharp line indicates the approximate limit of each group's home range.

0 _____ 1
1 mile
━ sleeping cliffs

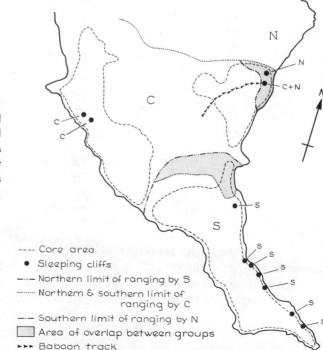

Fig. 2–5b. Areas occupied by C and S groups and southern limit of N group's range, indicating amount of overlap in home ranges and location of core areas.

---- Core area
● Sleeping cliffs
—··— Northern limit of ranging by S
········ Northern & southern limit of
　　　　 ranging by C
—·— Southern limit of ranging by N
▨ Area of overlap between groups
▶▶▶ Baboon track

stretch of steep cliffs, as on the east of the Cape Peninsula, may select any of 7 or more sections as a sleeping place.

### Home Range

Kaufmann (1962) has recently reviewed concepts of territory, home range, and similar methods for describing the spacing mechanisms of mammals. Our observations are very comparable to those of Kaufmann (1962) on the coati. That is, although we have never seen any indication of defended boundaries ("territorial defense"), this does not imply that groups moved about without reference to any fixed boundaries. On the contrary, baboon groups spend most of their time in circumscribed areas, "home ranges," and it is very difficult or impossible for observers to drive them outside the boundaries of this range. The sizes of these home ranges vary considerably for a variety of ecological and, perhaps, social reasons which are not yet well understood, but the size of the troop, concentration of food plants, and the proximity of neighboring troops seem most important. Table 2–4 shows the approximate size of the home range, compared to group size, for groups in Nairobi Park and the Cape Reserve.

TABLE 2–4. SIZE OF HOME RANGE OF BABOON GROUPS

| Name of Group | Group Size | Home Range (square miles) |
|---|---|---|
| Kenya (Nairobi Park) | | |
| MR | 12 | 2.0+ |
| LT | 17 | 9.2 |
| PP | 24 | 7.0+ |
| AR | 28 | 3.0+ |
| SR | 28 | 15.5 |
| SV | 40 | 9.6+ |
| KV | 77 | 11.7+ |
| HP | 87 | 13.8+ |
| Cape Reserve | | |
| N | 20 | 3.5 |
| S | 35 | 5.7 |
| C | 80 | 13.0+ |

While the ranges for only four of these groups is judged to be complete, sizes shown for the other five groups probably include 80 percent of their annual range. In general, a large troop contains more adult males (whose body weight and food requirements are about twice that of adult females)

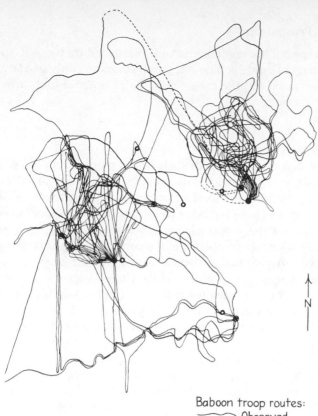

Fig. 2–6a. Day ranges by the SR group, Kenya, during 55 days, April to December 1959.

Baboon troop routes:
~~~~~~ Observed
- - - - - Reconstructed

Sleeping places:
- ● Frequent use
- ◉ Occasional use
- ○ Rare use

0    ½    1
mile

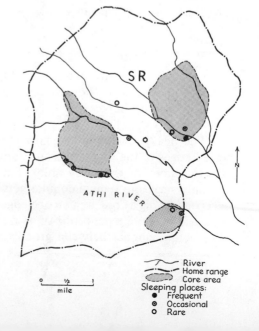

S R

ATHI RIVER

~~~~ River
—— Home range
▨ Core area

Sleeping places:
- ● Frequent
- ◉ Occasional
- ○ Rare

0    ½    1
mile

Fig. 2–6b. The home range and core areas of the SR group, derived from the day ranges shown in Fig. 2–6a. Note position of this group's range in Fig. 2–7.

and covers a wider range. This tendency is well illustrated by the AR and SR groups which both numbered 28. The AR group contained only one large adult male, the SR contained six; the range of the latter is about four or five times as large as the former.

## Core Area

Groups use only certain portions of their home ranges frequently. It is convenient to distinguish these areas of frequent use, which contain sleeping trees, water, resting places, and food sources; we refer to them as the core area(s) of the group. Because baboons cannot be driven beyond a certain boundary, the edges of the group's home range seem to have pyschological reality for the baboons themselves, but the core area is an abstraction created by the observer after watching the daily routes of the group during its day ranges. The day ranges for two groups in the Cape Reserve are shown in Figs. 2–5a & b, and 55 day ranges for SR group (Kenya) during an observation period of eight and a half months is shown in Figs. 2–6a & b.

From this record the month-to-month pattern of group activity in Kenya is obvious: certain sleeping sites are used far more frequently than others; from the sleeping site the group forages out in a meandering, roughly circular path each day, usually returning to the same sleeping site of the previous night; at irregular intervals the group shifts from one core area to another. Figure 2–6b shows the boundaries of SR group's home range and core areas, derived from the data shown in Fig. 2–6a. In Nairobi Park the majority of tall trees, preferred as sleeping sites, are fever trees. The fact that these trees grow only where the water table is high explains the clustering of sleeping sites along water courses, since only the Athi River at the southern edge of the park contained surface water throughout the dry season. The three core areas in Fig. 2–6b total only three square miles, or 20 percent of the group's total home range.

## Interactions of Groups

In most areas daily routines tend to keep baboon groups apart. In Fig. 2–7 it is clear that the home ranges of neighboring groups overlap extensively, while core areas (the areas where a group spends 80 percent of its time) overlap very little.

The heavy shaded areas show the observed extent of core areas (the jagged edges of the core areas and "open-ended" outlines of the range indicate the limits of the study area). The existence of alternative core areas probably serves to reduce contact between adjoining groups; when a group (A) is occupying a core area on one edge of its range, its neighbor on that side (B) tends to move to a portion of its range well away from the vicinity of A. Thus actual contact between groups is even less than might be expected

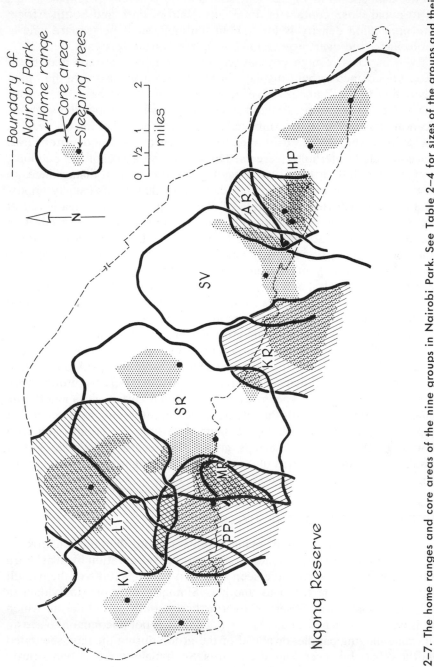

Fig. 2–7. The home ranges and core areas of the nine groups in Nairobi Park. See Table 2–4 for sizes of the groups and their home ranges. The park itself is slightly more than 40 square miles.

from the data shown in Fig. 2–7. It seems to be generally true that groups tend to avoid close contact in areas like Nairobi Park and South Africa, where population density is low (about ten individuals per square mile in Nairobi Park) and overt aggression between groups is very rare.

Even in areas of high population density different groups may be in close, daily contact without displays of intergroup aggression. In the Mana Pools region of the Zambesi River an aggregation of 118 baboons, constituting at least two groups, fed and drank side by side without the slightest indication of disturbance. In Amboseli Reserve, at the end of the dry season, many groups were gathered in a restricted area of food and water. Two small, connected waterholes were used by six groups, a total of 503 baboons, and more than 400 of these would aggregate there without disturbance. In fact, the individuals were so close to each other that it was usually impossible to distinguish the boundaries of the groups when they gathered at these waterholes, unless the arrival of each group had been observed. As a group began arriving at one edge of the waterhole, the group already there would begin feeding slowly away and perhaps leave the waterhole on the opposite side after an hour. A large group would gradually displace a smaller one at these waterholes, and a group of baboons would displace a group of vervet monkeys (*Cercopithecus aethiops*) feeding there, but there was no evidence of one group trying to chase another away.

This does not mean that all groups were always equally "relaxed" when near each other. On one occasion the group of 171 came to the waterhole usually frequented by the group of 185. Both groups paid close attention to each other; adult males clustered at the points where the groups were closest; and gestures and vocalizations indicated a nervousness among the animals that contrasted with the apparent lack of attention characteristic of groups which normally frequent the same waterhole. By comparison with the behavior of Nairobi Park groups, group 171 was probably on the edge of its range while group 185 was in its core area. And fighting between groups trying to settle in the same sleeping trees has been seen at Amboseli.

## POPULATION AND GROUP DYNAMICS

Baboon groups are closed social systems. During all of the field investigations reported here, and including 200 hours of observation by Washburn in Northern Rhodesia, we have seen only two baboons (both of them adult males) shift from one troop to another. Similarly only one individual (a nearly adult male) was observed over a three-month period during which time it was not attached to any group (Cape). It is not uncommon to see an adult male moving parallel or ahead of the group during the day, separated from the others by several hundred yards. Such males are only temporarily apart from the others, joining the group during rest periods and at the sleeping site. These males probably account for most of the "solitary" baboons reported by casual observers. The smallest unit of social significance for these baboons, then, is the entire group (although the one-male units of the hamadryas constitute an altogether different pattern).

## Formation of New Groups

None of our studies has covered periods of sufficient length for us to specify the conditions under which new groups are formed or established groups are split, but some of the Kenya data do suggest what may be involved:

> Large groups of baboons may temporarily subdivide, and groups of 88, 94, and 103 (Amboseli) and the group of 77 (Nairobi) frequently split. When the groups of 77, 88, and 94 split, all the small infants and their mothers were in one section of the group with the largest adult males. On one occasion group 171 (Amboseli) was also seen dividing in this way. When all the individuals in a group are together there is a clear distinction between the large, dominant adult males, mothers, and infants occupying the center of the group and the other, peripheral group members around them (described in the next chapter), and the temporary divisions seen in these large groups are divided along these lines. Such a subdivision lasts for only part of the day and the group reunites before nightfall.
>
> Another type of splitting, in which the group divides into two sections with a normal distribution of males, females, and juveniles in each section, also occurs in some large groups. Group 103 (Amboseli) sometimes split into two groups of 66 and 37, each group having a center, a periphery, and all the characteristics of a normal, independent group. It seems likely that this kind of splitting represents the first stage in the formation of a new group. Observations on groups 51 and 66 support this. These two groups stayed very close together; if one of them arrived at a waterhole, the other was likely to appear, and, after using adjacent sleeping trees at night, they often followed the same route away from the trees the next morning. It is tempting to regard this situation as representing a large group divided one stage further than was the case of group 103. The reason for regarding 51 and 66 as two groups is that individuals within them did not shift; repeated counts showed that the membership of these two groups was constant, and sometimes they were entirely separate from each other—once for a period of days. It appears that large groups may become unstable, and that divisions occur in groups larger than 70 individuals which are not seen in the small groups. If this division persists, and if the division contains a normal age-sex distribution, a new group may result (DeVore and Washburn 1963: 339–341).

## Group Composition

Accurate counts of baboon groups, even in open country, is no easy task. Repeated counts over many weeks are often necessary, and counts by more than one observer are indispensable. Small infants riding on their mothers' bellies, for example, are difficult to see at any distance, and older juvenile males may be mistaken for adult females. The large size of some groups, their tendency to cluster during movement, the fact that they may temporarily subdivide, and that they may aggregate in large numbers all contribute to the difficulty of taking an accurate census. For example, the group of 103 at Amboseli was originally counted as three groups (103, 66, and 37), and groups 51 and 66 seemed to form a group of 117 on some days. A single count at an Amboseli waterhole might include only part of a group, or an aggregation of 400 from adjacent groups. The group counts included in Fig. 2–4 include only those made in areas where counting was easy, or where an extended study period permitted repeated counting.

The classification of the animals of a group into accurate age and sex categories is even more difficult and requires prolonged familiarity with the groups. Adult males in Kenya, for example, vary greatly in body weight and development of the mantle of shoulder hair. It was not until after five weeks of study that a chance observation of the fully erupted, worn canines of two males in SV group (Kenya) disclosed that they were fully adult. There was nothing obvious in their size, appearance, or behavior to indicate that they were older than the subadult males they had been supposed to be during the early weeks of observation on this group. In areas outside parks or reserves groups are frequently shot at; in Kenya adult males are most often singled out for killing, and accurate group composition figures are impossible. It is with these reservations in mind that we have included population data only from protected areas in the following table:

TABLE 2–5. NUMBERS OF ADULT MALES, ADULT FEMALES, AND IMMATURES IN NINE BABOON GROUPS

| Name of Group | Adult Male | Adult Female | Total Adult | Total Immatures (both sexes) | Group Total | Adult Sex Ratio M : F | Ratio of Adult Females to Immatures |
|---|---|---|---|---|---|---|---|
| *Rhodesia (1961)–Hall* | | | | | | | |
| Kariba Main | 13 | 31 | 44 | 59 | 103 | 1 : 2.4 | 1 : 1.9 |
| *Cape (1961)–Hall* | | | | | | | |
| C | 8 | 18 | 26 | 54 | 80 | 1 : 2.2 | 1 : 3.0 |
| Table Mountain | 3 | 12 | 15 | 13 | 28 | 1 : 4.0 | 1 : 1.1 |
| N | 1 | 10 | 11 | 9 | 20 | 1 : 10.0 | 1 : 0.9 |
| Totals — Cape | 12 | 40 | 52 | 76 | 128 | 1 : 3.3 | 1 : 1.9 |
| *Kenya (1959)–DeVore* | | | | | | | |
| SV (Nov.) | 5 | 12 | 17 | 24 | 41 | 1 : 2.4 | 1 : 2.0 |
| SR | 6 | 7 | 13 | 18 | 31 | 1 : 1.2 | 1 : 2.6 |
| AR | 1 | 9 | 10 | 18 | 28 | 1 : 9.0 | 1 : 2.0 |
| LT | 2 | 3 | 5 | 12 | 17 | 1 : 1.5 | 1 : 4.0 |
| MR | 1 | 6 | 7 | 5 | 12 | 1 : 6.0 | 1 : 0.8 |
| Totals — Kenya | 15 | 37 | 52 | 77 | 129 | 1 : 2.5 | 1 : 2.1 |
| Over-all totals | 40 | 108 | 148 | 212 | 360 | 1 : 2.7 | 1 : 2.0 |

One of the most striking features on Table 2–5 is the low ratio of adult females to immatures in groups N (Cape) and MR (Kenya). While the average for all groups is consistently 1 : 2, both of these groups have a ratio of less than 1 : 1. These two groups shared other characteristics: both contained only one adult male; both occupied home ranges that were squeezed between larger groups on each side; both were the "wariest" groups encountered by the observers in the Cape and Kenya respectively. Group N used the same sleeping site as group C, when group C was not present. For all these reasons it is possible that these two small groups represent a different kind of new-group formation—the splitting away of a single adult male with associated females. If this speculation proves true, the unusual ratio of females to immatures would imply that offspring of two years of age or older remained in the parent group, and only females, or females with infants, left the parent group with an adult male.

The data in Table 2–5 confirm a statement that is repeated frequently in the literature on nonhuman primates, viz., that the adult females outnumber adult males by a ratio of 2 or 3 to 1. Since these studies have found only one instance of an adult male leading a solitary life, it is often difficult to understand why this unequal adult sex ratio should exist. While it is true that there is presumably a certain amount of differential mortality, because of the role of adult males in group defense, we have no evidence that intragroup fighting among males (which has often been suggested to account for higher mortality among them) is an important cause of death. One of the most important reasons for the disparate sex ratio in adult baboons is the fact that females mature in roughly half the time that males do. By the time she is three and one-half or four years of age the female is coming into estrus. By the age of five she is bearing young and has reached full physical growth. The young male, although he is sexually mature by five, takes from seven to ten years to attain full physical growth, that is, full eruption of canines, muscular and skeletal maturity, and development of secondary characteristics (such as shoulder hair or "mantle"). An observer counting baboons, then, will classify as "adult" all females with infants, or in estrus, or above a certain size. "Adult males," however, are usually only those which have attained the full measure of maturity. While it is possible to obtain data of the sort included in Table 2–5 after a reasonable period of study, the sex determination of every member of the group takes much longer, and it was possible to do so for only five of the Kenya groups. The results of such a determination are shown in Table 2–6. The most interesting conclusion from this table is that, in a series in which adult females outnumber adult males by 55 to 31, the total number of males in the series is about equal to the number of females. It is unlikely that females significantly outnumber males in any savanna baboon population. Different rates of maturation in the two sexes and sexual dimorphism, combined with early mortality of adults probably explain the apparent discrepancy.

TABLE 2-6. AGE AND SEX COMPOSITION OF FIVE GROUPS IN NAIROBI PARK, 1959 AND 1963

| Group Name | Adults M/F | Juveniles Old M/F | Juveniles Young M/F | Infants M/F | Total Sex Ratio M/F | Animals Not Sexed | Remarks |
|---|---|---|---|---|---|---|---|
| SR (Dec. 1959) | 6/7 | 1/3 | 5/0 | 2/4 | 14/14 | 3 | 3 infants born in December (not sexed). |
| SV (Sept. to Dec. 1959) | 6/14 | 6/3 | 8/3 | 0/1 | 20/21 | 4 | In Sept. 2 diseased females disappeared and an adult male joined; in Nov. an adult male and diseased infant disappeared; infant born in Dec. Four infants not sexed. |
| LT (May 1959) | 2/3 | 3/1 | 3/1 | 2/0 | 10/5 | 2 | A group member (probably adult female) shot in April; 2 infants born in Sept. (not sexed). |
| MR (June 1963) | 4/6 | 2/1 | 5/2 | 3/1 | 14/1̄0 | | |
| KV (June 1963) | 13/25 | 6/6 | 11/9 | 0/1 | 30/41 | 5 | 2 young juveniles and 3 infants not sexed. |
| Totals | 31/55 | 18/14 | 32/15 | 7/7 | 88/91 | 14 | |

## Group Structure and Ecology

Life in an organized group is so characteristic of baboons that the strength of the cohesive social forces appears to surmount all but the most severely disintegrative ecological factors. Under the stresses of overcrowding and near-starvation that occurred on a large island formed in Lake Kariba in 1961, however, all but two baboon groups (of 31 and 17) had split, and individuals were foraging singly, or in small parties of 2 to 9 animals (Hall 1963). The vegetation remaining on the island was mainly *Mopane* and *Terminalia* trees and grasses—a very inadequate selection of vegetable foods by comparison to the mainland habitat. None of the females sighted were in estrous cycles (malnutrition can cause the cessation of cycles [Goodman and Gilbert 1946]), and only one female was definitely carrying an infant. During this same study period many females were seen on the mainland with infants or in estrous cycles. The animals on the island were lethargic, and seemed to lack any social responsiveness such as vocalizations, juvenile play-fighting, mating, or gestures like presenting.

It is impossible to say from the first report on hamadryas (Kummer and Kurt 1963) whether the small one-male units characteristic of this species are adaptations to a harsh environment, but this would be one means whereby the normally larger foraging unit could subdivide under pressure. It seems unlikely that a group of the size typically found in Kenya or South Africa would be an effective foraging unit when food is in very short supply, that is, a group of 30 to 50 might well be unable to cover a sufficient feeding area in a day without exhausting its members. In areas where predators are rare and the need for males to protect the group is minimal, smaller foraging parties are probably more effective. However, an evaluation of the social and ecological factors operating in these hamadryas groups must await a more complete account.

## DIET

The most striking fact about baboon diet is its variety and eclecticism; no edible vegetable matter seems to be excluded, and it is almost easier to list the items which they do *not* eat than to describe the items which they do. They are almost entirely vegetarian and this aspect of their diet is treated in detail elsewhere, particularly in Hall (1962a) and Hall (1963). The present discussion will center on those aspects of diet which are most prominent or ecologically significant.

### Vegetable Foods

In the Cape baboons have been recorded eating 94 species of vegetable foods. In any one area the most ecologically significant items in the floral diet are those which make up the bulk of the diet during the year. The commonest plant-foods taken by groups in the Cape are shown in Table 2–7.

TABLE 2–7. MONTHS OF THE YEAR 1958–1959 DURING WHICH THE COMMONEST PLANT-FOODS WERE TAKEN BY THE CAPE RESERVE GROUPS.

| Species | Part Used for Food | Months in Which Feeding Was Prevalent | Number of Months |
|---|---|---|---|
| *Acacia* spp. (exotic) | Seeds | May to July ⎱ Nov. to Mar. ⎰ | 8 |
| *Carpobrotus edulis* | "Figs" and flowers | Nov. to April | 6 |
| *Cullumia squarrosa* | Flowers | July to Oct. | 4 |
| *Leucadendron* spp. | Cones | Sept. to April | 7 |
| *Leucospermum conocarpum* | Globe-shaped "flower" and young leaves | July to April | 10 |
| *Metalasia muricata* | Seeds | May to July | 3 |
| *Protea lepidocarpodendron* | "Flowers" | April to June | 3 |
| *Tetraria* spp. | Base of leaves | Dec. to May | 6 |
| *Watsonia* spp. | Bulbs | July to April | 10 |

Viewed in broader ecological terms, the most important aspect of their diet is the ability of baboons to adapt to different habitats, taking advantage of whatever staple food items the local area may offer. On the grasslands of Kenya, for example, baboons were seen eating grasses during every observation day in a ten-month period. Different portions of the plant are eaten, according to the season, but grasses seem most important during the dry season, when they compose an estimated 90 percent of the diet. In dry periods the baboons concentrate on the subsurface rhizomes, which have high water content even when the surface vegetation is parched and denuded by ungulates. In both Kenya and the Cape baboons will excavate holes as large as 24″ × 8″ and 15″ in depth in order to uncover roots, bulbs, or tubers (see Fig. 2–8*a*). In summary, the baboon diet, measured by the amount of time spent in feeding, was estimated to be 98 percent vegetarian in Kenya and 90 percent vegetarian in the Cape (where there is opportunity to search for marine food).

## Nonvegetable Foods

Baboons eat insects in all observation areas; how important these are in the diet seems to depend on the availability both of insects and of floral foods in an area. In Kenya and the Cape, for example, insects are ordinarily a very minor dietary item, but given the opportunity they can become a

Fig. 2–8a. An adult male in Nairobi Park digging for underground rhizomes.

Fig. 2–8b. A Nairobi Park male looking for ants and crickets under a stone.

principal foodstuff. When a heavy infestation of "army worm" caterpillars appeared in Nairobi Park, baboons (as well as vervet monkeys and Marabou storks) ate little else for ten days. Baboons were timed picking up 100 caterpillars per minute for 10 to 15 minutes without stopping. In South-West Africa both insects and reptiles are important food items. Groups in this area spend large amounts of time turning over stones or rock slabs and picking up objects under them (see Fig. 2–8b). Experiments carried out by Hall (1962a) on a tame juvenile and a wild juvenile from the area illustrate the importance of observational learning in the acquistion of food habits. When scorpions and live specimens of the snakelike, legless lizard (*Leptotyphlops scutifrous*) were presented to the two subjects, the tame juvenile reacted with fear and avoidance; the newly-captured juvenile ate scorpions, centipedes, and the legless lizards without hesitation. The scorpions were eaten sting and all, and reliable reports from the area indicate that baboons in South-West Africa also eat two common species of back-fanged snake. By contrast, in the Cape Peninsula insects (except ants) are unimportant in the diet, snakes are avoided, and lizards are ignored. A tame young male released into the S group, Cape, quickly learned to eat the local foods through observational learning (see Hall 1962a and Fig. 2–9).

Fig. 2–9. A tame male (*left*), released into S group, Cape, seven days earlier, is searching for bulbs in the exact spot where the young female beside him had just been foraging.

Fig. 2–10. An adult male in Nairobi Park eating a young Thomson's gazelle.

Baboon groups in the Cape fairly frequently collect marine foods along the seacoast, particularly black mussels and limpets. Mussels are pulled off by hand and cracked in the back molars; limpets are grasped and pulled away with the teeth. Crabs and sandhoppers were found in baboon feces.

Besides these invertebrates, baboons occasionally eat small mammals, eggs, and fledglings. This portion of their diet is described in detail in DeVore and Washburn (1963). Our 1959 observations indicated that the carnivorous tendencies of baboons have often been overestimated. In the ten months of study in Kenya baboons were seen to catch and eat animals on only six, perhaps seven, occasions. These included two half-grown hares (*Lepus capensis*), two or three fledglings (probably the crowned plover (*Stephanibyx coronatus*), two young Thomson's gazelles, and a young vervet monkey (Fig. 2–10). All of these instances of meat-eating seemed to be very incidental to the group's search for vegetable foods. No systematic search of a hillside covered in plovers' nests was ever seen, and fledglings are apparently found only when a baboon literally steps on them. Once a bird is caught by an adult it is eaten with dispatch, but one juvenile who caught a fledgling seemed puzzled by it and relinquished it to an adult male. Washburn saw a female catch a vervet near Victoria Falls, then release it unharmed. On subsequent visits to Kenya some baboon groups were catching more animals, especially vervets and hares, than they had previously. When a hare was flushed it was often chased and caught when it "froze" in concealment. These apparently contradictory attitudes toward live prey suggest that meat-eating is learned behavior, and may be frequent in some groups and rare or lacking in others.

Fresh carrion is ignored in Nairobi Park. Such observations indicate the limitations of meat-eating in baboons. Persistent reports of baboon predation on Karakul lambs in South-West Africa need investigation, but it is worth pointing out that the assertion that hardship and drought force the baboons to kill these lambs is not borne out by the Kenya observations, where the young gazelle were eaten during the rainy season when vegetable foods were most plentiful.

## RELATIONS WITH OTHER SPECIES

The terrestrial habits of baboons bring them into daily contact with dozens of other species. In the densely populated game reserves of Kenya they are seldom far from other animals, especially gazelle, wildebeeste (gnu), hartebeeste, zebra, warthog, giraffe, and less often, elephant, rhinoceros, buffalo, guinea fowl and ostrich (see Washburn and DeVore 1961). The baboons' relationship with most of these species is mutual tolerance, and most of the time the species simply ignore each other (Fig. 2–11). Baboons are most often near ungulates, and occasionally this proximity is mutually beneficial (DeVore 1962). Baboons and ungulates recognize each other's alarm calls or "startle barks," and all the species in an area are alerted if an alarm is sounded by an individual of any species. This is particularly true of baboon relationships with impala gazelle and bushbuck. On many occasions herds of impala, or solitary bushbuck, seem to actively seek out baboon groups and stay with them for most or all of the day. An aggregation of baboons and ungulates would be difficult for a predator to

Fig. 2–11. At the grassy border of a waterhole in Amboseli Reserve baboons feed with zebras, Grant's gazelle, and a gnu. Sleeping trees are in the background.

take by surprise; the keen eyesight of the baboons supplements the keen hearing and sense of smell of the ungulates. Furthermore, the impala may take advantage of the protective function of adult baboon males. On one occasion when a trio of cheetahs approached a mixed group of impala and baboons, the impala were very alert but made no attempt to flee; a large adult male stepped toward the cheetahs and turned them away. The response of the impala (a favorite prey of cheetahs) indicated that they had come to depend on the baboon males from past experience.

### Predator-Prey Relations

The role of baboons as predators is discussed above under diet. The relations between baboons and the animals that can prey on them is the most important single fact in the interpretation of baboon ecology and social behavior. Life on the ground exposes baboons to predation far more than is true of arboreal monkeys. In East and Central Africa today, and over most of Africa before the expansion of human activity, these predators included lions, leopards, cheetahs, hyenas, jackals, wild dogs, and raptorial birds. When baboons are away from trees, foraging in open country, the powerful muscles and large canines of the adult males are the group's only protection. When the group is moving in open country, the vulnerable members (mothers with infants and young juveniles) cluster in the group's center, around the most dominant and protective adult males. Other males surround the group, moving ahead, behind, and along its sides. The importance of these outlying males in preventing the rest of the group from being taken by surprise is described in detail in Hall (1960). During a year's field study it is unlikely that actual predation on baboons will be seen. Instead one sees sick or crippled individuals making strenuous efforts to keep up with the group, falling farther and farther behind daily, and finally disappearing. It is also not uncommon to see encounters between baboons and potential predators, and observe the baboons' defensive reactions, without seeing the predators actually attack. Finally, it should be remembered that the removal by predators of only a few individuals annually, from a sizeable population, would be almost impossible to detect during an average study, yet would exert very important selection on the evolution of the species.

The sexual dimorphism of baboons is most striking in those features which equip the male for defense. The fact that baboon and macaque males are aggressive and dominance-oriented, by comparison to other primates, is presumably a correlate of their special function as group defenders and has important consequences on social behavior and organization (next chapter). While there are demonstrable reasons why selection has favored the evolution of large males, it is not so obvious why it is an advantage for females to remain small. It can be argued that sexual dimorphism is a balance between social roles, and that females will be as much smaller as is com-

Fig. 2–12. SR group, Kenya, has taken refuge from a lioness by climbing into the trees. These trees are smaller than those used for sleeping.

patible with these roles. Females mature earlier and are only about half the body weight of males. Assuming that food is a limiting factor on the population, it is advantageous for females to be smaller because the reproductive potential of a baboon group, as measured by the combined body weights of all the individuals, is twice what it would be if males and females were of equal size (DeVore and Washburn 1963).

In addition to the effect predation has had in the evolution of physical characters, the danger of predators sets limits on baboon day ranges and home range. Refuge sites — trees, cliffs, "koppe" — limit baboon range as much as available food and water. A group's day range is limited by the necessity of returning to a safe sleeping site at night. Where large predators such as lions are numerous, as in Amboseli Reserve, the absence of trees in some areas may deny baboons access to rich food sources when food items in general are scarce (Fig. 2–12).

## BIRTH PERIODICITY

The fact that the Japanese macaque and rhesus macaque give birth during a brief period of the year is now well established (Lancaster and Lee, Chap. 14, this volume). There is evidence that in some areas baboon births are also somewhat seasonal. In Kenya rainfall is seasonal, with most of the rain falling between October and May, and the heaviest falling in the January to May period. The plants on which baboons depend for food are most abundant in the period from December to May, and in both the Nairobi and Amboseli areas most of the young are born in the months of October, November, and December, or just before the food supply reaches its peak. Wingfield (personal communication) has reported a birth peak at Kariba (Southern Rhodesia) at the onset of the rainy season (November), and Stevenson-Hamilton (1947) stated that most infants were born in a two- or three-month period, beginning in November, in the Eastern Transvaal.

The evidence, however, is by no means unequivocal. In contrast to the seasonal limits of copulation in Japanese macaques, some sexual activity occurs throughout the year in Kenya, and an occasional infant may be born at any time. In the Cape, where the seasons are less marked and the food supply is subject to less variation, there is no clear evidence of a birth peak. The 12 adult females collected by Zuckerman (1932) near Grahamstown, South Africa, included three lactating mothers with infants estimated to be 2 and 4 months old, 5 pregnant females with embryos of various sizes, and four females who were not pregnant. A further complicating factor is that, while most macaque females give birth every year, baboon females apparently give birth only every two years. Since the primary purpose of these studies was observation of undisturbed animals, females were not captured and examined, but from the observational data it would appear that estrous swelling and sexual activity does not resume in a female until her infant is about 12 to 15 months old. This interval, plus a gestation period of 6 months, would indicate that the usual interval between births is at least 18 months. In areas where birth peaks are pronounced this interval is apparently extended by the effect of seasonal variations on the reproductive cycle. How this may be brought about is not known, but the birth interval of 2 years is confirmed by Gilbert and Gillman's data on captive chacma females (1951).

## CONCLUSION

Local populations of the savanna baboon in widely separated areas have been found to be remarkably similar in all aspects of their ecological adaptations. Group size and composition, the length of the day range and size of the home range, sleeping habits, and intergroup relations are all basically alike wherever this species is found. Over all of its range the savanna baboon seems capable of adapting to whatever local foods are available, from pine cones in coniferous forests to crustaceans at the seashore, to grass roots on the plains. This catholic diet together with a social organization which permits the group to move into open areas in relative safety help explain why a single species has been able to spread over most of subsaharan Africa. The following chapter will examine their social behavior and its regional variations in some detail.

# K. R. L. HALL and IRVEN DEVORE

# 3

## ◆ Baboon Social Behavior

Zuckerman's (1932) field observations of chacma behavior were confined to a few days in the eastern Cape Province, South Africa, by far the bulk of his data coming from detailed observations on *P. hamadryas* in the Regent's Park Zoo, London. No data on behavior are yet available in English on the baboon colony at Sukhumi, Black Sea coast, although this colony has been established for about 30 years, and the Russian film "Threshold of Consciousness" indicates that behavior studies of at least one hamadryas group living in a compound have been carried out. The major captivity studies so far have been those of Kummer on hamadryas at the Zürich zoo (1956, 1957). This is at present the only species which has been thoroughly studied under restricted conditions as well as in the natural habitat, Kummer and Kurt (1963) having recently completed a year's field work on groups in Ethiopia. Bolwig (1959a) combined some detailed observations on the behavior of two young chacma baboons that he kept in captivity with data obtained from watching baboon groups foraging around the camp rubbish heaps in the Kruger National Park, but the scope of his study was restricted by these conditions. No systematic data whatever on the behavior of baboons elsewhere in Africa were available until the DeVore and Washburn studies.

Baboons have been used very little in laboratory studies of learning or "intelligence." As adults they have a reputation for being difficult to handle, and their comparatively large size makes them less convenient than macaques for most laboratory purposes. Where they have been used in problem-solving studies (Watson 1914; Harlow and Settlage 1934; Bolwig 1961), the data from one or two animals on one class of problem have yielded very little information that can be meaningfully related to field data.

Most of the behavior data we shall discuss were obtained by one or two observers, who worked at close range to the baboon group. A condition of neutrality between the observer and the animals was first achieved so that they were neither positively attracted toward the observer by expectation of food, nor frightened of him, unless he introduced some marked change into their environment. The presence of two observers permitted each to concentrate on a certain class of individuals in a group or upon a certain aspect of behavior, and film or tape recordings could be made without loss of observational data.

Marking of individuals was not attempted and, in fact, was not necessary for the immediate purpose of the studies, although it would be highly desirable as a basis for long-term investigations. All individuals of two Nairobi Park groups (SR and LT) were recognizable to DeVore, and most of the adults in four other groups in the same area were individually distinguishable. All individuals of one Cape Reserve group (S) were recognizable to Hall and Robert Wingfield, as were also many of the adults of the large C group and the Kariba main group in Southern Rhodesia. By memorizing blemishes and scars observed at close range as well as learning major physical differences such identification could be made.

Although sustained observation of the "natural" behavior of these animals was the main objective of these studies, minor experimental interferences were occasionally introduced to elicit unusual behavior. As a method of supplementing normal field data, we have hardly begun to explore the possibilities of systematic use of field experiments or of exploiting accidental occurrences not planned by the investigator but creating drastic alterations in the environment of a group.

## SOCIAL ORGANIZATION

The baboon group is organized around the dominance hierarchy of adult males. The nature of this hierarchy varies between groups according to the constitution of each group. The simplest form of organization is probably that of groups in which one, and only one, adult male is conspicuously dominant. Such groups, numbering from 15 to 35 animals, were the S group in the Cape, both in 1960 and 1961, the N group at all periods of observation, and the LT, AR, and MR groups in Nairobi Park in 1959 (see Table 2–4, previous chapter). A much more complex relationship was that observed in the SR group in Nairobi Park; during the time of study there were 6 adult males and only 7 adult females in this group, which totaled 28 animals. However, the proportion of adult males to adult females was nearer to the average in the SV group, the other group intensively studied in that area, in which there were 5 adult males and 14 adult females out of a total of 40 animals. In 1961 in C group, Cape, when the group totaled 80 animals, 8 identifiable large males took part at various times in threat behavior among themselves, and there were at least 30 adult females in the group. It was not possible during the limited observation period to work out the dominance relations among them. It remains one of the most important research tasks of the future to concentrate intensive observations for a long period on one group of this size or larger in order to work out accurately the complex interactions among the males and to learn how the adult females with their infants and the subadults and juveniles are organized in relation to them.

Pending a long-term study on a large group of the Kenya or southern African baboons, it is not possible to evaluate the apparent differences in social organization of the hamadryas baboons in Ethiopia, reported on in a preliminary account by Kummer and Kurt (1963). According to these observers, a one-male group is the characteristic social unit in the population area they studied. It consists typically of from one to four, rarely as many as nine, females who follow a single adult male, as do their offspring until they reach the age of one or one and one-half years. The juveniles and subadult males, and some adult males without females, live outside these units, yet all these, together with other one-male groups, tend to congregate in very large numbers at the sleeping cliffs. It would appear that tolerance between adult hamadryas males is significantly less than it is in olive or chacma baboons. However, until the full report of the Ethiopian study is available, we cannot judge whether the difference in social organization is one of degree, imposed upon the population by the ecological circumstances, or whether, as the authors suggest, it is so fundamental as to express itself in the same way even in captivity (*cf.* Zuckerman 1932).

### Male Dominance

Dominance is a complex conception assessed by observation of the frequency and the quality of several types of behavior in various kinds of situations, with reference both to the other animals within the group and to external events — such as the presence of a predator or some other disturbing stimulus. The "peck-order" concept of a linear kind of social relationship, derived from only one kind of situation — competition for food — is scarcely applicable to wild baboons, where in the normal course of foraging the animals are widely spaced and competition for any item of food is a rare event among adult males. Special food-incentive tests to determine relative dominance between a pair of adult males, used in several laboratory studies, have a limited usefulness in the field. In nature it is difficult to isolate the test pair so that it is unaffected by the presence of other adult males, though these may be temporarily in the background. Occasionally a situation occurs, such as in S group, Cape, in 1961, in a group numbering 38 animals that was sometimes to be found on the roadside about six miles to the north of S, and in the LT and AR groups, in which one and only one of the adult males has a consistent priority of access to any food object thrown down within its view.

Dominance as expressed in the natural behavior of a group can be illustrated by the straightforward system of S group, Cape. At the time of intensive study of this group there were only three adult males in the group, one somewhat larger than the other two. The key functions or behavior patterns most prominently associated with the largest male can be summarized as follows:

1. He mated exclusively with some, but not all, of the females as they came to maximum turgescence in the estrous period, and drove away males *2* or *3* from the female at this time. (Those females with whom he did not form an exclusive mating relation were not fully grown, and even when in full estrus were only occasionally mounted by him.)

2. The act of presenting, as a submissive gesture, was directed far more frequently to this male than to the others.

3. The number of aggressive episodes recorded for him within the group was far greater than that for any other male.

4. Whenever some disturbing situation occurred, as when the group was charged by an eland cow, and when a strange baboon was released in the vicinity of the group, this male went ahead of the rest of the group and threatened or attacked.

5. When there were mothers with black (recently born) infants in the group, they tended to cluster near him and to walk close to him during the day range. His retaliation against attacks on the mothers was immediate.

The quantifiable behavior patterns of this male in comparison with those of the other two adult males are summarized in Table 3–1, for the 1960 observation period, and the same kind of dominance relationship was still in evidence in this group in 1961.

TABLE 3–1. COMPARATIVE DATA ON MATING, PRESENTING, AND PARTICIPATING IN AGGRESSIVE EPISODES FOR THE $\alpha$ MALE AND MALES 2 AND 3 OF S GROUP, 1960

|  | *Male Animal* | | |
|  | $\alpha$ | *2* | *3* |
| --- | --- | --- | --- |
| Mating frequency | | | |
| female in full estrus | 101 | 37 | 56 |
| female less than full estrus | 8 | 4 | 28 |
| Total | 109 | 41 | 84 |
| Presented to | | | |
| by females and juveniles | 104 | 3 | 6 |
| by other males | 34 | 1 | 0 |
| Total | 138 | 4 | 6 |
| Aggressive episodes | | | |
| against females | 37 | 8 | 3 |
| against others in group | 15 | 6 | 6 |
| Total | 52 | 14 | 9 |

   This kind of dominance relationship may be no more "typical" of the chacma baboon than the one for the Kenya SR group is typical of the baboon groups in that region, but it reveals very clearly the general nature of the functions of dominance. The aggressive episodes are noisy, very menacing, and effective in breaking up squabbles among the other animals and in protecting mothers and infants from disturbance or injury. In addition, as was observed once in S group and three times in C group, when there is some cause for disturbance from outside the group, members of the group tend to close up rather than to scatter, the generalized aggressiveness of the *a* male being directed successively at many different animals within the group and having the effect of bringing them together or at least preventing them from wandering away. For example, this was observed the one time C group encountered N group at the limts of their home ranges, the first time a stuffed serval cat was placed near the sleeping cliffs of C group, and once when the observers were approaching S group through a thick mist that periodically lifted. The probable mechanism for this kind of generalized aggressiveness will be discussed below. In spite, or perhaps because, of the very pronounced dominance of the $\alpha$ male in S group, aggressive episodes were infrequent and were never observed to result in visible injury to any member of the group. The dominant male of this group was aggressive (as expressed in certain characteristic behavior to be described later) about once in every six and a half hours of daylight, except when some special situation arose.
   In C group, Cape, in the 1958–1959 observation period, when it numbered about 53 animals, threat behavior and chasing among the adult males was not recorded, and dominance relations may have been, temporarily, in the form of an established hierarchy. In 1961, however, several sequences were observed in this now much larger group (80 animals) in which two or more of the males threatened each other. One such episode resulted from an attack by one adult female on an adult female with an infant on her back. An adult male immediately chased the aggressor, who ran away from him but continued to try to get at the mother and infant. The first adult male now chased a second adult male who at first ran away; as is typical of these male-male encounters in this group, the animals did not make physical contact with each other. The second male then stood and repeatedly threatened the first male, turning his head rapidly from side to side. The second male was joined by two other adult males in threatening the first, and the four chased about without engaging each other. Several similar episodes occurred, usually while the group was still near the sleeping cliffs in the morning. On one occasion five adult males were charging about after each other, again without engaging with one another. As was also true in Kenya, all the other animals in the group kept well away from these adult males when such episodes were taking place.
   There was strong behavioral evidence that one of the adult males of C group (Saddleback) was often dominant over the others, but there was no way of working out the relations among the others. The probable explana-

Fig. 3–1. Yawning under tension, a young adult male, Mark, of the SR group displays his unworn teeth. The upper canines are not quite fully erupted.

Fig. 3–2. An old adult male, Pua, of the SR group displays the broken and eroded teeth characteristic of old age.

Fig. 3–3. An adult female, also yawning under tension, demonstrates the relatively small canine teeth of female baboons. LT group.

tion for these aggressive episodes may be drawn from the detailed close-range data obtained on the SR group, Kenya; in this group each of the six adult males was individually recognizable to the observer, and the interactions among them were studied continuously over a period of about three and one-half months. In contrast to most adult males in the Park, the six males of this group were all large and of approximately equal size. They ranged in age and physical fitness, however, from young prime (Mark) and prime (Kula) through late prime (Dano, Mdomo) to old (Pua) and very old (Kovu). There were far more aggressive episodes among these adult males than were observed in any other group, and the dominance pattern that emerges is one that cannot be reconciled with the model of a strictly linear hierarchy. It became clear that certain of the adult males constantly associated with each other and tended to support each other in aggressive interactions with other males. Some of these males associated so closely that they were scarcely ever observed acting independently in such episodes, and on this basis three of them came to be designated a "central hierarchy."

In trying to work out the dominance pattern in the SR group, several criteria were used, including: (1) success in achieving food objectives in paired tests given when other males were too far away to interfere directly; (2) frequency of successful dominance assertions in "natural" situations arising within the group, for example, success in gaining and maintaining access to an estrous female or in causing another male to move away from a particular resting place or feeding spot; (3) success of combinations of males against other individual males. The frequency data for criteria (1) and (2) given for the interaction of each of the six males in this group indicate only a fairly consistent subordination for Kovu and Mark and dominance for Dano (Table 3–2).

**TABLE 3–2. DOMINANCE INTERACTIONS AMONG ADULT MALES OF SR GROUP; NUMBER OF INTERACTIONS WITH DOMINANCE EXPRESSED***

*2a. Success-failure on experimental food-incentive tests*

| Success | Dano | Pua | Kula | Mdomo | Mark | Kovu | Total Success | Rank Order Successes | Failures |
|---|---|---|---|---|---|---|---|---|---|
| Dano | | 5 | 3 | 3 | 6 | 2 | 19 | 1= | 2 |
| Pua | 5 | | 1 | 6 | 2 | 5 | 19 | 1= | 5= |
| Kula | 3 | 4 | | 3 | 3 | 1 | 14 | 4 | 1 |
| Mdomo | 3 | 4 | 3 | | 1 | 5 | 16 | 3 | 3= |
| Mark | | 2 | | | | 2 | 4 | 5 | 3= |
| Kovu | | | | | | | 0 | 6 | 5= |
| Total Failure | 11 | 15 | 7 | 12 | 12 | 15 | | | |

*2b. Dominance-subordination in "natural" situations*

| Dominant | Dano | Pua | Kula | Mdomo | Mark | Kovu | Total Dominant | Rank Order Dominant Scores | Subordinate Scores |
|---|---|---|---|---|---|---|---|---|---|
| Dano | | 3 | 6 | 1 | 1 | 1 | 12 | 1 | 1 |
| Pua | | | | | | 2 | 2 | 5 | 5 |
| Kula | 1 | 1 | | 3 | 3 | 2 | 10 | 2 | 4 |
| Mdomo | | | 2 | | | 6 | 8 | 3 | 2= |
| Mark | | 1 | | | | 2 | 3 | 4 | 2= |
| Kovu | | | | | | | 0 | 6 | 6 |
| Total Subordinate | 1 | 5 | 8 | 4 | 4 | 13 | | | |

* The numerical tabulations represent the number of observed interactions in which the male in the vertical row on the left was dominant to the male in the horizontal top row.

The data in Table 3–2 indicate the difficulty of arriving at a linear rank-ing for the males by traditional criteria of dominance. Other criteria, such as instances of mounting between the males, confirm the positions of the males at the top and bottom of the hierarchy but do not clarify the posi-tions of all six. Some of the inconsistencies between sections 2*a* and 2*b* (Table 3–2) are due to the fact that the three central hierarchy males (Dano, Pua, Kovu) not only combined against the other males, but also were very uncompetitive among themselves with regard to food. These three males would feed side by side when food was thrown to them. Although Kovu was obviously less assertive in these situations, Dano and Pua were never asser-tive toward each other over food. Since only one male at a time can consort with an estrous female, however, even central hierarchy males sometimes competed with each other over access to a receptive female, and some scores reflect this. The rank order for "dominant scores," then, is the most accurate measure of individual dominance status (as shown in Fig. 3–4), but the most significant aspect of the dominance relations in this group is that the central hierarchy males, who stayed together in the center of the group, ordinarily acted in concert and together controlled access to incentives, determined group movement, and so on. In every instance where Dano, Pua, and Kovu or Dano and Pua combined, they were 100 percent successful against any of the other three males, who very rarely combined.

Thus a male's dominance status was a combination of his individual fighting ability ("linear dominance," see Fig. 3–4) and his ability to enlist

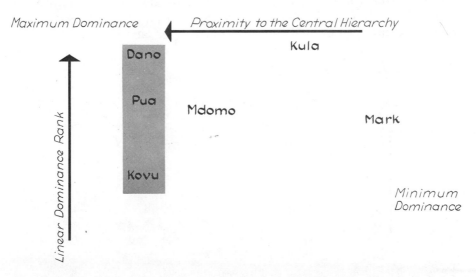

Fig. 3–4. The adult male dominance hierarchy in the SR group, Kenya. A male's position is a combination of his abilities as an individual (his "linear dominance rank"), and his ability to enlist the support of other males in the central hierarchy.

the support of other males ("proximity to the central hierarchy"). Dano emerges on these criteria as the *a* animal; that is, he was at the top of the central hierarchy. On several occasions, however, it was possible to test dominance between him and Kula when they were well away from other males. Kula was the more dominant and is shown (Fig. 3–4) as the highest ranking *individual*. The fact that Pua and Kovu would support Dano when he was challenged, however, meant that Dano was almost always in control and that Kula could only assert himself briefly.

In the SV group, numbering 40 animals (about the average size of groups in Nairobi Park), there were six adult males and the usual ratio of about twice as many adult females. This group has a special interest for the understanding of the dynamics of the dominance system. It was the only group intensively observed in which one adult male (Humbert) disappeared with a consequent alteration of the dominance balance, and to which an adult male from another, adjacent group (Lone from the AR group) attached itself, with interesting effects on the dominance pattern. All adult males and most adult females in the group were individually recognizable. The dominance pattern was characteristically stable—Curly, a younger and unusually aggressive male, being consistently dominant over the other males so long as the much older Humbert, with whom he allied, was in the group. In fact, Humbert, in spite of the physical disadvantage of worn-down canines, maintained a dominance over Gam (and the other smaller males) through a simple, triangular relationship that existed among the three of them (Curly dominant over Humbert; Humbert dominant over Gam; Gam dominant over Curly). The dominance pattern can best be illustrated diagrammatically (Fig. 3–5a) where the position prior to Humbert's disappearance can be compared with that four months later (Fig. 3–5b) when

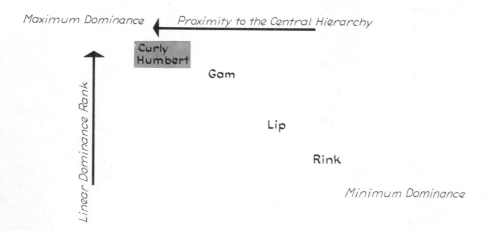

Fig. 3–5a. The adult male dominance hierarchy in the SV group, Kenya, in July 1959. As a central hierarchy Curly and Humbert dominate the other males, although Curly is individually subordinate to Gam.

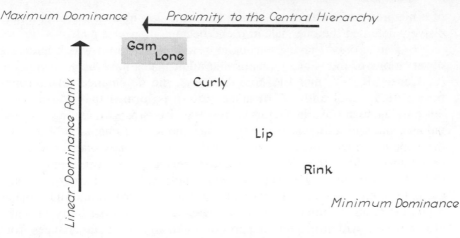

Fig. 3–5b. The SV group hierarchy in November 1959. With the disappearance of Humbert, Gam has asserted his dominant status over Curly, and with a new male, Lone, is beginning to establish a new central hierarchy.

Lone, the male from the AR group, had achieved his position in the SV group.

Before joining the SV group Lone had been very subordinate to the *a* male of the adjoining AR group. When the group was on the move he ranged well ahead of the others; when the group rested the α male frequently drove Lone away from resting spots or grooming clusters, and in general asserted his dominance over Lone continually. At first Lone kept 40 or 50 yards away from the SV group; then, after two days, he stayed within 20 yards of them and slept near them at night. During this period he engaged in several vicious fights with Curly and, probably, with Gam. Ten days after Lone was first seen near the SV group in October, he was walking among the SV animals, although Curly continually threatened him, forcing him to the edge of the group. Before Humbert's disappearance, when he and Curly together maintained a central hierarchy, Lone and Gam remained for a time in more peripheral positions, leading the group during progression. When Humbert disappeared in November, Curly dropped significantly below both Gam and Lone, between whom there had been less tension, with the rotating of the dominance relationship shown in Fig. 3–5b. At the end of the observation period (November) Gam and Lone seemed to be forming a new central hierarchy. Lip and Rink were small adult males who avoided fights and who had no observable effect upon the relations among the more dominant males.

During observations of chacma baboons in Northern Rhodesia in 1955, Washburn observed the only other instance we have seen of a baboon's leaving one group and joining another. In a situation analogous to that just described, a male was driven out of a group in which he was at the bottom of a hierarchy of six males. Shifting the same day to a new group, he decisively defeated the one male in it and became its new $\alpha$ male.

In four groups (having two or more adult males) on which intensive observations of individually identifiable adult males have been carried out (S, Cape; SR, SV, and PP, Nairobi Park), the dominance relationships have varied significantly. A dynamic pattern is formed that is dependent not only on such obvious factors as relative size, strength, and age of individuals, and their differences in experience and temperament, but also upon the support which combinations of two or three males may provide for each other. Although a stable and linear hierarchy sometimes exists, it is likely to represent only a temporary stage in the history of any one group, the pattern changing as younger males become full grown and older males disappear. Equally impressive is the evidence of the possibility of shifts in dominance within neighboring groups when an adult male changes from one group to another.

### Dynamics of Threat Behavior

The nature of the dominance functions of one $\alpha$ male, or of a group of central hierarchy males, is the clue that leads to an adequate understanding of the major aspects of baboon social organization. In addition, however, the complex relationships stemming from these dominance functions must also be fully studied as they affect the whole group. For example, threat behavior we now know can have at least four forms according to the kinds of social interaction with which it is associated. One of the commonest of these is called, in ethological terms, "redirection of aggression" (Bastock, Morris, and Moynihan 1953), corresponding to "transferred threat" (Altmann 1962). We have chosen the former term to indicate a wide range of behaviors that we believe can be so described. In its simplest form redirected aggression occurs when an animal threatens another, and the threatened animal redirects the aggression to a third party (chasing or threatening him) or, rarely, to an inanimate object (for example, bouncing against a tree or tugging vigorously at a rock). During the tense situation in the SR group, 33 instances of redirected aggression between individuals were recorded. A typical instance would be: Dano chases Mdomo, who chases an adult female. Initiation of a kind of chain reaction of aggressive acts downward through the group structure presumably serves periodically to reinforce the dominance pattern throughout the group.

Redirection of aggression was observed very clearly in a different context in S group, Cape, as a sequel to the release of a tame young male baboon near the group one evening close to the sleeping cliffs. Whenever the $\alpha$ male threatened the strange baboon, the latter took refuge behind or very close to the observer, and, apparently as a direct consequence of the $\alpha$ male's being prevented from attacking, he began to attack the other animals in the group more or less continuously during the day. His aggressiveness became ten times more frequent than on normal occasions. Aggression, in such a situation, is transferred from the object which elicited it to substitute objects or animals, probably with some kind of equivalence in the transfer. The generalized aggression of the S-group *a* male, however, gave the impression that he was attacking any animal that came near him or that he came upon. Similarly, during the period when Lone was joining the SV group, Curly's aggressiveness toward other group members was far more frequent than normal.

Threat behavior is often seen between combinations of individuals, indicating that an individual may sometimes seek support or "enlist" the threat behavior of another individual. This is done by gestures such as jerking the head rapidly from side to side. It is important, however, not to misinterpret the significance of this kind of social situation and the gestures involved in it. Head-turning and other gestures to be described later are expressive of agitation, and the support—if it comes—may be primarily in response to a conditioned association between the two animals for which the gestures are the signals. The situation where two animals "simultaneously threaten" another is of the same order. What Kummer (1957) described as "protected threat," on the other hand, refers basically to the situation in which a subordinate succeeds in escaping the threat or attack of a more dominant animal by running toward or standing in front of an animal that is still more dominant. The four terms we have used (redirection of aggression, enlistment of threat, simultaneous threat, and protected threat) all refer to social variants due to combinations of behavior within the general dominance pattern. This variety, observed in differently constituted groups, has served to bring out very clearly the dynamic quality of the adult male relationships.

### Harassment

The adult sex ratio was atypical in the SR group, as has been mentioned, and this factor seems to account for the occurrence of yet another form of aggressive behavior normally never seen in any other Kenya or southern Africa group, namely the harassing of an adult male when he is in consort with an estrous female. In a harassing sequence, similar to that which could almost invariably be induced in males of any Nairobi Park group by experimental feeding, the harasser would start by slowly pacing around the other male, accompanied by an audible tooth-grinding and yawning, directed straight toward the other in what can be described as a canine display. The harasser would gradually approach closer to the other who, in the consort situation, tended to increase his grooming of the female in an intense and agitated manner while occasionally mildly threatening the harasser. After several canine displays by the harasser, these tending to in-

Fig. 3–6. A diseased infant-two female takes offered food by the side of her protector, the B male, while male C harasses the B and A males. SV group.

crease in frequency the closer he approached, a chase, attack, or fight was the usual outcome. In such a situation other adult males would often join either the harasser or the harassed male. When the latter attacked the harasser, the usual conclusion was that a third male would appropriate the estrous female temporarily. Sequences of this sort were never seen in a group where a sufficient quota of adult females was available to the adult males, and never with regard to naturally available food.

## Dominance among Females

The dominance hierarchy among the females in the groups, even where all the adults were identifiable, has been much more difficult to determine objectively. This difficulty may in part reflect the tendency of female status to be more variable and perhaps rather more subtly defined than that of the male. Estrous condition is found to alter the status of a female very markedly; it is possible that the female hierarchy is typically unstable, that it is individually based rather than partly organized around coalitions as in the males, and that it is expressed in more-or-less continuous minor bickering with very little real attacking and biting. This description is indicated on the basis of the interactions between the SR females according to social criteria such as being forced from a feeding spot, from a grooming partner, or from the presence of a mother with an infant, together with an assessment on the indicators of female threat shown by the sudden stopping of the female in front of a subordinate and by eyelid-lowering (Fig. 3–8).

While these figures indicate trends of dominance during this observation period (Inama apparently being the most dominant and Notch easily the most subordinate), it is not possible at present to indicate at all accurately the meaning of these differences in the whole social organization of the group. To what extent these differences depend upon the individual character of the female, her age, experience, and so on, and to what extent they may be a function of some fairly consistent relationship with one or more of the adult males (independent of estrous manifestations of the sexual cycle), remains a problem for further research.

In S group, Cape, a similar picture of inconsistency arises from the 1961 data. One of the females (E), however, was consistently subordinate

Fig. 3–7. An adult male (*right*) displays his canines as he harasses another adult male who is grooming a fully estrous female. SR group.

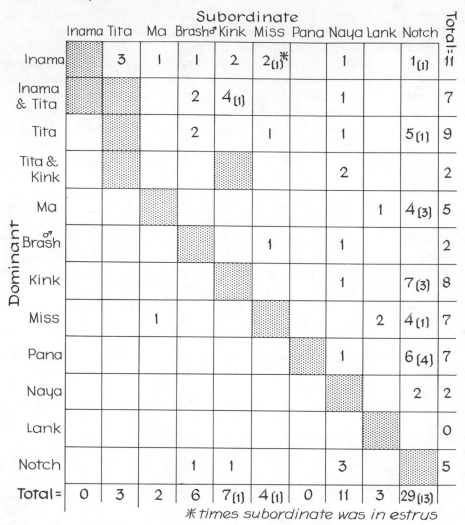

Fig. 3–8. Dominance interactions among females (and one subadult male, Brash) in the SR group, Kenya. The tabulations represent the number of observed interactions in which the female in the vertical row on the left was dominant over the female in the horizontal top row.

to all the others, including another low-ranking female who was physically smaller than E but far more aggressive. The most significant general finding from the 1960 observations on this group was the extent to which female aggressiveness against other females was correlated with the frequency of mating by the $\alpha$ male with the female who was in full estrus. This relationship seemed to indicate that the social pattern among all the adult females was considerably affected by the close attention of the markedly dominant $\alpha$ male to one of their number, for there is no significant

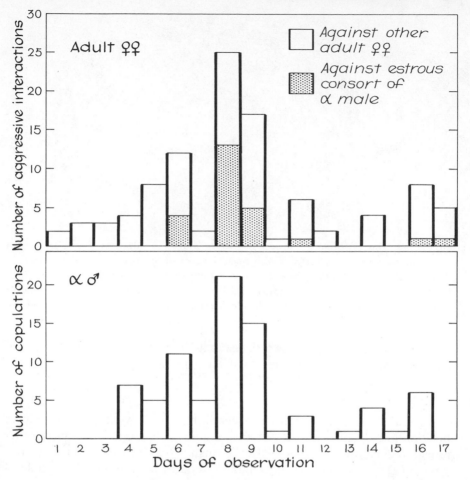

Fig. 3–9. Relationship between frequency of copulation by α male with a fully estrous female, and aggressiveness of adult females toward her and among themselves. S group, Cape.

correlation with the mating frequencies of the other males. Although their attacks on the fully estrous female with whom the α male was copulating increased markedly at the stage when he was consorting exclusively with her, there was also a general increase in aggressiveness among the adult females which indicates an unusual degree of disturbance of the relationship among them (Fig. 3–9).

Although there is evidence of a kind of individual ranking among the females, it is also common for two or more females to "gang up" in threatening and attacking another female. Instances of such simultaneous or enlisted threat were noted on the part of the two subordinate females, E and B. A striking instance of combination was observed in S group when the α

Fig. 3–10. The positions of group members during group movement. Dominant adult males accompany females with small infants and a group of older infants in the group's center. A group of young juveniles is shown below the center and older juveniles above. Other adult males and females precede and follow the group's center. Two estrous females (dark hindquarters) are in consort with adult males. Nairobi Park, Kenya.

male was attacking one of the females in a pond and several females threatened him so vigorously that he withdrew from his victim.

**Spacing within the Group**

As studies of the Japanese macaque have clearly shown, the relative position and distance of the various members of a group from one another reflect the nature of the social relationship between them (cf. Jay, this volume). Mothers carrying their infants tend to be found in the middle of a group when it is on the move; the less dominant males are to the front, at the sides, and to the rear; and the most dominant males are in the middle (see Fig. 3–10). This order of progression was invariable in all groups observed. When some crisis occurs, however, the $\alpha$ or central hierarchy males tend to go immediately to the front to meet the threat, a response observed consistently in all groups both in the Cape and in Kenya.

The so-called "sentinel" behavior of chacma baboon groups was found to be entirely consistent with this kind of organization. A subadult or a young adult male, ahead of the group by 200 yards or as much as one-quarter mile, would be observed to give the alarm bark, and one or more of the large adult males would come to the front to see the cause of the disturbance. It was almost always one of the "peripheral" males that continued to watch and to bark, while sitting at the edge of the area where the rest would soon resume feeding.

It is almost impossible to discover the extent to which adults other than dominant males "lead" a group in the sense of determining the route the group will take during the day range. For example, it sometimes appeared from their frontal position that one or more of the peripheral males might be initiating group movement and determining the direction the group was to take. Similarly, in S group, Cape, two of the adult females were often at the front of the group during the day range, and others appeared to follow them even when they changed the direction of movement. In fact, animals in the lead were probably taking a course which was habitual to the group, but might not otherwise be determining the group's behavior. It seems more correct to say that the group as a whole is continually alert to the behavior and location of the dominant males, and that those ahead are mainly anticipating or steering with reference to these males. This is suggested by their behavior whenever even minor disturbances from outside the group occur, and by the fact that the main body of the group occasionally changes direction, forcing the animals who had been in front to make a wide detour before rejoining the group.

The main characteristics of baboon social organization, as revealed in the Kenya and southern Africa studies, are derived from a complex dominance pattern among adult males that usually ensures stability and comparative peacefulness within the group, maximum protection for mothers with infants, and the highest probability that offspring will be fathered by the most dominant males. With all the variations so far apparent in groups of differing constitutions, it still remains to discover accurately the kind of relationship among the many adult males of a large group of 80 or more animals. The nature of the social structure of adult females, and its periodic variations, also remains to be worked out in detail over a longer period than has so far been available.

## SEXUAL BEHAVIOR

We have noted in the previous chapter the evidence on seasonal variations in births in different regions of the distribution area, and we have noted also some of the major physiological characteristics that may be assumed to underlie the manifestations of sexual behavior to be discussed in the present section. To recapitulate: the female estrous cycle averages, in captivity, about 35 days; the period of turgescence averages 19 days, deturgescence averages 16 days (Gillman and Gilbert 1946). Sexual swelling (see Fig. 3–7) increases gradually for about ten or twelve days until reaching the maximum, when it remains more or less constant for about eight days, and deturgescence takes place during the next one and one-half to five days. The mean gestation period is about six months. Nursing goes on for from six to eight months (Gilbert and Gillman 1951), and turgescence is usually not observed again until after lactation has ceased (although in some females it has occurred while the infant was still at the breast). These indicators are derived from data on chacma baboons in captivity and suggest that the minimum interval between successive births in the same female may be of the order of from 12 to 18 months. The Kenya field data, however, appear to indicate an even longer interval (see Chap. 2). The criteria for distinguishing cessation of lactation are difficult to establish in field studies, and these, together with actual observations of resumed sexuality by individual females in wild groups, need to be further studied in long-term field observation. A female begins her estrous cycles at about the age of three and one-half or four years, and the size of perineal swelling thereafter increases for a few years. Less is known about the chronological pattern of events in the male baboon, but puberty in captive hamadryas is reported to vary in onset between four and six years (Zuckerman 1932), this being similar to the age of first copulation in *M. fuscata*—reported as five years.

Much more needs to be discovered about the variants of sexual reproductive physiology of these animals in the wild. It is clear that standard findings derived in the laboratory may diverge importantly from those derived in the widely varying ecological conditions in which the animals live in nature. Nevertheless, it is now possible to describe rather fully the way in which the sexual behavior patterns fit into the over-all pattern of baboon social organization and to analyze in some detail the components of the behavior.

Comparisons of the Kenya and Cape Peninsula data are interesting in part because of the general similarity of the mating pattern in its social context, and in part because copulation has been observed in the Cape groups in all months of the year—with one or more females always in some state of estrus in C and S groups. In Kenya birth seasonality may have corresponding limitations upon estrous occurrences, because there are periods in some of the groups when no females in estrus are found and no mating actively takes place, though no satisfactory statistical data are yet available to determine whether these are seasonal trends. It is generally true that no mature males will attempt to mate with a female unless she is showing distinctive signs of estrous swelling (see below).

### Mating in Relation to Dominance

The mating pattern that we find to be typical of both Kenya and southern Africa baboons can be illustrated clearly from our field data. In S group, Cape, the $\alpha$ male copulated exclusively with each adult female that came into estrus only when her sexual swelling was most prominent. For two or three days he was extremely alert in watching for the female with whom he was consorting whenever she strayed away from him during the day range. This exclusiveness was not observed to take place in his relations

Fig. 3–11. A juvenile of about one-and-a-half years attempts to copulate with a low-ranking estrous female. S group, Cape (*Photograph by Dr. G. J. Broekhuysen*)

with the two lowest ranking young females when they came into estrus in 1961. Although both these females repeatedly presented to him and groomed him whenever he would tolerate their approach, he rarely mounted and copulated with them at any stage in estrus. Much younger males, two of them estimated at only from about one and one-half to two and one-half years old, repeatedly mounted these females and achieved intromission, (see Fig. 3–11) and males *1, 2,* and *3* copulated with them without increase in tension between them, and with no interference from the $\alpha$ male.

Prior to the $\alpha$ male's exclusive mating with the fully estrous adult females, other males in the group shared in the mating toward the onset of the female's turgescence. The nature of this relationship is shown by the frequencies of copulation by the $\alpha$ male and males *1* and *2* of S group with the same female during five complete day ranges (Fig. 3–12). On August 28 the group spent several hours in the visitors' car park, but, during the five observation hours before and after this, the $\alpha$ male copulated

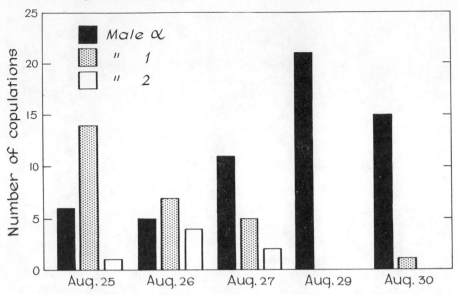

Fig. 3–12. Frequency of copulation by three males with one female (F4) during five full-day observation periods. S group, Cape, 1960.

with this female four times, male *1* three times, and male *2* not at all. On the third occasion when male *1* copulated with her toward evening, the $\alpha$ male, who was feeding 50 yards away from the pair, immediately leapt up and charged after and attacked male *1* who at once rushed away. On August 29, as indicated, male *1* made no attempt to copulate with the female, although she occasionally presented to him, and he remained near the $\alpha$ male without threatening him except very briefly on one occasion.

TABLE 3–3. FREQUENCY OF COPULATION OR ATTEMPTED COPULATION BY ADULT MALES WITH FEMALES IN A STATE OF FULL OR PARTIAL ESTRUS

| | S Group, Cape | | |
| | Completed Copulations | | |
| | Female in: | | With Full Estrus |
| Adult Male | Full Estrus | Part Estrus | Female (percent) |
| --- | --- | --- | --- |
| $\alpha$ | 101 | 8 | 93 |
| *1* | 37 | 4 | 90 |
| *2* | 56 | 28 | 67 |
| Others: | | | |
| Young adults | 20 | 11 | 65 |

| | SR Group, Kenya | | | | With Full Estrus |
| | Completed Copulations | | Attempted Copulations | | |
| | Female in: | | Female in: | | Female |
| Adult Male | Full Estrus | Part Estrus | Full Estrus | Part Estrus | (percent) |
|---|---|---|---|---|---|
| Dano | 18 | 0 | 12 | – | 100 |
| Kovu | 11 | 0 | 23 | – | 100 |
| Pua | 8 | 0 | 18 | – | 100 |
| Kula | 8 | 0 | 13 | – | 100 |
| Mdomo | 8 | 3 | 13 | 2 | 87 |
| Mark | 0 | 5 | – | 3 | 0 |
| Others: | | | | | |
| Brash (subadult) | 1 | 3 | 3 | 6 | 33 |
| Old juveniles | – | – | – | 9 | 0 |
| Young juveniles | – | – | 1 | 15 | 6 |

An elaboration of the kind of dominance-mating pattern of S group is shown in the Kenya SR group, in which there were six full-grown males of various ages, but of about equal size, and only seven sexually mature females out of the total of twenty-eight animals. At one time only one of these

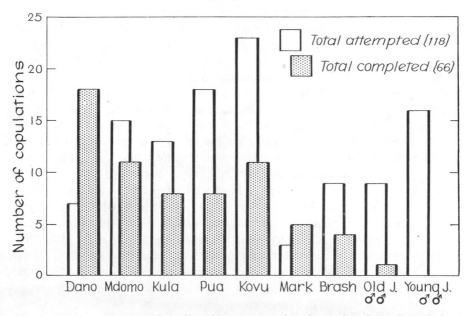

Fig. 3–13. A comparison of each male's attempted and completed copulations during 55 days of observation. SR group, Kenya, 1959.

females was in estrus. The tension among the males was very marked and was expressed in almost continuous harassing and fighting for her possession. Consequently, she did not remain in consort with one male for many hours. Later, when there were four females simultaneously in some state of estrus, consort pairs sometimes stayed together for several days. In this group the adult male's dominance is reflected by the number of times he was able to copulate successfully, as is shown by the frequency data for the six adult, one subadult, and juvenile males of this group (Fig. 3–13).

Interruptions of sexual relations were thus a prominent feature of the SR group, contrasting with a pattern of noninterference in other Kenya groups and in S group, Cape. Where several adult males are found in the more usual ratio of 1:2 adult females, as in C group, Cape, in 1961, and in most Kenya groups, the tendency has been for consort pairs to form for two or more days. These pairs usually remain at some distance from the rest of the group—as far as 200 yards or more in the Cape. This withdrawal is likely to ensure avoidance of interruptions and harassments. Indeed, except for the SR group, fighting between adult males over estrous females was never observed in any of the Kenya or southern Africa groups. That such fighting might occur in any group, under conditions similar to those in the SR, is indicated by the results of the artificial feeding experiments mentioned above. In any Nairobi Park group of more than two adult males, the complete harassment pattern (seen during mating activity in the SR) could be elicited by continuously offering a desired food item to the males.

Despite the prominence of harassment and fighting in the SR, the overall mating pattern was the same as that in other groups: juvenile, subadult, and less dominant adult males copulating with a female in the initial stages of her swelling; dominant males forming consort pairs with her and copulating during her period of maximum turgescence. This pattern is clear in Table 3–3, which includes all mating activity recorded for the S and SR groups. Despite the fact that in the SR group no females were in estrus some of the time and only one was in estrus most of the time, not a single copulation was attempted by the dominant males except when the swelling of a female's sexual skin had reached the maximum. Table 3–3 also illustrates how a male's position in the central hierarchy gives him an advantage over other adult males in mating activities. Kovu, an old male whose teeth were worn level with his gums and who was *individually* the least dominant adult male in the group, was nevertheless second only to the most dominant male in copulations completed at the time of maximum swelling in the female. Since ovulation occurs during the period of maximum swelling, it is likely that he was therefore one of the most effective breeders in the group.

The mating pattern in a large group with the usual adult sex ratio is still not entirely clear, as indicated in our discussion of the dominance relations in such a group. Although consort pairs are formed and maintained without evident interruption, we do not know whether a particular cluster of females tends to remain in the social milieu of one particular male for any period beyond the consort relationship. It is thus not known whether after her infant is born the female follows the male with whom she consorted for protection, and whether she maintains social contact with him during her gestation period by mutual grooming. Only prolonged study of a large group can determine the consistency or variability of the social and mating patterns and establish whether these differ significantly for the baboons of Kenya and southern Africa from the kind of social system reported by Kummer and Kurt (1963) for hamadryas. They state that in the one-male unit groups typical of their population the adult male makes strenuous efforts to prevent his females from straying into another group when several of these groups come together at the sleeping cliffs. The male does this by going after the female and biting her in the back of the neck, and the screaming female then follows him closely. To quote Kummer and Kurt, "In the one-male-group of *Papio hamadryas* the neck-bite obviously was selectively developed as the male's instrument to herd his group together in the crowd of the party." Certainly the neck-bite was never seen in such a context in the Kenya baboons and was only occasionally seen in S group, Cape, when the $\alpha$ male was trying to force an unwilling estrous female, with whom he had already been mating, to take up a position of readiness to receive him. In this latter situation the biting was gentle, the female did not scream, and the biting was accompanied by gestures of touching her on the side or flank with one hand. In other words, it was not a "herding" gesture. No herding behavior of any kind was observed except briefly, in SR, when a less dominant male in consort was being hard pressed by another. Kovu, for example, was seen four times to put an arm across the back of the estrous female he was with and try to pull her away from the area of the other males.

### Mating Behavior Details

It is possible that between the baboons of Kenya and those of southern Africa there are more clear-cut differences in mating behavior than in any of the other behavior categories. In both areas copulation as well as grooming and other social behavior occurred much more frequently early in the day, while the group was still in the vicinity of its sleeping place. In S group, Cape, for example, copulation was observed almost twice as often, in relation to the number of observation hours, during the first two or three hours after dawn as at any other time of day. The frequency again increases slightly toward evening. Although we have only negative evidence, the fact that the peak of sexual activity occurs in the early morning in both study areas indicates that it is unlikely that copulation occurs very often at night.

The first important difference that seems to exist in comparing data from the two areas is in the performance of the males in copulation. The quantitative data obtained for the three adult males of S group, Cape, sug-

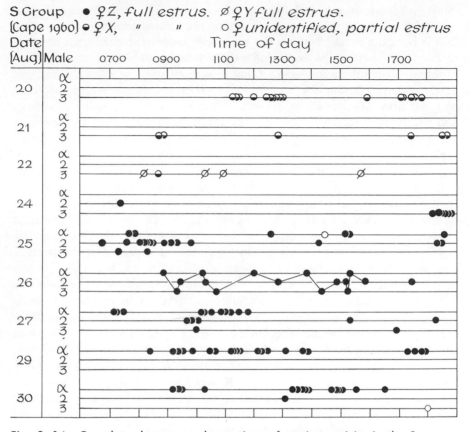

Fig. 3–14a Complete day-range observations of mating activity in the S group, Cape, to show copulatory series. Each dot represents one mounting by a male (see text).

gest that the typical pattern is a series of copulations with the estrous female similar to that described for the rhesus by Carpenter (1942a). For example, the α male of this group copulated with one fully estrous female 17 times between 0800 and 1400 hours on one day. There was then a three-hour interval when no copulation was observed between them, and four more copulations occurred between 1700 and 1800 hours as the group was nearing its sleeping place. Copulations in such a series occurred at about two-minute intervals, each consisting of between five and ten thrusts and lasting ten to fifteen seconds from time of mounting to time of dismounting. It was obvious that ejaculation did not always occur, and it is thus likely that it occurred only at the culmination of a particular series. However, the copulation ending with ejaculation could usually not be distinguished from any other copulation in the series. Because they may be of some comparative significance, the time relations of such series for a sample of complete day-range

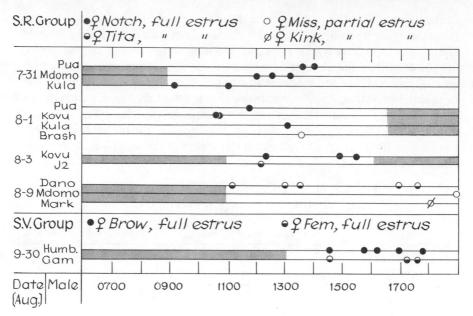

Fig. 3–14b. Mating activity in two Nairobi Park groups to indicate contrast in mounting sequences. Each dot represents a mounting with ejaculation. Shaded portions show times of day when group was not under observation.

observations are given for the adult males of S group, Cape (Fig. 3–14a) in which they are contrasted with data from Kenya (Fig. 3–14b). It is evident that the pattern is very different.

In contrast to the copulation series observed in the Cape, males in Nairobi Park typically ejaculated at the conclusion of only one mounting sequence. Such a copulation is brief, lasting 8 to 20 seconds, and averages only 6.2 pelvic thrusts (based on 54 observations). Rather than 2-minute intervals, the interval between copulations in Kenya was seldom shorter than 30 minutes and was usually longer. When tension was high among the males in the SR group, a male might make repeated, unsuccessful attempts to copulate, but this situation was clearly distinct from the lack of tension associated with copulations in other groups. In Nairobi Park ejaculation by the male is accompanied by a pause of from 2 to 4 seconds during which the male's whole body remains rigidly fixed in the mounting position. From numerous observations of the "rigid pause" at close range, where ejaculation could be seen, it was usually possible to ascertain whether ejaculation had occurred in mounting sequences which took place at longer distances from the observer.

The actual initiation of mating behavior is likely to vary between partners and between stages of the consort relationship. In Kenya the female initiates sexual activity during the first two-thirds of her cycle by going from one male to another. Although she does not solicit any but adult males, she allows mounting by juvenile and subadult males at this period. Bolwig (1959) describes the chacma female as always initiating mating by coming up to the adult male and stopping in front of him, where she presents to him. It seems likely that Bolwig was observing females during the early part of their swelling, although this is not clear from his account. The data on S group, Cape, show that the initiating act depends on the state of estrous swelling of the female, as well as on the status of the male who is currently mating with her (Table 3–4).

TABLE 3–4. COPULATION-INITIATING BEHAVIOR BY AND
TO THE MALES OF S GROUP, CAPE

|  | Initiative by Male | Initiative by Female |
|---|---|---|
| Other males | 7 | 18 |
| α male | 26 | 27 |
| Total | 33 | 45 |

From Table 3–4 it can be seen that prior to the establishment of a consort relationship the female takes the initiative, that is, when the non-dominant males are mating with her. But when a consort relationship is established with the dominant male, either partner might take the initiative.

The act of copulation closely resembles that of other monkeys, the male mounting the female as she stands in front of him, holding her back or side fur in his hands, and gripping her in the ankle region with his feet so that he is clear of the ground. The chacma male (only) sometimes grimaces, his lips being drawn away to expose his teeth, and occasionally the female turns her head to the side in the direction of the male (as does the rhesus female). As the male dismounts, the chacma female gives a distinctive muffled growling call in which her cheeks puff out and her mouth is almost closed. This occurred in 92 percent of the copulations observed at close range in South Africa and Rhodesia (Washburn, personal communication), but vocalizations by either male or female were very infrequent in Kenya (see Table 3–5, item 10), and males were not seen grimacing. After the male has dismounted, the female characteristically runs or walks a few yards away from him, this reaction occurring even when copulation has taken place on a narrow ledge or the top of a bush from which she will leap down. Running away from the male occurred in about 33 percent of the copulations observed in Kenya and in about 75 percent of those observed in the Cape. In S group, Cape, frequency data show that this flight has been far more frequent from the α male than from the other males, and its significance is not yet clear. In Kenya the female sometimes ran away from the male until she came to another male to whom she indicated her readiness to mate, but this is probably typical only of the early phase of estrus. No such running from male to male has been seen in the southern Africa groups. Grooming between partners often occurs before copulation and sometimes directly after copulation, initiated by either the male or the female. In this the baboons of both regions are similar.

Although the dominance pattern associated with mating seems essentially the same for both areas of study, there are apparently behavior differences in the details of copulation that require further intensive investigation. The copulation call of the female chacma is so distinct and so constant an accompaniment of the male's dismounting that if it had occurred it would have been noted in the close-range observations of the Kenya groups. But an even more prominent difference in behavior between the two areas is the copulation *series* of the chacma, as well as the indication, from the behavior samples obtained in the Cape at regular intervals throughout the year 1958–1959, that copulations occur in any month. It is possible, then, that regional differences in sexual reproductive activity are accompanied by differences in the form and frequency of its behavioral expression.

## SOCIALIZATION

In dealing with the development of social behavior from birth to maturity, we are probably more dependent upon the continuous checking of field with laboratory data, and vice versa, than in any other aspect of non-human primate behavior. The interactions of social learning, of play and exploration, of sensori-motor coordinations, and of reflex systems are such that they can be described only tentatively from field data. It must be left to experiment to try to sort out the complex of factors that determine the final behavior of the mature animal within the group. It is probably a correct assumption that the developing primate learns its functions in the group and its skills in coping with its physical environment in ways that differ importantly according to its age and growth stage. It is likely, however, that learning is necessary for all specific meaningful connections and modifications to be made in the built-in forms of the behavior repertoire. Thus, an infant baboon does not have to learn the basic threat-behavior gestures and vocalizations of its species, but it must continually learn to inhibit, modify, and refine the ways in which its repertoire is used to accord with varying social conditions. Exactly how these learning processes proceed in the natural group can, at present, be inferred chiefly from laboratory studies of habituation, conditioning, and observational learning, and a more complete account awaits the result of naturalistic experimental studies of free-ranging animals carried out over several years.

The stages in baboon development from birth to more or less complete independence from the mother will be outlined here under eight arbitrary chronological headings with which various progressive changes in behavior and social relationships within the group are associated. A provisional "typical" picture is thus sketched, but it must be noted that there is much variation between individuals. Furthermore, the data are not yet sufficiently based upon a long-term follow-up of identified individuals through all the stages. We present, rather, a synthetic account derived from observations of the young animals of nine groups in Nairobi Park and of three groups in the Cape Peninsula, together with data compounded from miscellaneous observations of other groups in Kenya and southern Africa. The longest series of observations of an identified individual was made in Kenya in a group observed continuously from June through mid-September, with intermittent data up to late December of the same year (DeVore 1963*b*). The scheme thus derived is shown below where average behavior correlates are set against each of eight stages in age growth. Following this is some elaboration on the behavior stages and their social significance, together with an assessment, largely in the nature of hypotheses for further study, of the main factors affecting normal behavioral development within the group (other than those of nutrition, sickness, injury, and so on).

A composite account of the chronological stages of normal development and associated social behavior in baboons from birth to adulthood follows.

Fig. 3–15. A mother grooms her infant two or three days after its birth. SR group.

1. *Newborn, birth to one month. Infant:* locomotion confined mainly to body surface of mother; grasping her ventral surface and suckling.

   *the Mother:* shortly after birth, supporting infant's head with one hand, licks blood from rock on which she has sat and from her fingers, moves closer to other baboons; continues to support infant's head on day ranges and supports its rump on upper surface of her feet when she is sitting; grooms infant frequently; tends to come close to a dominant male and remain in his vicinity; little vocal communication between mother and infant because of direct physical contact (Fig. 3–15).

   *Others:* soon are attracted to approach close to mother and infant, lip-smacking, touching infant with hands and mouth, and grooming mother; this may include the *a* male; "attractiveness" of mother-infant manifest.

2. *Infant-one, first to fourth month. Infant:* begins to ride briefly on mother's back at about five weeks, though changes its position back to her belly quite readily; infant's developing locomotor and sensory coordination allow occasional movement away from mother; signals from mother to infant now appear; occasionally touches with hands food plants which the mother is eating, or puts to mouth without chewing.

   *Mother:* allows infant to move some feet away, but sometimes takes hold of it and draws it to her for grooming; tends to remain close to a dominant male.

   *Others:* fully adult and even young adult males are completely tolerant of the infant as it crawls near or over them; they may touch the infant with one hand, and the dominant male may grunt at high frequency while looking at the infant; immediate retaliation by a dominant male against attacks on the mother.

3. *Transition, fourth to sixth month* (period of color change from black to light brown). *Infant:* begins to sit up, "jockey style," (Fig. 3–16) on mother's back, though when mother runs or climbs, lies face down and clutches with hands and feet, as at stage 2; begins to eat some solid foods whereas previously only touched or chewed at them; occasionally picks up objects such as sticks, and stones, carrying them sometimes in the hand or mouth; an important stage in exploring immediate physical environment, moving as much as 20 yards or more from the mother, and in beginning social play with peers; much play movement, such as climbing and jumping and tussling.
*Mother:* grooms the infant regularly, but not so consistently as earlier because of its wandering.
*Others:* peers and older young participate in play; adults considerably reduce their attentions to the infant, although both females and males may sometimes carry the infant, as though in play, and adult males maintain their protective function.

4. *Infant-two, six months to one year. Infant:* progressive increase in play relations with other young, and increased exploration of physical environment; by about ten months, nurses only rarely, though tends to follow mother closely when she is feeding, and feeds often from the same plants and uses the same feeding movements; probably an important stage in learning feeding habits and discriminations.
*Mother:* remains tolerant of infant's close presence and of its wandering away from her.
*Others:* increasing play relations of other young with infant; adult females occasionally threaten or even attack the infant, holding it down or giving it a "token bite"; screeching of the infant may elicit a counterattack by the mother, or by an adult male; adult males remain completely tolerant and protective of the infant.

5. *Weaning, eleventh to fifteenth month. Infant:* tends to be rejected by mother both from taking the nipple and from riding on her back; the infant may continue to press its attentions upon the mother, following her and sometimes grooming her, while the rest of the time it is continually active in playing and exploring.
*Mother:* females vary considerably in the stage and in intensity of rejection; in general the independent activity and irritability of the mother increases with her sexual swelling; the temporary "privileged" status of the mother, due to the presence of the infant, is now lost.

6. *Young juvenile, second year of life.* The increasing independence of the young animal is partly shown by the fact that now, when danger threatens the group, it tends to flee to the protection of the adult males and not to the mother or other adult females; the juvenile spends most of the day

with its peers, feeding with its age group or with other young animals, and playing with these early and late at the sleeping place.

7. *Older juvenile, third and fourth year.* Accurate age estimates beyond the second year were not possible, but the category "older juvenile" conveniently describes the transition from the young, dependent juvenile to the independent young adult. In the early portion of this stage the individual is still oriented to play in a peer group, but play has become rougher and dominance interactions more intense. Adult males no longer tolerate play by older juveniles and in fact threaten them when the juveniles play too roughly with infants and young juveniles. During this period older juvenile females leave the juvenile play group and join the grooming clusters of adult females. By the end of this stage the female's sexual cycles have begun, she is almost fully grown, and her behavior is that of an adult.

8. *Subadult male, fourth year to complete physical maturity* (eighth year?). Although the male probably produces viable sperm by about the fourth year, his period of growth is much longer than that of the female. No records are available, but full skeletal and muscular growth, complete eruption of the canine teeth, and development of the shoulder mantle (olive baboon) may take eight years or even longer. By the fifth year the subadult male is larger than adult females and establishes dominance over them. He is still much smaller than the fully adult males and tends to avoid them. Temperamentally the subadult male is pugnacious within the group and "daring" in his behavior generally. Although in some species of monkeys males of this age may leave the group, no subadult male baboon left his natal group during our studies. Nevertheless, males of this age are more behaviorally peripheral to other group members than is true of either sex at any other stage of development.

In considering this outline scheme it is necessary both to elaborate on it and to attempt some generalization from it. At stage 1, we have no observations of actual birth, but one female of C group, Cape, was seen at 1735 hours sitting on a rock at the sleeping cliffs and holding a wet infant to her belly. Her posterior was bloody, and she was in full view of the observer until dusk at 1850 hours. During this period none of the other animals in the group actually approached her. On the contrary, on several occasions she tried to move close to some of them, and these sometimes moved away from her. For example, juveniles walked close by her and gazed at the infant and the mother (lipsmacked toward her), but they passed on without stopping. Several times she walked on three legs, holding the infant's head with one hand, toward juveniles or females with other infants, none of whom made any attempt to touch her or the infant, and most of whom moved away from her. When she took her infant and sat near the one adult male among this cluster of animals, he made no response to her or the infant. The next day she tended to be to the rear of the group during its foraging, and was seen with a large male and another female with a black infant at one time as much as 400 yards from the rest of the group. In Kenya healthy mothers with infant-ones were typically toward the center of a group, close to one or more adult males, but on several occasions an adult male was seen to drop behind the group and walk with a mother who was having difficulty keeping up with the rest of the group.

It is not yet possible to state precisely what it is in the combination of mother with infant-one that begins so strongly to attract the attentions of the other animals in the group. Certainly the temporary lack of such attention soon after the birth is not an unusual occurrence in baboons, whereas not a single instance has been recorded from either area where a mother and infant-one did not soon begin to attract these attentions. Possibly it is the beginnings of movement in the infant as it crawls about the mother's body that sets off the reactions of friendly behavior, or it may be such minimal movement combined with perception of the infant face with its relatively large, pink ears, and contrasting facial and body coloration. The clearest answer to such a question can best be obtained from experimental study.

Throughout the stages we note the protective function afforded to the mother-infant combination by the adult males. This protection seems to extend, at least in individual cases, well beyond the color-change transition period. The adult males vary quite markedly in this respect, but it is usual for older males to approach fairly frequently and to touch the infant. On several occasions adult males in Kenya and southern Africa have carried infants on their bellies—for twenty minutes on one occasion. The *a* male of S group, Cape, was notably attentive and tolerant of infants and even juveniles. He once carried a black infant ventrally up the sleeping cliffs in the morning, often picked up or touched other infants, and was also seen to sit with one juvenile against his chest for several minutes on a day of strong cold wind. In the SV group, Kenya, an infant-two female with a disease of face and scalp became the constant companion of the B male (Humbert), remaining with him all day, feeding close to him, grooming him, and sleeping beside him at night (Fig. 3–6). She even stayed beside him while he was in consort with an estrous female, and took food in front of him (DeVore 1963b).

Precisely what it is that stimulates the aggressive retaliatory behavior of an adult male in relation to mother and infant was often not clear in rapidly occurring events. Sometimes an infant shrieked, apparently because it was separated from its mother, and an adult male looked around slowly and even approached it. A similar sounding shriek, on other occasions, elicited an immediate aggressive charge by the male, as did also the shrieking of a mother with an infant when she was set upon by another female. It is thus doubtful if there is any one kind of stimulation having a "releaser" effect for this behavior by the male, and it is probably elicited by combinations of stimuli the social significance of which is learned. The prominence of this protective and tolerant behavior by adult males toward infants and juveniles is such that, in general, it prevents injuries from fighting within the group and also prevents predation. What is not yet known from field studies is the association of adolescents and young adults with the adult males. Although some young adult or subadult males are somewhat peripheral, or complementary, to a group, others appear to be assimilated into close relationship with dominant males (see Social Organization above).

In describing the gradual independence of the infant from its mother as it comes to explore the physical environment and to establish play relations with other young, we are dealing with a behavior phenomenon that is characteristic of other young primates and mammals. However, since this is the first time this exploratory play behavior has been systematically observed in wild baboons, it is important to try to evaluate its probable significance. It can be said at once that play-climbing, play-fighting, play-manipulating, running, somersaulting, and so on are strongly in evidence among the young of all stages after stage 1, and continue in evidence even to the subadult stage. It is the first behavior to be seen at the sleeping places before dawn and the last behavior to cease at night. The developmental trend might be generalized as a progressive focussing of the play-manipulatory repertoire of movements and gestures upon particular objectives, early efforts being much more random. It is usually assumed that the frequent social play of young monkeys is a very important kind of trial-and-error experience that may determine adult dominance and the pattern of adult sexuality, but we have to rely upon the experimental evidence (Harlow 1962; Mason this volume) to demonstrate what can happen in macaques when the social norm is drastically changed.

## EXPRESSIVE AND COMMUNICATIVE BEHAVIOR

A straightforward description of the repertoire of expressive movements, postures, gestures, and vocalizations observed in our wild baboon groups would not be realistic or meaningful unless it was accompanied by comments on the social situations in which they occurred and on the variations in individual performance that seem to reflect the particular status of the baboon within its group. Descriptions of the repertoire of baboons are to be found in Zuckerman (1932), Kummer (1957), and Bolwig (1959a), and here we shall attempt chiefly to coordinate our own observations and to relate them to the kind of scheme exemplified by the studies on captive rhesus monkeys of Hinde and Rowell (1962), Rowell and Hinde (1962). It will already be apparent from the previous sections that individual patterns of communication vary according to sex, age, and status. With regard to the vocalizations of these animals, it is notable that many hours of the day are spent in almost complete silence. Probably the commonest kind of sound is the grunt. A specialized investigation remains to be carried out of the significance of the many variations in grunting, and in the other types of calls, distinctive to the human listener at least, that are heard during the routine of social behavior. It is not unlikely that the major system that mediates interindividual behavior for baboons is one of visual cues from facial expressions, intention movements, and attitudes, while auditory, tactual, and olfactory cues are of descending order of importance. Except where specifically stated, no difference was observed in either study area in the quality, frequency, or situations of occurrence of movements and gestures. Tables 3–5, 3–6, and 3–7 list the vocalizations and elements of visual and tactile expression so far distinguished in the two study regions, with a summary of the situations in which they occur.

Accurate and detailed comparisons of the vocal repertoire of rhesus macaques and baboons cannot be undertaken until the vocalizations of both species have been tape recorded and analyzed, but it is worth noting briefly what we believe to be similarities. References below are to Rowell and Hinde (1962) and Altmann (1963).[1]

| *Baboon* | *Rhesus* |
|---|---|
| 1. Two-phase bark | No apparent equivalent |
| 2. Grunting | Comparable to Altmann No. 48 |
| 3. Roaring | Probably same as Rowell and Hinde "roar" |
| 4. Grating roar | No apparent equivalent |
| 5. Screeching | Identical to Rowell and Hinde "screech"; Altmann No. 36 |
| 6. Yakking | Probably same as Rowell and Hinde "gecker" |
| 7. Chirplike clicking | Probably identical (Rowell and Hinde) |
| 8. Shrill bark | Probably identical (Rowell and Hinde; Altmann No. 55) |
| 9. Ick-ooer | Probably identical (Rowell and Hinde "rising clicks"; Altmann No. 24) |
| 10. Muffled growl | No apparent equivalent |
| 11. Chattering | No apparent equivalent |
| 12. Dog-like bark | Perhaps same (Rowell and Hinde "bark") |
| 13. Grunting | Probably same, including "chorus" given by rhesus in sleeping trees on Cayo Santiago |
| 14. High-frequency grunting | No apparent equivalent |

[1] Through the courtesy of Dr. Stuart Altmann, DeVore was able to visit the rhesus colony on Cayo Santiago in 1958; and through the courtesy of Dr. Carl Koford, Hall was able to visit the colony in 1963 after the tabulation of baboon vocalizations had been completed.

TABLE 3–5. BABOON VOCALIZATIONS

| Description | Class of Animal Vocalizing | Area and Situation in Which the Vocalization Was Observed | |
| --- | --- | --- | --- |
| | | South Africa | Kenya |
| | | A. ATTACK-THREAT | |
| 1. *Two-phase bark* (very far-carrying; audible for 1/2+ mile in mountainous districts; often repeated at about 1 per 2–5 sec. according to intensity of arousal). | Adult males only. | a. Extragroup danger situations; reaction to humans and large predators. | Same. |
| | | b. Intragroup aggression; occurring in adult males' threat among themselves, and in attacks on, e.g., females | Apparently *not* in evidence in such in-group situations; see roaring. |
| 2. *Grunting* (soft, sometimes two-phase uh-huh). | Adult males only. | Occasionally adult male grunts in this way as a prelude to mild threat gestures toward another animal. | Same, except that it usually begins as single grunts, becoming two-phase as the male begins threat gestures. May blend rapidly into (3). |
| 3. *Roaring* (loud, two-phase grunting; a crescendo of grunting with a two-phase character; uh-huh [intense expression of two-phase grunting]). | Adult males only. | Not recorded. | Occurred during all fights between adult males. This accounts for 90 percent. |
| 4. *Grating roar* (resonant but of low intensity). | Adult males only. | Not recorded. | Heard only 5 times. Given by dominant male after fight in the group. The male sits with chin pointing up and brings his head down in a series of 3 or 4 jerks, expelling the vocalization with each jerk. |

TABLE 3-5. BABOON VOCALIZATIONS—Continued

|  | Class of Animal Vocalizing | Area and Situation in Which the Vocalization Was Observed | |
|---|---|---|---|
|  | | South Africa | Kenya |
| Description | | | |
| | | B. ESCAPE-FEAR | |
| 5. *Screeching* (repeated, high-pitched; sometimes modifies to a repetitive churring noise). | Any animal | High intensity vocal reaction, accompanying other behavior indictions of escape-fear, as when fleeing from adult males. | Same. |
| 6. *Yakking* (? Rowell and Hinde 1962, "Gecker"; single sharp yak sound, repeated perhaps 2 or 3 times). | Any adult or near adult. | Accompanying fear grimace, when animal withdraws from a threat. | Same. |
| 7. *Chirplike clicking* (Rowell and Hinde 1962) | Infant and juvenile. | Probably juvenile equivalent of yakking; occurs when juvenile is frustrated, as when separated from mother. | Same. |
| 8. *Shrill bark* (Rowell and Hinde 1962; single sharp explosive sound). | Any animal, except possibly adult males. | Has occurred on seeing a snake, or on discovering a scorpion (in the Cape), and on *suddenly* seeing eland or a hyena appear; a startle reaction that usually elicits an instantaneous avoidance response in other baboons near the barker. | Same; has occurred in response to sudden appearance of bush-buck, and mongoose, as well as to large predators, such as lions. |
| 9. *Ick-ooer* (a repeated sharp ick, followed by longer drawn *ooering* sound, thus a two-phase vocalization). | Infants primarily; juveniles occasionally. | Accompanied by twitching of the head, shoulders and arms, and by grinning; apparently a frustration response that may occur in situations similar to (7). | Same. |

| | | C. SEXUAL | |
|---|---|---|---|
| 10. *Muffled growl* (mouth almost closed; cheeks puff out with inspiration-expiration, audible at 50–100 yards). | Estrous females only. | Occurred in 92 percent of copulations, coinciding with the male's dismounting; also occurred occasionally during defecation. | An indistinct call, apparently of a similar kind but with no blowing out of the cheeks, was heard in 10 percent of copulations; uncertain whether from the male or the female. |
| | | D. FRIENDLY | |
| 11. *Chattering* (nasal, very rapid, short-phased gruntlike series of sounds). | Juveniles | During play. | Probably does not occur. |
| 12. *Doglike bark* (higher-pitched, less staccato and sudden than shrill bark and somewhat quavering). | Probably any adult or young adult. | Seems only to occur when, for example, one animal, or a party of animals, has been temporarily separated from the rest and is about to rejoin them. | Same. |
| 13. *Grunting* (varies in frequency from slow, about 1 per 2 seconds to very rapid, sometimes as a "chorus" through group). | Any animal, except possibly infants. | The most frequent baboon sound, heard at intervals when feeding close together, as well as at night. | Same. The chorus was regularly heard when group was congregated near or in sleeping trees at nightfall, as well as during day; infants and juveniles also gave ooer sound toward end of grunting chorus. Also occurs when the animals are becoming calm after being frightened. |
| 14. *High-frequency grunting* (slightly higher-pitched; possibly an intensity variation of 13). | Adult males only. | When close to, and possibly about to touch, an infant-one. | Probably does not occur. |

Nine out of the fourteen most conspicuous vocalizations occur in both study regions in similar situations. Two of the other four (items 11 and 14) probably do not occur in Kenya; item 4 probably not in the Cape. Two more (items 3 and 10) are so infrequent in one region, so common in similar situations in the other, that they may constitute important area differences. One (item 1) seems to differ between the regions in the situations of its occurrence. While sampling differences in the kinds of observations made in the two regions may account for some of this variation, the vocalizations in question are sufficiently distinctive to indicate some qualitative as well as quantitative variations in the vocal repertoires.

TABLE 3–6. VISUAL COMMUNICATION AND EXPRESSION

| Description | Class of Animal | Directed at Another Baboon | Areas Where Observed | Comments |
|---|---|---|---|---|
| *Head and face* | | ATTACK-THREAT | | |
| Tooth-grinding | Adult males only | Yes | Kenya | In threat displays of two or more animals at close range to each other |
| Yawning (always accompanied by ear-flattening, eyebrow-raising, etc.) | Adult males | Yes | Kenya | In harassment sequences |
| Staring (directed) | Any adult or young adult | Yes | Both regions | |
| Eyebrow-raising | Any adult or young adult | Yes | Both regions | |
| Ear-flattening | Any adult or young adult | Yes | Both regions | Occurs also in friendly behavior |
| Jerking of head down and forward | Adult and young males only | Yes | Both regions | |
| *Body and limbs* | | | | |
| Mantle hair raised | Adult males only | Yes | Both regions | |
| Rearing on hindlegs | Any adult or young adult | Yes | Both regions | Can prelude attack or escape |
| Shoulders forward | Any adult or young adult | Yes | Both regions | |

| | | | | |
|---|---|---|---|---|
| Slapping ground with hand | Any adult or young adult | Yes | Both regions | |
| Rotating movement of hands on ground | Any adult or young adult | Yes | Both regions | |
| Shaking of rocks, branches | Any adult or young adult | Yes | Both regions | |
| Hitting-away reaction with hand | Any adult or young adult | No | South Africa | Response to noxious small object, especially scorpions |
| Charging run | Any adult or young adult | Yes | Both regions | Attack |

ESCAPE-FEAR-UNCERTAINTY

*Head and face*

| | | | | |
|---|---|---|---|---|
| Staring (undirected, eyes wide open) | Any animal | Yes | Both regions | |
| Grin | Any subordinate animal | Yes | Both regions | |
| Looking away | Any subordinate animal | Yes | Both regions | |
| Sideways jerking glances | Any adult or young adult | Yes | Both regions | |
| Yawning | Most frequent in adult males | No | Both regions | Occurs in situations of uncertainty |

TABLE 3-6. VISUAL COMMUNICATION AND EXPRESSION—*Continued*

| Description | Class of Animal | Directed at Another Baboon | Areas Where Observed | Comments |
|---|---|---|---|---|
| *Body, limbs, tail* | ESCAPE-FEAR-UNCERTAINTY | | | |
| Tail erect | Any subordinate animal | No | Both regions | Usually adult females, particularly mothers with infants |
| Body prone to ground, animal rigid if fear is extreme | Any animal | No | Both regions | Most intense fear response; very rare in adult males |
| Twitching of head, arms, shoulders | Infant, juvenile | No | Both regions | Separation from mother, insecurity |
| Throwing aside of arms | Any animal | No | South Africa | Response to noxious, small object, especially snake |
| Scratching | Any animal | No | Both regions | Occurs in situations of uncertainty |
| Shoulder-shrugging | Adult or young adult male | No | South Africa | Response subsequent to startle-reaction |
| Muzzle-wiping with hand | Adult or young adult male | No | Both regions | Response subsequent to startle-reaction |

**FRIENDLY**

| *Head and face* | | | | |
|---|---|---|---|---|
| Lipsmacking | Mostly adults and young adults | Yes | Both regions | |
| Ear-flattening | Mostly adults and young adults | Yes | Both regions | |
| *Body and limbs* | | | | |
| Presenting | Any animal | Yes | Both regions | |
| Stand on hindlegs in front of another | Uncertain; mostly adults or young adults | Yes | Both regions | |

**SEXUAL**

| *Head and face* | | | | |
|---|---|---|---|---|
| Turning head back | Adult females in estrus | No | Both regions | Only occasional |
| Grin | Adult males | No | South Africa | Occasional during copulation |

**Tension Differences in Normal Posture or Locomotion**

The stance of a baboon, independently of any specific gesture, may indicate differences in tension and of individual status. The dominant male macaque walks deliberately and stiffly, with tail elevated. The dominant male baboon tends to walk very directly and "confidently" through different parts of a feeding area or when moving across country. It is too subjective a task to try to judge whether the proximal section of his tail tends to be more upright than that of subordinate animals. Intentions are declared by changes of pace, by halting, and by looking around, and it is such changes in ordinary locomotion that may be inferred, from the behavior of others in the group, to be the main cue to which they respond when moving away from the sleeping place or altering direction during the day range. No vocalization from a dominant animal normally accompanies or precedes such movements. The general tension in the attitude of a watchful animal is clearly to be seen when it is sitting, standing, or walking about, and alertness is sometimes shown by its climbing to a high point or by its standing on hind legs.

Relaxation is equally clear in lying or sitting attitudes. In relaxed sitting the head is lowered, the back is arched, the hands rest loosely near the knees. When the animal is lying down, a variety of doglike postures are seen, including lying on the back, on the stomach, or on the side.

All such postural differences between a tense and a relaxed animal are likely to be in a general way communicative to one or more animals in the group, and thus may affect their behavior, as in determining the distance they keep from the animal and whether they look toward it or ignore its presence.

**Attack and Threat**

The intensity, duration, and complexity of attack and threat behavior varies greatly with the social situation and its stresses. A dominant male may sufficiently indicate his intention or mood by simply standing up, raising his muzzle, and staring, or by remaining seated and, while staring, slapping once with one hand in the direction of another animal. Or he may go immediately into an attacking charge which culminates in his seizing his victim in his jaws, biting it, holding it, and rubbing it on the ground with his hands. In the latter case the chacma male will repeatedly utter a loud two-phase bark, while the olive male roars in the same situation (Table 3–5). More complex expressions of attack and threat occur when the participants are of more equal status, as in the "harassment" sequences between adult males, or as when several females or young males engage in a quarrel. Quantification of attack-threat episodes, both where no physical contact was made with a victim and where such contact as grappling, beating, and

**TABLE 3-7. TACTILE COMMUNICATION AND EXPRESSION**

| Description | Class of Animal | Areas Where Observed | Comments |
|---|---|---|---|
| | | ATTACK-THREAT | |
| *Head and face* | | | |
| Biting | Any animal; more frequent in males | Both regions | End result of attack; victim sometimes lifted from ground; usual bite areas are nape of neck; occurs in play sometimes as a gape; in Kenya females usually bite at the base of the tail |
| *Body and limbs* | | | |
| Grappling with hands | Adult males | Both regions | Attack |
| Rubbing against ground | Adult males | Both regions | Attack |
| Slapping | Adult males | Kenya | By the attacker, when a threatened adult male is deliberately looking away from the threat. (rare) |
| | | ESCAPE-FEAR | |
| Mounting to the side | Any adult, juveniles | Both regions | |
| | | FRIENDLY | |
| *Head and face* | | | |
| Mouth-to-mouth touching | Any animal | South Africa | |
| Genital-stomach nuzzling | Mostly by adult females and young adults of both sexes, to infants | Both regions | Rare in Kenya |

**TABLE 3–7. TACTILE COMMUNICATION AND EXPRESSION**—*Continued*

| Description | Class of Animal | Areas Where Observed | Comments |
|---|---|---|---|
| | | FRIENDLY | |
| *Head and face* | | | |
| Putting nose to perineal region | Adult males, usually to estrous females | Both regions | Rare; usually sexual |
| *Body and limbs* | | | |
| Posterior grasping | Adult males | Kenya | Response of male being harassed |
| Mounting | Dominant animals | Both regions | Animals tense during mounting |
| Touching on side | Adult males | South Africa | |
| Tweaking (hands between hindlegs of other) | Adults and young | South Africa | |
| Grooming | Adults and young | Both regions | |
| | | SEXUAL | |
| *Head and face* | | | |
| Biting gently at nape of neck | Adult males to estrous females | South Africa | Rare |
| *Body and limbs* | | | |
| Pushing with hands | Adult males to estrous females | South Africa | Rare |

biting occurred, showed in S group, Cape, that aggression by adult males was of the contact kind twice as often as aggression by adult females. In *all* the episodes observed, no-contact threat was a far more frequent culmination than physical attack. Certain components of no-contact threat were relatively more frequent in the females, but all such frequency data are representative only of the dominance structure and of adult male-adult female relationships within the particular group, and no generalization can at present be attempted.

Expressions of attack-threat, very similar to those described for *P. hamadryas* by Kummer (1957) and for *Macaca mulatta* by Hinde and Rowell (1962), are listed here.

CHARGE OR ATTACKING RUN: This is most clearly seen in the behavior of a dominant male, who may start the attack by leaping to his feet, raising his muzzle, and immediately launching himself after his objective without any preliminary threat gestures. He barks loudly and repeatedly and his mane fur tends to stand up around him, enlarging his appearance. If he catches his victim, he grapples with it and seizes it in his jaws, usually near the nape of the neck, or he may beat it with his hands as it lies prone on the ground. A female thus attacked has been seen to be briefly lifted off the ground in the jaws of the male. Such attacks have usually been of very short duration, and, even when they sound and appear extremely vicious, have only once been seen to result in visible physical injury to the victim. Often the victim evades the attacker by jumping or climbing down a steep cliff, hiding under a boulder, or running up into a tree, in which case the attacker soon gives up. Although such attacks come chiefly from adult males, one instance was recorded in Kenya of two adult females attacking

Fig. 3–17. The female on the left eyebrow-threatens while the female on the right lifts the head of a female they are simultaneously attacking. SR group.

and viciously biting another female and persisting in so doing for twenty minutes (Fig. 3–17). At the end of this attack the animal was badly mauled and bleeding from numerous wounds.

THREAT: Facial expressions observed in threatening animals consist of "staring," sometimes accompanied by a quick jerking of the head down and then up, in the direction of the opponent, flattening of the ears against the head, and a pronounced raising of the eyebrows with a rapid blinking of the pale eyelids. This reaction, as Van Hooff (1962) points out, is seen in all the macaques, mangabeys, and baboons, and is particularly obvious because the upper eyelids and the skin above them are white.

Grinding of the teeth, the function or significance of which is not clear, has been observed in adult males of Kenya groups when closely threatening each other, as in harassment sequences. Yawning has likewise occurred frequently as two adult males come close to one another. In yawning the large canine teeth of the adult males are clearly displayed and, as Zuckerman (1932) has suggested for baboons, and Hinde and Rowell (1962) for macaques, this may have a secondary intimidating effect. An animal may also frequently yawn, without necessarily directing its gaze toward the source of disturbance, in situations where a conflict of tendencies is highly likely and hence "anxiety" (see below) is present, but this can easily be distinguished from the threat yawn which is always accompanied by other threat gestures, such as ear-flattening, eyebrow-raising, and so on.

Threat gestures and movements of the limbs that may either accompany or follow facial expressions include a variety of intention movements made from sitting, standing, and sometimes crouching positions. They include rapid down-pressing movements of the arms, with accompanying jerking forward and back of head and body, and rapid forward and backward scraping movements with the hands against the ground. Sometimes these are suggestive of ambivalence in the animal, that is, uncertainty as to whether to threaten more closely or to go away. They occur often in young animals or subadults that are disturbed by the presence of an intruder or predator. All such reactions are usually without vocalization, but in the Kenya males a low grunting which grew to a roaring crescendo of rapid two-phase grunts always accompanied movements forward, such as a short run, lunge, and slapping of the ground in the direction of the opponent. Low grunting sometimes occurred in the Cape males in similar circumstances. A grating roar (Table 3–5, item 4) has been heard in the Kenya males on only five occasions, and always after fighting in the group.

Baboons sometimes shake tree branches violently, or pull vigorously backward and forward against rocks, when, for example, they are excited by the too close approach of human beings or large predators. This kind of reaction has rarely been observed in encounters between individual baboons, and it is possible that it is a redirection of aggression onto substitute objects (Bastock, Morris, and Moynihan 1953) rather than a part of interindividual threat behavior.

Although in the main the basic attack-threat repertoire of baboons resembles closely that of macaques, some differences of detail or of social significance may emerge from intensive comparative study. It is not clear, for example, that the behavior described as "backing threat" and "showing hindquarters" by Hinde and Rowell have had their counterparts in our baboon groups.

### Escape-Fear

As with attack-threat a range of behavior is included under this heading, from the obvious running away to slight gestures of mouth or limbs.

RUNNING AWAY: When, for example, a female is chased by a dominant male, she typically runs away screeching continuously (Table 3–5, item 5), her tail may go to a vertically upright position, and she may defecate and urinate as she goes. If caught, or even if she escapes down a cliff and continues to be threatened by the male above her, she tends to crouch to the ground, and her teeth are bared as she repeatedly utters a long-drawn, high-pitched, repetitive "churring" (Table 5, item 5). Occasionally, when running away from a charging male, a female has succeeded in temporarily arresting his aggression by quickly halting and presenting in front of him.

FEAR GRIMACE: This, the "grimace" of Altmann and the "frightened grin" of Hinde and Rowell, is characterized by retraction of the lips so that the teeth are exposed but not separated. The ears are usually flattened against the head, and the eyes may have a staring appearance. In chacma baboons this occurs quite frequently as a gesture by a subordinate animal when passing close to a dominant one, and it also occurs when an animal is offered food but is afraid to approach nearer to get it. The fear grimace is rarely seen in adult males. In Kenya only the old male Kovu, when very hard pressed, grimaced. But any unexpected attack on a female, juvenile, or infant almost invariably caused them to grimace. A more intense form of this expression occurs with the mouth open and accompanied by a sharp short "yakking" vocalization (Table 3–5, item 6) usually as the animal begins to withdraw and is looking back over its shoulder (Fig. 3–18).

STARTLE REACTIONS: These have been most clearly shown in field experiments with S group, Cape, and in field observations of this and C group when reacting to snakes. The action of an individual baboon on seeing a snake in a bush or on the ground has been sometimes to leap instantly away from the spot with all four limbs clear of the ground. It then stands, turns its head cautiously to look at the snake, and walks slowly away. When the whole of C group walked close by a coiled mole-snake about 6 feet long, each animal looked at the snake, but only some of the infants riding on their mother's backs were seen to have their tails go vertically upright. No vocalization was heard. On one occasion, a young female, on seeing a snake, uttered a sharp shrill bark (Table 5, item 8) and looked toward the rest of the group, none of whom appeared to respond to her.

In 1961 the animals of S group were discovered to have a complete aversion to live scorpions when these were experimentally given to them. The animals typically showed their aversion by immediately leaping back from the scorpion, with arms spread apart at fullest extent, and usually with the "yak" bark of alarm (Fig. 3–19). Following this the animal would sometimes draw one hand down over its muzzle — apparently a "nervous" reaction with no particular significance. Some of the animals followed their startle behavior by hitting away several times with one hand the scorpion or the bag or box which contained it.

The startle reaction to the very sudden appearance of another kind of animal, such as a group of eland in the Cape and a hyena in Southern Rhodesia, has consisted of one very sharp bark (Table 3–5, item 8), almost explosive in quality, by the baboon that first saw the intruder. Any baboons nearby will instantaneously dash away or up into trees. This is a reaction quite distinctive from the far-carrying, repeated barking of baboons when a lion or other large predator is in sight, or when a human intrudes on a group unaccustomed to human presence. Startle reactions of baboons vary enormously from situation to situation. If the observer comes suddenly upon an unhabituated group, it is likely to rush away silently, and only later to begin barking. Under such circumstances it is likely to disperse rather than keep together.

**Behavior in Uncertainty**

In many situations affecting behavior of baboons toward humans or other animals that arouse some fear of hostility, or both, as well as in some situations of interaction between baboons, attack-threat and escape-fear expressions may both occur. In addition, behavior expressive of tension or uncertainty may be observed. Yawning has been seen on several occasions in individual baboons in both regions when it was neither preceded nor followed by any expression of attack-threat (Fig. 3–20). In these cases it may be primarily a displacement activity and secondarily a part of threat display. It occurs occasionally in adult females, but less commonly.

Scratching the arms or back, wiping the muzzle with the hand, shrugging the shoulders, and fiddling with food objects have all been observed under similar circumstances, the actions tending to be desultory, jerky, and of short duration. When a male in the SR group is being sharply harassed, his normal grooming of the estrous female often increases in rapidity until he is brushing at her side in a frantic, ineffectual way. A rapid copulation was frequently observed when general chasing and fighting had broken out among the males of this group. On a few occasions mounting was observed and apparently true copulation by adult males of the Cape groups when disturbed by experimental objects. Similar "out of context" behavior is

Fig. 3–19. The startle reaction of a subadult male who has just discovered a live scorpion. S group, Cape. (*Photograph by Dr. G. J. Broekhuysen*)

Fig. 3–20. An adult male yawns while he sits expectantly beside another male eating a young gazelle. SR group.

reported by Carpenter for the howler monkey (1934) and for *M. mulatta* (1942a). It seems likely that in baboons and probably other monkeys, agitation or uncertainty leading to anxiety may express itself through any behavior system that happens to be or to have recently been activated, while the cues as to which system will receive the expression may also come from the presence of the relevant stimuli in the environment. The situations in which certain behavior of infants and young juveniles occurs — such as being ignored by the mother or separated from her — indicate a high degree of frustration or insecurity. In these situations the infant gives a repeated ick-ick-ooer (Table 3–5, item 9) accompanied by spasmodic or twitching movements of the head, shoulders, and arms, and by grimacing.

### Agitated Behavior of Unclear Function

Occasionally during quarrels in S and C groups, particularly in the latter, where adult females or subadult males were primarily involved, one animal would appear to mount another, with hands resting lightly on its back, but tending to stand with hindlegs a little to the side. Both animals pointed with their muzzles directly toward one or more other individuals

104

whom they were threatening. The movements of both were jerky, their attitudes tense. Similar behavior has also been observed in Kenya groups in quarrels among adult males and, occasionally, juveniles. It is not clear at present whether this is an action that forms a part of "enlisted threat" and, it it does, whether it derives from mounting.

## Friendly Behavior

As in the other categories of behavior, friendly behavior patterns may occur in varying social contexts. Thus, presenting, which is usually a gesture of submission, is often accompanied by nervous, even fearful, behavior on the part of the presenting animal, whereas mounting, conversely, in baboons is usually an indicator of relative dominance. However, all the forms of behavior to be discussed here seem to have as their chief function the establishing or maintaining of peaceful social relationships within the group.

GROOMING: Grooming in baboons is a very prominent form of social behavior, occurring in the wild most frequently early in the day, during a midday quiet period, and when the group approaches its sleeping place at the end of the day. Initiation of grooming may be made by an adult male, for example, by going up to a female and lying down beside her. The grooming response of the female is usually immediate. A female who is anestrous or partly in estrus may approach an adult male and present to him, upon which he may briefly pick over the perineal fur with his hands and put his nose close up to her. Initiative may come from the animal who intends to groom, as when a female, lipsmacking, approaches a mother with an infant and begins to groom the mother. The groomer usually lipsmacks while grooming. The movements of grooming are very similar to those observed in other monkeys, namely a brisk parting of the fur with the fingers of both hands and a picking off by hand or directly by mouth of extraneous items on the skin. These items are often swallowed.

Analysis of 220 grooming events in the Cape baboons indicated that grooming of female by female was easily the most common (Fig. 3–21), and females also spend much longer (averaging $6\frac{1}{2}$ minutes per grooming event) in grooming than do males (averaging $1\frac{1}{3}$ minute)—patterns of grooming behavior which are also true of baboons in Kenya. Adult males spend longer in grooming the estrous females with whom they are in temporary consort relationship than they do in other grooming situations. Females with infants, as already noted, are particularly attractive to other females, who frequently approach and groom them. In S group, Cape, it was also noted that, in female grooming pairs, females nearing or at full estrus were the groomed animals nearly four times as frequently as the converse. This is probably a direct reflection of the increase in all kinds of social activities by an estrous female, and of some alteration in her status, but the significance of the observation is not yet clear.

Fig. 3–21. One adult female grooms another while an infant-one clings to her mother's belly. S group, Cape.

Infants are frequently groomed by their mothers and by other females, and young animals frequently groom each other, although it is not known whether the young males tend to be groomers markedly less often than the young females. Although a female low in the dominance order may be groomed by other females superior to her, she may also be driven away fairly often by another female.

The nature of the dominance relations within a group are reflected in the amount of grooming attention an individual receives; a dominant, central male, for example, is more frequently groomed than a peripheral or less dominant male. Nevertheless, it seems that all members of the group to some extent receive and give grooming attention, and the function of grooming is assumed to be not simply a cleaning of the body surface but a continuing reinforcement of the social bonds.

LIPSMACKING AND "GREETINGS" BEHAVIOR: Lipsmacking occurs, as we have stated, when a would-be groomer approaches another animal and also during grooming. It also occurs as a prelude to or accompaniment of a series of gestures which are provisionally described as "greetings" behavior. This behavior was most clearly and frequently seen in S group, Cape, as a sequel to the release near the group of a tame young male baboon (about four years old). Once the aggressiveness of the $\alpha$ male had subsided, baboons of about the same age and of both sexes approached the stranger on many separate occasions and exhibited several reactions to him, which were sometimes reciprocated by him. These included standing on hind legs; embracing the hindquarters of the other when it was standing on all fours, one arm

106

placed between the hind legs, the other holding the buttocks from the rear; putting the muzzle down to the genital-pelvic area; placing the mouth up to the mouth.

On the few occasions when this behavior was seen at other times in S group, it seemed that the initiative usually came from the more dominant animal of a pair. Thus, the $\alpha$ male was observed to rise briefly on his hind legs, while lipsmacking, as some adult females passed close to him. Also, female B, dominant over female E, approached lipsmacking up to E, held the latter briefly with her hands between E's thighs and put her head right down to E's pelvic region. In the beginning the initiative always came from the animals in the group toward the tame baboon although later he initiated some exchanges. Such behavior was seen rarely in the Kenya groups also, and it is doubtful if all the components in the sequences described for the Cape occur there. Adult females have been observed standing on hind legs in front of adult males, and when two adult males are approaching each other lipsmacking, one may put its nose to the genital area of the other and even grasp the other's penis.

This type of performance is clearly very similar to that which females, or sometimes males, would carry out after approaching a black infant. The usual sequence was to walk, lipsmacking, toward mother and infant, then stand on hind legs, pick the infant up by its back legs, and briefly touch or "kiss" the infant's backside. Such performances frequently occurred in S group in the winter of 1961 when there were five black infants in the group. What is common to the situation of both the tame baboon and the infants is that they were all newcomers to the group. These performances were not accompanied by any vocalizations. Although the adult male (Lone) who joined the SV group, Kenya, did not elicit greetings behavior, such sequences occurred in that group occasionally when a female approached a young infant.

Another kind of "friendly" behavior that is difficult to describe fully, because it is usually fleeting and has no very pronounced gestures in it, occurs between baboons, often young animals, when they are several yards away from each other. The communicating animal briefly flattens its ears against its head, but without any other facial or gestural element common to threat behavior, and looks in the direction of the other animal. Among chacma baboons the animal also utters an intermittent "chattering" call (Table 3–5, item 11), a call that is also heard between young animals playing with one another. Also, when one or more baboons have become separated from the main body during the day range and when they begin to approach the group again, a loud, rather high-pitched bark (Table 5, item 12) is heard, usually from the smaller party, in both Kenya and the Cape. Apart from the apparent pitch difference and apart from the nature of the situation, it is difficult for the observer to distinguish this from an alarm bark.

When most of the members of a group are feeding quietly and at ease fairly close to one another, as among the thick bush areas in part of the Cape Reserve, a chorus of grunting (Table 3–5, item 13) may occasionally be heard without any other signs of communicative behavior. In Kenya this chorus inevitably occurred once or more as the group settled into its sleeping place for the night. What initiates these vocalizations is not clear, although sometimes they appear to start with the deep and repeated grunting of the $\alpha$ male, to which the others may have been responding.

PRESENTING AND MOUNTING: Among baboons, presenting is usually done by a subordinate animal, and mounting is usually done by a dominant one. The presenting animal approaches and stands in front of the other, sometimes backing toward it, tail raised or turned to the side. Distances at which the presenting animal approaches its rump to the other have varied considerably, from two feet or less up to several yards. The farther away the presenter stands, the more nervous it usually appears, sometimes looking back at the other, and sometimes jumping away as if in expectation of attack. In all the groups studied the act of presenting is one of the clearest indications of relative status. In S group, Cape, where at the time of study the $a$ male was clearly and consistently dominant over the other males in the group, he presented to no other animal. On one occasion when the $a$ male was sitting near the top of a gully up which the group was moving, seven different animals (five adult females, and males 2 and 3) presented briefly to him in six minutes. The $\alpha$ male responded (by mounting) to only one of the seven.

At least four different situations may occur where presenting is seen, and there are some postural variations in each:

(1) A female in estrus stands in front of a male and turns the tail to the side, lifting it slightly. The male varies his response according to her state of estrus and probably according to her dominance rank among the females. If she is in full estrus, he may pick over her perineal fur, or mount and copulate. Otherwise, he may briefly put his nose to her genital region, or he may ignore her altogether.

(2) Females not in estrus tend to present much more briefly, as do juveniles who may present to a dominant male, peering at him, then scamper away.

(3) Adult females, when approaching another adult female with an infant-one, would sometimes lower their hindquarters toward her, looking over their shoulder at her and lipsmacking (Fig. 3–22). The mother sometimes responds by briefly grasping the presenting female's hindquarters, but never mounts her.

(4) An adult male may walk quickly over to another adult male and lower his hindquarters, which action usually elicits grasping of the posterior. This sequence is rarely followed by mounting, in fact, it is usually the *dominant* male who initiates this sequence, and whose rump is grasped.

Fig. 3–22. An adult female approaches a mother slowly, with hindquarters lowered. SR group.

It is probably significant that the hindquarters are lowered substantially more in situations (3) and (4) than in normal presenting, and that mounting is unlikely to follow this lowered-hindquarters type of presenting. In any case, presenting and mounting among adult males was most frequently observed in a group in which there was tension or excitement among the adult males, as in the Kenya SR group in the presence of estrous females or feeding experiments. When in consort with an estrous female the male Dano of this group trotted over to Mdomo and mounted him, dismounting after two pelvic thrusts. Both males lipsmacked vigorously during the mounting. Mounting at other times is a very brief gesture, and quite infrequent in groups where the male dominance relations are stable.

## CONCLUSION

Within the limited sampling of baboon habitats represented by the Kenya and southern Africa studies, the range of ecological variation has been considerable. Animals that can maintain themselves successfully in mountainous riverine and savannah habitats are by definition adaptable, and the evidence for the diversity of feeding within the general vegetarian scheme indicates a readiness to make use of local natural resources, just as they make use of man-created food opportunities.

It is also of special interest that baboons seem capable of organizing themselves into groups, or, as among hamadryas, forming loose associations between groups in a variety of ways that indicates the flexibility of the basic social scheme. For example, a viable social structure appears in groups as diverse in composition as SR, Kenya, S Cape, C Cape, and so on, and with group members totaling from a low of 9 to a high of 185. Going beyond our own data to that of Kummer and Kurt (1963), we find an even more significant variation, but one which is still based upon the same sort of dominance relationships.

Adaptability in coping with a diversity of physical conditions, therefore, is inseparable from the adaptability revealed in the pattern of social organization. The remarkable success of the pattern of interaction between aggressiveness and protectiveness must, it seems, be attributed to the propensity these animals have evolved for learning continually during development to modify, extend or inhibit the form and frequency of their expressive and communicative behavior. This is essentially a perceptual, social learning, and it appears to be founded on a fairly narrow range of vocal and other expressive gestures and postures.

When we look back over the data synthesized in the two baboon chapters, the basic similarity of the findings from two widely separated regions of Africa should not lead us to neglect the possibility that some major differences may be found in the behavior patterns characteristic of what are sometimes designated as two separate species. For example, although the dominance relations look fundamentally alike in the two regions, the details of mating behavior show some differences. The rhesuslike copulation series characteristic of the Cape chacma does not seem to have its counterpart in the Kenya groups, and in mating behavior detail, the female vocalization of the chacma and the male "grin" have not been reported in Kenya. The attack-threat behavior patterns seem essentially alike, but it is not yet evident that the full sequence of what is provisionally termed greetings behavior is ever shown in the Kenya animals, although some components of it undoubtedly occur. In evaluating such comparisons, however, it is necessary to emphasize that the full extent of behavior variations within the regions of study has not yet been sufficiently sampled. Particularly where quantitative differences in behavior are in question, the difficulty in making significant comparison is very great.

CHARLES H. SOUTHWICK, MIRZA AZHAR BEG,
and M. RAFIQ SIDDIQI

4

# ◆ Rhesus Monkeys in North India

## INTRODUCTION

Rhesus monkeys (*Macaca mulatta* Zimmerman) have been studied intensively in laboratory and colony conditions, and much information is available on their biology and behavior in confinement and in seminatural habitats. Relatively little work has been done, however, on the ecology and behavior of rhesus monkeys in natural habitats in India. Only a few such studies have been published. Nolte (1955a) made brief observations on two rhesus groups in northern India, but she did not have time to obtain complete group counts or to analyze group social behavior. Prakash (1958) observed three groups of rhesus near Jaipur, India, and obtained records of births during two years, but he did not undertake a general study of ecology and social organization. Numerous scientific and popular accounts of Indian mammals, or of primates in general, contain some descriptions of rhesus ecology and behavior, but such accounts are entirely anecdotal and are not based upon specific field studies (Pocock 1929; Prater 1948; Sanderson 1957).

This study was undertaken to provide comparative data on the ecology and social behavior of naturally occurring rhesus groups in northern India. The ecological data were obtained in field surveys in Uttar Pradesh and adjacent provinces from September 1959 to June 1960, and in Bengal from October to November 1962. This work was planned to provide a broad

This work was conducted under grants from the National Institutes of Health, U.S. Public Health Service (RG–6262, RG 6262 S1, and A1–04154) to Ohio University and The Johns Hopkins University, and a fellowship from the U.S. Educational Foundation in India. During the 1959–1960 study period, the senior author was a Fulbright Research Fellow at Aligarh Muslim University.

111

picture of the population status, group sizes and compositions, habitat selection, and general ecological relationships of rhesus monkeys in northern India. The results of most of this work have been published previously (Southwick, Beg, and Siddiqi 1961a, 1961b), and will be presented only in summary in this paper. All subsequent statements on the ecology and population structures of rhesus monkeys in India are based upon these previous publications unless otherwise cited.

The behavioral data were obtained in a more intensive observational study of four groups of rhesus monkeys inhabitating a Hindu temple area in Aligarh, Uttar Pradesh. This study was undertaken from October 1959 to June 1960. Its purpose was to provide more specific information on social behavior, group organization, and intergroup relationships of rhesus monkeys. These data have not been published previously except those relating to intergroup relationships (Southwick 1962).

Rhesus groups inhabiting the grounds of Hindu temples have obvious advantages for behavioral study. The monkeys in temple grounds are fed and partially protected by local people; they are relatively free from trapping and molestation and are tame and easy to observe. Temple groups are typically larger and more completely age-structured than groups in most habitats. Thus they have more normal numbers of infants, juveniles, and adults than are found in most groups, which are subjected to trapping and molestation. Temple grounds are also among the few habitats in India where different social groups of rhesus come into frequent daily contact. No other habitat category in India ordinarily possesses all of these factors favorable for the study of social behavior.

Temple habitats also have a number of disadvantages for behavioral study. Temples are frequently in crowded urban areas where the congestion of buildings and people makes behavioral study difficult. Temple monkeys live in close association with people and rely so much on them for food that they are essentially living in an unconfined zoo. These environmental features undoubtedly result in certain behavioral distortions in comparison to the behavior of groups living in forest environments. For example, temple rhesus definitely exhibit more aggressive tension than do forest-dwelling rhesus.

In the total pattern of rhesus population distribution temple habitats probably contain only a minor segment of the rhesus population of northern India. In Uttar Pradesh, it was estimated that temple habitats contained approximately 2 percent of the total population.

For these reasons temple groups are not necessarily typical of rhesus groups in general, and the results of behavioral study of temple groups cannot necessarily be extended to include all rhesus groups. It is our belief, however, that the behavioral differences of rhesus monkeys in different habitats are basically quantitative rather than qualitative. Temple groups, then, represent a logical starting point in the study of social behavior of rhesus monkeys in India.

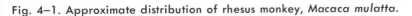
Fig. 4–1. Approximate distribution of rhesus monkey, *Macaca mulatta*.

## STUDY AREAS

### Ecological Survey

The State of Uttar Pradesh (formerly United Provinces) was selected as the primary locale for this survey because of its favorable geographical location and its traditional reputation as an area of great abundance of rhesus monkeys. Uttar Pradesh is situated in the northcentral portion of the range of the rhesus monkey in India, which is usually described as extending from western Kashmir eastward to Assam, and south to the rivers Tapti (150 miles north of Bombay) in the west, and Godavari (100 miles north of Hyderabad) in the east (see Fig. 4–1 taken from Pocock 1939 and Prater 1948). This description of range needs revision, however, since the rhesus is reported to be common around Hyderabad.

Uttar Pradesh extends from 24 to 31 degrees north latitude and from 77 to 84 degrees east longitude. It is composed of 113,454 square miles of which 79 percent are alluvial plains of the Ganges, Jumna, and Ghaghara rivers, 5 percent are upland plateau, 5 percent are Himalayan foothills, and 11 percent are Himalayan mountains.

Approximately 65 percent of the total land area of Uttar Pradesh is under cultivation. The major crops in decreasing order of acreage are wheat, rice, gram, barley, mustard, millet, pulse, sugar cane, corn, ground nuts, potato, and cotton. Forest areas, largely in foothills and mountains, compose 14 percent of the total land area.

The human population of Uttar Pradesh was listed in the 1961 census as 73,752,914, with a density of 650 people per square mile. Eighty-six percent of the population was rural. A recent enumeration of villages in the state listed a total of 108,941 villages with less than 2,000 people per village.

The climate of Uttar Pradesh varies considerably. The winter season (October to early March) is warm in the day throughout the plains (60° to 80° F.) and cool at night (40° to 50° F.). In the Himalayan foothills and mountains it is much colder, with snow prevailing in many regions. The summer season (late March until June) is hot and dry in the plains with day temperatures exceeding 100° F. in May and June, and night temperatures ranging from 60° to 80° F. In the foothills and mountains more moderate temperatures prevail. The monsoon season (July to September) is hot and humid, with temperatures generally 80° to 95° F. night and day throughout the plains. Rainfall is almost entirely confined to the monsoon with the exception of a few scattered winter rains. The annual rainfall averages from 30 to 50 inches in the plains and from 40 to more than 100 inches in the foothills and mountains.

Bengal, in northeastern India, was selected in 1962 for a comparative study of regional differences in rhesus abundance and ecology. Bengal extends from 22 to 27 degrees north latitude and from 86 to 89 degrees east longitude. It is composed of 33,928 square miles, of which the majority are alluvial plains of the Ganges and Hooghly rivers. Bengal had a human population of 34,967,634 in the 1961 census, with a density of 1031 people per square mile. The greatest population concentration occurs in the Calcutta area, but approximately 80 percent of the human population dwells in rural villages.

Fig. 4–2. Map of Uttar Pradesh showing regional divisions in roadside and railroad survey.

The major agricultural crops of Bengal are rice and jute in the southern and central regions, and tea in the northern terai and foothills. Forests are limited to reserved areas, primarily in the north, in the conservation districts of the centrally located Damodar Valley, and in the southern delta area known as the Sundarbans.

The climate of Bengal is more moderate and has more rainfall than

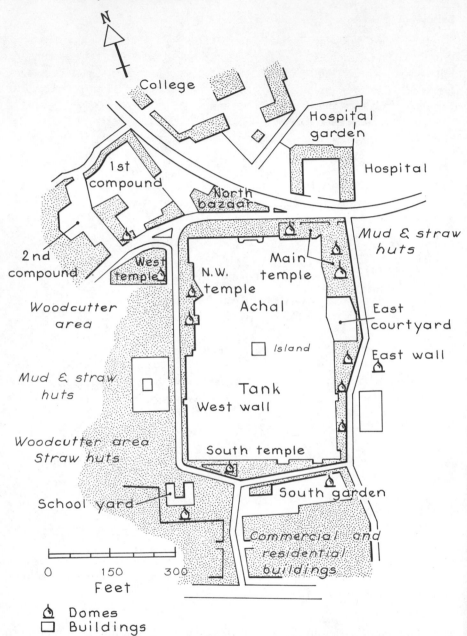

N

College

Hospital garden

Hospital

1st compound

North bazaar

Mud & straw huts

2nd compound

West temple

N.W. temple

Main temple

Achal

East courtyard

Woodcutter area

East wall

Mud & straw huts

Island

Tank

West wall

Woodcutter area
Straw huts

South temple

School yard

South garden

Commercial and residential buildings

0     150     300
Feet

△ Domes
▢ Buildings

Fig. 4–3. Diagram of Achal Tank, temple area, Aligarh, Uttar Pradesh.

Uttar Pradesh. At Calcutta daily temperatures in the winter vary from 50° to 80° F., and in the summer from 75° to 95° F. Average annual rainfall varies from 62 inches at Calcutta to 126 inches at Darjeeling.

**Behavioral Study**

The study area for intensive observations of behavior consisted of a group of Hindu temples located in the city of Aligarh, in Uttar Pradesh, 80 miles southeast of Delhi. Aligarh is a city of approximately 150,000 people located in the western region of the Upper Gangetic Basin between the Jumna and Ganges rivers.

There were approximately twelve Hindu temples, plus numerous small shrines, in the study area. They were constructed around the edges of an artificial lake, known as Achal Tank, with a surface area of approximately 4 acres (Fig. 4–3). The temple area was surrounded by crowded residential and commercial districts of several types. Immediately to the north was a crowded bazaar area (north bazaar), composed of fruit, vegetable, and food sellers, lining one of the main streets of Aligarh, the Grand Trunk Road to Kanpur.

East of the temple area was a variety of dwellings; some were mud and straw huts; others were middle-class homes of brick and adobe, with tree-shaded courtyards. To the south of the temple area was a shaded garden (south garden) that contained the living quarters of several *sadhus* (Hindu holy men). Beyond the garden was a middle-class residential and commercial area composed of apartment dwellings and shops along another main street which led to Agra.

The entire area was the scene of constant human activity throughout most of the day and part of the night, with commercial and pedestrian traffic of all types passing through. The area shown in Fig. 4–3, composed of approximately 30 acres, served as the main residence and area of activity for more than a thousand people, and in the course of a typical day hundreds of other people passed through or stopped for varying periods at the temples. Many people, primarily sadhus, slept and lived in the temples, while others slept in the streets surrounding the temples.

Most of the temple area had numerous shade trees, primarily pipal (*Ficus religiosa* L.), banyan (*Ficus bengalensis* L.), neem (*Melia azadirachta* L.), imle or tamerind (*Tamarindus indica* L.), mango (*Mangifera indica* L.), and acacia (*Acacia leucophaea* or *A. modesta*). These trees provided shelter and natural food for the monkeys. Trees were particularly abundant in temple courtyards, the south garden, and the campus of the college.

## FIELD METHODS

**Ecological Survey**

The ecological survey was designed to obtain data on abundance, habitat distribution, and group compositions of rhesus monkeys. Field effort was divided into six categories: (1) a roadside survey, which included cursory inspections of fields, woodlots, and gardens bordering roadsides; (2) a canal bank survey, which also included the bordering fields and woodlots; (3) a railroad survey, with particular emphasis on railway stations; (4) a village and town survey; (5) a temple survey; and (6) a forest survey in the Himalayan foothills. These surveys were planned to provide a sample of all major rhesus habitats found within Uttar Pradesh, and involved 20,000 miles of travel within northern India, and more than 6000 man-hours of field work.

In each type of survey we attempted to find as many rhesus groups as possible and to obtain a sex-age count of groups whenever possible. Systematic field procedures were adopted for each type of survey to permit quantitative indices of abundance. Detailed descriptions of field survey methods have been published previously.

The ecological surveys in Madhya Pradesh and Bengal consisted only of limited roadside surveys, accompanied by interviews of villagers, herdsmen, and forest officers. A limited forest survey was undertaken in northern Bengal, but it was not done systematically as in Uttar Pradesh.

In all surveys the individuals observed were placed in one of four categories: adult males, adult females, infants, and juveniles. Infants were identified as young which were generally dependent upon the mother, not yet weaned, usually carried by the mother during group progression, definitely less than four pounds in body weight, and judged to be less than one year old. Infants frequently moved on their own some distance from their mothers during play or feeding, but most of the time they remained closely associated with the mother. If a young individual was seen to ride upon the female for any distance, or was seen to nurse successfully, it was classified as an infant.

Juveniles were identified as young that were largely independent of the mother, definitely weaned, more than four pounds in body weight. They were judged to be more than one year of age and less than four. In general the differences between infants and juveniles, as here defined, were clear-cut, but occasionally borderline animals were seen and after close observation were arbitrarily assigned to a category.

Juveniles were distinguished from adults by their smaller size and lack of red sexual skin. Both these characteristics are highly variable, however, and subjective judgments were necessary on many occasions.

The division of this population survey into six habitat categories led to certain obvious problems of classification. For example, where villages were located along roadsides, a group of monkeys living in the vicinity might be considered either a village group or a roadside group. Monkeys living at points where road bridges crossed canals could be considered either roadside groups or canal-bank groups. These problems of classification were handled by determining which locale represented the usual and most frequent habitation of the group. The home ranges of the monkeys were often very restricted and the main sleeping and feeding areas quite specific. This usually warranted placing a group in a particular category, and in a few cases where two habitat categories seemed to be used equally an arbitrary designation was made depending upon how or where the group was first seen.

## Behavioral Study

Field observations on the rhesus monkeys inhabiting the Achal Tank area were made on a total of 85 days from October 13, 1959, to May 12, 1960. From 1 to 10 hours per day were spent in observation with a total observation time of 412 hours by the senior author, and approximately 350 hours by the other two authors. A typical day consisted of 5 hours of observation from 6:00 to 9:00 A.M., and from 5:00 to 7:00 P.M. These were the hours of greatest activity in group movements, feeding, and sexual behavior.

Two observational techniques were used. One was to start out with a particular group of individual monkeys and simply follow them around, staying with them wherever they went. The second was to remain at one spot, usually on the edge of Achal Tank, from which a good view of the entire tank area could be obtained, and to observe patterns of group movement and behavior from this location. The west wall was particularly suitable for this procedure since it afforded a good view of most of the central area.

Usually two of us were in the area during each observation period. We found it most profitable to split up and observe different groups or different parts of the area, meeting every hour to compare notes. We attempted to remain as neutral as possible in relation to the monkeys. We did not feed them except for specific purposes. We did not trap or handle them, nor did we annoy or threaten them in any way. After a few months, they generally disregarded our presence. We could observe most individuals freely from a distance of a few feet.

We did not mark animals for individual identification. Over a period of two months we became familiar with all the adult males and many of the adult females by their individual appearances. It would have made the study more meaningful to have marked other individuals, but we felt there were good reasons for not doing so in an area crowded with Indian people. There probably would have been no serious objection, but undoubtedly it would have created great curiosity and would have required countless daily explanations. As it was, our presence in the area aroused much curiosity, and it was not unusual to collect crowds of 20 people by simply using binoculars. A camera, particularly a movie camera, created even greater interest. We gave up the use of walky-talkies as a method of maintaining voice contact between two observers because they generated too much curiosity from the local people. Thus it was necessary at several points to compromise field techniques to maintain more suitable public relations.

TABLE 4–1. POPULATION SURVEY OF RHESUS MONKEYS IN NORTHERN INDIA: INCIDENCE AND STRUCTURE OF GROUPS

| Type of Survey | Miles Traveled | Number of Stations, Villages, and Temples | Groups Seen | Incidence of Groups (percent) | Miles per Group | Groups Counted | Average Group Size | Adults | | Subadults | |
|---|---|---|---|---|---|---|---|---|---|---|---|
| | | | | | | | | ♂♂ | ♀♀ | I I | J J |
| Roadside | 6093 | | 412 | | 14.8 | 230 | 15.1 ±0.6 | 3.5 ±0.1 | 6.9 ±0.3 | 3.8 ±0.2 | 0.9 ±0.2 |
| Canal bank | 200 | | 37 | | 5.4 | 26 | 19.0 ±2.0 | 4.4 ±0.4 | 8.4 ±0.9 | 5.5 ±0.6 | 0.7 ±0.3 |
| Railroad | 2730 | 443 | 84 | 11.3 | 32.5 | 34 | 11.4 ±1.4 | 2.6 ±0.4 | 5.0 ±0.7 | 2.7 ±0.4 | 1.0 ±0.2 |
| Village | | 280 | 50 | 15.7 | | 50 | 17.4 ±1.2 | 3.5 ±0.2 | 7.2 ±0.5 | 4.6 ±0.3 | 2.0 ±0.4 |
| Town | | 30 | 39 | 68.8 | | 39 | 22.4 ±2.5 | 4.4 ±0.5 | 9.7 ±1.1 | 5.9 ±0.7 | 2.4 ±0.5 |
| Temple | | c. 200 | 15 | <10.0 | | 15 | 41.9 ±4.6 | 7.9 ±0.9 | 15.2 ±1.9 | 9.5 ±1.3 | 9.3 ±1.5 |
| Forest | 10 sq. mi. | | 7 | | | 5 | 49.8 ±5.8 | 5.6 ±0.7 | 19.2 ±1.7 | 11.4 ±0.7 | 13.6 ±2.9 |

## RESULTS OF THE ECOLOGICAL SURVEYS

Rhesus monkeys were found in a wide variety of habitats, from crowded cities and villages to relatively remote forest areas.

A total of 645 groups of rhesus monkeys were seen during these field surveys: 412 groups in roadside habitats, 89 in villages and towns, 84 in railroad stations and along railroad rights-of-way, 37 along canal banks, 15 in temples, and 8 in forest areas (Table 4–1). These data *per se* do not provide an accurate concept of the relative importance of these habitat categories in the over-all pattern of population distribution. They merely give some indication of the relative ease of finding rhesus monkeys in these various habitats. Projected estimates of the actual habitat distribution of the rhesus populations of Uttar Pradesh are shown in Fig. 4–4. The bases of these estimates are given in Table 4–2.

Reliable counts were obtained on 399 groups (60 percent of all groups seen), totaling 7003 individuals. The average group size was 17.6 individuals, and was composed of 3.7 adult males, 7.7 adult females, 4.5 infants, and 1.7 juveniles. There were, however, significant differences in group

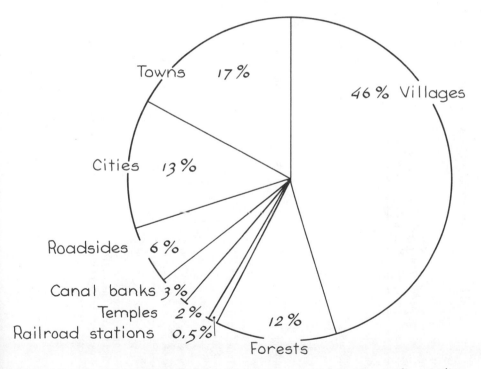

Fig. 4–4. Estimated habitat distribution of rhesus population in northern India, 1959–1960.

TABLE 4-2. HYPOTHETICAL ESTIMATE OF TOTAL RHESUS MONKEY POPULATION IN UTTAR PRADESH

| Habitat | Rhesus Population Estimate | Percent of Total Population | Basis of Estimate | Calculation |
|---|---|---|---|---|
| Roadsides | 48,000 | 6.0 | $\dfrac{\text{(total mileage of roads in U.P.)}(\bar{x})}{\text{miles per group in roadside survey}}$ | $\dfrac{(35,851)(15.1)}{11.2}$ |
| Canal banks | 25,000 | 3.0 | $\dfrac{\text{(total mileage of large canals in U.P.)}(\bar{x})}{\text{miles per group in canal bank survey}}$ | $\dfrac{(7,236)(19.0)}{5.4}$ |
| Railroads | 4,000 | 0.5 | $\dfrac{\text{(total mileage of railways in U.P.)}(\bar{x})}{\text{miles per group in railroad survey}}$ | $\dfrac{(10,000)(11.4)}{32.5}$ |
| Villages | 372,000 | 46.0 | (total number of villages in U.P.)(I)(G)($\bar{x}$) | (108,941)(.157)(1.25)(17.4) |
| Towns (small and medium) | 133,000 | 17.0 | (total number of small and medium towns in U.P.)(I)(G)($\bar{x}$) | (3,104)(.688)(2.78)(22.4) |
| Large towns and cities | 100,000 | 12.5 | pure guess | |
| Temples | 20,000 | 2.5 | pure guess | |
| Forests | 100,000 | 12.5 | (sq. mi. of forest in U.P.)(I)($\bar{x}$)(c.f.) | (15,877)(.7)(49.8)(.20) |
| Total | 802,000 | | | |

$\bar{x}$ = average group size
I = Incidence of rhesus groups in villages, towns, and forest survey areas
G = average number of groups per village or town with resident monkeys
c.f. = correction factor for dry season concentration

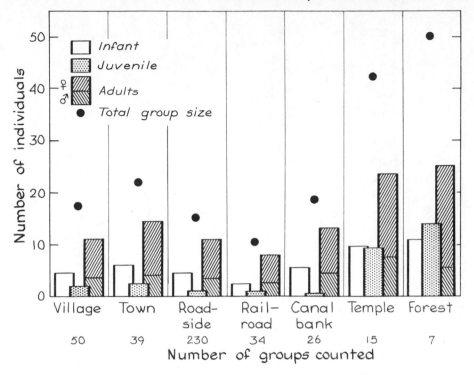

Fig. 4–5. Rhesus group sizes and compositions, according to habitat, 1959–1960.

sizes and compositions between different habitat categories (Fig. 4–5).

The most productive and valuable types of survey in this study were: (1) roadside surveys, for obtaining large numbers of group counts, (2) village, town, and forest surveys, for providing samples of the largest segments of the rhesus populations of northern India, and (3) temple surveys, for the close and detailed study of behavioral interactions.

## Roadside Surveys

In a total of 6093 miles driven in the course of specified road survey studies, 412 groups of rhesus monkeys were seen, an average of one group every 14.8 miles. There were prominent regional differences in the abundance of roadside monkeys (Table 4–3). The region of greatest abundance was central Uttar Pradesh, around Lucknow, Faizabad, and Gorakhpur where 94 groups were seen in 388 miles, an average of one group every 4.1 miles. An outstandingly high concentration of roadside groups occurred near Ajodhya where 17 groups were seen in 5 miles.

**TABLE 4–3. INCIDENCE AND GROUP STRUCTURES OF RHESUS MONKEYS OBSERVED IN ROADSIDE SURVEY OF NORTHERN INDIA**

| Location | Miles | Groups Seen | Average Miles per Group | Groups Counted | Average Group Size | Adults ♂♂ | Adults ♀♀ | Subadults I I | Subadults J J |
|---|---|---|---|---|---|---|---|---|---|
| Western U.P. | 2655 | 191 | 13.9 | 65 | 16.2 ± 1.3 | 3.6 ± 0.3 | 6.9 ± 0.6 | 4.6 ± 0.4 | 1.1 ± 0.3 |
| Central U.P. | 538 | 79 | 6.8 | 63 | 14.2 ± 1.1 | 3.6 ± 0.3 | 7.1 ± 0.4 | 3.2 ± 0.4 | 0.3 ± 0.2 |
| Eastern and Southern U.P. | 626 | 72 | 8.7 | 62 | 12.4 ± 0.7 | 2.9 ± 0.2 | 6.0 ± 0.4 | 2.9 ± 0.3 | 0.5 ± 0.2 |
| Northern U.P. | 542 | 57 | 9.5 | 36 | 19.3 ± 1.9 | 3.7 ± 0.3 | 8.2 ± 0.8 | 5.2 ± 0.5 | 2.2 ± 0.6 |
| Central M.P. | 281 | 7 | 40.1 | 4 | 18.5 ± 7.0 | 3.5 ± 0.9 | 11.0 ± 4.0 | 1.8 ± 1.0 | 2.2 ± 1.1 |
| Bengal | 1451 | 6 | 241.8 | 0 | not counted accurately | | | | |
| Totals | 6093 | 412 | 14.8 | 230 | 15.1 ± 0.6 | 3.5 ± 0.1 | 6.9 ± 0.3 | 3.8 ± 0.2 | 0.9 ± 0.2 |

In all of Uttar Pradesh, and including adjacent sections of Rajasthan and the Punjab, roadside monkeys were least abundant around Delhi, where only one group was seen every 29 miles traveled.

In a very brief roadside survey in central Madhya Pradesh around Jubbulpore, only seven groups were counted in 281 miles. This was in hilly country with scattered shrubby forests, however, and hence this sample was not comparable with those from the flat plains of Uttar Pradesh.

The most striking scarcity of roadside monkeys in all regions surveyed was in Bengal in 1962. Only six groups of rhesus were seen in 1451 miles of systematic roadside survey; an average of one rhesus group every 242 miles (Southwick, Ghosh, and Louch 1964). Although the roadside vegetation of Bengal is frequently too dense for survey purposes, the majority of this mileage was through roadside habitat suitable ecologically and also observationally.

To evaluate the reliability of roadside survey methods, one section of typical roadside 104 miles in length from Delhi to Hathras was selected. Frequent surveys on this road indicated that 14 groups of rhesus monkeys lived along the roadside. In ten repetitions of the trip under similar conditions, the lowest count of groups seen during a single trip was three, the highest count was eleven, and the average was seven groups per trip. On no single trip were all groups seen. This suggests that an average roadside survey trip on the plains, under standard conditions, reveals about 50 percent of the total number of groups which inhabit the roadside. In hilly and/or forested country, or in areas with excessive roadside vegetation, roadside survey methods are not satisfactory for locating rhesus monkeys.

## Village and Town Surveys

Villages and towns probably represent the most important single habitat category of rhesus monkeys in the populated sections of northern India.

Sixteen percent of 280 villages sampled throughout four regions of Uttar Pradesh had resident rhesus monkey groups (all of which had apparently been there for at least five years), an additional 20 percent reported that monkeys came into the village occasionally, and an additional 14 percent reported that monkeys had been present within the last five years, but were no longer there (Table 4-4). Most villages having monkeys had just one group; the maximum number of groups per village occurred in Kamta, a large village in southern Uttar Pradesh, where five groups were seen.

The region with the greatest number of resident monkeys was eastern Uttar Pradesh around Azamgarh, where 32 percent of 50 villages surveyed had resident monkeys.

The town survey indicated more resident monkeys in towns than in villages: 69 percent of 30 towns sampled in three regions had resident

**TABLE 4-4. INCIDENCE OF RHESUS MONKEYS IN VILLAGES AND TOWNS OF UTTAR PRADESH**

| Districts | Number of Villages or Towns Surveyed | Number with Resident Monkeys | Percent | Average Number of Groups per Village or Town | Number with Monkeys as Occasional Visitors | Percent | Additional Number of Villages or Towns Which Had Monkeys in Last Five Years | Percent |
|---|---|---|---|---|---|---|---|---|
| Village survey | | | | | | | | |
| Aligarh (Western U.P.) | 108 | 12 | (11) | 1.0 | 12 | (11) | 11 | (10) |
| Azamgarh (Eastern U.P.) | 50 | 16 | (32) | 1.0 | 8 | (16) | 9 | (18) |
| Banda (Southern U.P.) | 69 | 10 | (14) | 1.8 | 22 | (32) | 14 | (20) |
| Dehra Dun (Northern U.P.) | 53 | 6 | (11) | 1.3 | 13 | (24) | 5 | (9) |
| Total | 280 | 44 | (16) | 1.25 | 55 | (20) | 39 | (14) |
| Town survey | | | | | | | | |
| Aligarh | 16 | 11 | (69) | 2.3 | 1 | (6) | 3 | (19) |
| Azamgarh | 9 | 6 | (67) | 2.0 | 2 | (22) | 0 | |
| Banda | 5 | 4 | (80) | 5.7 | 0 | | 1 | (20) |
| Total | 30 | 21 | (69) | 2.78 | 3 | (10) | 4 | (13) |

monkeys, an additional 10 percent indicated that monkeys came as visitors, and an additional 13 percent that monkeys were present within the last five years but had been driven away or trapped.

Larger villages and towns tended to have more rhesus groups than small villages: 14 percent of small villages throughout Uttar Pradesh had resident rhesus, 18 percent of medium-sized villages, 22 percent of large villages, 53 percent of small towns, and 91 percent of medium-sized towns.

**Temple Survey**

It is not possible to express precisely the percentage of temples which had resident monkeys or monkeys as occasional visitors, since temples are not definable units. It can be stated quite definitely that monkeys are not present in most Hindu temples.

A survey of approximately 200 moderate- to large-size temples revealed only 15 resident temple groups in 12 different temples (Table 4–5). This list does not represent a thorough survey of temples in the survey regions, nor does it represent a random survey, since we specifically visited temples

TABLE 4–5. GROUP SIZES OF TEMPLE MONKEYS IN UTTAR PRADESH

| Location | Group Size | Adults | | Subadult | |
|---|---|---|---|---|---|
| | | $\male\male$ | $\female\female$ | I I | J J |
| Aligarh: Achal Tank, Group 1 | 51 | 12 | 14 | 6 | 19 |
| Achal Tank, Group 2 | 34 | 7 | 10 | 8 | 9 |
| Benaras: Durga Temple | 46 | 7 | 14 | 8 | 17 |
| Sarnath Temple | 31 | 5 | 11 | 7 | 8 |
| Chitrakut: Jagvedi Akhara Temple | 78 | 17 | 35 | 20 | 6 |
| Bara Math Temple (1) | 26 | 5 | 11 | 6 | 4 |
| Bara Math Temple (2) | 32 | 9 | 13 | 7 | 3 |
| Delhi: Temple at Hindan Bridge | 21 | 5 | 9 | 6 | 1 |
| Hardwar | 34 | 6 | 10 | 7 | 11 |
| Hathras: Group 1 | 49 | 11 | 16 | 14 | 8 |
| Group 2 | 74 | 11 | 28 | 16 | 19 |
| Kamta: Mukharbind Temple | 28 | 6 | 14 | 4 | 4 |
| Lucknow: Temple at Monkey Bridge | 54 | 9 | 18 | 13 | 14 |
| Mathura: Group 1 | 55 | 6 | 18 | 16 | 15 |
| Group 2 | 16 | 2 | 7 | 5 | 2 |
| Total | 629 | 118 | 228 | 143 | 140 |
| Means | 41.9 | 7.9 | 15.2 | 9.5 | 9.3 |
| Standard Error | ±4.6 | ±0.9 | ±1.9 | ±1.3 | ±1.5 |
| Population Composition | | 18.7% | 36.2% | 22.7% | 22.3% |

**TABLE 4–6. FOREST SURVEY OF RHESUS MONKEYS IN NORTHERN UTTAR PRADESH: INCIDENCE AND GROUP STRUCTURES**

| Location | Forest Type | Altitude (feet) | Man-Hours Observed | Square miles | Langur Groups Seen | Rhesus Groups Seen | Rhesus Group Size | Adults ♂♂ | Adults ♀♀ | Subadults II | Subadults JJ |
|---|---|---|---|---|---|---|---|---|---|---|---|
| Corbett National Park Dhikala and Sarupduli areas | Tropical dry mixed deciduous | 1000–2000 | 50 | 4 | 4 | 6 | 60 | 6 | 24 | 14 | 16 |
| | | | | | | | 32 | 4 | 14 | 9 | 5 |
| | | | | | | | 40 | 4 | 16 | 11 | 9 |
| | | | | | | | ca. 45 | – | – | – | – |
| | | | | | | | ca. 40 | – | – | – | – |
| | | | | | | | 49 | 6 | 21 | 12 | 10 |
| Corbett National Park Dhikala area | Sal or Sheesham | 1000–2000 | 18 | 2 | 1 | 0 | | | | | |
| Naini Tal Bhowali, Kale Khan and Malli Tal areas | Pine-oak or Pine-fir | 4000–7000 | 54 | 4 | 5 | 1 | 68 | 8 | 21 | 11 | 28 |
| Totals and Averages | | | 122 | 10 | 10 | 7 | 49.8 ±5.8 | 5.6 ±0.7 | 19.2 ±1.7 | 11.4 ±0.7 | 13.6 ±2.9 |

that were most likely to have monkeys, and considered only those with at least one quarter acre of temple grounds containing trees and an available water supply.

The average size of temple groups was 41.9 individuals, twice as large as village and town groups. The smallest temple group counted consisted of 16 individuals, the largest of 78. Temple groups also had a higher proportion of juveniles (22.3 percent) than the other groups listed heretofore.

### Forest Survey

In forested areas of northern Uttar Pradesh rhesus monkeys were found in both mixed deciduous and mixed coniferous forests up to altitudes of 6000 feet.

In 10 square miles of forest area surveyed in Uttar Pradesh, representing five distinct forest types, seven groups of rhesus were found (Table 4–6). Six of these groups were found in 4 square miles of mixed dry deciduous forests of Corbett Park, and one in a pine-oak forest near Naini Tal. The mixed deciduous forests of Corbett Park were typical secondary forests of the Indian terai. They afforded excellent cover and adequate natural food for rhesus monkeys (leaves and fruits of *Ficus religiosa, Ficus bengalensis, Bauhinia variegata, Melia azadirachta, Tamarindus indica*, and the like [see Champion 1936]). In the same areas pure stand forests of sal (*Shorea robusta*) and sheesham (*Dalbergia sissoo*), which were managed for timber production, were less favored rhesus habitats.

The abundance of rhesus monkeys in the mixed dry deciduous forests of Corbett Park probably represented a seasonal concentration. Water supplies in these terai forests are abundant during and after the monsoons, but as the dry season progresses most streams become dry and the monkey population becomes concentrated along major watercourses. All the forest areas studied in this survey contained available water or were adjacent to rivers. The forest work in Corbett Park was done along the Ramganga River. There were extensive forest areas farther up the slopes that were devoid of surface water and probably also devoid of monkeys at the time of the survey (the month of May at the end of the dry season). This statement is based upon our own observations and also upon the opinions of the Corbett Park forest officers.

The average group size of forest monkeys was the largest observed in this study (49.8 individuals), probably an underestimate of true group size in forest areas. Rhesus groups in the forest were very difficult to count. The animals were wild and shy, and often spread over an area 100 or 200 yards in diameter. The could only be counted when seen crossing a dry-stream bed, a forest road, or some similar opening. The counts obtained suggest that some adult males were missed, quite possibly the peripheral males characteristic of most rhesus groups.

Forest groups of rhesus also had good percentages of juveniles (27.3 percent). In this regard they were similar to temple monkeys, but unlike all other groups.

In the forests of northern Bengal seven groups of rhesus were found in a two-week period. We encountered six of these groups while driving on forest roads. Accurate counts of these groups were not obtained, but the smallest group was estimated at from 20–30 individuals, and the largest at from 80–120 individuals. The groups were completely age-structured with favorable numbers of infants and juveniles.

## Population Composition

Of the total 7003 individual rhesus monkeys counted, 21.4 percent were adult males, 43.6 percent were adult females, 25.5 percent were infants, and 9.5 percent were juveniles. Males constituted 30.7 percent of the adult population, infants 58.4 percent of the infant/adult female population, and subadults 35 percent of the total population. Some significant differences in population composition between different survey categories did occur, however.

The percentages of adult males in groups of different categories were generally from 19 percent to 23 percent, except in forest groups where it was only 11.2 percent. This was probably an observational failure, that is, the failure to count peripheral males in dense forest cover.

Males normally made up from 31 percent to 34 percent of adults in all survey categories, except in forest groups where only 22.6 percent of adults were male.

The percentages of females, infants, and the infant/adult-female ratio was quite similar in all types of groups. Adult females composed from 36 percent to 46 percent of the total populations, infants composed from 23 percent to 29 percent of the total populations and from 55 percent to 66 percent of the infant/female populations.

The greatest variation in population composition occurred in the percentages of juveniles. Roadside and canal-bank groups had less than 6 percent juveniles; railroad, village, and town groups had approximately 10 percent juveniles; whereas temple and forest groups had 22 percent and 27 percent juveniles respectively. If the age structure in these temple and forest groups is considered normal, all other groups surveyed had significantly deficient percentages of juveniles ($X^2 = 698.904$; $P = < 0.01$).

## Seasonal Patterns of Reproduction

Seasonal peaks of sexual activity were observed in November, December, and January (see Table 4–11 below), and a seasonal peak of births was observed in April and May (see Chap. 14, Fig. 14–3). Of 343 adult females observed in 32 groups in April and May, 37 percent had infants less than one month old. If all of these groups could have been observed in the latter part of May, undoubtedly a higher percentage of newborn infants would have been seen. In contrast to this, of a total of 622 adult females seen in September and October only 1.1 percent had newborn infants, and of 2092 adult females seen from November to March none had newborn infants.

A similar seasonal pattern of births has been observed by Prakash (1958). In three large groups of rhesus near Jaipur in northern India most births occurred from March 25 to May 7, but a few were observed from September 28 to October 8. None were seen at other times of the year. On Cayo Santiago births occur in the spring from January to May with a peak in March and April (Koford, Chap. 5, this volume).

### Estimates of Rhesus Population Size

It is virtually impossible to obtain a reliable population estimate of rhesus monkeys in any major area of India. At a risk of considerable error, we would venture a guess at less than one million individuals for the total rhesus population of Uttar Pradesh. Table 4–2 presents the basis of this estimate. It is offered only on the premise that it may be more accurate than many popular estimates that there are from 10 million to 20 million monkeys in Uttar Pradesh.

In Table 4–2 there is some sample basis for the population estimates for roadsides, canal banks, railroads, villages, and small or medium towns. The figures for large towns, cities, temples, and forest areas involve pure guesses, and might contain errors of several hundred percent. It is inconceivable to us, however, that the rhesus population of Uttar Pradesh could greatly exceed one million. In ten months of intensive field work throughout most of Uttar Pradesh we saw fewer than 12,000 rhesus monkeys.

On the basis of roadside and village surveys, we feel that the regions of greatest rhesus abundance in Uttar Pradesh are central and eastern Uttar Pradesh, extending from Shahjahanpur through Lucknow to Gorakhpur.

Other areas of high rhesus abundance were the *terai* (tarai) and *bhabar* of northern Uttar Pradesh and northern Bengal. The terai is a narrow bank of lowland jungle between the plains and the Himalayan foothills. The bhabar is an adjacent band of rocky, hilly terrain at the base of the foothills, covered by scrub forest. The two types of terrain are frequently interspersed, and together form a belt from 2 to 20 miles wide running most of the length of the Himalayan chain. Typical terai and bhabar country occurs in the vicinities of Dehra Dun, Corbett National Park, Nainital, and Tanakpur. Rhesus monkeys were abundant in these regions as evidenced by the Dehra Dun village survey, the Corbett Park forest survey, and the Tanakpur road survey.

### Habitat Distribution and Human Interactions

Villages and towns were the most important habitat categories in this survey, having probably more than half of all the rhesus monkeys in Uttar

Pradesh. These small communities afford ideal physical habitat for rhesus monkeys: large trees for cover and food, buildings and walls for shelter from duststorms and monsoon rains, abundant food supplies in fields and gardens around the village, and available water in wells, in irrigation ditches, and in ponds.

The major disadvantage of the village and town habitat for monkeys is frequent molestation from the people. Rhesus monkeys exist in villages and towns only by the tolerance and consent of the people, a tolerance that has been maintained for centuries by social tradition and religious custom. Rhesus monkeys have been permitted to live in villages and towns and to feed upon agricultural crops, but currently social traditions and customs in India are undergoing rapid change, and the tolerant attitudes toward monkeys are also changing. Many villagers told us that they could no longer afford to have monkeys in their villages. Hence, monkeys in some villages and towns are being trapped, driven away, or even killed. The village survey data indicated a decline in village monkeys of almost 50 percent during the five years prior to 1959.

This decline in village monkeys does not necessarily indicate an equivalent population decline, and it is possible that groups driven from villages and towns have retreated into roadside or canal-bank habitats. It is our opinion, however, that most of the decline in village monkeys has been an actual population decline, rather than just a shift in habitat distribution. We could obtain no evidence that there had been a marked increase in the rhesus population of roadsides or of any other habitat.

Roadside and canal-bank habitats contained a relatively small segment of the total rhesus population, but probably a more stable segment than did villages. Both roadside and canal banks frequently have rows of large trees, providing food and cover for monkeys, and neighboring fields of agricultural crops. The obvious advantage of canal banks is the abundance of water. Along roadsides monkeys were usually limited to places where irrigation ditches ran along the road. The dry season in northern India covers nine months; water is a critical factor determining monkey distribution.

Both roadsides and canal banks are public property in India, and, in a sense, the monkeys are also public property. Living within the public domain, the monkeys are not so obviously in direct competition with any one village for food. When they venture into neighboring fields, they are frequently driven back by *chawkidars* guarding the fields, and they retreat again to the roadsides where they are relatively free from molestation.

In temples and railroad stations monkeys also exist as "public property" within the public domain. When the monkeys venture from these specific habitats into surrounding bazaars or residential areas, they are often chased and driven back by shopkeepers and residents. In this respect temples, railway stations, roadsides, and canal banks all represent "refugia" where the monkeys are relatively free from constant molestation and where they are also fed.

Within these "refugia" rhesus monkeys are a source of entertainment for the people of India. Along roadsides and canal banks passersby often stop, rest, and feed the monkeys. In temples and railway stations rhesus monkeys are even more abundantly fed. They are given gram nuts, peanuts, fruits, vegetables, and occasionally cooked foods such as *chapatis*. Many people have a daily routine of feeding the monkeys. They apparently do it for amusement, or for an outing with children. Occasionally, they appeared to do it in a spirit of worship. Rhesus monkeys are not sacred for most Hindus (Lydekker 1893; Pocock 1929), although they enjoy varying degrees of religious association. The langur is the sacred monkey of India; Hanuman, the monkey god of Hindu mythology, is usually portrayed as a langur. Rhesus monkeys, however, have become partially sacred by association. Thus, rhesus monkeys are often fed and protected in temples and holy places. The greatest concentrations of rhesus monkeys observed in this survey were all in places of particular religious significance for Hindus: Ajodhya, Benaras, Chitrakut, Hardwar, Kamta, and Mathura.

Temples and railway stations are also significant habitats from other standpoints. They offer the most intimate contacts between monkeys and large numbers of itinerant people of any habitat in India. Infectious diseases reservoired in rhesus monkeys which might be passed to human beings could spread more rapidly across India via temple and railway-station groups than by groups in any other type of habitat.

No specific survey of rhesus monkeys in large towns and cities was attempted in this study. There are fifteen cities in Uttar Pradesh with populations of more than 100,000 people, and numerous large towns with populations from 15,000 to 100,000. Probably all these have some rhesus monkeys present; we were able to find rhesus groups in all major cities except Allahabad.

In large towns and cities rhesus groups were usually associated with temples, railway stations, roadsides leading into the cities, or bazaars, and this survey has included many city groups under these categories. Rhesus groups in bazaars were common, but were exceptionally difficult to count and study.

## Population Trends

Two aspects of the data from the 1959 survey of Uttar Pradesh indicated that the rhesus population in that area had declined significantly. The village data showed that the incidence of village rhesus had declined from 30 percent to 16 percent during the five years preceding 1959—a decline of nearly 50 percent in village-dwelling rhesus.

The age-structure data also indicated declining populations. Normal primate age structures should contain at least as many juveniles as infants, but the only survey categories attaining this condition were temple and forest groups. In all other categories there were considerably fewer than one half as many juveniles as infants. This suggested that breeding adults would not be adequately replaced in future years.

We believe that the primary factors for the declining rhesus populations in the 1950s were: (1) social changes in the protective attitudes of the people of India toward rhesus monkeys, (2) trapping of juvenile monkeys for export (14,000 juveniles per month were exported from New Delhi in 1959), and (3) more intensive land utilization for agriculture and applied forestry.

The scarcity of rhesus monkeys in Bengal in 1962 suggested that these factors had been operative there, probably stimulated by the exceptionally high human population density.

In Aligarh District of western Uttar Pradesh recounts of approximately 20 rhesus groups by Siddiqi since 1960 show that the total population has been maintained with relative stability at between 300 and 400 monkeys, but the number of groups has increased and the average group size has decreased.

In the district surveyed the number of rhesus groups increased from 17 in October 1959 to 21 in October 1963, and average group size declined from 19.8 to 15.1, a decline of 24 percent in the four-year period (Table 4–7). The decline was most evident in adults. Infants remained proportion-

TABLE 4–7. RECOUNTS OF RHESUS MONKEYS IN ALIGARH DISTRICT, UTTAR PRADESH, 1959–1963.

| | Total Rhesus Counted | Number of Groups Counted | Average Group Size | Average Group Composition | | | |
|---|---|---|---|---|---|---|---|
| | | | | Adult Male | Adult Female | I I | J J |
| October 1959 | 337 | 17 | 19.8 | 4.2 | 8.2 | 6.0 | 1.4 |
| March 1960 | 300 | 17 | 17.6 | 4.0 | 8.3 | 3.9 | 1.4 |
| July 1961 | 359 | 20 | 17.9 | 3.3 | 6.8 | 6.0 | 1.8 |
| October 1961 | 377 | 21 | 17.9 | 3.7 | 6.9 | 6.2 | 1.1 |
| March 1962 | 332 | 21 | 15.8 | 3.6 | 6.9 | 4.7 | 0.6 |
| July 1962 | 403 | 21 | 19.2 | 3.8 | 6.9 | 5.6 | 2.9 |
| October 1962 | 378 | 23 | 16.4 | 3.4 | 6.0 | 5.1 | 1.9 |
| March 1963 | 299 | 21 | 14.2 | 3.0 | 5.6 | 4.0 | 1.6 |
| July 1963 | 371 | 21 | 16.9 | 3.4 | 6.25 | 5.45 | 3.45 |
| October 1963 | 318 | 21 | 15.1 | 3.1 | 5.4 | 4.2 | 2.4 |

ately stable, whereas juveniles declined until March 1962, and then increased.

It is difficult to interpret these data in terms of over-all population trends. In open unconfined areas such as Aligarh District, where considerable movement into or out of the area can occur, total population counts are not too reliable. Fortunately, in this survey, most of the groups have been spatially stable; that is, at every recount (at four-month intervals) most groups could readily be found in their former locations. Also, all of the groups seemed to be locally protected to a certain extent; that is, some trapping has been permitted but not complete removal. It is not definitely known, however, whether the increase in the number of groups was due to group fissioning, or to the movement of new groups into the area. We think it was probably the latter.

The new groups in this population sample appeared in roadside and canal bank habitats, especially along the lower Ganges Canal. This canal is one of the few open water supplies in the entire region which is completely stable throughout the year. Many smaller canals, lakes, and tanks dry up in March, April, and May. Hence, this canal undoubtedly represents an ecological magnet for rhesus monkeys.

Logically, the decline in average group size could be attributable to three major influences: (1) a true population decline, (2) a basic sociobiological change in the rhesus tending toward smaller group size, or (3) a habitat change so that the ecological determinants of group size contribute to smaller group numbers. No evidence exists for the last possibility, and the second possibility is unlikely in so short a period of time. We tentatively believe, therefore, that the decline in average group size represents true population decline, and that the increase in groups has resulted from new groups entering the area.

This hypothesis is supported to a certain extent by population data on howling monkeys on Barro Colorado Island. In the late 1940s an extensive population decline of approximately 50 percent or more was accompanied by a 50 percent decline in average group size, whereas the numbers of groups had actually increased (Collias and Southwick 1952; Southwick 1963). The rhesus data from Aligarh District might well be analagous to this. The best resolution of this question will require extensive population surveys of all of Uttar Pradesh, essentially repeating or extending our field work of 1959 and 1960.

The rhesus groups in Aligarh District have been remarkably productive in terms of infants born. In July of 1961, 1962, and 1963 the percentages of adult females observed carrying infants have been 88 percent, 82 percent, and 87 percent respectively. The relative increase in the numbers of juveniles beginning in July 1962, suggest relief from trapping pressure. Whether or not this is significant for the total rhesus population of Uttar Pradesh obviously cannot be stated from such a small sample.

Fig. 4–6. The temple area surrounding Achal Tank.

## THE BEHAVIOR OF TEMPLE MONKEYS

### Group Compositions

Slightly more than 100 rhesus monkeys of all ages lived in the temple area surrounding Achal Tank. When first observed in October and November 1959, 104 monkeys were divided into three social groups, with the compositions listed in Table 4–8. Three additional monkeys were peripheral adult males which normally maintained an extragroup position.

In the winter a subgroup of Group 1 split from the parent group and became a distinct social group that was designated as Group 1B. Hence, by March, there were four distinct social groups in the area with the compositions listed in Table 4–9.

TABLE 4–8. AVERAGE GROUP COMPOSITIONS OF ALIGARH TEMPLE MONKEYS, OCTOBER–NOVEMBER 1959

| Group | Adult Males | Adult Females | Infants[a] | Juveniles[b] | Total |
|---|---|---|---|---|---|
| Group 1 | 12 | 14 | 6 | 19 | 51 |
| Group 2 | 7 | 10 | 8 | 9 | 34 |
| Group 3 | 5 | 7 | 5 | 2 | 19 |
| Peripheral | 3 | | | | 3 |
| Total | 27 | 31 | 19 | 30 | 107 |

[a] Infants: preweaned individuals dependent upon the mother, judged to be less than one year of age, and less than four pounds in body weight.

[b] Juveniles: postweaned, immature individuals, independent of mother, judged to be from one to three or four years of age, more than four pounds in body weight, lacking red sexual skin.

Group sizes and compositions were not entirely rigid, and some daily variation occurred. Group 1, which averaged 40 individuals after Group 1B had split from it, varied from 37 to 44 individuals. Group 1B, which averaged 11, varied from 7 to 11. Group 2, which averaged 34, varied from 31 to 37. Group 3, which averaged 17 during most of the study period, varied from 16 to 19. With the exception of Group 1B, random group counts usually varied less than 10 percent from the averages.

This variation was due in part to individuals' mixing between groups. Juveniles frequently mixed between groups for several hours at a time. Occasionally certain females would enter a different group for a brief period, and twice adult males were seen to change groups temporarily.

In addition, certain individuals, particularly young adult males of subordinate social rank, left their group for periods of a few hours to several days and apparently led a temporary extragroup existence, accounting for some of the variation in group sizes and compositions. It was difficult to

TABLE 4–9. AVERAGE GROUP COMPOSITIONS OF ALIGARH TEMPLE MONKEYS, MARCH–APRIL 1960

| Group | Adult Males | Adult Females | Infants | Juveniles | Total |
|---|---|---|---|---|---|
| Group 1 | 9 | 12 | 4 | 15 | 40 |
| Group 1B | 3 | 2 | 2 | 4 | 11 |
| Group 2 | 7 | 10 | 8 | 9 | 34 |
| Group 3 | 5 | 5 | 5 | 2 | 17 |
| Peripheral | 2 | | | | 2 |
| Total | 26 | 29 | 19 | 30 | 104 |

determine what the individuals did during these periods — they would simply disappear into surrounding portions of the city and would reappear in their group within a few days. The three peripheral males, which normally maintained a solitary existence, would occasionally enter the fringes of either Group 1 or Group 2.

Some permanent changes in group compositions other than the fissioning of Group 1B also occurred during the study period. Two adult females in Group 3 and one peripheral male were known to have died during the study period. Three infants were born into Group 1 in April and May, and two infants were born in Group 2 in the same months. These were the only births which occurred in the groups during the study period. Four juveniles disappeared from Group 1 in May, and we were told by local shopkeepers that these monkeys had been trapped in the north bazaar by commercial monkey trappers.

**Group Movements and Daily Routine**

Daily movements of all groups except Group 3 occurred within a 30-acre area surrounding the temples. None of the groups maintained precise territorial boundaries, but all displayed strong traditional attachments to certain areas and characteristic patterns of movement.

Each group had a characteristic night lodging position (Fig. 4–7). Group 1 normally lodged for the night on the rooftops of the main temple or in trees in the main temple courtyards. Group 1B usually spent the night on the rooftops or trees of the northwest temple, and occasionally in the north bazaar. Group 2 usually lodged in the south garden, but was seen lodged in the northwest temple on four occasions, and in the eastern courtyard on one occasion. Group 3 usually lodged in the hospital garden or along the edges of the college. Frequently, however, Group 3 would leave the area for several days and would venture as far as two miles into the city. Group 3 was the only group which left the area for extended trips of this sort.

In their nighttime lodging positions the monkeys slept huddled in small groups. In the winter these groups were usually five to fifteen individuals closely huddled together. In the hot weather of April and May there were usually from two to six individuals in the sleeping groups.

Group movements began about a half hour before dawn. Dawn occurred at approximately 7:00 A.M. in mid-December, and advanced to 6:30 A.M. by mid-March. The monkeys would begin moving slowly and randomly out of their sleeping clusters. Within 15 or 20 minutes parts of the groups would begin definite progressions or directed movements. Most of Group 1 moved along the north edge of the tank toward the northwest temple. Group 1B characteristically moved into the north bazaar and first compound. Group 2 moved around within the south garden or into the schoolyard in the southwest corner of the tank. Group 3 usually moved through the hospital garden along the boundaries of the college.

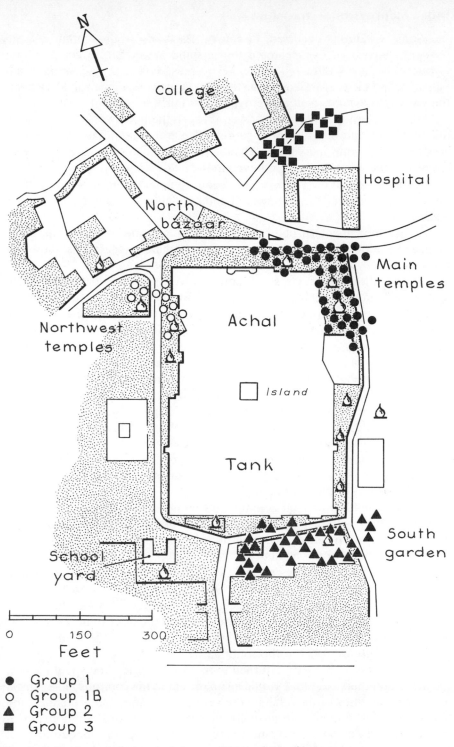

N

College

Hospital

North
bazaar

Main
temples

Northwest
temples

Achal

Island

Tank

South
garden

School
yard

0          150          300
Feet

● Group 1
○ Group 1B
▲ Group 2
■ Group 3

Fig. 4–7. Typical nighttime lodging positions of temple groups.

Some variations occurred, of course. Parts of Group 1 often entered the north bazaar or even entered the hospital area. If this occurred both Groups 1B and 3 retreated from these areas. Group 2 occasionally advanced along the east wall as far as the east courtyard. Generally, however, the group movements were stereotyped and fairly predictable.

Most of Group 1 normally moved through the northwest temple, along the west wall, and into the south garden. The group did not move as a unit, however, and some individuals usually remained behind in the northwest temple, in the north bazaar, and even in the main temple.

As most of Group 1 entered the south temple, Group 2 would retreat on to the rooftops of the commercial and residential buildings south of the garden.

These movements usually occurred over a period of about one hour. Hence, by 8:00 A.M., the groups were customarily located as shown in Figure 4–8.

During these movements the monkeys were usually alert and actively looking around or watching other monkeys. Frequently they would stop and feed in a tree or eat food given them by people passing along the streets. The peak of human activity generally coincided with the peak of monkey activity. The streets at this time were crowded with people beginning their day's activities or passing through the area en route to work.

By 9:00 or 9:30 A.M., the monkeys' activity in moving and feeding generally quieted down. Adults typically assumed resting and mutual grooming positions. In the cold months of December and January when the night temperatures would fall to 40° F., the monkeys often sat in sunny spots until 10:00 or 10:30 A.M., at which time temperatures would be reaching the high 60s or low 70s. In the hot months of April and May the monkeys would seek shade early in the morning, since the temperatures shortly after dawn would be rapidly approaching the 90s.

As the adults rested and groomed, the infants and juveniles formed play groupings. Play activities involved chasing, wrestling, climbing, and jumping, and were often centered around favorite trees, bushes, rocks, or other structural features of the habitat.

Occasionally the groups remained in basically the positions shown in Fig. 4–8 throughout most of the day. Usually, however, Group 1 returned to the main temple once or even twice during the day. This movement was often, but not always, timed with the entrance into the main temple of *sadhus* who left food for the monkeys. As Group 1 returned to the main temple, Group 2 usually returned to the south garden.

Normally Group 1 then returned to the south garden and spent most of the afternoon there. Group 2 would again retreat to the rooftops. The typical afternoon activities of the adults were resting, sleeping, and grooming, and again the infants and juveniles usually engaged in play. Small random movements took place, but usually no major group movements occurred until

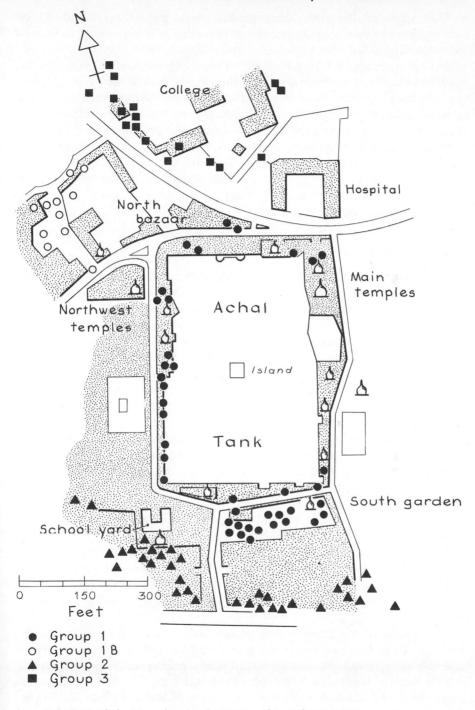

N

College

Hospital

North
bazaar

Main
temples

Achal

Northwest
temples

Island

Tank

South garden

School yard

| 0 | 150 | 300 |

Feet

● Group 1
○ Group 1B
▲ Group 2
■ Group 3

Fig. 4–8. Typical daytime dispersal pattern of temple groups.

4:30 or 5:00 P.M. Then the groups gradually returned over a period of one or two hours to their lodging positions. The evening movement of the monkeys also coincided with increased human activity in the area. By sunset, which occurred about 5:30 P.M. in mid-December and 6:30 by mid-March, most individuals of all groups were in the general area of their typical lodging positions. The last hour before darkness was characterized by an increased amount of aggressive interaction between individuals within a group. Each night there appeared to be a certain amount of reshuffling of individuals until final sleeping clusters were formed and favored sleeping locations were established. Nothing comparable to this was observed in the morning. The only other situation in which intragroup aggression increased notably was when a group was fed fruits or vegetables by people, and then fights often occurred over the food.

## Intergroup Relationships

Behavioral relationships between different social groups were characterized by marked intergroup intolerance. Although most parts of the temple area were jointly used by two or more groups, and there was an 80 to 90 percent overlap of home ranges, group movements occurred so that groups usually avoided contact with each other. A similar pattern of intergroup behavior was observed on Cayo Santiago (Altmann 1962a).

A prominent intergroup dominance hierarchy existed. Group 1 was dominant to all groups at any location. Group 2 was dominant to Groups 1B and 3. Groups 2 and 3 did not normally come into contact, however, and only one interaction was observed between these groups. Group 1B was dominant to Group 3 in the north bazaar and the first compound, whereas the reverse was true in the hospital and college area. Intergroup dominance status between the subordinate groups, then, depended upon location.

Since Group 1 was dominant to all groups throughout the area, it had the greatest freedom of movement. All other groups usually retreated when they saw members of Group 1 approaching.

This entire system of avoidance of the dominant group apparently depended upon visual cues. The subordinate group retreated only when it saw the dominant group approaching. Group movements were usually silent, not accompanied by conspicuous vocalization as in many species of primates.

If a subordinate group failed to see a dominant group approaching, with the result that two groups came into sudden and unexpected contact, a severe intergroup fight would occur. Twenty-four severe intergroup fights and numerous minor ones were observed in 85 days of observation. All these resulted from two groups coming into sudden contact owing to the failure of one group to retreat. Normally the adult males began the fight, but females and juveniles also became involved. These fights were ferocious and dangerous to the monkeys, often resulting in severe wounds, and most adult males bore wound scars around the face, shoulders, or rump. Wounded individuals were fewer among rhesus in rural habitats and forest areas, suggesting that the crowded conditions of temple and urban environments resulted in more aggressive activity. In forest areas more space and protective cover greatly reduced the number of intergroup contacts.

Intergroup fights among the temple monkeys usually lasted just a few minutes until the subordinate group retreated. Occasionally, however, there would be a prolonged fight of 15 or 20 minutes duration. This typically occurred if there happened to be a close dominance balance between the particular individuals involved. For example, if only a small part of Group 1 attacked all of Group 2, a severe and prolonged fight might ensue, but invariably Group 1 would win as more members of Group 1 arrived at the scene and joined the fight. An intergroup fight often produced noise that could be heard throughout the area. At the sound of fighting and threat, monkeys would come running to the scene of the fight. Most of the individual monkeys would simply join in threat vocalization, but as more became involved in the conflict, group dominance would be quickly established. One could very readily observe the dominance balance swing in the direction of the favored group. Such fights provided clear examples of social facilitation in group aggressive behavior.

Certain members of each group had the tendency to initiate intergroup fights more readily than others. These were the young adult subordinate males within each group. This topic will be discussed later under the section on intragroup social structure.

Although the home ranges of all groups except Group 3 were moderately well defined and quite restricted, these ranges could not be designated as territories since they were not consistently defended against intruders. Probably the closest approach to a territory was the main temple, which was the almost exclusive property of Group 1. When any members of Group 1 were in the main temple courtyards, no other groups would enter. However, if all members of Group 1 were elsewhere, in the south garden for example, Group 1B would frequently enter the main temple. Group 2 was seen there once, and Group 3 entered on several occasions. When these subordinate groups were in the main temple, however, they were conspicuously alert and actively watching for other monkeys. At the first sight of a Group 1 male, the subordinate group would quickly retreat.

On the one occasion in which Group 2 entered the main temple, all individuals except one adult male quickly escaped from the area before Group 1 returned. This one adult male, however, which happened to be number 2 dominant male in Group 2, was trapped in a corner of the temple courtyard bordering the water and all escape routes were blocked. He was immediately attacked by four adult males of Group 1, and his only retreat was to jump from a high ledge about ten feet into the water. He swam along the edge of the east wall, and made frequent attempts to come up on the land again, but at each attempt the males of Group 1 vigorously threatened him from the bank. Finally, he swam toward the small artificial island in the center of the tank. This male had a badly withered and crippled hind limb and swimming this distance appeared to be difficult for him. When he reached the island he barely succeeded in climbing up the rough rock wall about two feet high which surrounded it. He spent two hours on the island and then swam back to the south garden after Group 1 had quieted down in the main temple.

Sometimes, however, there was a definite relaxation of intergroup antagonism. This was noted several times between Groups 1 and 2 in the south garden. Group 1 and 2 males came within 15 or 20 feet of each other in the south garden on three occasions without aggressive interaction. At such times Groups 1 and 2 would have temporarily appeared to be one large group. We could not explain these occasions; they seemed to be simply brief periods when all normal aggressive tendencies had disappeared. It was a common observation that Group 1's aggressive drive toward other groups was greatest in the main temple area, and definitely weaker in the more peripheral areas of its range. In addition to this, however, there were variations in the aggressive interactions between groups for which we could find no obvious correlates.

### Intragroup Social Organization

The organization of individuals within a social group was characterized by fairly consistent patterns of subgrouping. The term "subgroup" is used here to denote a fairly large assemblage of individuals within a social group that displayed recognizable affinity from day to day. A subgroup is a social aggregation within a group that is more stable than the temporary associations of individuals engaged in mutual grooming, juvenile play, or sexual consort relationships. These latter associations occurred primarily between members of a subgroup, but not exclusively so.

The pattern of subgrouping within a group was primarily associated with the pattern of adult male dominance. The social organization of Group 1 is diagrammed in Fig. 4–9. Group 1 consisted of three subgroups.

The central male subgroup consisted of two dominant males, one subdominant male, and an aggregation of approximately eight females, two infants, and eight juveniles. This subgroup formed the main core of Group 1, and largely determined the patterns of movement and daily routine of Group 1. The two dominant males in this subgroup were both old individuals, and they were of almost equal social rank; that is, they were virtually codominant. They were usually closely associated, and only rarely did any aggressive conflict occur between them. One of them, designated "Fat-intact male" was slightly dominant over the other, known as

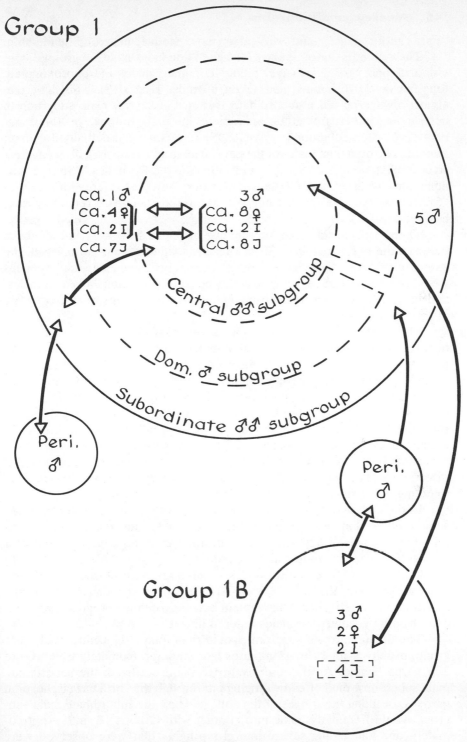

Fig. 4–9. Diagram of social structure of Groups 1 and 1B.

"Fat Cut-lip male," and was also more active in group leadership.

The second subgroup, known as the "dominant male subgroup," consisted of one very aggressive, highly dominant male, and approximately four females, two infants, and seven juveniles (Fig. 4–9). This subgroup almost always played a subordinate role to the central male subgroup in determining patterns of group movement and daily routine, yet the dominant male of this subgroup (known as "Shifty male") was actually dominant over the two dominant males of the central male subgroup. In a direct aggressive conflict between "Shifty" and either of the fat males, "Shifty" was dominant. Both of the fat males together, however, were dominant to "Shifty." Aggressive conflict between the three males was relatively rare, however.

There was considerable interchange of females, infants, and juveniles between the two subgroups. Since these individuals were not marked, the extent of this interchange could not be accurately determined. Adult females were observed to change subgroups during consort relationships with males, and juveniles were observed to change or mix subgroups most frequently in their play patterns.

The third subgroup of Group 1 was composed of five young adult males of subordinate social rank. These five males did not enter either the central male subgroup or the dominant male subgroup. The five males were occasionally joined by two peripheral males, both adults, one of which was occasionally successful in penetrating the central male subgroup for brief periods of time. This subordinate male subgroup normally ranged around the fringes of the other two subgroups, and did not participate directly in regular group movements. These males were active when the other subgroups were active, but they usually ranged farther and often in different directions. They were highly aggressive and were particularly active in initiating intergroup conflicts.

In the course of typical group movements of Group 1, the central male subgroup would initiate group movements and determine their general direction. For example, the first progression of the morning usually consisted of the central male subgroup's moving around the western side of the tank to the south garden. The central males themselves were not necessarily the first individuals in the progression. Often juveniles or females were in the forefront, but rarely did any movement become a definite progression unless one or both of the central males entered into it.

The dominant male subgroup would then follow the central male subgroup, usually from 10 to 15 minutes later and approximately from 100 to 200 yards behind. As this orderly progression occurred, the subordinate male subgroup would often be ranging out through the north bazaar, hospital gardens, or along the fringes of the college. Here the subordinate male subgroup would frequently come into contact with Groups 1B or 3. Approximately one half of the severe intergroup fights that were observed were started by the direct aggressive action of the subordinate male subgroup.

The central male subgroup would also primarily determine the time and pattern of movement back to the main temple area during the day and later on in the evening.

Group 1B was a homogeneous group not divided into subgroups (Fig. 4–9). It was originally considered a subgroup of Group 1, in October and November. Throughout the winter it became behaviorally more independent of Group 1, so that by March it displayed entirely independent movements.

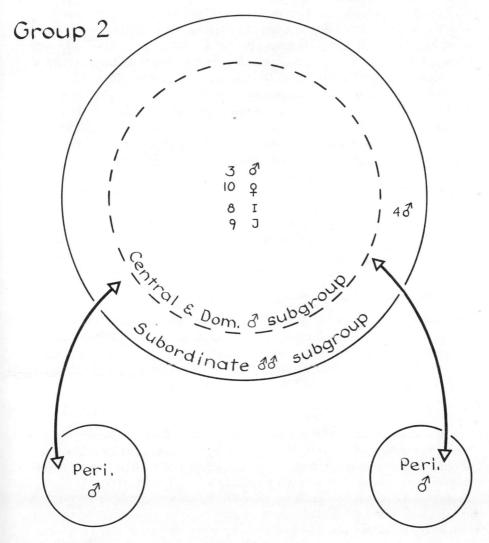

Fig. 4–10. Diagram of social structure of Group 2.

It also displayed agonistic behavior to Group 1 at all times after February, and it consistently lodged by itself in the northwest temple. Hence, by March Group 1B exhibited all the criteria which were used in this study to define a distinct social group.

This process of group fission was gradual and required several months. The primary driving force seemed to be adult male antagonism that led to increased social independence of the subgroup. The general description of this phenomenon given by Carpenter (1942a) fitted this situation accurately. Group fission has occurred several times on Cayo Santiago in recent years (Koford, Chap. 5, this volume).

The four juveniles in Group 1B continued to associate occasionally with the juveniles in Group 1, even after Group 1B had attained the status of a distinct social group. Group 1B also shared a peripheral male with Group 1 (Fig. 4–9). This male, which normally led a solitary existence, was seen on several occasions in the fringes of Groups 1, 1B, and 2.

Group 2 had a social organization consisting of two subgroups (Fig. 4–10). In Group 2 the dominant male was also the central male. The main subgroup consisted of three adult males, ten adult females, eight infants, and nine juveniles. The second subgroup of Group 2 consisted of four subordinate adult males. These males ranged the periphery of the male subgroup, and they were also particularly active in movement and aggressive behavior. The peripheral males mentioned in connection with Group 1 also entered the subordinate male subgroup of Group 2 for brief periods.

The social organization of Group 3 was not studied in detail. By all appearance it had a homogeneous structure without subgrouping, similar to that of Group 1B.

### Relationships between Individuals within a Group

Observations were made on the following dyadic relationships within groups: male-male, male-female, male-infant, male-juvenile, female-female, female-infant, female-juvenile, infant-infant, juvenile-juvenile, and infant-juvenile. This is basically the type of analysis first used by Carpenter in his study of howling monkeys (1934).

#### Male-Male Relationships

The relationships between adult males varied from peaceful, even cooperative, associations, to highly agonistic relationships. Moderately sharp dominance hierarchies existed. The male dominance pattern was relatively simple when encounters involving only two individuals were considered. Table 4–10 records the outcome of 119 two-male aggressive encounters in Group 1. This tally includes both natural encounters and forced encounters where food was placed equidistant between two adult males.

TABLE 4–10. DOMINANCE RELATIONSHIPS OF ADULT MALES IN GROUP 1.
NUMBER OF AGGRESSIVE INTERACTIONS WITH DOMINANCE EXPRESSED.*

| Dominance Rank: Highest to Lowest | Shifty | Fat-intact | Fat Cut-lip | Thigh-wound | White-face | Young Cut-lip | Cleft Chin | Blue Chest | Gray Cheek |
|---|---|---|---|---|---|---|---|---|---|
| Shifty | | 8 | 2 | 6 | 3 | 2 | | 2 | 1 |
| Fat-intact | | | 3 | 3 | 2 | 2 | | 1 | 2 |
| Fat Cut-lip | | | | 5 | 4 | 2 | 1 | 1 | 1 |
| Thighwound | | | | | 8 | 5 | 6 | 3 | 2 |
| Whiteface | | | | | | 2 | 1 | 3 | 7 |
| Young Cut-lip | | | | | 2 | | 9 | 6 | 5 |
| Cleft Chin | | | | | | 1 | | 2 | 2 |
| Blue Chest | | | | | | | | | 4 |
| Gray Cheek | | | | | | | | | |

* The numerical tabulations represent the number of observed interactions in which the male in the vertical row on the left was dominant to the male in the horizontal top row.

In this table Shifty was the dominant male of the second subgroup; Fat-intact and Fat Cut-lip were the leader males of the main subgroup; Young Cut-lip was the third male of the central male subgroup.

Table 4–10 shows an orderly and consistent dominance hierarchy. In only three encounters out of 119 did subordinate animals exhibit dominance over normally dominant individuals. This table, however, is an oversimplification of the true structure of the dominance system. Additional complexities were imposed upon this system by the pattern of subgrouping, and by social facilitation of aggressive behavior; that is, the combined aggressive force of two or more individuals attacking together.

The pattern of subgrouping definitely reduced the frequency of contact between males of different subgroups. For example, there were relatively few contacts between the three dominant males and all the subordinate males except Thighwound and Young Cut-lip. Thighwound was the dominant member of the subordinate male subgroup. On the other hand, the frequency of contact between the subordinate males was relatively high. Hence, the dominance hierarchy was stratified on the basis of subgroupings. This stratification influenced the frequency and intensity of aggressive encounters. Figure 4–11 attempts to portray this relationship and shows a modified straight-line hierarchy with a steep slope in the center representing the gaps in dominance interactions resulting from subgroup stratification. This graph is based upon subjective judgments of the relative dominance strength of individuals, but we believe that it portrays the situation more satisfactorily than a mere tabulation of encounters.

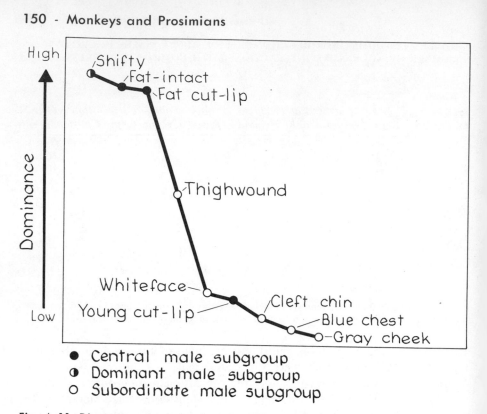

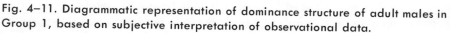

Fig. 4–11. Diagrammatic representation of dominance structure of adult males in Group 1, based on subjective interpretation of observational data.

Table 4–10 is also an oversimplification because it tabulates only those encounters involving two males. Aggressive encounters between males often involved several individuals, and this added variability and complexity to the dominance structure. For example, the two fat males together were dominant to Shifty. The three lowest ranking males (Cleft Chin, Blue Chest, and Gray Cheek) were dominant on two occasions to Young Cut-lip when they attacked in unison. Young Cut-lip was dominant on two occasions to Whiteface in the presence of Fat-intact, but he was normally subordinate to Whiteface when alone. This phenomenon has been termed "dependent rank" by Kawai (1958) in contrast to "basic rank." Kawai defines basic rank as the ". . . dominance-subordination relationship between two individuals not interfered [with] by the group to which they belong." Dependent rank is defined as the dominance-subordination relationship between individuals modified by other individuals or by group dynamics. It is this phenomenon which creates complexity, variability, and instability in the total male dominance system within a group.

Many prominent examples of cooperative male-male relationships existed. One of the most striking was the peaceful, cooperative relationship between the two fat males. Aggressive encounters between these individuals were rare, despite the fact that they lived in close association. They frequently fed together, moved together, and rested together. It was usually impossible to force agonistic behavior between them. An item of food placed between them at feeding time would not usually provoke conflict — one time one would take it, on the next occasion the other might. Separately these males were slightly subordinate to Shifty; together they were definitely dominant to Shifty.

Another example of cooperative male behavior was the relationship of the Young Cut-lip male to the two fat males in the central male subgroup. This young adult male was a close associate of both fat males. He was permitted to feed and rest in close proximity to them, but he was very subordinate to both. Agonistic encounters were rare, possibly because of the wide dominance gap between them (Fig. 4–11).

The subordinate male subgroup represented a third example of cooperative behavior between adult males. Despite the high incidence of agonistic behavior between these males, they would unite cooperatively in group attacks against other groups.

### Male-Female Relationships

The most conspicuous aspect of male-female relationships was sexual consort behavior. Sexual consort pairs exhibiting what was judged to be true copulatory behavior were seen in all months of the study period except March. A peak of observed copulatory behavior in the consort pairs in the temple groups occurred in December (Table 4–11). Several brief mountings were observed in March, but they did not occur in typical consort pairs and lacked the characteristics of true sexual behavior.

TABLE 4–11. SEXUAL CONSORT BEHAVIOR IN ALIGARH TEMPLE MONKEYS — CONSORT PAIRS OBSERVED COPULATING

| Month | Hours of Observation | Consort Pairs Observed Copulating | Consort Pairs Observed Copulating per Hour of Observation |
|---|---|---|---|
| October 1959 | 14 | 4 | 0.28 |
| November | 70 | 24 | 0.34 |
| December | 54 | 36 | 0.66 |
| January 1960 | 55 | 24 | 0.44 |
| February | 70 | 14 | 0.20 |
| March | 99 | 0 | 0 |
| April | 50 | 8 | 0.16 |
| Total | 412 | 110 | 0.27 |

We do not consider these data representative of the total rhesus populations of western Uttar Pradesh. When incidental data from other groups observed during population surveys are added to the temple data, a peak of copulatory activity in October is obtained. These data are not included here, however, because the behavior observations made during population surveys could not be systematically tabulated owing to varying observational conditions and periods. Nonetheless, the survey observations may represent a more typical picture of copulatory frequency for the rhesus populations of western Uttar Pradesh.

Another reason for suspecting that the seasonal frequency of copulatory activity in the Aligarh temple groups was atypical is the fact that the first birth in the temple groups did not occur until April 24, whereas the first birth in the population survey sample was March 7. This suggests that the peaks of reproductive activity in the temple groups were approximately six weeks behind those in the more general survey sample.

In the temple monkeys consort periods varied considerably from just a few hours to a few days. During these periods the male and female would remain in close association, moving together, feeding together and engaging in frequent grooming.

Little or no display preceded copulation. The male would mount at frequent intervals, placing his hands on the female's back, and grasping her hind legs with his feet. After several thrusts, the male would return to the former resting or grooming behavior with the female. Typically, from 5 to 25 mounts occurred in a period of from 10 to 20 minutes. Each mount normally lasted only 3 or 4 seconds and consisted of several thrusts. Most mounts did not appear to terminate in ejaculation. Those mounts which obviously did terminate in ejaculation had greater vigor and intensity. The male frequently bared his teeth and issued a high pitched staccato note during mounts leading to ejaculation. The female would frequently turn her head sideways toward the male, as if attempting to see him, and often reached back toward him with her foreleg. The observations of adult male-female sexual behavior in this study fitted the descriptions of Carpenter (1942b) and Altmann (1962a).

Consort relationships were quite changeable. One female was seen to copulate with three different males in the course of one day, and one male with two females in one day. These were not typical occurrences, however. Normally, a consort pair remained together for one or two days, and engaged in several periods of mounting during this time.

Dominant males tended to form consort relationships more readily than subordinate males. However, females definitely formed some consort relationships with subordinate males. Unfortunately, accurate data concerning the frequency of true copulation in relation to dominance rank were not obtained.

Several types of male-female interactions occurred other than sexual consort relationships. Normally males and females maintained peaceful cooperative relationships and all aspects of normal daily behavior usually occurred in close association. Grooming was a particularly prominent type of behavior between males and females. Most commonly, adult females groomed males, and they did so at all times, but more frequently during consort relationships. Grooming activity of adult males on females was typically confined to the sexual consort period.

Some agonistic behavior occurred between males and females. Males occasionally attacked females, particularly in the early stages of estrus prior to the formation of consort relationships. At times other than estrous periods, males might attack females who would accidentally bump them, or get in their way during feeding periods. Males were usually dominant to females, although on a few occasions females expressed definite dominance over males in acquiring food.

### Male-Infant and Male-Juvenile Relationships

Throughout most of the normal daily routine of the temple monkeys, the relationship between adult males and infants or juveniles appeared to be a fairly neutral or indifferent association. Sometimes, however, there were prominent interactions between them.

Adult males frequently attacked infants or juveniles, particularly at feeding times. If an infant or juvenile got in the way of an adult male who was feeding, the adult would often attack it, picking it up, biting it, and throwing it to the ground. These attacks occurred most commonly on infants; juveniles appeared to stay their distance and to avoid contacts with males more successfully.

Sometimes there were peaceful social interactions between adult males and infants or juveniles. On three occasions infants were seen playing with adult males, climbing over them and remaining in close association for several hours. These were rare occurrences, however. Infants also had fairly close and peaceful contacts with adult males when their mothers were in sexual consort. Usually, however, the male ignored the infant during such periods. The type of "paternal" behavior between adult males and infants described by Itani (1959) for the Japanese macaque was not observed in this study.

Juveniles frequently had positive social contacts with adult males in grooming. Quite commonly one or two females and one or two juveniles formed a resting and grooming cluster around an adult male. Juveniles often groomed males; the reverse was seen on only a few occasions.

### Female-Female Relationships

The social relationships between adult females were usually positive with a minimum of agonistic interaction. Adult females commonly moved, fed, rested, and groomed in close association. Particularly close social bonds

Fig. 4–12. Three generations of female rhesus.

Fig. 4–13. An adult female threatens.

were observed between certain females. Patterns of spatial distribution and food priority suggested that some dominance structure existed between adult females, but data on female dominance hierarchies were not obtained.

Agonistic interactions between adult females were most commonly associated with estrous periods. An increase in female aggressive behavior often occurred just before and just after estrous peaks.

### Female-Infant Relationships

One of the strongest and most persistent social bonds within the group was that between female and infant. Most of the infants and mothers observed remained in intimate association throughout the study period. This relationship probably lasts about a year and is not disrupted until the next sibling is born (Altmann 1962a; Koford, Chap. 5, this volume).

At the beginning of the study period all infants were judged to be several months old. Newborn infants were not seen until April and May 1960, at the end of the study period. Hence, a continuous chronological account of female-infant relationships cannot be given.

Of four newborn infants observed in April and May, detailed observations were made on one infant born in Group 1 on April 24. The mother with the infant retired somewhat from normal group activities and was more restricted in her movements for a few days before and after the birth. Most females with newborn infants were shy and could not be approached more closely than 20 or 30 feet, but the mother of this infant was unusually tame and permitted an observer within a few feet.

The infant was probably born in the early morning hours, since it was still wet when first seen at 8:00 A.M. For the first day the infant's activity was confined to sleeping and nursing. The mother groomed and nudged the infant and held it closely to her breasts. The infant's face could be seen from the side, but it showed no reactions to the presence of an observer 4 feet away.

During the second day the infant was more active in moving its head and limbs, and it appeared to react to objects of its environment outside its mother. It would look directly at an observer without showing any fear. The infant's general pattern of behavior was to remain awake and nurse for from 15 to 20 minutes and then to sleep for from 30 minutes to an hour.

By the third and fourth day the infant's perceptual environment continued to expand. It began to crawl around feebly on its own and it showed an alarm reaction to the shadow of a bird that passed over it. The infant's activity in crawling was obviously limited by weak motor ability, particularly in the hind legs, and also by restraint from the mother, who held on to the infant and prevented its crawling more than a few inches.

During this time, the female was not the center of attention of other females or infants. We were surprised to observe that all individual social relationships within the group appeared quite normal. No prominent differences in group social behavior were seen. One adult male showed mild interest in the mother and newborn infant, and was seen within 10 or 12 feet of the mother, but he was not seen to approach any closer. When the infant was six days old, two females approached the mother, and one attempted to pick up the infant, but the mother retreated with her infant. When the infant was seven days old, a juvenile approached and groomed both the mother and infant for approximately 30 minutes. This was the first contact the infant had had with any other individual than the mother.

At seven days of age the infant was able to crawl a foot or two from the mother, but normally the mother restrained its movements. On one occasion, when the infant was seven days old, the mother walked 6 feet away from it, and another female approached and started to pick it up, but the mother quickly retrieved her infant.

Unfortunately, the study of this group terminated in May, and subsequent observations on this infant were not made.

Many general observations were made throughout the study on infants in the age range of from three or four months to one year. By three months, and probably earlier, infants leave the mother for periods of play, exploration, and feeding. While adult females rested and groomed, infants in this age range often played with each other at distances of 10 or 20 feet from the mother. During group progressions infants usually rode on the mothers, but they frequently hopped off whenever the mothers stopped, or they often walked along with her, sometimes running ahead or dropping behind to investigate some object. During group feeding periods infants often fed on their own, and they were particularly active in investigating new foods, either natural leaves and fruits or foods given to them. Infants continued to nurse throughout this time, however, until they were probably about one year of age. Weaning definitely occurred when the next sibling was born.

### Female-Juvenile Relationships

The weaning process, by which an individual changed from the infant to juvenile status, appeared to be gradual. The young monkey became more independent of the mother in movement, feeding, and most aspects of normal daily routine. Probably the most abrupt event in the weaning process was the birth of a new sibling. The weaning process, which was apparently well advanced by this time, was then forced to completion. The juvenile, however, retained some association with the female, and thus appeared to be the closest associate of the new infant other than the mother. It was common, therefore, to see mother, infant, and juvenile in frequent association. Juveniles were observed on several occasions to attempt to nurse, and were usually repelled with a threat gesture from the female.

Since specific ages of juveniles were not known, it cannot be stated from this study how long juveniles tended to associate with their mothers.

Koford's work on Cayo Santiago indicates that a filial relationship persists between mother and juvenile for several years.

### Infant-Infant Relationships

This relationship represented a positive social attraction that increased in strength, frequency, and duration throughout the life of the infant. The relationship between infants may be based initially on investigative behavior but very quickly becomes dominated by play behavior. The earliest ages at which infants begin to play with each other cannot be stated from this study. Infant play definitely began by three or four months of age, and probably earlier. The most common forms of infant play were chasing, jumping, and wrestling. Mounting behavior was also a common form of interaction between infants.

Infant play groups usually consisted of two or three individuals. Two important results of infant play are the development of positive social bonds between individuals, and the development of motor skills such as running, climbing, grasping, and manipulation.

### Juvenile-Juvenile Relationships

Juvenile play was an even more conspicuous behavior pattern than infant play in the daily routine of rhesus groups. Juvenile play groups frequently consisted of from four to ten individuals, and their play, based primarily upon play chases and play wrestling, assumed more complicated forms than infant play. It often involved dextrous climbing through tangled vines and jumping from tree to tree. Juveniles often played in and around water—jumping from rock to rock in the water, jumping off walls into the water, and swimming around after each other. Surprisingly, juveniles swam more in the cold months of December and January than in the hot months of April and May.

Juvenile play also often centered around cattle in the streets and temple courtyards. Juveniles climbed on the backs of cattle, jumped from one cow or bullock to another, and wrestled on their backs. They frequently teased cattle by pulling their tails or swatting their noses.

Occasionally juvenile play was object-oriented. Juveniles sometimes stole items of clothing from open windows or washlines, and these would become the centers of games of chase. On two occasions a juvenile was seen with a piece of broken mirror, which was the object of play chase for more than an hour. In the areas where woodcutters lived juveniles often played on piles of cut firewood and climbed over the thatched roofs of the huts. In better residential areas juveniles played along balconies of apartment buildings and slid down rainpipes. In general, they were a frolicsome, amusing nuisance to the people in these areas.

Juveniles engaged frequently in mounting behavior. This interaction was not studied in detail, but it appeared to be a form of social response indicating a certain relationship between individuals. It did not seem to be consistently related to relative dominance status. (Data were not obtained on dominance structures within juvenile play groups, but, as with adult females, general observations suggested that some form of hierarchy existed.)

### Juvenile-Infant Relationships

Juveniles and infants did not mix extensively in play groups, usually playing with individuals of their own general age group. Some juvenile-infant interactions occurred in grooming and resting behavior. The closest associations seemed to be between siblings, although we could not be certain of this since these individuals were not marked. Koford's recent work (personal communication) has demonstrated stronger and more persistent sibling bonds than were previously suspected.

## CONCLUSIONS

Rhesus monkey populations of India afford outstanding opportunities for further research in primate ecology and behavior. There is a particular need for more field work in rural and forested areas. It is becoming increasingly apparent that significant variations in ecological and behavioral adaptations may occur within a primate species in various habitats or in various parts of its range.

The rhesus monkey in northern India occurs in such a wide variety of habitats that it is an ideal species for the study of adaptational variations. It is, in fact, difficult to assess what the natural habitat of the rhesus actually is. It has lived in close ecological contact with man for centuries, and in frequency and persistence this commensal relationship in villages, towns, temples, and roadsides represents a natural relationship. The rhesus is also abundant in forest areas, where it appears to be a natural member of the forest community. In mixed forest and agricultural areas, rhesus groups often exhibit behavior which might suggest that they live in forests secondarily because they have been driven from human habitation. For example, if villages and plantations are fringed by forests, rhesus groups in the forests make frequent attempts to enter the villages or plantations despite continual harassment from people. Such groups do not seem to desert human habitations completely unless they are hunted or trapped heavily. This is not meant to imply, however, that all rhesus groups in remote forest areas have been driven there by human pressure.

In considering the habitat adaptability of the rhesus and particularly its close association with man, it cannot be stated at the present time whether this association is primarily a species characteristic (as, for example, the commensal habit of the house mouse), or an ecological necessity dependent upon the availability of food and water, or a product of human behavior, that is, the Hindu social tradition. All factors have undoubtedly interacted, but it remains an interesting question to assess their relative importance and to determine why other species (for example, *Macaca silenus*, the lion-faced macaque of southwestern India) have not adopted the commensal habit as readily as the rhesus. This question introduces the type of ecological problem that requires considerably more field research before adequate evaluations can be made.

The ecological surveys reported in this chapter trace the broad outlines of population ecology and habitat distribution of the rhesus. The behavioral study focuses on the social interactions of temple groups and hence forms just the beginning of the naturalistic study of this species. In comparison with the rhesus groups in other habitats, the Aligarh temple monkeys exhibited certain behavioral differences, as, for example, more restricted home ranges and increased aggressive behavior. It has been tentatively concluded, however, that these differences are primarily quantitative rather than qualitative differences of basic behavior patterns. All rhesus observed, regardless of habitat, seemed to possess a basically similar behavioral repertoire, but this is a subject which requires systematic study.

No primate species other than the rhesus spans such a wide ecological continuum from complete domestic commensalism with man to a remote forest life. Herein lies the major value of the rhesus as a research subject in the field as well as in the laboratory.

# CARL B. KOFORD

# 5

# ◆ Population Dynamics of Rhesus Monkeys on Cayo Santiago

## INTRODUCTION

More than 400 rhesus monkeys (*Macaca mulatta*) run free on Cayo Santiago, a wooded 40-acre islet off the east coast of Puerto Rico, near latitude 18 degrees north, longitude 66 degrees west. These animals are supplied with food pellets and water at several widely spaced feeding stations; they are essentially free of common laboratory diseases and are accustomed to almost daily observation at close range. All monkeys more than one year old are distinctively marked, and younger ones are identified by their close association with their mothers. The island monkeys are descended from stock released at the end of 1938 (Carpenter 1942a). During the following 17 years, under various administrations, the colony was maintained but food was often minimal. Several hundred monkeys were removed for laboratory use, but none was added. The National Institute of Neurological Diseases and Blindness assumed control of the remnant colony in mid-1956, and thereafter the food supply was adequate and regular. During the period from mid-1956 to mid-1958, Altmann (1962a) tattooed and measured most of the animals and observed their social behavior. My observations began at the end of 1958.

## POPULATION COMPOSITION

By mid-1959, when every monkey was accounted for, there were 277 individuals. Thereafter the net annual increase was about 16 percent. In

The work for this study was conducted at the Laboratory of Perinatal Physiology of the National Institute of Neurological Diseases and Blindness, National Institutes of Health, Public Health Service, U. S. Department of Health, Education and Welfare, San Juan, Puerto Rico.

Fig. 5–1. Aerial view of Cayo Santiago, off the east coast of Puerto Rico.

Fig. 5–2. Adult females and immatures feed at a hopper inside a trapping cage (October 6, 1961).

Fig. 5–3. A high-ranking female with her two-week-old male infant (May 22, 1963).

the total population about one fifth of the animals are infants, born during the current year; two fifths are immatures, from one to three years old; and two fifths are sexually mature, at least four years old. (In this age classification, all animals move up one year on January 1.) The monkeys are considered full adults at six years of age, when they have full dentition and growth.

Since late 1960 the population has comprised 6 groups. By mid-1961, at the end of the birth season, these groups consisted of 122, 117, 43, 31, 30, and 30 members respectively, and there were 3 solitary adult males. The only animals removed during the preceding five years were 5 very old females and 3 infants. Since then, 47 selected individuals have been taken off the island. Of these, 29 were yearling males, 10 were low-ranking or solitary mature males, 3 were mature females, and the remaining 5 were immature females. These removals had no apparent effect on the organization or behavior of the groups. At the beginning of 1963 the groups contained from 21 to 130 members each.

## SEASON OF BIRTHS

As in most wild animal populations, reproduction in the monkeys of Cayo Santiago is seasonal. This fact is clearly shown by the distribution of birth dates from 1960 to 1962 (Fig. 5–1). These dates were determined by field observation by me and, since 1962, John H. Kaufmann. Nearly all births are known within plus or minus one day. With few exceptions infants were born only during the first six months of the year. The start and peak

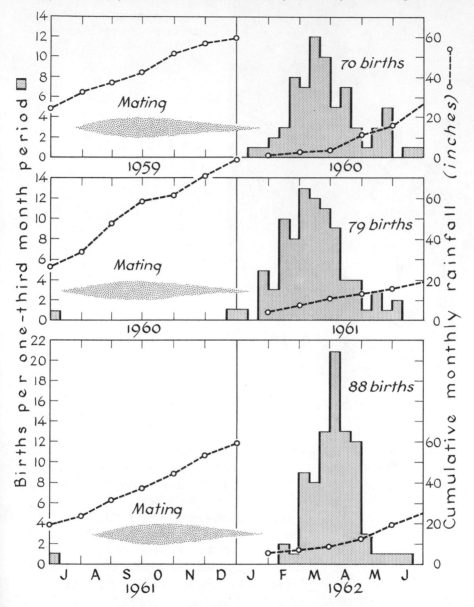

Fig. 5–4. Occurrence of mating and births during three years. Each hatched square indicates one birth during a one-third month period. The length of the horizontal lenticular bar indicates the period of copulations; the width, approximate relative frequency of copulation. Broken line indicates cumulative rainfall for each year by months. Rainfall data provided by J. A. Gavan and D. S. Sade.

of the birth season varied moderately from year to year. Over a period of five years, from 1959 to 1963, the difference between the earliest and latest

Fig. 5–5. An adult male mounts an estrous female (October 6, 1961).

initial birth of the season was 46 days. The earliest initial birth dates were: January 30, 1959; January 14, 1960; December 29, 1960; February 13, 1962; and January 7, 1963. The spread of the median birth dates for three years, 1960 to 1962, was only 29 days. For these years the median birth dates were: March 21, 1960; March 8, 1961; and April 5, 1962. The latest birth dates were: July 20, 1959; July 3, 1961; and July 26, 1962. (In 1960, the latest birth date was before July 26.) In 1957 and 1958, also, nearly all births occurred from February to May (Altmann 1962a). Of 38 estimated birth dates the earliest in 1957 fell during the last week of January, and in 1958, about February 22.

## MATING SEASON

The season of births is a consequence of an earlier mating season, during which females come into estrus and males copulate with them. Because males sometimes mount females without inseminating them, only mountings during which ejaculation was seen are considered as copulations. In 1959 and subsequently the first copulations were seen in mid-July, except for 1961 when they began a month later. These observations coincided roughly with the dates of initial conceptions as judged by subtracting 168 days, the average gestation period (Hurme and Van Wagenen 1956), from the date of birth. By this criterion, for the period 1959 to 1963 the earliest initial conception occurred about July 11, 1960, and the latest about August 29, 1961. Inasmuch as Altmann (1962a) noted that "in 1957, intensive breeding began about the first week of September," and the previous year it apparently commenced after mid-October, the onset of mating might tend to become earlier as the population grows.

The present mating period is at least four months later than that observed on Cayo Santiago by Carpenter (1942a) in March and April 1940. During that period at least 40 of "approximately 150 adult females" passed through periods of "sexual receptivity," and copulations were frequent. Inasmuch as that period of intense mating immediately followed the release of the animals from six weeks of isolation in cages, the timing might not have been typical of free animals.

Approximately a month before copulations occur the skin of the perineum and adjacent areas of many adult males reddens and may become ridged. Masturbation to ejaculation is comparatively frequent during this premating period. The sex skin of females also reddens, and in some it becomes grotesquely swollen. Copulations begin soon after females come into estrus and solicit the attention of males.

Judged by birth dates the latest conceptions of the mating season occurred late in January. In each of the past five years I have seen copulations in January, and I saw one on February 1. On a few occasions in mid-February a male was seen to mount a female repeatedly, as if in copulation, but there was no apparent ejaculation. With these exceptions, males did not copulate from February to June, and their sex skin was dull and faded at this period. The histology of the annual testis cycle as determined from biopsy material is at present under study by C. H. Conaway and D. S. Sade. These studies reveal a distinct annual cycle with testis regression and cessation of spermatogenesis in the nonbreeding season (Conaway and Sade, unpublished manuscript).

Parous females without infants, and therefore not lactating during the mating period, tended to mate and give birth earlier than others. Non-lactating females bore seven of the first nine infants born in 1960, eight of the first ten in 1961, three of the first four in 1962, and five of the first six in 1963. Yet these females constituted only from 10 to 20 percent of those giving birth. Apparently, then, reproductive failure or early mortality of infants tends to make the following birth season early. Newly mature (four-year-old) females gave birth at about the same time as normal lactating females. But the rare (less than 1 percent) births to precocially mature (three-year-old) females all occurred late in the birth season.

Fig. 5–6. A high-ranking subadult male grooms his resting leader (August 4, 1962).

## ECOLOGIC INFLUENCES ON REPRODUCTIVE TIMING

Some females consistently gave birth early or late, or retained from year to year their approximate position in the order of births. Others were highly variable. The same old adult female who was first to give birth in 1958 (Altmann 1962a) was also first in 1959, 1960, and 1963; second in 1961; and fourth in 1962. She was lactating during mating for at least three of these births. In the same group, however, another female gave birth near the median for her group in 1960 and 1962, but next to last in 1961. And yet another gave birth after the median in 1960 and 1961, but was first of her group in 1962. Because of such year-to-year variations among individuals, an internally regulated physiological cycle could not be responsible for maintaining a regular annual breeding season in the population (Bullough 1961). Breeding is probably synchronized by annual variations in ecological factors.

The principal environmental factors that influence the breeding cycles of terrestrial vertebrates are temperature, increase of day length, and food. Inasmuch as temperature ranges only about 10° C. over the entire year, it is probably not influential on Cayo Santiago. At the latitude of the island, 18 degrees north, day length, from sunrise to sunset, varies about 130 minutes during the year. But the rate of change is slight, less than half a

166

minute a day, and is decreasing at the onset of mating. Therefore I do not think that day length has a dominant effect on the observed breeding cycle. Although the food provided is nutritionally uniform throughout the year, the monkeys also eat bark, leaves, fruits, and other natural foods which seasonally change in quantity and qualities, such as vitamin and protein content. Variations in natural foods are difficult to measure, but they depend greatly upon the distribution of rainfall. Thus, if the start of reproduction depends upon natural foods, there should be a correlation between rainfall and the onset of mating. Rainfall totals from 60 to 80 inches a year. Only about one seventh of this rain falls in the first third of the year, from January to April, and during this period many plants dry up or shed their leaves. Mating usually commences in July, but nutritional influences that might stimulate a rise in sex hormones probably begin earlier, in May or June. Inasmuch as these months normally include the early part of the wet season, when there is abundant new plant growth, I think that the distribution of rainfall during the first half of the year is a major factor in determining the time of mating. It may be significant that although the dry season of 1961 was not intense, rainfall during the first half of that year (19.1 in.) was about a quarter lower than during the same period in 1959 (24.3 in.), 1960 (27.0 in.), or 1962 (25.5 in.), and mating began a month later in this drier year than during the other years (Fig. 5–1). In all four years mating began when the cumulative rainfall for the year was between 25 and 30 inches.

In northern India most births occur in March and April, in the hot, dry "summer" season (Southwick, Beg, and Siddiqi, this volume). Mating,

Fig. 5–7. An old female grooms her subadult (four-year-old) son (October 11, 1962).

five and one-half months earlier, therefore occurs mostly in October and November. This period follows shortly after the wet monsoon season, July to September. In general, then, the timing of mating in relation to month and the start of the wet season are roughly similar in northern India and on Cayo Santiago.

It is clear that climatic factors alone do not determine precisely the time of breeding because the birth period differs somewhat among the six groups. In single years the variation among groups in the initial birth dates has been from 47 to 67 days, and in the median birth dates, from 21 to 34 days. In three out of four years the median birth date in one of the two largest groups occurred two or three weeks before the median in the other. These variations in timing were probably caused by differences in the complex sexual and social relations within groups during the mating season (Conaway and Koford, in press).

## REPRODUCTIVE RATE

The reproductive rate, as shown by the ratio of newborn infants to mature females, also varied with the year and group. For all mature females the rate increased from about 73 percent in 1959 to 85 percent in 1962 (Table 5–1). For newly mature females, four years old, there was a more striking increase in the rate, from about 63 percent in 1959 to 100 percent in 1962. This high rate is notable because in many mammals, such as rodents and deer, the reproductive rate of the youngest class of breeding females is usually lower than that for older animals.

TABLE 5–1. REPRODUCTIVE RATE OF FEMALES FOR FOUR YEARS

| Year | All Mature Females | | | Newly Mature Females | | |
| | No. | Births | Percent | No. | Births | Percent |
| --- | --- | --- | --- | --- | --- | --- |
| 1959* | 88 | 64 | 73 | 24** | 16 | 67 |
| 1960 | 91 | 70 | 77 | 12 | 9 | 75 |
| 1961 | 100 | 79 | 79 | 16 | 14 | 88 |
| 1962 | 104 | 88 | 85 | 19 | 19 | 100 |

* In 1959 some infants probably died before being identified; hence number of births may be slightly low.
** There were more four-year-olds in 1959 than in following years. Presumably their mothers died or were removed before the 1956 birth period.

Among individual groups reproductive rate ranged from 56 percent to 100 percent, but the rate did not follow the order of group size. For the two largest groups, with from 28 to 35 mature females, the range of reproductive rates was from 71 to 89 percent. The mean rate was highest, 94 percent, in a medium-sized group having 9 to 13 mature females.

### TABLE 5-2. INFANT SEX RATIO AND MORTALITY RATES

| | Births | | | | | | | | Ratio | Deaths | | | | Mortality Rate | | |
| | Alive | | | | Stillborn | | | | mm. per | during Year | | | | (Percent of Live Births) | | |
| Year | mm. | ff. | ? | Total | mm. | ff. | ? | Total | 100 ff. | mm. | ff. | ? | Total | mm. | ff. | Total |
|---|---|---|---|---|---|---|---|---|---|---|---|---|---|---|---|---|
| 1959* | 34 | 29 | 1 | 64 | 0 | 0 | 1 | 1 | 118 | 2 | 2 | 1 | 5 | 5.9 | 6.9 | 7.8 |
| 1960 | 30 | 36 | 2 | 68 | ? | 1 | 1 | 2 | 81 | 1 | 1 | 2 | 4 | 6.7 | 5.6 | 5.9 |
| 1961 | 40 | 39 | 0 | 79 | 0 | 0 | 0 | 0 | 102 | 3 | 4 | 0 | 7 | 7.5 | 10.3 | 8.9 |
| 1962 | 39 | 45 | 0 | 84 | 1 | ? | 4 | 5 | 89 | 4 | 5 | 0 | 9 | 10.2 | 11.1 | 10.7 |
| Total | 143 | 149 | 3 | 295 | 1 | 1 | 6 | 8 | | 10 | 12 | 3 | 25 | | | |
| Mean | | | | | | | | | 96 | | | | | 7.7 | 8.7 | 8.5 |

*1959 observations are probably slightly incomplete for birth data.

## MORTALITY RATES

From year to year the ratio between the sexes at birth varied moderately (Table 5–2). Over a period of four years this sex ratio ranged from 81 to 118 males per 100 females. The mean sex ratio in 294 births was 96 males per 100 females. Newborn found dead were considered stillborn. It was difficult to determine their sex because the mother usually clutched the corpse tenaciously and carried it with her, even after it decayed. The eight stillborn seen constituted 2.7 percent of the observed births. But surely a few were missed, for some abandon their dead infants at obscure sites. The true proportion of stillbirths was probably about 4 percent.

Many infants die before the end of the calendar year. Over a period of four years the infant mortality rate ranged from 5.9 to 10.7 percent (Table 5–2). This rate tended to increase with the size and reproductive rate of the population. The mean mortality rate for 295 live births was 8.5 percent. That rate was slightly lower for males (7.7 percent) than for females (8.7 percent).

Excluding infants, the mean population mortality rate for three years was 6.5 percent, with negligible difference between the sexes (Table 5–3).

### TABLE 5-3. POPULATION MORTALITY (EXCEPT INFANT) FOR THREE YEARS

| | Number at Start | | | Deaths during Year | | | Percent Loss | | |
| Year | Males | Females | Total | Males | Females | Total | Males | Females | Total |
|---|---|---|---|---|---|---|---|---|---|
| 1960 | 113 | 150 | 263 | 9 | 9 | 18 | 8.0 | 6.0 | 6.9 |
| 1961 | 133 | 174 | 307 | 8 | 11 | 19 | 6.0 | 6.3 | 6.2 |
| 1962 | 130 | 191 | 321 | 8 | 13 | 21 | 6.3 | 6.8 | 6.5 |
| Total | 376 | 515 | 891 | 25 | 33 | 58 | | | |
| Mean | | | | | | | 6.7 | 6.4 | 6.5 |

Fig. 5–8. An adult female rests with her yearling and two-year-old young (August 31, 1962).

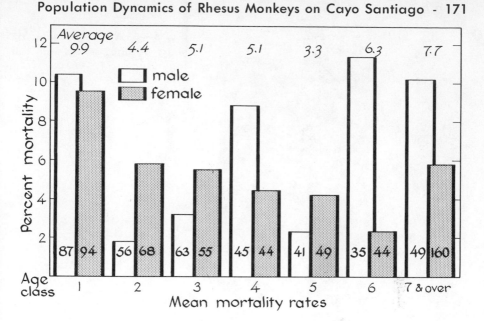

Fig. 5–9. Mean mortality rates of yearling and older monkeys from 1960 to 1962. Data for three years are lumped for each age class. Stippled bars indicate males; white bars, females. Numbers over bars are rates for sexes combined. Numbers in bars indicate number of monkeys used to determine rate. Animals removed early in the year were not included in the computations; those removed late were considered survivors.

By years the mean rates for both sexes combined ranged from 6.2 to 6.9 percent. Considering the effects of individual, group, and year-to-year differences, this uniformity is remarkable. So far there has been no indication of increased mortality with population growth, except slightly in infants.

By age classes for yearling and older monkeys the three-year-mean mortality rates ranged from 3.3 percent in five-year-olds to 9.9 percent in yearlings (Fig. 5–9). The latter figure is abnormally high, for at least a fifth of that yearling rate was directly caused by handling accidents. For animals older than yearlings the mean mortality rates were highest in adults, at least six years old, but there were considerable differences between the sexes.

During the period from two to six years of age the mortality of males tended to increase, while that for females tended to decrease. These differences among sex and age classes were probably caused by differences in social relations. For example, two- and three-year-old females experience their first periods of estrus and consort with adult males, which sometimes attack them. Consequently, these females may suffer more injuries than

Fig. 5–10. A group leader, six years of age, stands with tail high (August 11, 1961).

Fig. 5–11. A high-ranking male, at least eleven years old, threatens a female above him.

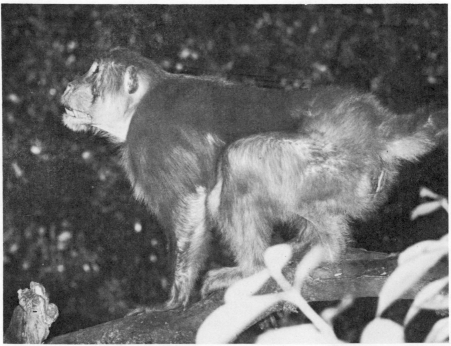

Fig. 5–12. The second-ranking male of a group grins submissively as the first-ranking male walks close behind him.

Fig. 5–13. An adult male (063 tattooed on medial thigh) grins at the photographer (September 21, 1961).

males of the same age. On the other hand, females in postpuberty, four and five years old, stay in the central part of the group and associate closely with their mothers, whereas most adolescent males leave their mothers and often their natal group to become peripheral males. These males lose the comfort and protection of the central members of the group, which are hostile toward them. In trying to get food, to which they have lowest precedence, they are often attacked by adults of their own and alien groups (Koford 1963). Thus peripheral males are lean and furtive, almost continuously under tension, and often wounded. Among adults social tension and the frequency and seriousness of fights are considerably higher in males than in females. The high mortality of males from four to six years old probably reflects these social relations. Evidently females survive to greater age than males, for in 1956 Altmann (1962a) found on the island nine females whose tattoos indicated that they were born in 1943 or earlier, but he found no such tattooed males. Because of the higher mortality rate in males, adult females outnumber adult males more than two to one.

It is planned to allow the Cayo Santiago population to increase and to continue basic observations. In addition, observations have commenced on two new island colonies of rhesus monkeys. These were established in 1962 in southwest Puerto Rico, where rainfall is less than half that of Cayo Santiago. Comparison among the colonies will allow more significant analyses of population dynamics.

PAUL E. SIMONDS

# 6

# ◈ The Bonnet Macaque in South India

## INTRODUCTION

The bonnet macaque (*Macaca radiata*) is the common macaque of the Indian subcontinent, ranging from about 19 degrees north to Cape Comorin in the south, up to the Godavary River in the east, and at least as far as Satara (18 degrees north) in the west. In Kerala State the bonnet macaque is found in or near the forest inhabited by *M. silenus*, the lion-tailed macaque. The closely related toque macaque, *M. sinica*, inhabits Ceylon, and in north India the rhesus macaque, *M. mulatta*, replaces the bonnet macaque.

In appearance bonnet macaques are slender, long-tailed monkeys, weighing between 6 and 17 pounds as adults (Nolte 1955). Their fur is a gray-brown on the back and white or gray on the belly. Facial skin is light pink, but some individuals have red faces. The head hair is parted in the center and radiates from a central cowlick. They exhibit considerable sexual dimorphism in body size and canines.

Bonnet macaques are to some extent ground-living, spending about one third of the day on the ground. They have a well-marked home range, which they do not leave, and their diet is widely varied.

Two major ecological niches are occupied by the bonnet macaque: a variety of forests, and areas of human cultivation. They inhabit the forests from the lowlands of Kerala State to the highlands of the Nilgiri Hills, occurring there as high as 7000 feet and near sea level in Nellore District of Madras State. They are found in the rain forests of Kerala State and the semidesert of the central Deccan.

In the cultivated areas the bonnet macaque lives in banyan trees (*Ficus bengalensis* and *F. benjamina*) lining the roads. If there are no banyan trees, there will probably be no macaques. The surrounding fields may be planted with such crops as peanuts, castor beans (which the monkeys do not eat),

175

Fig. 6-1. Female with newborn infant being groomed by another female. Note arrangement of head hair forming a bonnet.

beans, squash, rice, and gram (*Dolichos byflorus*). The bonnet macaque is seen only in areas where there are at least a few large trees, and, given a supply of food and water, the presence of some large trees seems to be the only limitation to their adaptation. Banyan trees that fan out and reach a height of 100 feet apparently provide the optimum environment. The population seems to be considerably less dense in forested areas of low trees and bushes, areas in which the langur (*Presbytis entellus*) may be common (see Chap. 7, this volume).

Prior to the present study the only recorded observations of the social behavior of bonnet macaques was a 16-day study by Angela Nolte (1949, 1955a, b). In the present study intensive observations were made on a group of *M. radiata diluta* in southern Mysore State from October 1961 through January 1962, and from late April through early June 1962. (In the period from mid-February to mid-April a survey of primates in Ceylon was made.) The locality chosen for the intensive study was on the edge of the Somanathapur Sandal Reserve, a low forest merging into a bamboo forest a few miles south. The home range of the group studied (the Somanathapur group) was entirely within a cultivated area but extended to the edge of the sandal reserve forest. The macaques of the Somanathapur group were never seen entering the forest. Peanuts and horse gram (*Arachis hypogea* and *Dolichos byflorus*) were the major crops planted in the fields. The core

176

area of the group consisted of a mile-long double row of banyan and tama-rind (*Tamarindus indica*) trees on the roadside. A few other varieties of trees grew in the area, but only the banyans and tamarinds provided a major source of food, and they also formed the main shelter. The monkeys ranged out into the fields for a part of their food supply, but a major part consisted of banyan fruit which is available throughout the year.

Several forest groups were observed briefly, both those nearby in the bamboo forests and those high in the Nilgiri Hills. The major sources of food for the bamboo-forest macaques are the two forms of bamboo, *Bambusa arundinacea* and *Dendrocalamus strictus*. Seeds are plentiful throughout the year, but new bamboo shoots are available only during the wet season from April to September.

No forest group came into contact with the Somanathapur group during the period of observation. There were no bonnet macaques in the sandal forest which apparently was a barrier, and the Somanathapur group never made any attempt to enter it. There was a neighboring macaque group which also occupied a row of banyan trees (the Hangala group).

The best information on home range and core areas for bonnet macaques comes from the Somanathapur and Hangala groups. The pattern observed for them is not unlike that described for baboons (this volume). The monkeys have a fairly well-delimited home range, which for the Somanathapur group occupied two square miles (Figs. 6–2 and 6–3). The group covered from one third to one half of the total home range on any single day. One stand of sleeping trees was observed in use 90 percent of the time; a second was used the remaining 10 percent, except for one time when a third stand of trees was used. The two secondary stands of sleeping trees were often used for dozing and grooming in the midday. Approximately 20 percent of the home ranges of the Somanathapur and Hangala groups overlapped, but the core areas did not seem to do so. For part of the study period a group of common langurs occupied the major sleeping trees of the Somanathapur group and the macaques chased them to the tops of the trees several times. The only threat behavior observed between the macaque groups occurred when a subadult male dropped out of a tree into the wrong group and was chased away. No seasonal change in home range was observed for the macaques, but the langur group may have occupied the area only seasonally. They were observed in the Somanathapur group's home range in May and June 1962 and in February 1963. They were not present from October 1961 to January 1962.

## POPULATION DYNAMICS

The ages of monkeys given in this chapter are based on estimates made of the observed macaques during the study. Most infants are born in Febru-ary and March; therefore the one-year-old juveniles form a distinct age

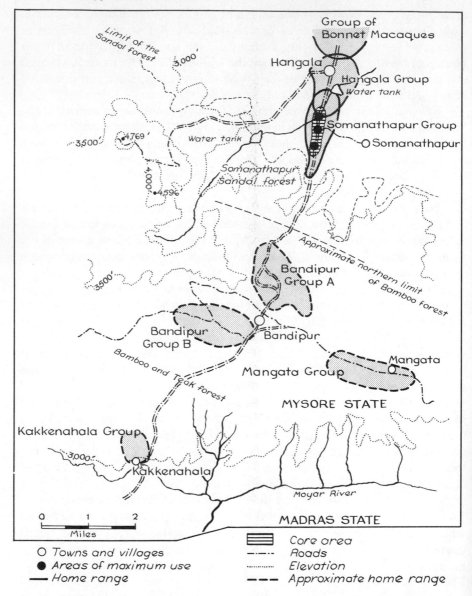

Fig. 6–2. Map of home ranges of bonnet macaque groups near Somanathapur, Mysore State, India.

class, which is easily recognizable—as are also the two-year-old juveniles. Estimates of older juveniles and subadults are not so accurate, since individual growth rates may vary, but may be considered correct plus or minus a year.

Fig. 6–3. Somanathapur Sandal Reserve — the troop home range consists of trees in the center and the adjacent fields.

The estimated age at which females reach sexual maturity is from two and a half to three and a half years. The male is sexually mature at about the same age, but is not socially mature until from two to three years later. The female bears her first infant within a year after reaching sexual maturity and probably continues to bear infants yearly throughout her life.

The reproductive success of the Somanathapur group, as expressed by the ratio of births to adult females (see Koford, Chap. 5, this volume), was fairly high. There were 19 females who were in reproductive cycles during the period of observation. Five of them entered the cycle in the fall of 1961 by becoming estrous and were included only in the 1962 ratio. In 1961, with 14 adult females there were 14 infants, or a reproductive success of 100 percent. In 1962 there were ten births between the end of January and the end of April. An eleventh female that was pregnant in January did not have an infant in April but was no longer pregnant. There were also three females who gave birth some time in the summer or early fall of 1961, probably June and July, who had not given birth at the termination of the study in 1962. If the lost infant and the projected births are counted, the total for 1962 would be 14 infants for 19 adult females, or a reproductive success of 74 percent. The average reproductive success is, then, 84 percent.

Only three monkeys are known to have died during the period of observation and there was no evidence of disease during the study. An infant female was killed by dogs; a subadult male was killed during a dominance fight (observed and reported by a villager); and an extremely old male was

179

missing after the break in observations. Generally, deaths due to wounds are probably not common. After a major male fight in which the alpha male was deposed, nearly all the adult males in the group were wounded, some very badly. Some of the wounds were slashes as much as four inches long and others were deep puncture wounds. One subadult male had two long slash and puncture wounds on his hips and other cuts on his head and shoulders. Within one month all wounds had successfully healed and three months later they were not detectable from a distance of six feet.

TABLE 6–1. COMPOSITION OF BONNET MACAQUE GROUPS

| Group | Adult and Subadult Males | Adult and Subadult Females | Juveniles M F ? | Infants M F ? | Total | Date | Remarks |
|---|---|---|---|---|---|---|---|
| Somanathapur group* | 18 | 18 | 5 3 | 8 6 | 58 | Nov. 61 | 10 infants born January to April 1962 (5 males, 5 females) |
| Hangala group | 19 | 11 | 6 2 1 | 2 1 4 | 46 | Dec. 61 | |
| Mangata group | 10+ | 8+ | 5+ | 5+ | 28+ | May 62 | |
| Kakkenahala group | 1 | 4 | 1 | | 6 | May 62 | |

* The Somanathapur group is the only group for which there is an accurate count of subadult males as distinguished from fully adult males. There were 11 adult and 7 subadult males in that group.

The composition of the groups is shown in Table 6–1. Infants are those monkeys between birth and one year of age. Juveniles range between the ages of one and three. Subadult males are males over three that have their canines fully erupted or nearly so but have not attained full body size, weight, or musculature. Full physical and social adulthood for males is probably attained in approximately the sixth year (Fig. 6–4). For females it is attained in the fourth year. The females are approximately half the size of the fully adult males and do not have large, projecting canines.

In the Somanathapur group there were both old females and old males. One of the males showed signs of extreme age including drooping eyelids, reduced musculature, stiffness of the joints, extra folds of skin, and skin with the mottled appearance of age. The general impression he gave was similar to that of a human in the eighties or nineties.

Nolte (1955a, b) made two group counts in the forests near the area in

Fig. 6–4. Fully adult male. Note size of canines.

which the author worked. Her totals were 32 and 33 monkeys per group. Her categories differ from the author's in that she apparently classes what are called subadults in this paper as juveniles and some of the juveniles as infants.

In general estimates of group size in the forest are hazardous, but in addition to Nolte's data Dr. Kawamura's team of primatologists in northern Mysore State reported the forest groups to range from 20 to 30 monkeys. The Bandipur forest groups were probably no larger, as Nolte's data indicate for groups near by. This contrasts with from 40 to 60 monkeys in groups outside the forest.

The categories of infant and juvenile can be further subdivided. The infants may be classified as either dark infants (from birth to two months) or light infants (from two months to a year). Juveniles, because of the yearly birth peak, fall into two age classes: one to two years of age and two to three years of age.

## SOCIAL BEHAVIOR

Bonnet macaques are extremely social and live in groups including both sexes and all sizes. These groups are highly organized and the individuals are ranked relative to one another. The ranking is quite clear among subadult males and is probably at least in the formative stage among juvenile males. It is more difficult to demonstrate rank among the females than among the males, but there is a definite dominance hierarchy among the socially most active females.

The ranking of male bonnet macaques is most evident when a single portion of food is placed between two males. One of the males will consistently take the food, except sometimes when the food is placed directly in front of the subordinate monkey, and even then the dominant monkey may take the food. The Somanathapur group was not fed regularly but on perhaps 20 occasions the food test was used to determine relative dominance. Once relative dominance had been determined in this manner a series of other indicators was isolated.

A subordinate monkey consistently gives way on the approach of a dominant monkey, or makes one of several subordination gestures that are equivalent to moving. This is true of females as well as males. Looking away from the dominant animal may be substituted for actually moving, or the subordinate monkey may lip smack or present to the dominant monkey. Lip-smacking is a rapid opening and closing of the lips while the ears are held tightly against the head. The jaw is not opened and closed in this gesture. Presenting consists of raising the tail and turning the hindquarters toward the monkey to which the presenting is directed, often with the tail held to one side. Presenting in dominance situations is similar to the position the receptive female takes as a male approaches to mount for copulation, but differs in that the presenting monkey in a dominance interaction is usually more tense. Both lip-smacking and presenting are clear indicators of subordination and the monkey to which they are directed is almost always the dominant monkey in that social situation.

The sniffing of the face of one monkey by another is a consistent indication of dominance, the sniffing monkey always being the dominant. Another gesture made by dominant monkeys is neck-chewing. Neck-chewing is often, but not always, combined with embracing. Often in the morning, two males approach one another, embrace, and one may chew on the neck of the other. The skin is not broken. Also, as the final gesture in a threat sequence, the dominant monkey may approach and embrace the subordinate monkey and chew on the subordinate's neck, apparently as a reaffirmation of the dominance relationship. Face-sniffing is used in the same

Fig. 6–5. Old male mounting subadult male.

manner. Face-sniffing and neck-chewing are always done by the dominant monkey, but embracing is usually done by both monkeys, and it is not always possible to tell which is embracing which.

The mounting of one monkey by another in bonnet macaques is not a certain indication of dominance (Fig. 6–5). For instance, during a two-and-a-half-month period, dominant males mounted subordinate males 23 observed times, whereas clearly subordinate monkeys mounted dominant monkeys 11 times. Sometimes when subordinate monkeys mounted dominant ones, the dominant had forced the subordinate to do so by backing into it and reaching back to grab it. In these situations the dominant monkey was not presenting and its whole attitude was different from that of a presenting subordinate monkey. The subordinate monkey might try to avoid mounting, but the dominant monkey would continue backing into it until it did mount, lip-smacking while mounting. However, such mountings accounted for only about 15 percent of the total subordinate-dominant mounting situations. In the others no clear differentiation was observed to set them off from mountings by the dominant monkeys.

With the help of these various gestures indicating the relative ranking of males within a bonnet macaque group, a central hierarchy of dominant males may be distinguished. In the Somanathapur group there were 5 of the 11 males that could be considered highly dominant (Table 6–2). They were active in the social interaction of the group, moving quickly toward most threat situations involving subordinate monkeys and terminating the threatening by their presence, acting as the focus of the group with the females and infants remaining in their vicinity, and often determining the direction in which the group moved. These central males were not

TABLE 6–2. MALES IN DOMINANCE ORDER, SOMANATHAPUR GROUP (MOST DOMINANT ANIMAL TOP LEFT)

|  | Dan | Zeb | Pim | Hala | 1-Eye | Kink | Andy | Rock | Butch | Shorty | Sanna | Slim | Al | Crest |
|---|---|---|---|---|---|---|---|---|---|---|---|---|---|---|
| Dan |  | 6 | 1 | 1 | 2 |  |  |  | 1 | 1 | 2 |  | 1 |  |
| Zeb |  |  | 10 | 4 | 2 |  | 1 |  |  | 1 |  | 2 | 2 | 1 |
| Pim |  |  |  | 4 | 1 | 6 | 2 | 3 | 2 | 3 | 5 | 2 | 3 | 1 |
| Hala |  |  |  |  | 2 | 2 |  |  | 1 | 2 |  | 1 |  |  |
| 1-Eye | 1 |  |  |  |  |  |  |  | 1 |  | 3 |  | 1 | 3 |
| Kink |  |  |  |  |  |  |  |  | 3 | 4 | 7 | 3 | 1 | 1 |
| Andy |  |  |  |  |  |  |  | 1 | 1 |  | 1 |  | 1 |  |
| Rock |  |  |  |  |  |  |  |  | 11 | 6 | 2 | 4 | 1 |  |
| Butch |  |  |  |  |  |  |  |  |  | 6 |  |  |  |  |
| Shorty |  |  |  |  | 1 |  |  |  | 1 |  |  | 5 |  |  |
| Sanna |  |  |  |  |  | 1 |  | 1 | 7 | 3 |  |  | 5 |  |
| Slim |  |  |  |  |  | 1 |  | 2 | 2 | 4 |  |  | 1 |  |
| Al |  |  |  |  |  |  |  | 2 |  |  |  |  |  | 2 |
| Crest |  |  |  |  |  |  |  |  |  | 1 |  |  | 1 |  |

The numbers indicate the total incidents in which the monkey in the column acted in a dominant manner toward the monkey to the right during a two-and-a-half-month period. This includes causing the other to give way, face-sniffing, neck-chewing, slapping, stare threatening, eyelid threatening, open-mouth threatening, and growl threatening. (Slim, Al, and Crest are subadult males; Sanna rapidly becoming full adult.)

Those incidents to the left of the diagonal line represent dominance behavior of subordinate monkeys over more dominant monkeys. Note that they are almost confined to subadult males.

threatened by subadult males and their presence was usually sufficient to terminate a threat sequence, or, conversely, on their approach a subordinate female or old male might begin to threaten a subadult male.

Four of the Somanathapur adult males were subordinate to the central males and somewhat different in their behavior. They were not part of the focus of the group, and tended to avoid threat situations when possible. Their presence did not often tip the balance of dominance away from subadult males in a threat sequence and, in fact, they were often the target of threats by the subadult males.

There were several differences between these two major classes of males. The central males were generally considerably larger than the other adult males and had greater musculature. They had excellent canines for the most part, whereas the other, less dominant males had, without exception, inferior or missing canines. The less dominant males were less active generally. And there was a personality difference, as well, which may have been a result of their subordinate position rather than the cause of it. For instance, one of the older and smaller males never initiated a threat sequence without the support of a more dominant male, but he would join any threat sequence in which other males threatened those immediately below him in dominance. After such a sequence he always chewed on the neck of the subdued monkey. He could be characterized most simply as a cowardly bully. More dominant males, particularly the central males, would not rely so heavily on the support of other males and would often initiate threats on their own.

A single, very old, canineless male must be considered separately. He was subordinate to the central males and not very active in threat sequences or other agonistic behavior. But his presence did have the effect of the presence of a central male. A threat sequence would stop if he sat in the middle of it. No subadult male was ever observed threatening him, and yet he was less capable of defending himself against their canines than some of the other less dominant adult males who were threatened regularly. He was dominant over those other males and it is likely that he belonged to the central males in his younger days.

An eleventh adult male achieved that status during the study of the Somanathapur group. Throughout the study his relative dominance changed and he was ranked below the lowest ranking noncentral male at the beginning of the study and was equal to the alpha male at the end of the study nine months later. During this time his musculature increased dramatically in size. Apparently he was experiencing the final phase of his growth. Throughout the study he threatened more and more dominant males until he was displacing the number 2 male fairly regularly. He was not, however, part of the central core of dominant males at the end of the study. They tended to threaten him jointly, and their combined dominance exceeded his.

There were no males denied access to the central part of the group in the Somanathapur group. Subadult males, subdominant adult males, and juvenile males moved through any part of the group with impunity if they made the proper gestures on approaching more dominant monkeys. Only if they molested another monkey (female or infant, usually), which screeched, did the dominant central males chase them or threaten them. It was usually the subadult males who were involved in such incidents. No isolated males were observed and the group composition included males of all ages, indicating that males probably do not tend to leave the group as they approach full adulthood.

Of the 18 females in the Somanathapur group, 4 of them were easily ranked in dominance. Of the remaining 14 females, it could only be said they were more or less dominant. It is likely that they were ranked among themselves, but the means of ranking them did not become evident during the study.

The alpha female in the Somanathapur group could count on the assistance of the original alpha male when she became involved in a threat situation with any other monkey in the group. When he was reduced in dominance, following a loss of an upper canine and a major dominance fight, she was no longer able to dominate the other males. Previously she had been able to take food from the number 2 male. The number 2 male became the alpha male and would not allow her in his presence during at least the first month of his dominance. She did not, however, lose her dominance over the other females.

**Grooming**

There is no significant difference between the amount males and females groom in a bonnet macaque group; the female bonnet macaque is not the major groomer, either in number of grooming interactions or in the time spent in grooming. Both sexes groom every age and either sex category in the group (Fig. 6–6).

Many of the grooming interactions take from a few seconds to a few minutes. These are the most readily observed, since they tend to occur while the group is moving on the ground, but the major amount of grooming takes place during the midday, from 10:00 A.M. to 2:00 P.M., when the group retires to the trees to doze and groom. Then there may be small groups of monkeys that continue to groom for from half an hour to two hours, with dozing mixed in. There is often a great deal of shifting back and forth in grooming sequences, especially if four or five monkeys are involved. Two or three may groom one monkey for a few minutes, then one will switch and groom another, and later the monkey originally groomed will begin grooming another. Each individual interaction may last from only a few seconds to a few minutes, but continuous grooming of one monkey by an-

Fig. 6–6. Female grooming older infant.

other, without interruption, may last as long as 30 minutes. Self-grooming does occur, but is rare.

Adult males often groom each other and for long periods of time. Two adult males have been observed sitting together in the trees for more than an hour, alternately dozing and grooming. The dominant male does not necessarily groom the subordinate less than the subordinate grooms him, nor does a male groom a female less than the female grooms the male. Adult, highly dominant males will groom each other. Table 6–3 shows the total number of grooming interactions observed in the Somanathapur group, indicating the sexes involved. Note that monkeys of like sex tend to groom each other somewhat more often than monkeys of opposite sex. Females were observed in a slightly greater number of grooming interactions than males were, but males groomed other males considerably more often than females groomed males. Often a male would groom a female without her reciprocating the grooming at all, and the reverse was also true. The general picture of bonnet macaque grooming is that males groom long and often,

187

TABLE 6–3. TOTAL NUMBER OF GROOMING INTERACTIONS,
SOMANATHAPUR GROUP

| Groomer | Groomed | | Total |
|---------|---------|---------|-------|
| | ♂ | ♀ | |
| ♂ | 353 | 248 | 601 |
| ♀ | 242 | 410 | 652 |

their grooming activity being equal to that of the females both in intensity and frequency. There seems to be no consistent pattern of who grooms whom. Some males, for instance, groom a lot while others are groomed a lot (Table 6–4). There is no relation to dominance rank. Nolte's (1955 a, b) observations support this conclusion.

More grooming is probably done in a bonnet macaque society than in rhesus macaque, Japanese macaque, or baboon societies, since more individuals take an active part in the grooming.

TABLE 6–4. COUNT OF MALE-MALE GROOMING INTERACTIONS

| | Dan | Zeb | Pim | Hala | 1-eye | Andy | Rock | Butch | Shorty | Sanna |
|---|-----|-----|-----|------|-------|------|------|-------|--------|-------|
| Of other males | 16 | 20 | 34 | 34 | 10 | 9 | 7 | 9 | 17 | 24 |
| By other males | 34 | 22 | 14 | 20 | 9 | 21 | 4 | 14 | 32 | 11 |

Although juveniles and infants are not regular groomers, they do a small but significant portion of the total grooming. Table 6–5 gives the age categories as well as the sex categories of the groomers and those groomed.

Wounded monkeys present for grooming often and are often groomed. There seems to be a direct relationship between the seriousness of the wound and the amount of grooming activity. The subadult male with two slash wounds more than three inches long coupled with deep puncture wounds presented to monkey after monkey for grooming, and when one ceased grooming moved immediately to another. The grooming involved picking any dirt or other foreign matter out of the wounds and then licking them clean.

When infants were born other monkeys would groom the new mother in order to be near the infant. This was dramatically demonstrated when a subdominant female gave birth to the first new infant of the season. For much of the first week the female and her new infant were avoided. In the second week following the birth nearly every female in the group groomed

TABLE 6–5. GROOMING INTERACTIONS, SHOWING AGE AND SEX CATEGORIES

| | | | | Groomed | | | | | |
|---|---|---|---|---|---|---|---|---|---|
| Groomer | ♂ | ♀ | Subadult ♂ | Juvenile ♂ | Juvenile ♀ | All Juveniles | Infant ♂ | Infant ♀ | All Infants |
| ♂ | 186 | 219 | 52 | 15 | | 15 | 1 | 2 | 3 |
| ♀ | 175 | 355 | 21 | 19 | 11 | 31 | 24 | 22 | 55 |
| Subadult ♂ | 62 | 20 | 15 | 1 | | 1 | | | |
| Juvenile ♂ | 13 | 6 | 4 | 1 | | 1 | | | |
| Juvenile ♀ | 3 | 15 | | | 1 | 1 | | 2 | 2 |
| All juveniles | 17 | 23 | 4 | 1 | 1 | 2 | | 2 | 2 |
| Infant ♂ | 3 | 1 | | | | | | | |
| Infant ♀ | | 4 | | | | | | | |
| All infants | 5 | 8 | | | | | | | |

The categories *all juveniles* and *all infants* include monkeys not identified as to sex, as well as both sexes.

her whereas many of them had not been observed to groom her in the previous four months. Mothers groom infants frequently, usually doing so each time they sit.

## Play

Play begins for bonnet macaques when they are first able to walk about. The first manifestations of play are attempts to hop; infants of about a month old will hop together for several minutes. By the age of two months they begin mild chasing, and as coordination increases the chasing becomes more and more violent. Some time before six months of age wrestling begins, and as the infant grows this becomes the major play activity. Violent wrestling is generally confined to the older juvenile males, subadult males, and adult males.

Swimming becomes part of the monkey's play activity during the second six months of life. Females rarely swim; only one female was observed swimming, although a few swimming monkeys were not identified as to sex.

In the Somanathapur group play was not restricted to age mates. Adult males would play with monkeys of all ages, from infants about six months old to other fully adult males. Increasing intensity of play activity would separate out the younger individuals. Play that started as chasing and turned to wrestling would eliminate the younger infants. As the wrestling became

Fig. 6–7. Bonnet macaques at play. Note adult male playing with juvenile in the foreground.

more violent, all infants and all females would drop out. The most violent wrestling, indulged in by the subadult males, would find even the older juveniles watching from the sidelines.

Adult male bonnet macaques play regularly and often (Fig. 6–7). On one occasion in the Somanathapur group the number *2* and number *4* males wrestled in the grass for several minutes, rolling, mouthing each other, and grappling. This wrestling was like that of juveniles and subadult males. There were no threat gestures used, and no signs of attack, no biting to break the skin, no growling or screeching, nor the lunging and slapping that take place during a threat sequence. These males were clearly playing and their preliminary gestures were like those used by juveniles and subadult males in an approach to a play situation (a bouncy walk, head twisted to one side, reaching with the hand, and slightly open mouth). There was no tenseness in the action of either male.

Some of the adult males played regularly and others played rarely or not at all. Four of the eleven adult males in the group were never observed playing. Of the remaining seven, two played often, usually with juveniles and subadult males. Table 6–6 gives age, dominance position, and play partners for the adult males in the Somanathapur group.

Adult males generally confined their play to wrestling; they did not chase each other in play, nor were they seen swimming, with the exception of one newly adult male. Subadult males, too, wrestled far more than they chased. Chasing play is primarily infant play. Infants and juveniles might use low growling, eyelid threats, and other mild threat gestures fleetingly in their play, but subadult and adult males did not. If such a gesture was used while an adult male was playing, the play stopped immediately and a threat sequence might ensue.

The two males that played regularly were the number *3* and number *10* males. The number *3* male was never threatened by subadult males. The number *10* male was the recipient of daily threats by subadult males, either singly or in combination. Still, he was observed playing with them four times. There was no question about the difference involved in the two kinds of behavior, threat and play. Threat behavior was violent and tense, and could result in the infliction of wounds. Play behavior was considerably more relaxed and none of the chewing was observed to result in wounds. And yet, in some respects, the threatening of the number *10* male may have been an intensification of play behavior.

### TABLE 6–6. RELATIVE DOMINANCE POSITION, AGE, AND TIMES ADULT MALES OBSERVED PLAYING

| Male | Dominance Position October 61 | June 62 | Age | Infants | Juveniles | Subadult Males | Adult Males |
|---|---|---|---|---|---|---|---|
| Dan | Alpha | 4 | Prime | Never observed playing | | | |
| Zeb | 2 | Alpha | Prime | 1 | 2 | 2 | 1 |
| Pim | 3 | 5 | Late prime | 4 | 7 | 3 | 3 |
| Hala | 4 | 3 | Early prime | | 1 | 1 | 1 |
| 1-Eye | 5 | 2 | Early prime | Never observed playing | | | |
| Kink | 6 | 6 | Prime | 2 | | | |
| Andy | 7 | deceased | Very old | Never observed playing | | | |
| Rock | 8 | 7 | Very late prime | Never observed playing (cowardly bully) | | | |
| Butch | 9 | 8 | Old | | | 1 | |
| Shorty | 10 | 9 | Old | 1 | 1 | 4 | 2 |
| Sanna | 11 but rising | = to Alpha in 1–1 encounters | Attaining prime | | 6 | 5 | |

The subadult males would threaten the number *10* male (or the number *8* or number *9* males) without apparent provocation. When one began several others often joined. At the beginning of such a sequence a subadult male would usually be sitting with one of the old, toothless males in the same tree or within a few yards on the ground. The subadult would look about, then assume a threatening posture and begin growling and screeching with the appropriate gestures (eyelid threats, slaps, and lunges). In contrast, agonistic behavior on the part of the older males and the females was usually elicited by some incident. A subadult male might approach a female sexually who was not receptive, or a subordinate monkey might approach too close to a dominant monkey without making the proper gestures of subordination.

There are two possible explanations of the threat behavior of the subadult males. Since the play of infants and juveniles essentially involves kinds of behavior that will be useful in later social interaction (chasing, wrestling, and some of the threat gestures), it is possible that the threatening by subadult males of older, subdominant males is a continuation of the exercises in social gestures and fighting behavior. On the other hand, the subadult male is approaching adulthood and the first adult males he will pass in dominance are the older, subdominant males. The subadult male that became fully adult during the study of the Somanathapur group was no longer threatening the older, toothless males. Instead he threatened a subdominant male with small canines who was above the older adult males in dominance position. When the subadult male became clearly dominant over the small-toothed male, he no longer threatened him.

### Female-Young Interactions

The mother-infant relationship in bonnet macaques is intense and continuous for the first few weeks of life. The mother does not allow other females to hold her infant, and if a dominant female picks up the infant of a subordinate female, the mother will hold a part of her infant even though the dominance difference is very great. By the end of the first two months of life the mother may leave her infant in the trees or bushes while she goes into the fields to eat.

The female bonnet macaque never feeds her infant solid food. The only nourishment it gets from her is her milk. Mothers have been observed taking food from their infants. Once a mother was observed to open the mouth of her infant and remove whatever food the infant had been chewing and then eat it herself.

The infant is able to cling tightly early on the first day of life and is carried under the belly of the mother, who may make jumps of eight or ten feet on the first day without giving any assistance to the infant. If the infant is slipping, the mother will pause in walking and raise the infant with her hand. Between the ages of two and six months, the infant may ride on its mother's back a small part of the time (perhaps 5 percent), but after six months of age, back-riding seems to be given up completely.

If the infant is playing near the mother and danger threatens (for example, a monkey may give a warning bark), the mother will scoop up her infant and run for the trees. She will also do so if the infant is threatened by a dominant male, but if it is threatened by a lesser monkey, she will usually return the threat.

The female grooms her infant often. As the group moves, individual monkeys will pause after walking 10 or 20 yards. When a female with an infant does so, she often makes a few passes at grooming the infant. Female bonnet macaques do not seem to play with their infants. When the infant is within reach it is groomed; when beyond reach it is often playing with other infants.

Weaning occurs between eight and twelve months of age, apparently; that is, the infant is progressively allowed less and less access to the mother's nipples. The flow of milk may have ceased before that but the infant is allowed to huddle at the mother's breast, nipple in mouth, up to the birth of the next infant. Several months before that, however, the mother will chase the infant from her nipples on some occasions. The infant will try time and again to reach the nipples, either with a hand or its face. Each time the infant approaches, the mother will give a mild threat and the infant will draw back, chirping. Later in the same day, the infant will be found again at the mother's breast, nipple in its mouth but making no sucking motions. No female was observed allowing last year's infant to nurse after the birth of a new one.

The birth of the new infant loosens the bonds between the mother and last year's infant, now a juvenile. The juvenile still will doze with its mother and be groomed by her, but more and more of its time is taken by play with its age-mates and other young monkeys. Female-juvenile relationships beyond two years could not be traced because of the shortness of the study.

## Sexual Behavior

In bonnet macaque females the sexual skin does not swell very much. Only one female out of 18 in the Somanathapur group had noticeable swelling. The estrous and nonestrous periods of the others could not be differentiated by this means. Variation in the color of the sexual skin was also slight. Some did have bright red sexual skin, but it remained red throughout the month. Variation may have existed, but it was no greater than that caused by differences in lighting in the sun and shade. Females were recorded as in estrus if they were seen copulating. It is doubtful that different categories of males copulated with the female at different stages of her estrous period since a female might copulate with a dominant male, a subadult male, and a juvenile within a few minutes of one another, but, owing to the difficulty of determining the onset of estrus, this is not otherwise demonstrable.

There are two major differences in the sexual behavior of bonnet macaques as compared to rhesus macaques, in particular. Among the bonnet macaques, the male does the majority of soliciting for copulation. And the copulation consists of one mounting.

There were 28 copulations observed from the beginning of the approach to the completion of the copulation. Of these 28, only one was initiated by the female. In addition, there were 31 incomplete copulations observed from the beginning of the approach to the interruption or separation of the monkeys involved. Of those 31, only three were initiated by the female. Females rarely presented for copulation without the prior approach of the male in a soliciting manner. The male would run up to a female, flip her tail to one side and examine her genitalia. The female would either present or run when the male began such an approach. On many occasions a male would walk or run up to a sitting female, grasp her by the root of the tail and lift her to a standing position, then examine her genitalia. It was only rarely that a female would walk up to a male that was sitting and present to him; the total number of such incidents is less than 5 percent of the total approaches made for copulation or solicitation for copulation. During the mating season the males actively examined most of the females every day.

In bonnet macaque copulation usually consists of only one mounting. There were 108 copulations observed during the study. Of the 28 that were observed from the beginning of the approach to the separation of the monkeys concerned, males were only twice seen to dismount, sit or groom, and then mount again to complete the copulation to ejaculation. In one of these interrupted copulations a juvenile male mounted four times before ejaculation. The normal pattern is for the male to approach the female, briefly examine her genitalia and smell them, flip her tail to one side with the back of his hand and mount, grasping the small of her back with his hands and her ankles with his feet. The copulation is completed with 5 to 30 pelvic thrusts and ejaculation. The male then dismounts, and either may groom the other briefly before they separate.

Only one long-term relationship between a particular male and female was observed that might be called a consort relationship. In all other copulations, although the male sometimes followed the female a short distance, the male and female involved separated shortly thereafter and either copulated with other monkeys or had the opportunity to do so before copulating with each other again. Once in the space of four minutes three males copulated with one female, and one of those males copulated with another female. There was no attempt by any of these males to disrupt the copulation of the subordinate males, even though all were within a few yards of one another. In the one possible consort relationship, the alpha male followed the alpha female for at least two days. They were not seen copulating, but much of the time they were out of sight in the trees. There seemed to be no part of the estrous cycle in which juvenile males or subadult males were denied access to the females. There was never any attempt on the part of the dominant males to break up a copulation. They would help a female chase a subadult male away if he solicited copulation and she threatened him, screeching, but if the female made no objection the dominant males would pay no attention.

For breeding and birth seasons, see Lancaster and Lee, Chapter 14, this volume.

## INTERGROUP AND INTERSPECIFIC RELATIONS

The Somanathapur group's home range overlapped the neighboring Hangala group's range by approximately one-half square mile or more. The two groups were observed in contact with each other on five occasions. When the two groups met the subadult and adult males would move toward the other group, and then sit and look at each other with approximately 20 feet between them. Then the males in one of the groups would begin to drift back in the opposite direction and the groups would separate. On all but one occasion the Hangala group retreated; on that one occasion there was some screeching among the females of the Somanathapur group as the males sat looking at the Hangala males. The Somanathapur males ran back to the females and the Hangala males ran after them for a distance of about 30 yards. The Somanathapur group then continued retreating and slept in sleeping trees other than their usual ones, which they had left behind in their retreat.

Normally macaques and langurs occupied the same ranges without conflict. The macaques always displaced the langurs, but without active threatening. Even so, on three occasions, bonnet macaques and langurs (*Presbytis entellus priamus* or *Presbytis johni*) were observed intermixed in the same trees, eating or sitting. However, in the course of the study one group of priamus langurs moved into the Somanathapur group's home range and was chased to the tops of the banyan trees whenever the two groups made contact. Apparently the more peaceful interaction is a result of later accommodation.

## FOREST GROUPS

Several forest groups were observed sporadically. The problems of observation in the forest were not overcome during this study. The bonnet macaques were extremely shy, often melting away into the forest at the first sign of man. In contrast to the crashing flight of langurs, the bonnet macaques would disappear silently and completely.

A few brief observations were made. One small group, consisting of a single adult male, four females, and one juvenile male was observed (Table 6–1). Eating and grooming were the major aspects of this small group's behavior. One of the females, a young one apparently, played briefly with the juvenile male.

Other forest groups were too shy for any but fleeting observations. They were observed to feed mainly on bamboo seeds and shoots, and ate banyan fruit if a tree was available in their home range.

## SUMMARY AND CONCLUSIONS

The general social behavior of bonnet macaques falls within the range of that reported for other macaques and baboons (this volume). Bonnet macaques live in highly organized groups, which include adult males, adult females, subadults, juveniles, and infants. They have a dominance hierarchy that is well marked in the males and rather less clear among the females. Their social communication is very elaborate, consisting of gestures and vocalizations.

In contrast to other macaques and baboons, there tends to be a greater tolerance in bonnet macaque groups of male for male. Males approach each other for grooming and play, and they do not interfere with copulations. They do not force individual males out of the group during their subadult years, with the result that a bonnet macaque group may consist of a higher number of males and, perhaps, thereby gains an adaptive advantage.

Flight to the trees provides bonnet macaques the main escape from predation. During such flights the males drop to the rear and are the first to come in contact with the predators. It is possible that the higher number of males in the group provides that much greater a margin of safety under stress of predation. In any event, it seems that male tolerance, with perhaps some reduction in the intensity of dominance behavior, is an adaptation that favors bonnet macaques.

PHYLLIS JAY

# 7

# ◈ The Common Langur of North India

## INTRODUCTION

Man and monkey have shared the forests, villages, and cities of India for thousands of years. One kind of monkey, the langur, has also had an important part in the traditions and epics of India and is often referred to in its role as the monkey deity Hanuman. The common langur monkey of North India, *Presbytis entellus*,[1] and very closely related forms distributed widely throughout India, are related to the langurs of south and southeast Asia.

Before the present study very little information on the Indian langur monkey was available. Pocock's interest in the behavior of langur monkeys was incidental to his main concern with langur taxonomy and distribution (1931, 1938, 1939). In 1928 McCann described his occasional contacts with langurs and added brief communications from other observers of langur behavior. This article was followed in 1933 by another short account of encounters with langurs in several areas of India. The literature includes articles on other types of southeast Asian langurs (Pocock 1934; Hill 1934, 1927; Phillips 1935; Washburn 1944; and Stott and Silsar 1961).

Ayer's book *The Anatomy of Semnopithecus entellus* deals exclusively with anatomical problems and is the most complete published physical description of langurs (1948). The Indian langur is a quadrupedal monkey with a specialized stomach adapted to digesting large quantities of relatively

---

[1] References in the literature to Indian langurs of the species *entellus* include the use of three generic names: *Pithecus* (Wroughton 1918, 1922; McCann 1928, 1933; Pocock 1931; Zuckerman 1932), *Semnopithecus* (Hutton 1867; Cunningham 1904; Hill 1936; Heape 1894; Prater 1949; Champion 1934; Pocock 1939), and *Presbytis* (Simpson 1945). Following Simpson (1945) the generic name of *Presbytis* will be used in this chapter. Although there is great diversity in the literature regarding the generic and subgeneric nomenclature, *entellus* is commonly used in reference to the species observed in this field study.

unnutritious, mature leaves. Because of their ability to digest mature leaves and to live for months without drinking water, langurs can live in extremely dry areas that are inhospitable to monkeys unable to subsist on mature leaves during summer months. Many langur groups survive the summer with no water other than that from leaves and bark (Kawamura, personal communication). Whenever possible, langurs supplement their leafy diet with fruit, vegetables, buds, and sprouts, but they were not observed eating meat or insects or digging in the ground for roots.

A team of research workers from the Japan Monkey Center is currently observing langurs in Mysore State, south India. The results of this two-year study will be available soon. In addition, S. Ripley is completing a study of the Ceylon gray langur. When the results of these field studies are available the present confusion of taxonomic relations of these very closely related forms should be settled, and the degree and nature of their differences in behavior and adaptations to various environments assessed. At the present time even boundaries of langur distribution are poorly defined. There are two major forms of the Indian gray langur, one in the north and the other in the south. It is possible to tell them apart on sight by the way the tail is carried and by the pattern of fur length and distribution on the crown of the head. The southern langur has a conelike peak of fur on the top of its head and the tail is carried up with the end pointing down and behind the monkey. The north Indian langur has a round-appearing head with no peak of fur. Its long tail is carried up over the back toward the head in a large single loop (see photographs). We do not know if these forms of langur overlap in distribution. Just as the Godavari River has been traditionally considered the boundary between rhesus and bonnet macaques (see Southwick, *et al.*, Chap. 4, this volume), it may also correspond with the division between northern and southern forms of langurs. A thorough survey of central India will be necessary to determine the degree, if any, of overlapping between north and south forms of both langurs and macaques. The Ceylon langur is clearly another variation of *entellus* and is probably not distinct on more than a subspecific or racial level. The Ceylon langur carries its tail differently from either Indian variety and has a tuft of fur that comes to a pointed peak on the top of its head.

The behavior of all the gray langurs of India and Ceylon is extremely similar. The size of the home range for the north Indian groups is larger than for the Ceylon langurs, and the home ranges of both these forms are still larger than those of south Indian langurs. North Indian langurs are probably the most aggressive of the three forms, and they also spend more time on the ground. There are subtle differences in the vocalizations of these three varieties, but the calls can still be identified as very similar among all three forms. Differences in behavior and vocalizations are much greater between the Ceylon gray langurs and the arboreal purple-faced langurs of Ceylon, which overlap in distribution, than among the gray langurs, which probably do not overlap in distribution.

Fig. 7–1. In a typical North Indian habitat the Kaukori group moves leisurely in the late afternoon to tall trees it will use for the night.

## The Field Study

The common langur of North India was observed for more than 850 hours during an eighteen-month field study in India, from October 1958 through April 1960.[2] Approximately 75 percent of the total hours of observation were undertaken with excellent observation conditions where the majority of group members could be seen at one time. Observations were concentrated on four groups, although more than 1000 langurs were counted in 39 groups. From November 1958 through November 1959 three groups in the forest near Orcha village, Bastar District, Madhya Pradesh, were observed. Survey trips into the surrounding hills made it possible to determine the size and composition of other groups. From December 1, 1959, to March 30, 1960, intensive observation was undertaken on one group near Kaukori village, 14 miles from Lucknow in Uttar Pradesh. A brief resurvey

[2] For complete results of this study see Jay 1962.

Fig. 7–2. Study areas of langur monkeys in North and Central India.

of the Kaukori group was made in February 1963. Another langur group of approximately 20 langurs and one adult male rhesus macaque was located near the village of Halwapura, three miles from the Lucknow-Hardoi road and approximately five miles from Kaukori. In 1959 only the one group of langurs at Kaukori was recorded for an area of approximately eight square miles. Kaukori is on the densely populated Gangetic Plain where peasant agriculturalists utilize every available plot of land that can be irrigated and

will support a crop. In contrast, Orcha is a tribal area of minimum cultivated acreage and very low population density. Kaukori and Orcha are
located on the map in Fig. 7–2. Table 7–1 presents an ecological comparison of the two locations. Langurs were also observed in other areas
representing a wide range of environments. In 1959–1960 brief observations
were undertaken at Mussoorie and Agra in north India, and at Nagpur,
Kondagaon, and Narayanpur in central India. The latter three places were
checked periodically during 16 months to determine whether a birth season
existed and if any major changes in social behavior occurred in the course
of the year.

Detailed observation of many aspects of social behavior was difficult
and often impossible in the Orcha forests because of restricted visibility.
However, it was possible to observe and understand many basic patterns
of langur behavior and details of the ecological adaptations of three groups
over a period of 16 months. Orcha was surrounded by reserved forest with
a full complement of wild animals, including potential predators. Both animal population and forest have remained essentially undisturbed ·by man.
After an initial 12 months at Orcha in 1958–1959, observations were shifted
to Kaukori in North India. Conditions at Kaukori were excellent for the
investigation of special problems that required the prolonged following of
well-known individuals. The Kaukori group could be located and followed
at any time of day and the group members could be kept in sight. This made
it possible to investigate many details of maternal behavior, socialization,
and dominance — details that could not be observed at Orcha because it was
difficult there to maintain contact with the animals.

Although Orcha and Kaukori provided very different contexts for group
life, there appeared to be no important alterations in basic patterns of
social behavior between the two environments. Excellent observation conditions at Kaukori made it possible to record long, detailed sequences of
all patterns of social behavior, and, by contrast, Orcha forests made it more
profitable to study group ecology and intergroup relations. These two areas,
Kaukori and Orcha, presented different research opportunities and it was
essential to undertake appropriate problems of investigation and observations in each location.

In February 1963 additional data on langur behavior was recorded for
groups living near Dharwar, Mysore State, and for groups living along
roadsides between Bangalore and Dharwar, and between Bangalore and
Ootycamund.

### Study Methods

Interactions were recorded as they were observed and photographs
were taken of all major forms of behavior. Fieldnote entries included time,
actors, and interaction. Group movement and weather conditions were recorded daily.

TABLE 7-1. ECOLOGICAL COMPARISON OF ORCHA AND KAUKORI
GROUPS OF INDIAN LANGUR MONKEYS

| Characteristics | Orcha (Abujhmar Hills) | Kaukori |
| --- | --- | --- |
| Land under cultivation or dwelling | .3 percent (maximum) | 98 percent |
| Human population density | 8 per sq. mi. | 650 per sq. mi. |
| Source of langur's food: | | |
|     Man's crops | 1 percent | 90 percent |
|     Forest | 99 percent | 10 percent |
| Surrounding land in virgin condition or in forest regrowth | 90 percent | 1 percent |
| Summer hot season | Moderate (90–100°) | Severe (100–118°), with wind and dust storms |
| Annual rainfall | 80 in. | 30–50 in. |
| Monsoon rainfall | Approx. 60 in. | 20–40 in. |
| All-year water supply | Rivers and streams good | One large reservoir; wells barely adequate and not easily accessible |
| Altitude | 2500 ft. | 400 ft. |
| Coldest months | December–February | December–February |
| Winter showers | 1–4 in. | Less than 1–4 in. |
| Associated fauna | Man, domestic animals, jackal, hare, mongoose, hyena, tiger, leopard, wild dog, deer, sambar, wild pig, peacock, jungle chicken, etc. | Man, domestic animals, jackal, mongoose, hyena |
| Possible predators | Man, wild dog, tiger, leopard | Man (rarely) |
| Reaction to man | Flight | None, except flight when chased |
| Range overlap | With langur and rhesus groups | With one rhesus group |
| Intergroup relations | With many langur and rhesus groups | With langur and rhesus groups |
| Use of "whoop" vocalization | Intergroup positional cue, and intragroup use | Intragroup use only |
| Time on ground in day | Approx. 30–50 percent | Approx. 70–80 percent |
| Sleeping trees | Many | Many |
| Birth season | Insufficient data but births in most months | Birth concentration in April–May |
| Observation conditions | Poor | Excellent |

Before a group was chosen for observation each area was surveyed to estimate population concentration and average group size and composition. Time was limited and the purpose of this study was to investigate behavior characteristic of normal free-ranging groups, and therefore norms of group size and structure were first determined in order to avoid the selection of either extremely large or small groups, or groups of unusual age or sex compositions. An average observation day lasted from six to eight consecutive hours. Most observations were made during daylight, but evening and night activity was also recorded by alternative observation hours every four or five days. Night observations were limited to nights of full moon when it was possible to recognize individual monkeys.

Observation techniques varied with the reaction of monkeys to my presence and with visibility conditions. In Bastar forests systematic observations were difficult. Langurs in that area seldom saw man and their immediate reaction to my presence was flight or concealment in treetops. It was not possible to follow an individual for more than a few hours. Observations were made from semiconcealment but it was extremely difficult to remain concealed for more than an hour. The monkeys were very alert and within that time one of the group usually noticed me. Forest groups gradually became used to me and I could follow them at a distance of about 50 feet. However, if any sudden movement in the brush startled them, they immediately fled from sight.

Groups living in towns presented special observational problems. Frequently part or all of the group climbed over walls and into yards or houses where I could not see them. When this happened people usually chased the group. Because city langurs are chased frequently and are often crowded into areas much smaller than their natural range, their behavior is tenser and more aggressive than the behavior of monkeys living in less crowded and less stressful surroundings of forest and open field. A similar change in social behavior among rhesus monkeys is recorded by Southwick *et al.* (Chap. 4, this volume). Rhesus macaques living in a city fight more frequently and severely and are tenser than forest rhesus.

The Kaukori group was accustomed to man, although it did not tolerate people too close unless food was thrown or the people were not paying attention to the animals. For the first ten days of observation I stayed approximately from 50 to 100 feet from the monkeys and did not try to conceal my presence. I wore the same colored clothing each day and avoided making any sudden movements. When the group moved I followed them at a distance, stopping each time they did. After approximately ten days I moved to the edge of the group where I sat within ten feet of the least shy animals. I was careful not to look directly into a langur's face since this is a form of threat. Within another week I moved to the center of the group and from that time until the end of the study I recorded behavior from within the group. Whenever an animal threatened I turned or moved away, as is characteristic of subordinates, and never returned the threat. My rapport with the group depended in part on my subordinate position and refusal to interact with group members. No animal, regardless of how subordinate he or she was to the rest of the adults in the group, found it necessary to avoid me. No attempt was made to feed or provision the animals or to keep them nearby. As soon as the members of the group were used to my presence their social behavior was apparently normal.

Variations in size, coat color, scars, temperament, and reactions to other animals made it possible to recognize many of the group after only a

Fig. 7–3. North Indian langurs may spend part of the day in trees, as this group is doing. In the foreground a mother sits with her newborn infant shortly after its birth.

few days of observation. After two months it was not difficult to identify most animals at from 50 to 75 yards by their manner of movement and general appearance. Individual recognition and thorough knowledge of the individual personality were extremely important to this study and were possible mainly because observation conditions at Kaukori allowed close and prolonged contact with each member of the group. The personalities of every adult monkey and most of the juveniles were well known.

## ECOLOGY

Because the distribution of arboreal monkeys is closely related to forest distribution, many localized populations of monkeys have become distinct on a racial level. Minor variations in coat color, fur length, and other characteristics have been the basis for a confusingly large number of classifications of langurs.

The common langur of north India is probably the most ground-living of langurs. It is distributed over most of north India with the exception of the western deserts. Pocock (1939), Blanford (1888–1891), and McCann (1928) discuss langur distribution in detail. Groups of langurs live in areas ranging from dry scrub, with only occasional low trees, to thick wet forests. They are extremely adaptable and their ability to live on mature leaves without drinking water enables them to occupy many vegetation zones. The langur is found from sea level to altitudes as high as more than 8000 feet at Nanital. Here the groups occupy deciduous oak forests and are reported to move to lower elevations during the coldest months of winter (Southwick, personal communication). I have observed langurs at Mussoorie. Hingston (1920) reports langurs to the timber line at 11,000 feet in the foothills of the Himalayas, and notes that they have been observed in fields of snow. He also reports that these langurs appear to be less quarrelsome than langurs living at lower altitudes, although when the langur is driven to lower elevations during the winter, "pitched battles are said to occur between the two species."

### Population Structure and Ecology

*The Group and Ecology*

The effect of ecological conditions on group size and population density among monkeys is poorly understood. It appears that among langurs drinking water is much less important than type of vegetation as a limiting factor on the number of groups an area can support. In regions where part of the year is completely without any rain, langurs do not drink for several months. At least a minimal quantity of new growth is available all year through in the Orcha forest area but this is not true in many other areas. In some of the dry central and northern regions of India little if any winter rain falls, and these areas are covered only with low scrub that provides a minimum of new vegetation during extremely dry summer months. The presence of suitable sleeping trees also affects langur group distribution more than does the edibility of the vegetation.

Groups in central India tend to be larger and are spaced to take advantage of artificial water sources used to irrigate crops. Orcha groups are smaller and the population is spread evenly throughout the forest (Table 7–2).

In areas of water scarcity groups that otherwise might not have any contact with one another come together at wells and reservoirs. When several groups use the same areas around water reservoirs their interactions are peaceful. Smaller groups tend to stay at a distance while larger groups drink, but on seven occasions more than two groups were observed to drink from the same pool at once. Very small streams in the Orcha forests do not flow during the summer months but pools of water remain. Several groups may use the same pool at different times but if they arrive together the smaller group usually waits or moves to the opposite side to drink.

*Group Size*

More than 1000 langurs were counted in 39 groups. The smallest group was a group of 5 and the largest consisted of more than 120 monkeys. Group sizes (recorded in Table 7–2) averaged from 18 to 25 in the Bastar forests and from 25 to 30 in the dry central regions. The largest group was observed one-half mile from a water reservoir in the late winter and in the dry season. Large aggregates of langurs at water reservoirs are usually temporary, and although several groups may mingle for an hour along the edges of a river or a pool, they separate and return to their own home ranges.

A langur group appears to be a closed social system and monkeys rarely change groups. The membership of a group remains constant except for deaths, births, and the departure of a few adult males that leave to live as nongroup males. The reasons a male leaves or is forced to leave the group are not known. A total of 53 nongroup males were observed living alone or in groups of from 2 to as many as 10 males. The sizes of these all-male groups were:

| Number of Groups | Number of Males |
|---|---|
| 9 | 1 |
| 2 | 2 |
| 4 | 3 |
| 1 | 4 |
| 1 | 6 |
| 1 | 8 |
| 1 | 10 |

A group of nongroup males occupies a range that overlaps the ranges of adjacent bisexual groups, but the males avoid using overlapping areas when the group is nearby. Three nongroup males lived next to the Kaukori group, and since there were no other langurs for several miles it is probable that these males came from the large group. It was not possible to determine the group origin of other nongroup males with ranges surrounded by those of bisexual groups. One of the three males living near the Kaukori group attempted on two separate occasions to follow the group. Each time he was repelled by adult males and by one old female in the group. The fighting that occurred during these contacts was the most severe I ever observed among langurs.

## Group Structure

Group composition for three Orcha groups and the Kaukori group is presented in Table 7–2. Although the number of males and females of all ages in the total population is probably approximately equal, there appear to be more adult females than adult males. In group counts, on an average, there are usually between 1.5 to 2 adult females for each adult male.

**TABLE 7–2. COMPOSITION OF KAUKORI AND ORCHA GROUPS**

| Group | Inf.-1* | | Inf.-2 | | Juvenile | | Subadult | | Adult | | Total | | Total | Nongroup Males | Rhesus Macaque | |
|---|---|---|---|---|---|---|---|---|---|---|---|---|---|---|---|---|
| | | | | | | | | | | | | | Both Sexes | | | |
| | M | F | M | F | M | F | M | F | M | F | M | F | | M | M | F |
| Kaukori | 1 | – | 8 | 5 | 5 | 5 | 2 | 3 | 6 | 19 | 22 | 32 | 54 | 3 | 1 | 1 |
| West Orcha | – | – | 4 | 1 | 2 | 2 | – | 1 | 3 | 5 | 9 | 9 | 18 | | | |
| North Orcha | 1 | 1 | 3 | – | – | 5 | 1 | 2 | 6 | 9 | 11 | 17 | 28 | } 1 | | |
| East Orcha | – | 1 | 1 | 1 | – | – | – | 1 | 2 | 4 | 3 | 7 | 10 | | | |

* See p. 223 for definitions of age stages      M = male
                                                    F = female

Females are counted as adult from the time they give birth to their first infant, at about three and one half to four years of age, whereas a male is not socially an adult until he has reached full physical development and his canines are fully erupted, at about six to seven years of age. Thus females enter the adult category as long as four years before a male is considered adult.

## Daily Round

Activity starts just before dawn, when a few monkeys shift positions in the sleeping trees. As soon as the first light can be seen movement increases, infants squeal, and adults move from branch to branch. When the sun is visible the group comes to the ground or suns in the treetops. Early morning is spent eating and moving; estrous females are active and the young play. Midday usually is spent quietly, with adults resting and grooming while infants and juveniles play or rest with their mothers. Feeding and movement start again in the late afternoon and continue until the group moves to trees it will use for the night. The group prefers large sleeping trees but usually sleeps in different trees each night. Settling down takes from 45 minutes to one hour and during this time there is constant moving and grunting from adults and squealing from some of the young. Females and young form small sleeping groups with adult males scattered throughout the group. Night is spent quietly with occasional waking and slight shifting of positions. During the hours of darkness, whenever a monkey shifts its position or disturbs a neighbor, there is a wave of urination and defecation from adjacent monkeys. As soon as it is light another daily cycle of activity begins.

The daily activity cycle lasts from approximately 8 hours during monsoon months to more than 12 hours during long summer days. Hours of

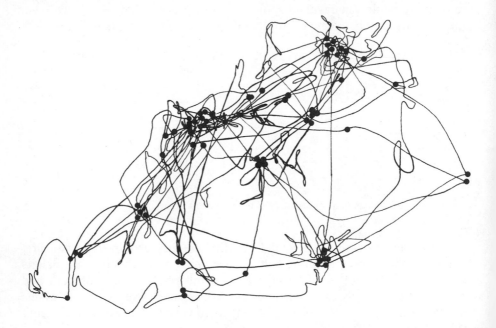

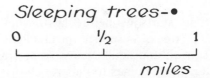

Sleeping trees-•

0        ½        1

miles

Fig. 7–4. Daily travel of the Kaukori langur group for 80 consecutive days.

sleep at night vary from more than 15 in the monsoon to 10 in the summer. The 2 to 4 quiet midday hours are spent resting and grooming or eating. A group usually moves from 1 to 2 miles a day, less during the monsoon months and more during summer.

*Group Range*

Langur group ranges vary in size from approximately 1/2 square mile to as large as 5 square miles, with average sizes of from 1 to 3 square miles. Figure 7–4 presents the daily routes of the Kaukori group for 80 consecutive days. From this figure the range map in Fig. 7–5 was drawn, illustrating

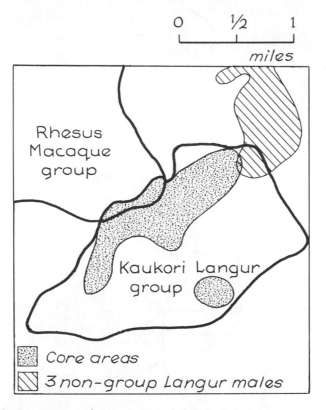

Fig. 7–5. Home range and core areas of the Kaukori langur group, and home range of three nongroup langur males.

boundaries of the group range and, within this, the core areas, those used most frequently. As was also true of Orcha groups, the core areas coincided with preferred sleeping trees (more than 80 percent of which were in core areas) and, sometimes, with water sources, those of the Kaukori group

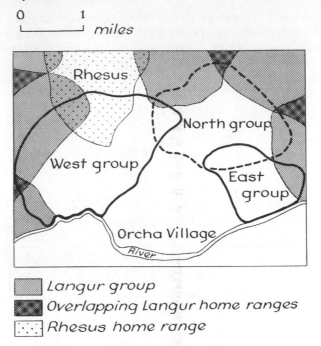

Fig. 7–6. Overlapping home ranges of langur and rhesus groups.

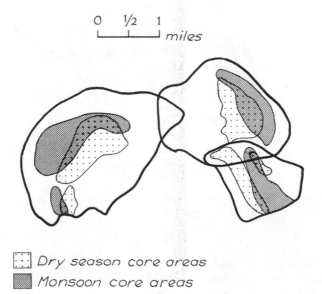

Fig. 7–7. Core area shifts in langur home ranges during summer and monsoon season.

being centered around water reservoirs, since during five months of the year all other wells and irrigation systems were dry. In Fig. 7–4 the plotted daily routes of the Kaukori group show that parts of the home range are seldom used except as the group travels from one core area to another. Figure 7–6 summarizes range size for four Orcha groups, and Fig. 7–7 illustrates the annual home range and core areas for three Orcha groups. In this forest area there is a definite seasonal use of different parts of the range. Dark areas in Fig. 7–7 represent concentrated use during dry months when cultivated areas are overgrown and forest is relatively open, with visibility restricted in grassy open areas and in fields, and greatly improved in the forest and on the forest floor. Lighter areas represent core areas in wet monsoon months, when the forest becomes almost impenetrable and the fields are cleared of plants that obstruct crops. Treetops are covered with a thick

Fig. 7–8. An adult female langur is being groomed by an adult female rhesus macaque, a member of the langur group.

canopy of vines that provides some shelter from the rain and during wet months groups move less during the day in order to remain under this vine canopy.

Rhesus macaque groups use part of the area included in langur group ranges at Kaukori and Orcha. On nine occasions members of Orcha rhesus and langur groups were observed eating together in the same trees and on fifteen occasions they ate together in harvested fields. The two groups mixed peacefully, with neither threats nor aggressive behavior. The Kaukori rhesus group seldom came in contact with the langur group, since the rhesus remained in the village. However, two rhesus macaques, an adult male and an adult female, lived in the Kaukori langur group during the entire period of observation.

Langur group home ranges may overlap extensively, but core areas do not. Areas of range common to several groups are usually occupied by only one group at a time, although when two groups are in the same area they do not threaten each other. Fighting between two groups was never observed; if they both happen to be nearby, the larger group usually takes precedence and the smaller remains at a distance until the larger moves away. Langur groups seldom come together in the forest or in open fields since groups are separated very effectively by their daily routes and patterns of range use. An effective spacing mechanism that allows groups to determine each other's position is a deep, resonant "whoop" vocalization produced by adult males when a group is about to move suddenly or for a long distance.

**Interspecific Relations**

Kaukori is extensively cultivated with almost no ground cover of brush or scrub. As a result there are few animals other than man and his domestic animals. No instance of predation on langurs of the Kaukori group was observed. Because the Orcha area includes large reserved forests where hunting is not permitted, it is very rich in wild life. In addition to man and domestic animals, there are tiger (*Felis tigris*), leopard (*Felis pardus*), wild dog (*Cuon dukhunensis*), wild pig, hyena (*Hyaena striata*), bear (*Melursus labiatus*), many large ungulates, sambar (*Cervus aristotelius*), bison (*Bos gaurus*), spotted deer (*Cervus axis*), barking deer (*Cervulus muntjac*), hare, mongoose, squirrel, small forest mammals, peacock (*Pavo cristatus*), red jungle fowl (*Gallus ferrugineus*), and other birds. It is possible that wild dogs, tigers, and leopards prey on Orcha group langurs, but no instance of predation was ever observed. It is extremely unlikely that a healthy langur would fall prey to a ground-living carnivore even though several Indian predators, such as leopards and jungle cats (*Felis chaus*), can climb trees. Because of the langur's skill in climbing and jumping, a predator would find it difficult to catch and kill even an injured langur if the monkey reached the safety of trees. There is a very large ungulate population in Orcha which makes it unlikely that a leopard would expend great effort trying to catch a monkey. On three occasions langurs gave alarm barks and moved up into the treetops when a leopard appeared, twice the group gave an alarm but continued eating in the trees, and once a langur group slept within 100 feet of a tiger and his kill.

Although forest langurs did not associate with any other species for more than a few hours at a time, langurs were extremely alert to sudden movement or warning calls of other species in the forest. Several times a herd of spotted deer grazing nearby barked and alerted the langurs, and peacock often alerted the monkeys since these birds, with their exceptionally keen eyesight, saw man and predators long before the langurs noticed them.

### Female Reproductive Cycle

A female langur is sexually receptive for the first time when she is approximately three and one half years old. The first sexual cycles of three females in Orcha groups were irregular and spaced at longer than normal intervals. A female is sexually receptive only during estrus, a period of from five to seven days midway between menstrual periods, which occur approximately once every thirty days. The period of estrus corresponds to

Fig. 7–9. An adult male langur copulates with an estrous female.

the portion of her monthly cycle when ovulation is most likely to occur. Perineal swelling or "sexual skin" does not occur in langurs, and the female initiates sexual behavior by displaying three gestures not associated as a sequence in any other social context—only the sexually receptive female simultaneously shakes her head, drops her tail on the ground, and presents to adult males.

Sexual behavior actually plays a very small part in the life of an adult female. She is pregnant for approximately six months and is not sexually receptive again until her infant is weaned at from ten to twelve months of age; she will not give birth again for another six to eight months. Births in many areas are spaced at approximately two-year intervals. When a female is not in estrus, adult males show no sexual interest in her. She is the sole initiator of sexual activity and she is not mounted unless she solicits the male.

TABLE 7–3. NUMBER OF ESTROUS FEMALES IN KAUKORI GROUP

| Number of Estrous Females | Number of Days Per Month | | | | Total Number of Days |
|---|---|---|---|---|---|
| | December | January | February | March | |
| 1 | 14 | 8 | 9 | 8 | 39 |
| 2 | 1 | 6 | 4 | 3 | 14 |
| 3 | — | 8 | 3 | 1 | 12 |
| 4 | — | — | 2 | 1 | 3 |
| 5 | — | — | — | 1 | 1 |
| Total days per month | 15 | 22 | 18 | 14 | |

In a group containing many females there may be one female in estrus during most days of the year. Figure 7–10 indicates the days during which females of the Kaukori group were sexually receptive in a four-month period, and Table 7–3 indicates the number of days during which more than one female was in estrus. Although estrous females do not solicit males in any particular preference order, there is a tendency for the most dominant males to consort with estrous females at the height of their activity at the middle of their estrous period, the time at which ovulation and conception probably occur.

**Birth Season**

In central India births are concentrated in the months of April and May. In February and March of 1959 only four newborn infants were observed in groups along the roadside, but in April 27 newborn infants were counted within six of the same groups. In contrast, groups in Bastar forests contained

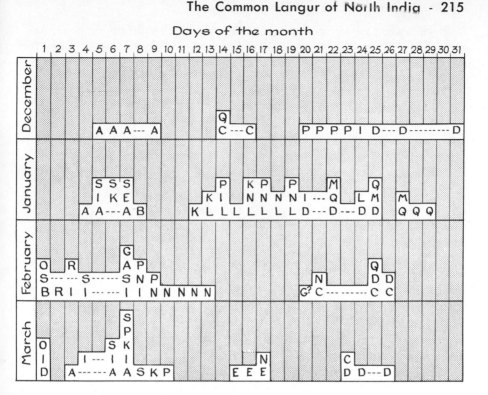

Fig. 7–10. Days of the month when adult females in the Kaukori group were in estrus. (Dashed lines indicate days during which females were probably in estrus but were not observed to copulate.)

newborn infants in most of the months of the year, although it is possible that there may be a concentration of births during some months, a concentration that was not clearly observed because of the difficulties of repeated surveys.

Infants born in April and May, the first months of summer, begin to eat solid food early in the beginning of the monsoon, in June and July, when tender leaves and shoots are plentiful. During April and May wells dry and irrigation systems are empty, crops are harvested, and very little new growth is available as food. The infant is dependent on its mother's milk during these first months of life until new leaves are available. Since there is rainfall and new growth throughout the year at Orcha, the necessity for a specific birth season is probably not so acute as in dry regions of central India.

Among the langurs of south India most births occur in January and February, at the beginning of the dry months (Kawamura, personal communication). Langurs in some areas of the south do not drink water for several months, but there, as in northern India, the young begin to eat leaves at the time when such new growth is available after the start of the monsoon season. However, a definite correlation between an infant's dietary need for available new growth of leaves and the spacing of births has not been established.

## BEHAVIOR

### Social Organization: The Group

The context for langur social life is a stable well-organized group composed of monkeys of all ages and both sexes. Such a group is the basic unit of the species. Although it is possible to survive living apart from a social group, only a small number of adult males live outside bisexual groups, and probably only for part of their adult life.

The social life of langurs makes the group as a unit possible. Individual members assume roles and activities that assure group cohesion and pacific intragroup relations. Langur groups can be characterized as peaceful and relaxed; their members are seldom aggressive and serious fighting is rare. A langur spends most of its life in a relaxed manner, eating, sleeping, and grooming. A group has a dominance structure that is not obvious in daily life, and each adult animal may interact freely with other members regardless of dominance status. Because dominance relations are subtle and seldom expressed, it often takes an observer a long time to determine male or female hierarchies. The relaxed tenor of langur behavior is a contrast to the tenser behavior of rhesus, among which aggression and serious fighting are more frequent.

Although an arboreal monkey is not under as great pressure to remain in a group as is a ground-living monkey, there are advantages to it also in a group way of life. Many langur group activities cannot be accomplished by the individual or are most effectively carried out by the group. Among the most important activities is socialization of young. The presence of a newborn langur infant is an extremely strong cohesive factor for all females in the group. Intense female interest assures the young of the protective environment and care they need until they are independent members of the group. The necessity of contact with age-mates in a social setting for the development of a normal adult rhesus monkey has been demonstrated in laboratory analysis (Mason, Chap. 15, this volume). Without a stable group such contact would not be possible. In an average-size group of from 20 to 25 langurs there will always be an adequate peer group in which the young monkey matures.

The group is a context for activities such as mutual, relaxed grooming, which may occupy more than five hours every day. Grooming is also extremely practical since dirt and parasites are removed from the fur and wounds and injuries are picked clean.

The group provides protection because each member is alert and warns all others as soon as danger is sighted. The chances that a monkey will be warned are many times greater if he lives in a group than if he lives alone. A common social tradition is shared among the members of a group; this includes knowledge of food and water sources, sleeping trees, and places that are safest from predators. In addition, as part of the social tradition, all group members are united in a dominance structure that provides a system of predictable behavior among familiar animals.

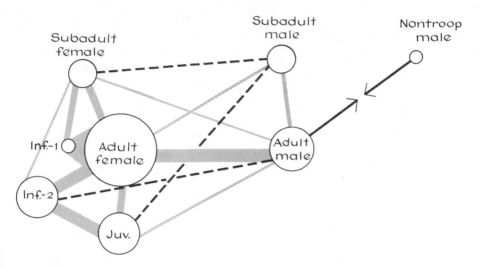

Fig. 7–11. Social structure of a langur group.

Patterns of interaction within a group can be conceptualized as a clearly defined network of social relationships among its members. A model can be constructed to represent the interrelationships of each major category of age and sex. Figure 7–11 illustrates group social structure and the interactions occurring most frequently. Not all possible interactions that might occur are observed. Some age-sex categories seldom interact with each other, as for example there are no interactions between infant-ones and adult males. Circles represent age-sex categories and the size of each circle is equal to the approximate proportion of that category to total group size. Lines connecting circles represent social interactions: the thicker the line the more frequent and intense the contact. Since social interactions do not all involve the same activity, this diagram can be altered to represent the various important forms of social interaction. Figure 7–12 represents grooming patterns, the major form of group interaction. Figure 7–13 illustrates dominance interactions, and since dominance is not a simple concept, it is divided into its major types from subtle to very aggressive.

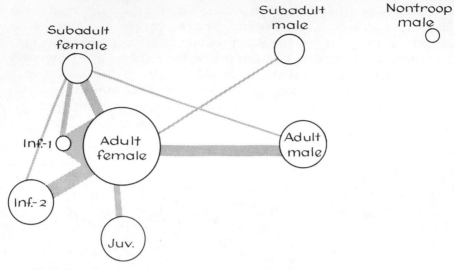

Fig. 7–12. Grooming relationships within a langur group.

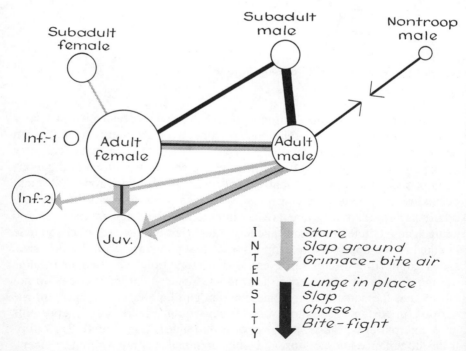

Fig. 7–13. Dominance interactions in a langur group.

Temporary changes in social relationships are observed as, for example, when fighting occurs within the group. Figure 7–14 illustrates changes in social interactions during a dominance fight. Males separate from females and interaction between the two sexes stops. As soon as fighting ends normal social interactions are resumed. Fighting is very seldom observed, and changes in social relation due to this cause are very infrequent. Although these alterations do occur, they are temporary and there is no basic change in the social structure. Novelty is minimal and any important change in behavioral relationships within a group could result only from such causes as alterations in ecological conditions, genetic change, or a repeatedly abnormal sex ratio in birth.

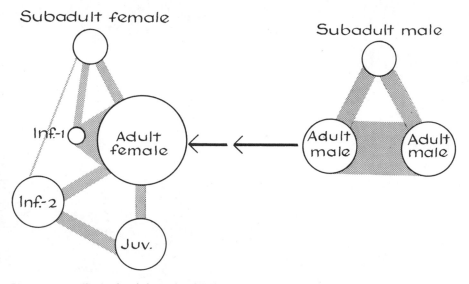

Fig. 7–14. Effect of adult male dominance fighting on the social interactions of a langur group.

Models of social structure illustrate that at each stage of maturation the individual participates in different social relationships. These are discussed in detail in the following sections.

### Socialization: The Ontogeny of Social Behavior

Social maturation is an orderly and well-integrated process characterized at each step or stage by new and changing relationships and behavior patterns.[3] As a monkey matures it learns social skills within a group of age-

---

[3] For a more complete account of socialization see Jay 1963a.

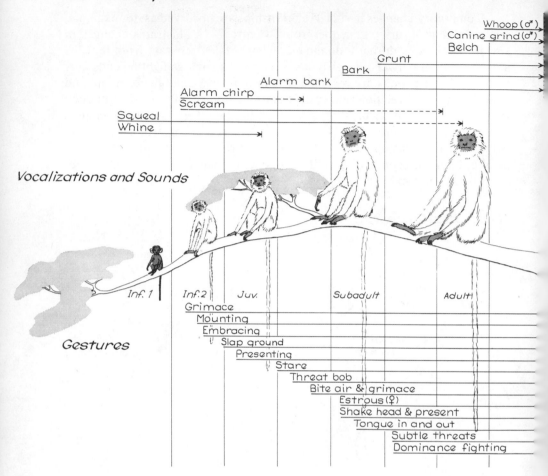

*Vocalizations and Sounds*

*Gestures*

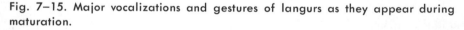

Fig. 7–15. Major vocalizations and gestures of langurs as they appear during maturation.

mates and gradually assumes roles and patterns of behavior characteristic of each level of social development. The social maturation of the individual is the concern of the entire group. A monkey's life in a social group consists of constantly reacting to and interacting with other monkeys; it is a complex adaptation in learning to get along with others. Patterns of social behavior described in the following sections are based primarily on observations of the Kaukori group in north India.

Figure 7–15 illustrates the major vocalizations and gestures that appear at different stages of maturation. Some elements of communication are replaced, whereas others are supplemented to produce the full complement of gestures and vocalizations forming the communication system of the adult. Although elements are designated as if discrete, in reality they interact to form an almost continuous series of socially meaningful behavior patterns.

## Maternal Behavior and Infant Social Development

The mother–newborn-infant relationship is the strongest and most intense bond in the life of a langur monkey (Jay 1962). At birth the brown-colored infant langur is dependent on its mother for nourishment and transport, but it is by no means completely helpless. It is a clinging, vocal animal, capable of controlling to a great extent its relations with the mother. It can cling to her unaided within a very few hours after birth and can secure itself so tightly under her body that she can run on the ground or make long jumps through the air without dislodging it. The infant is able to move independently of its mother long before the change in its natal coat color, which remains dark brown for approximately the first three to five months of life. The mother and adult females are most intensely interested in the infant during that period.

The birth of an infant is an extremely important event in a langur group. As soon as females in the group, whether adult, subadult, or juvenile, notice a newborn infant they immediately cluster closely around its mother. She is surrounded by a group of from four to ten females, all reaching out gently and trying to touch, lick, and smell the newborn infant.

The mother inspects, licks, grooms, and manipulates the infant from the hour of its birth. When it rests quietly she grooms and strokes it softly without disturbing or waking it. She usually turns her back to the waiting females until a few hours after birth, when the infant is dry, and then she allows several of them to handle it. Within a few minutes one of these females takes the infant from the mother's arms and holds it; as soon as the favored female has the infant in her arms she inspects it minutely, gently manipulating, nudging, licking, and smelling the infant. Special attention is directed to inspecting the infant's head, hands, and genitals. At the first sign of discomfort in the newborn it is taken by another of the waiting females, although if the mother is sitting nearby she often reaches out and intercepts the infant before another female can take it. As many as eight females may hold the infant during the first day of its life, and it may be carried as far as 50 feet from its mother. However, she can take her infant from any female in the group regardless of that female's dominance status. Passing infants among adult females is reported by Kawamura for south Indian langurs and by Ripley for Ceylon gray langurs.

Among north Indian langurs, if there are several females with newborn infants, they usually stay together near the center of the group. This protected area, where mother and infant are surrounded by the rest of the group members, assures maximum security for young infants.

Female langurs are intensely interested in newborn infants but there is considerable variation in skill among mothers in caring for their infants and among females in holding infants of other females. Not all females can keep an infant quiet and content, and a few are awkward and clumsy, but the majority experience little or no trouble caring for infants. Range of ability to handle an infant extends from incompetent to extremely competent. Competent females are casual but firm, apparently unaware of the movement of the often very active infant, whereas less capable females are uncertain of themselves and constantly readjust the infant and shift it from side to side. A very few females, much less than 1 percent, are inept with infants. They hold the infant too tightly, upside down, or away from their body while they inspect it constantly. These same females also appear to have difficulty making a newborn cling and nurse in a comfortable position.

Females vary in their behavior toward the newborn of another female. Some females pull the infant away from their breast each time it succeeds in finding a nipple, whereas many females let the infant press against their chest and at least take a nipple in its mouth. Of all females observed holding another female's infant, less than one fourth deliberately helped it locate and grasp a nipple.

The length of time a female can hold a newborn infant before it is uncomfortable, that is until it squirms and squeals, is a measure of her ability to handle it. Older females that have given birth to many infants appeared, in general, more efficient mothers than very young females. These older and more experienced mothers are usually more confident and expend little effort keeping a newborn calm and quiet. This suggests that experience is important in developing skill in caring for an infant. Because langur mothers allow other females to hold their infants, no langur female is completely without experience in infant care.

The female's temperament or personality also affects her interest in and aptitude for holding infants. A tense, nervous, and easily irritated female frequently startles the infant with quick or unpredictable motions, whereas a calmer and more relaxed female makes few sudden movements.

Dominance is not important in the daily life of a langur female and her status is seldom apparent in her relations with other group members. It is unlikely therefore that her status has any significant effect on the development of her offspring. Infants of all females in the group have free access to other infants in play and can venture into any part of the group without being threatened by the adults. Some females tend to stay together more than other females but these preference groupings are temporary and not exclusive. It is probable that the dominance status of a langur mother is not as influential on the development of her young as is her temperament.

TABLE 7–4. STAGES OF LANGUR DEVELOPMENT

| Stage Designation | Age | Basis for Stage Designation |
|---|---|---|
| Infant-one | Birth to from 3 to 5 months | Brown coat color; color change from approximately 3 to 5 months of age |
| Infant-two | From 3 to 5 months to 12 to 15 months of age | From end of color change to weaning at from 12 to 15 months |
| Juvenile | From 15 months to 4 years (M) or to 3 years (F) | Intense peer orientation; play is major activity |
| Subadult | From 4 years to complete physical maturation at approximately 6 to 7 years (M); from 3 to 4 years (F) | No play, orientation to adults, dominance important. Male marginal, little participation in group activities; female displays intense interest in infants and spends much time grooming with adult females |
| Adult | At approximately 6 to 7 years for male, canines fully erupted, full muscular development; female from birth of first infant at approximately 3½ to 4 years | Entrance into adult dominance hierarchies; assume all roles of the adult |

### Infant-One

Several obvious characteristics of a newborn or very young infant set it apart from all older monkeys. Brown natal coat color is present during the first few months of life, when the infant most needs nourishment from its mother and protection by all adult monkeys. The young infant's movements are uncoordinated, hesitating, and awkward. When it needs help in steadying itself or in clinging, it grasps its mother's fur or touches her and she immediately supports it or helps it to cling. These movements of an infant-one as it touches the mother, shifts positions, clings, or falls appear to stimulate her so that she holds, adjusts, and fondles the infant.

The second month of life is one of rapidly increasing muscular coordination and greater independence from the mother. The infant spends several hours a day exploring a rapidly expanding environment of new and strange objects to lick, smell, and touch. The infant is carried but it is no longer necessary for the mother to pull it under her body when she is about to walk. At about two and one half months the infant wanders as far as ten feet from her but makes frequent trips back to nurse briefly. If they are sitting in a tree, the mother often restrains the infant by pulling it back by a leg or its tail. As the infant goes farther from the mother it encounters age-mates and adult females, and instead of hopping from one place to another it starts to focus its attention on other monkeys. By three months the infant supplements its milk diet with solid food. It samples plants the mother picks and takes bits of food she drops.

The two months of color change from dark brown to light gray coincide with important alterations in the social relations of an infant. It is often left by its mother with another female and her infant so that one female may sit with several infants at once. Active interest of adult females in the infant declines rapidly as the infant turns white, although they continue to be tolerant of the infant when it climbs and tumbles on them. The mother is less solicitous but she is constantly aware of the infant's whereabouts and continues to care for and protect it. If the group is alerted suddenly, she signals her tensions by a grunt, patting the ground, or moving quickly toward the infant, and it rushes to her.

The social unit for the protection and care of the newborn langur does not include adult males. They are indifferent to a newborn and seldom are within 15 feet of one. The loudest squeals of a newborn do not draw the attention of an adult male, and when an infant needs help it is the mother or another adult female which gives assistance. If an adult male accidentally frightens an infant, the mother instantly threatens, chases, and often slaps the male.

### Infant-Two

Infant-two is a period of increasing independence from the mother and gradual orientation to age-mates. The young monkey learns to produce vocalizations and gestures and to use them in appropriate situations. As an infant-one the monkey displayed rudimentary and mostly unrecognizable motions that communicated only the most general states of discomfort or comfort.

By five months of age the infant-two runs 20 or 30 feet from its mother but she is constantly aware of its whereabouts and moves to it whenever the group is alerted. Because she vocalizes to draw its attention, her protective role is more obvious than when she had only to take a few steps to reach it. When the group is relaxed she no longer signals short moves away from her infant while it is playing, and it must follow her if it wishes to nurse or cling.

By six months of age the infant-two plays with age-mates for several hours every day. Play groups may include as many as 16 young monkeys but the average size is from two to four, and half of all play groups have fewer than three members. Running, jumping, chasing, wrestling, and tail-pulling are supplemented by more complicated forms of play, sometimes oriented toward objects such as twigs, potsherds, cloth, or any other object — not necessarily a movable one. Play is usually interpersonal and exploratory. When the young are approximately eight months old the males are much larger and stronger than the females of the same age and large play groups divide into smaller ones composed of young of approximate size. Mothers

Fig. 7–16. A young infant-two drops down from his mother as she stops.

Fig. 7–17. A small infant-two reaches hesitatingly away from his mother and keeps one hand tightly grasping her fur. (*Courtesy John Wiley & Sons, Inc.*)

Fig. 7–18. An infant-two reaches for a piece of food in her mother's mouth.

Fig. 7–19. Large play groups are composed of both infants and juveniles. (Courtesy John Wiley & Sons, Inc.)

seldom intervene even when play gets very rough. Squeals and grunts are heard during active play but sharp or loud outcries and continuous squealing are rare since these cries may draw the attention of adult females, which break up the play group by slapping the ground or mildly threatening the playing animals. Adult interference in play is more frequent in small langur groups with few young members, where play groups must include infants and juveniles of unequal size and strength. When the infant is ten months old it spends from four to five hours a day in group play and frequently travels with age-mates when the group moves.

Most basic patterns of social behavior, including dominance and sex, first appear in play groups. As a context for learning to get along with other monkeys the play group provides social environment in which experimentation and mistakes go without punishment or the threat of danger from other monkeys. Dominance among young langurs is poorly defined and is not established until they are much older.

Whereas adult females orient themselves, as mothers and protectors, to all the young in the group, it is the infant itself which must draw the attention of adult males. The male infant has no contact with adult males until he is approximately ten months old. At this time the infant first approaches the adult in a highly specialized manner. The infant runs, squealing tensely, to the moving adult and veers away just before its touches him. Gradually the infant appears to gain confidence and touches the male's hindquarters. Within a week after this the infant approaches and mounts by pulling himself up over the adult's hindquarters. Infant mounting of an adult male is similar in form to a male mounting a female or to dominance mounting between two adults, but when displayed by the infant it is neither sexual nor dominance behavior. In a few weeks another element is added and the infant runs around to face and embrace the adult. Touching, mounting, and embracing occur thereafter either as a series or as separate events.

226

One adult male may be mounted and embraced by as many as four infants and juveniles in rapid succession. As shown below, this approach is displayed by the young male until he is approximately four years old.

TABLE 7–5. TOUCHING, MOUNTING, AND EMBRACING OF ADULT MALES
BY MALE INFANT-TWOS AND JUVENILES

| | Frequencies by Age Groups | | |
| Form of Approach | Small Infant-Two | Large Infant-Two | Juvenile |
| --- | --- | --- | --- |
| Touching the hindquarters | 4 | 19 | 33 |
| Mounting | 0 | 10 | 38 |
| Embracing | 0 | 12 | 61 |

The female infant-two, in contrast to the male, has no contact with adult males. Instead she spends more time than does the male infant grooming and being groomed by adult females. The year-old infant, male or female, takes active roles in the group including grooming and alerting the entire group with an alarm bark if danger approaches.

From the eleventh to the fifteenth month the infant is weaned, an extremely stressful period for both the infant and the mother. In addition to physical rejection, an important part of weaning is the emotional rejection

Fig. 7–20. A male infant-two is about to mount an adult male.

of the infant. The mother, who has been the major source of protection and security, becomes hostile and denying. The infant can no longer run to her when it is frightened by an adult. The infant must resolve its conflicts with other members of the group unaided by a protecting mother.

Early rejection is mild. At first the mother avoids her infant by moving away and taking long jumps from one tree to another, making the infant maneuver long distances down to the ground and up into her tree. When the infant catches her she merely turns away, and only if the infant persists in trying to nurse does she hold it off with outstretched arms. The infant squeals and its movements are quick, tense, and jerky. It crouches, peers into her face, and runs around to stay in front as she turns from it.

For weeks the mother alternates between temporarily rejecting her infant and allowing it to cling. After several months of rejection even 30 minutes of being followed and harassed by the infant may not wear down her resistance, as did the shorter periods of infant persistence during the early weeks of weaning. Even the most boisterous weaning tantrum seldom draws attention from other adults. If a female is disturbed by the noise and movement, she moves or threatens the mother. Rather than return the threat, the mother usually moves and is followed by the infant.

Severity of rejection varies among females. Some females make little effort to reject their infants until after the resumption of estrous cycles. A rare female may be very positive in her rejection and after only a few weeks may strike the infant whenever it approaches. The mother's temperament is also important in determining the amount of hostility or physical force used in rejection. Irritable females are usually also more irritable with their infants. Older multiparous females appear to reject their infants with less effort than do younger adult females, but there are exceptions. Very few females bite infants during rejection but when they do, the infant is not visibly hurt.

In the last month of weaning even the most permissive mother persists in her rejection of the infant in an effort to break the remaining ties of infant dependency. Her tension, increasing irritability, and flight from the infant suggest that this final period is unpleasant and strenuous for her. The daily routine of both mother and infant is affected by the intensity of their encounters and antagonism between the two reaches a peak toward the end of weaning. The infant strikes her and screams as it jumps about her and shakes the branches.

When the infant is approximately 14 months old it no longer receives preferential treatment by adults and is threatened if it disturbs an adult. Active running and wrestling of male infants bring them in contact with adults more than the quieter play of female infants. As a result adults threaten and chase male infants more than twice as often as they do female infants (see Table 7–6).

TABLE 7–6. DOMINATIONS BY ADULTS OF INFANT-TWOS AND JUVENILES

*Domination by Adult Males of Infant-Twos and Juveniles*
*Number of Dominations of Each Age Group*

| Sex | Small Infant-Two | Large Infant-Two | Juvenile |
|---|---|---|---|
| Female | 0 | 5 | 5 |
| Male | 0 | 11 | 50 |

*Domination by Adult Females of Infant-Twos and Juveniles*
*Number of Dominations of Each Age Group*

| Sex | Small Infant-Two | Large Infant-Two | Juvenile |
|---|---|---|---|
| Female | 3 | 9 | 21 |
| Male | 2 | 18 | 41 |

### Juvenile

The fifteen-month-old juvenile is weaned and independent of its mother. When the juvenile is approximately two years old its mother gives birth to another infant and all remaining social ties with her last infant are completely severed. Sibling relationships did not exist in the Kaukori group. Juveniles moved freely among adults and it was not possible to determine the mother of any particular juvenile. The young juvenile assumes an independent life in the group, where its protection is provided by its own alertness and that of the group, and not by the mother's signaling changing group tensions.

The juvenile stage is a period of expanding social relationships with adult and subadult members of the group. A gradual familiarization with the range of normal group behavior is important in the development of behavior patterns that will characterize adult social interaction. The juvenile learns by experience which patterns of behavior, vocal and gestural, are appropriate in a given situation and learns also the consequences of inappropriate responses. Since the juvenile is no longer protected by its mother, it is essential that the juvenile develop those forms of social behavior that allow a maximum of integration into group life with a minimum of interindividual aggression.

Threat gestures directed by a large juvenile to an adult are responded to with threat or aggressive behavior. Similarly, a submissive gesture may avert impending adult threat or aggression. The juvenile's skill in displaying gestures and its longer consistent sequences of gestures and vocalization contribute to effective communication of the juvenile's emotional state, whereas the infant intersperses recognizable social gestures with random, often play, behavior.

Play is the most consuming and important activity of the juvenile. Since play groups are composed of other juveniles and infant-twos, the young juvenile is assured of a context in which inappropriate motions will not result in serious injury, although physical contact in rough play among older male juveniles may turn into fighting if one juvenile is hurt or repeatedly chased by other large juveniles. Early patterns of dominance appear in this context and although dominance among juveniles is mostly a function of relative size, the juvenile gains experience and becomes familiar with both dominant and subordinate situations.

Dominance interactions occur among female juveniles but less frequently than among males. The female spends only a few hours a day in play and when she plays it is more likely to be with other female juveniles and infants and in a less active manner than males play. Group play among large juveniles is almost entirely unisexual, since large female juveniles seldom play with large male juveniles for more than two or three minutes at a time.

The social bonds of the juvenile with adult females are much less intense than those of the infant with adult females. Grooming remains the main form of relaxed social contact between the juvenile and the adult female. The male juvenile seldom initiates grooming with an adult unless it is to placate the adult or to get closer to food.

The male juvenile mounts and embraces adult males more than four times as often as does the male infant-two (see Table 7–5). The following are typical of adult male and male juvenile interactions:

KAUKORI
December 17, 11:15 A.M. A juvenile male ran screaming to alpha male, embraced, grasped alpha's fur, and then groomed him. The adult returned the embrace and put his face into the fur of the juvenile's shoulder but the juvenile tried to move to one side in order not to remain directly in front of the adult. In a minute alpha ran off and the juvenile ran squealing after him but did not attempt to touch the adult again.

KAUKORI
March 2, 4:05 P.M. A large juvenile male ran squealing to beta male and groomed beta while he lay on a branch. The juvenile continued to give a steady weak squeal and when he stopped squealing beta raised his head and looked at the juvenile, which started squealing again. As long as the juvenile squealed, beta did not look directly at him.

The juvenile may occasionally take part in the harassing of older males when the latter are in consort with estrous females. The following two examples illustrate this behavior:

KAUKORI

January 17, 9:00 A.M. An estrous female was sitting beside a juvenile male when an adult male came to her in response to her presenting. The adult male slapped the branch at the male juvenile, which ran down the tree and sat 15 feet away watching the pair. The juvenile continued to move about after a few minutes of sitting quietly and watching. He squealed constantly. When another adult male came to the base of the tree and threatened the copulating male, the latter chased the juvenile out of the tree, hitting him and threatening the second male, which withdrew 20 feet and sat.

KAUKORI

February 4, 12:15 P.M. An estrous female was mounted by alpha male. After the copulation alpha chased away another adult male, which had been circling them vocalizing and gesturing. A male juvenile ran up to the female while alpha was chasing the other adult male and the female hit the juvenile. Alpha returned and mounted. The juvenile ran up to the female's head and hit at the the male but the female pushed the juvenile away. Alpha did not react to the juvenile and did not dismount. When alpha completed the second copulation, he dismounted and the female ran after the juvenile, hit it, and grimaced. (The grimace is a pulling back of the corners of the mouth as in a broad grin; the teeth may or may not be exposed.)

## Subadult

The subadult stage is a period of transition from the juvenile stage, in which peer-group orientation, play, nonaggressive behavior, and reliance on the group for direction are important to the adult stage, in which dominance hierarchies, sexual behavior, maternal behavior for the female and leadership of the group for the male replace the dependency of the young monkey. During the years when not yet physically mature the subadult cannot compete with adults for a position in the adult dominance hierarchy. However, it orients toward adults and experiences and participates in many forms of adult activity without entering dominance competitions. The subadult stage is characterized by display of predominantly submissive gestures to adults. Although the subadult female is subordinate to all adult females, the subadult male is not. Contacts between subadult males and adult females are tenser than female-subadult/adult-female interactions. From approximately four to five years of age the male repeatedly tries to assert his dominance over as many adult females as possible.

During the two years from approximately four to six years of age, the subadult male has fewer social bonds within the group than at any other time in his life. He is, in many respects, an extremely marginal participant in group life. Although he has free access to any part of the group, he spends most of the day on its edge and near adults only when they are resting quietly.

Subadult males compete with each other for food, right of way on paths, positions in trees and on the ground, and for estrous females. Dominance interactions among them are characterized by more physical contact, aggressive threats, and chasing than is dominance among adults. In one instance a large subadult male in the Kaukori group was mounting an estrous female when a second subadult ran up to the pair, jumped on the first and knocked him off. The larger subadult turned, threatened, slapped, and chased his attacker.

Subordinate to all adult males, the subadult never disputes this lower position. During adult male threats and fighting the subadult stays a safe distance away, usually more than 50 feet. The subadult is tense and often slightly nervous when he is near an adult male. In an extremely stressful situation, as for example if an adult threatens and does not continue his threatening behavior, the subadult occasionally approaches tensely and embraces the adult in a gesture of subordination. Mounting is a gesture of dominance among adults, and the subadult no longer displays this approach as he did when a juvenile.

Contact of subadult males with subadult females is rare, except in relaxed mutual grooming. When the subadult female first displays estrous behavior the subadult mounts her whenever he is solicited, but this, too, is not frequent. Subadult-male contacts with adult females are more frequent than with subadult females. These also consist mainly in relaxed mutual grooming. Most adult females are able to dominate small subadult males. Larger subadults, however, gradually can dominate most adult females in a group. Only if a female attacks a large subadult or adult male suddenly, or if the male is relaxed when she threatens him, is she able to dominate him. Alliances of two or more females can always dominate even the largest subadult male. Because the subadult male works his way up through the female dominance hierarchy before he enters the adult male dominance structure, there is often tension when subadult males and adult females are near each other unless the group is very relaxed. If an adult female is threatened by a more dominant adult, she may turn and threaten a small subadult male instead of the more dominant animal. This redirected aggression often initiates fights involving both subadult males and adult females.

Infants have no contact with the subadult male. Juveniles may approach, touch, mount, and/or embrace subadult males in the same manner as they approach adult males. During the contact there is less tension and occasionally the subadult initiates wrestling or plays with the juvenile.

Although the subadult female has a much wider radius of activity than has the male subadult, she does not have strong ties with any segment of the group. Her approaches to adult males are hesitant and she moves away from adult females when they are irritable or aggressive.

As a subadult the female is very interested in young infants and when she has the opportunity she plays and wrestles gently with them. Her relationship with adult females is usually relaxed and they often spend four or five hours a day together in mutual grooming. Subadult females readily join grooming groups of adult females but may hesitate to approach certain of the more irritable adult females if they are sitting alone.

The subadult female is subordinate to all adult females, but dominance is seldom observed. At the first hint of aggressive behavior the subadult usually moves away. She is seldom the focus of aggression until her first estrous periods, when she actively solicits mounting by adult and subadult males. Her sexual behavior is like that of the adult female, which is discussed in the following section.

**Adult Female**

The most important and time-consuming role of the female langur, and her primary focus as an adult, is maternal behavior, motherhood. She raises one infant after another from the time she assumes adult roles at the age of about four years until the time she dies. More than two-thirds of her life is spent nurturing and protecting her infants. She is pregnant approximately 25 percent of her adult life. She lactates and cares for a dependent infant 33 percent of her adult life and weaning occupies another 20 percent. Weaning may overlap the resumption of her estrous cycles, but often it does not. Her dominance status, associations with adult males, female companions, and daily activities are to a large extent a function of her status as a mother and her phase of the reproductive cycle.

The next most important and time-consuming activity, one which she engages in throughout her life, is mutual relaxed grooming. A female has close grooming ties to most of the members of the group and by far the majority of her contacts with adult males occur in mutual relaxed grooming.

### Adult Female Dominance Relations

It is not possible to assign a female langur to a position in the female dominance hierarchy except within a general level of dominance that includes females of approximate rank. The female dominance hierarchy is relatively unstable and poorly defined. A female's dominance position fluctuates with the different stages of her reproductive cycle. However, by far the majority of interindividual contacts do not involve expressions of dominance. At least one-third of the activities involving dominance are of such a subtle nature that it is only after the group members are well known that any hierarchical arrangement can be described. Dominance is often a matter of degree and an adult female that is dominant in one situation may not be in another.

The female dominance structure is best conceptualized as a series of levels of dominance. An individual female occupies a rank within a general level and she is dominant over those females in a lower level and submissive in most situations to the females in the next higher level (see Table 7–7). In Fig. 7–21 adult female dominance hierarchies for three Orcha groups and the Kaukori group are presented. The hierarchies of small groups usually represent a cross section of age grades and tend to be linear with most or all females of unequal status. Relationships among females within one level are often poorly defined and may vary slightly in short periods

TABLE 7–7. ADULT FEMALE DOMINANCE HIERARCHY OF KAUKORI GROUP

| Female | Dominates Frequency | Dominates Most Frequent | Dominated Frequency | Dominated Most Frequent | Present to Female | Associated Young |
|---|---|---|---|---|---|---|
| A | 30 | G, D | 10 | C | 2 | F Infant-2 |
| B | 21 | K | 6 | C, L | 3(A, H) | Pregnant |
| C | 19 | A, B | 6 | A, B | 1(A) | Pregnant (?) |
| D | 13 | K | 10 | A, C, I | | F Infant-2 |
| E | 10 | | 4 | B | | F Infant-2 |
| | | | | | | Pregnant (?) |
| F | 8 | G, C | 11 | D, G | 5 | M Infant-2 |
| G | 8 | | 8 | | 2(F) | Pregnant |
| H | 8 | | 6 | A | | M Infant-2 |
| I | 6 | A, B, D | 3 | A, B, J | 1 | M Infant-2 |
| J | 4 | D | 3 | A, C | | Pregnant |
| K | 4 | G | 12 | B, D | | M Infant-2 |
| L | 3 | B | 2 | B | 1(D) | Pregnant |
| M | 2 | | 8 | I | 1 | F Infant-1 |
| | | | | | | Pregnant (?) |
| N | 2 | | 8 | | | Small M |
| | | | | | | Juvenile |
| O | 3 | | 9 | | | M Infant-2 |
| P | 2 | | 10 | | | M Infant-2 |
| Q | 2 | 10 | 10 | | | F Infant-2 |
| R | 1 | | 8 | I, D, E | | —— |
| S | | | 8 | | | F Infant-2 |
| Subadults | | | | | | |
| a | 3 (in alliances) | | 12 | | | —— |
| b | | | 13 | | | —— |
| c | | | 10 | | | —— |

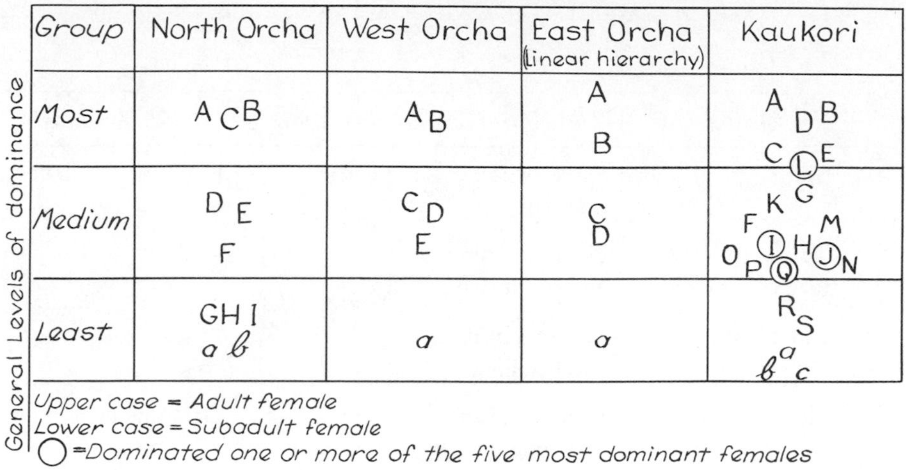

| Group | North Orcha | West Orcha | East Orcha (linear hierarchy) | Kaukori |
|---|---|---|---|---|
| Most | A C B | A B | A<br>B | A D B<br>C ⓛ E |
| Medium | D E<br>F | C D<br>E | C<br>D | K G<br>F M<br>O ⓘ H ⓙ N<br>P ⓠ |
| Least | GH I<br>a ℓ | a | a | R S<br>ℓ a c |

General Levels of dominance

Upper case = Adult female
Lower case = Subadult female
◯ = Dominated one or more of the five most dominant females

Fig. 7–21. Adult and subadult female dominance hierarchy in four langur groups.

of time. Actual fighting during dominance interactions is rare. Interactions are quick and usually last only from five to thirty seconds. Female dominance interactions, unlike those among males, are seldom preceded by a gradual building up of tension. In female fighting physical contact is usually limited to slapping, and no adult female was visibly wounded in such fighting. In 150 encounters recorded for one group, biting was observed in only three.

Table 7–8 summarizes the aggressive gestures and vocalizations in order of increasing aggression. These are displayed by both males and females, although the female often skips some elements during her quick interactions. Table 7–9 summarizes the submissive gestures and vocalizations used by both adult females and males. Table 7–10 summarizes gestures and vocalizations given by dominant and subordinate adults and juveniles and illustrates that most gestures and vocalizations are used by many individuals in a group, and that few of these elements of communication are specific to a very limited number of situations.

The very dominant female is not necessarily involved in dominance interactions more frequently than other females; she is able to take food whenever she wants and when she is irritated or tense she is often avoided by less dominant females. Female *L* is relaxed and direct in her movements, and does not take part in many interactions, but she can walk up to females *A* and *B* and take a piece of food lying at their feet.

Reduction of all dominance interactions to numbers of successes and failures is only a partial reflection of the dominance structure and needs qualification. Patterns of social interaction most difficult to evaluate, such

TABLE 7–8. AGGRESSIVE GESTURES AND VOCALIZATIONS

| | Male | | Female | |
|---|---|---|---|---|
| | *Gesture* | *Vocalization* | *Gesture* | *Vocalization* |
| I N C R E A S I N G | Stare | Silent or low grunting | Tense | Grunting or silent grunting |
| | Tense, turn to face other monkey | Silent or grunting and belching | Stare | |
| | Intense stare | Silent or grunting and belching | | |
| | Slap ground | Silent or grunting and coughing | Slap ground Grimace | Grunting or barking |
| | Grimace | Silent or grunting | | |
| | Crouch, then stand suddenly | Barking, grunting or sharp coughing | Bite air, toss head | Barking, grunting or coughing |
| | Slap ground and bob head | Grunting, coughing or barking | | |
| A G G R E S S I O N | Bite air, toss head | Silent or grunting | | |
| | Lunge in place | Silent or grunting and barking | Lunge in place | Barking, grunting o coughing |
| | Chase | Silent or grunting or barking | Chase | Silent or barking |
| | Hit or slap | Silent, grunting or barking | Hit or slap | Silent or barking and coughing |
| | Bite | Silent, grunting or barking | Bite | Silent or barking and coughing |
| | Wrestle | Silent | Wrestle | Silent or barking and coughing |
| S U B S I D E N C E | Monkeys separate and dominant sits | Grunting or belching | | |
| | Hand on other monkey | Silent | Female sits | Barking, grunting |
| | Subside | Belching or canine grinding | | |

as avoidance, are extremely important in understanding dominance. Table 7–7 summarizes dominance interactions during four months' observation of the Kaukori group. Approximately one third more dominations occurred, but interactions are tabulated only if it was possible to identify both or all participants.

All the females listed in Table 7–7 were well known as individuals. Differences in personality, age, and experience often accounted for differences in status. Whereas some females are relaxed and slow to threaten, other females are irritable and appear to have little tolerance for disturbance.

On 13 occasions two or more adults formed temporary alliances, which lasted from 30 seconds to approximately two-and-one-half minutes, during which the females simultaneously chased and threatened another monkey or other monkeys. The target of the alliance can be either a dominant or subordinate male or female. The alliances are apparently spontaneous and voluntary. The members of the alliance act with little reference to each

TABLE 7–9. SUBMISSIVE GESTURES AND VOCALIZATIONS
(IN ORDER OF INCREASING SUBORDINATION)

| Gestures Male and Female | Accompanying Vocalizations | |
| --- | --- | --- |
| | Male | Female |
| Avoid visual contact | Silent | Silent |
| Turn head; look away | Silent, or belching or soft grunting | Silent or soft grunting |
| Turn back | Silent or soft grunting | Silent or soft grunting |
| Move tongue in and out of mouth | (Rare) silent or soft grunting | Grunting or soft squealing |
| Grimace | Silent or grunting | Grunting or soft squealing |
| Embrace | (Rare) coughing | Grunting, coughing or soft squealing |
| Walk away | Silent, or grunting, belching | Silent or grunting |
| Present | Silent or grunting, belching | Grunting or squealing softly |
| Combine turning back, presenting, and grimace | Grunting or coughing | Grunting, coughing or squealing |
| Run away | Silent or grunting | Silent or grunting and coughing |

other and often the alliance fractionates and individual females turn their attention in separate directions. The following are two illustrations of female alliances:

    1. Five adult females were eating in a thick lentil-bush patch when one of the five, a dominant female designated as *1* in this sequence, brushed against female *2*, which turned and slapped the ground toward *1*. Female *3* sitting nearby ran toward *1*, which backed away five feet. When she saw *3*, *2* also ran toward *1*; and female *4*, sitting near, stood and ran toward *1*. Then *1* ran out of the field followed by *2*, *3*, and *4*. The three females chased *1* 30 feet and

**TABLE 7-10. VOCALIZATIONS AND GESTURES GIVEN BY DOMINANT AND SUBORDINATE ADULTS AND JUVENILES**

| *Vocalization* | *Adult Male* | *Adult Female* | *Juvenile* | *Subordinate* | *Dominant* | *Equals* |
|---|---|---|---|---|---|---|
| Whoop | X | X | | X | X | X |
| Belch | X | r* | | X | X | X |
| Canine grind | X | | | X | X | X |
| Cough | X | X | | X | X | X |
| Bark | X | X | r | X | X | X |
| Grunt | X | X | X | X | X | X |
| Squeal | r | X | X | X | X | X |
| Scream | | X | X | X | | X |

| *Gesture* | | | | | | |
|---|---|---|---|---|---|---|
| Grimace | X | X | X | X | X | X |
| Stare threat | X | X | | | X | X |
| Bite air | X | X | | X | X | X |
| Slap ground | X | X | X | r | X | X |
| Bob head | X | X | | r | X | X |
| Lunge in place | X | X | | | X | X |
| Chase | X | X | X | | X | X |
| Slap | X | X | X | X | X | X |
| Bite | X | X | X | | X | X |
| Wrestle | X | X | X | | X | X |
| Dominance pause | X | X | | | X | X |
| Embrace | X | X | X | X | X | X |
| Present | X | X | X | X | | X |
| Tongue in & out | X | X | r | X | r | X |
| Hand on monkey | X | r | | | X | |
| Turn back | X | X | X | X | r | X |

*r = rare, seldom observed

disbanded; *1* sat, barked toward *3* and *4*, which grimaced and slapped the ground, and *2* returned to the lentil patch, followed shortly by *4* and *1*.

2. Four other females were involved in this sequence. One was sitting in a tree eating a mango and dropped half of it. When female *D* ran and picked it up, one threatened her by slapping the branch on which one was sitting, and three, also in the tree, jumped down toward female D. Female one then jumped down, and female three, which had been sitting nearby, ran toward female D. D, with the mango in her hand, ran into the mango tree grove followed by females one, two, and three. Female one ran directly up to female D and slapped her; female D in turn slapped three. Then one, two, and three again chased female D, which dropped the mango and ran up into a tree; two grabbed the mango and ran off into another tree.

More than half of all temporary alliances recorded led into a long sequence of dominations. The sequence diagrammed and described below is a more complicated example of a long, connected series of dominance interactions. The female designated as *1* is one of the most dominant females, and *2* and *6* are also dominant. The entire sequence lasted one minute and ten seconds.

Female *1* was being chased in a mango tree by *2*; one then chased *3*, which presented to *1*; *4* chased *1*, which ran down out of the tree and over to *3* and back to the tree, where *4* chased *1* again; *1* ran up into the tree and was chased down by *3*; and *3* ran after *1*, which repeatedly presented while running; *6*, which had been sitting in the tree, jumped down and presented to *1*, and then ran up to *7*, which was sitting nursing her infant. Seven presented to *6*; *1* displaced both *5* and *3* and ran back into the tree; *3* displaced *1* and *4* and at this point the female rhesus monkey came running and scattered all the female langurs (diagrammed in Fig. 7–22).

Since most adult females do not display patterns of individual preference for each other, chance dictates the nearness of a female which might join in a combined threat or alliance.

Male dominance is never contested by a female unless a male accidentally frightens an infant or a female with an infant. When this occurs he is liable to immediate attack from the mother of the infant and nearby females. On one occasion male *D* walked under a mango tree in which a small infant-two was playing. The mother was sitting under the tree and as the male approached she reached up to grasp the infant, who became alarmed and jumped up to the next branch just out of her reach. The female jumped up and chased the male 150 feet while the infant raced around squealing in the tree. The adult male ran up into a tree and whooped; she stopped and he turned to look at her and belched.

### Sexual Behavior

Sexual behavior plays a very small part in the life of an adult female. She is sexually receptive only when in estrus, which lasts for from five to

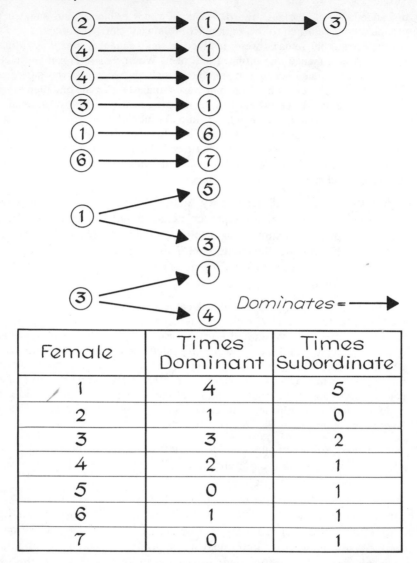

Fig. 7–22. A complex series of dominance interactions among adult females.

| Female | Times Dominant | Times Subordinate |
|--------|----------------|-------------------|
| 1 | 4 | 5 |
| 2 | 1 | 0 |
| 3 | 3 | 2 |
| 4 | 2 | 1 |
| 5 | 0 | 1 |
| 6 | 1 | 1 |
| 7 | 0 | 1 |

seven days a month, when she is not pregnant or lactating. The proportion of time would be far less than 1 percent of her adult life. When she is not in estrus adult males show no sexual interest in her. A female langur exhibits no perineal swelling and must indicate to the male that she is receptive by shaking her head rapidly from side to side, presenting, and dropping her tail on the ground. No female associated with an infant-one was ever observed to display estrous behavior. Figure 7–10 presents the record of sexual activity for females in the Kaukori group and Table 7–3 shows the number of days per month for a four-month period that one or more females was in estrus.

There is a tendency for an estrous female to solicit the most dominant males in the group at the height of her receptivity, the time ovulation is most likely to occur. However, some males are preferred over others at all times. Table 7–11 illustrates the frequency of copulation and solicitation of the adult males in the Kaukori group.

TABLE 7–11. FREQUENCY OF SEXUAL BEHAVIOR

| Adult Male | Solicited by Estrous Females | Copulates |
|---|---|---|
| A | 47+ | 18 |
| B | 35 | 10 |
| C | 19 | 6 |
| D | 55+ | 10 |
| E | 6 | — |
| F | 4 | 4 |
| Subadult Male | | |
| G | 17 | 14 |
| H | 3 | 2 |
| Total | 186+ | 64 |

Consortships last only a few hours. Once a consortship is formed the male follows the female. When she moves away he follows slowly and he very seldom threatens her. The consort pair may be harassed by less dominant males, which run about the pair and bark, threaten, and slap at the consort male. The aggressive behavior of a harassing male is directed almost exclusively to the consort male and not to the estrous female. In general the dominance status of a female increases when she is in consort with any male, and the dominance of the female with a high-status male is potentially greater than that of the female with a low-status male.

## Adult Male

### Adult Male Roles

Every adult male in a group can be described as a unique personality with variations in behavior that set him apart from all other males in the group. These differences are not obvious until the male is well known and has been observed in a wide variety of interactions with the other members of the group. Differences in maternal behavior as well as in tolerance for other monkeys were described for adult females, and variations in behavior of similar magnitude are characteristic of individual males. These variations are expressed in intensity of reactions, gestures, and vocalizations. It was possible to identify most adult males in the Kaukori group without looking at them by the way in which they produced certain vocalizations. For example, the "belch" always was given by one male in a rapid series, while other males emphasized parts of the sound or the volume. Variations of this magnitude were distinguishable only after long familiarity with the individuals. Changes in dominance status may affect the degree of confidence or of hesitation with which many forms of vocalization are given, but only one major change in a male dominance hierarchy occurred during the period of observation and neither of the two males involved noticeably changed their vocal patterns.

Adult males are leaders and coordinators of group activity. Their roles are extremely important in the maintenance of group unity and stability as well as in determining the group's use of its range and its relationships to other langur groups.

Males initiate and determine the direction of group movement. Male leadership determines the part of the range that will be used, where the group will feed, and which trees it will use for sleeping. In addition, the male coordinates intergroup relations by producing the whoop vocalization that is an effective means of informing all nearby groups of the location of his group. Adult males also coordinate intragroup activity and group movement by whooping, and thereby minimize the possibility of leaving any member behind. The "whoop" call is necessary for quick and effective gathering of a group in forests where visibility is poor and it is difficult for monkeys to stay in sight of one another. Adult males maintain internal group stability by establishing and asserting a stable male dominance hierarchy that structures the relationships of adult males within a group. Since adult males are dominant over adult females, the stable, linear male hierarchy is far more effective than is the poorly defined female hierarchy in determining the outcome of disputes which arise among group members.

In the Kaukori and Orcha groups the adult males invariably initiated a display characteristic of north Indian and Ceylon langurs. (This is probably true also for south Indian langurs but data are lacking.) This display consists of whooping and dashing about in trees and on the ground, jumping against branches and trunks with all four feet, and taking great leaps from place to place. The males whoop during the entire series of leaps. Females occasionally begin to run about, banking off objects with all four feet, but in the Kaukori group the females did so only after the display was initiated by the adult males. The cause of this display was not always obvious, but frequently it was due to some disturbance outside the group, such as an airplane overhead or a shot in the distance. Langurs in Ceylon displayed this sequence more frequently than did the north Indian langurs, and in Ceylon females as well as males began the display. It was elicited as often by dominance interactions within the group as by events outside the group. Here too the animals would attempt to jump down deliberately as hard as possible on limbs, which might break and fall crashing to the ground. Often very large limbs were broken in this manner. When the commotion settled, males sat quietly belching and grinding their canines. Gradually the tension subsided and the group was quiet.

### Dominance

A dominant adult male langur does not stand out in a relaxed group. The male dominance hierarchy can be determined accurately only after patterns of aggressive and submissive behavior are familiar. When the group is relaxed, which it is most of the time, adult males mingle freely with most of the group members. There is usually little tension and very few aggressive interactions to indicate which males are more or less dominant. Those adult males in the Kaukori group most noticeable because of their activity were actually among the less dominant males.

A dominant male is less active in minor disputes than is a subordinate male. The high-status male is able to take positions, food, and estrous females from other males, and when he is tense and irritated he is surrounded by a wide area of potential threat or personal space. Beta males are usually more active in dominance interactions than are alpha males whose high dominance status is uncontested by the rest of the group.

Adult male dominance is established and maintained with a minimum of aggressive behavior. Subtle pauses and hesitations predominate in dominance interactions. If a male pauses in passing another male as the two are alongside one another, this is a dominant gesture and the sitting or stationary male either looks away or moves. The dominant animal may pause without breaking the rhythm of his stride. If the passing animal pauses when he is slightly in front of the stationary male, this indicates that the passing male is subordinate.

Physical nearness is often used as a subtle gesture. Repeated approaches to a less dominant male is a subtle means of forcing him to move. A characteristic gesture of dominant males seldom displayed by a female is placing the hand on a less dominant monkey. Often it signifies the end of an interaction, a dismissal by the more dominant animal.

Another subtle indicator of status is the size of a male's "personal space," an intangible area surrounding him into which another monkey cannot enter without the danger of threat from the animal within the space. The more dominant the male, the larger the area of space he can maintain for his exclusive use. When a male is relaxed he does not maintain an area of personal space. Females may also maintain a surrounding area into which another female or a less dominant monkey may not enter without making his or her intentions clear to the more dominant animal. To conclude, in all instances the potential threat is only to less dominant members of the group.

Slight postural shifts and the direction of visual focus are two extremely subtle movements that communicate a potentially changing emotional state and an awareness of surrounding activity or tension. Subtle movements by an adult of low-dominance status are usually ignored by a more dominant animal unless the high-status animal is irritated and tense.

Often a seemingly inappropriate mixture of dominant and subordinate gestures and/or vocalizations is used in a sequence. To illustrate: a female may grimace, slap the ground, tense her body, and then present to a more dominant female; a female lunges in place, slaps at another adult female, then presents. Such ambiguous sequences are commonly observed in females of intermediate dominance status. In part this reflects a rapid alteration of mood, but it is also observed in interactions between two animals of very different status. The total impression of a series, and the reaction of the animal to which the sequence is directed, depends upon which gestures are emphasized or repeated and which are displayed last. The effect of an aggressive threat followed by presenting is usually submission. In many other combinations the effect is not so easily predicted since it depends on the relative dominance status of the animals involved and the sequence of gestures displayed.

### The Dominance Hierarchy

Table 7–12 summarizes the dominance hierarchy for the six adult and two subadult males in the Kaukori group. The degree of marginal participation is indicated by the horizontal dimensions of this diagram. The status of each individual is well defined and constant for long periods of time. Adult males act independently during a dominance interaction and do not support each other or form even temporary alliances. Ranks on Table 7–12 take into consideration more than the numbers of dominations credited to each male. Table 7–13 illustrates several aspects of adult-male social behavior important in the assessment of adult-male dominance. Table 7–14 details the dominance interactions which were recorded.

**TABLE 7–12. ADULT MALE DOMINANCE HIERARCHY OF THE KAUKORI GROUP**

A (Slate)
B (Rip)
      C (Slit)
D (Patch)
          E (Rat)
            F (Mangle-ear)

- - - - - - - - - - - - - - - - - - - - - - - - - - - - -

G (Subadult)
H (Subadult)

TABLE 7–13. SUMMARY CHART FOR ADULT MALE DOMINANCE
(KAUKORI GROUP)

| Male | A | B | C | D | E | F | G | H |
|---|---|---|---|---|---|---|---|---|
| Dominates other males | 48 | 57 | 20 | 4 | 6 | 1 | 1 | 1 |
| Dominated by other males | 4 | 16 | 10 | 31 | 16 | 12 | 24 | 7 |
| Solicited by estrous females | 47+ | 35 | 19 | 55 | 6 | 4 | 17 | 0 |
| Copulations | 18 | 10 | 6 | 10 | 0 | 4 | 14 | 2 |
| Groomed by adult females | 33 | 66 | 65 | 26 | 32 | 16 | 18 | 10 |
| Presented to by adult males and grooms them | 1 | 5 | 1 | 0 | 2 | 0 | 0 | 0 |
| Relative size (1 = largest) | 3 | 2 | 1 | 4 | 2 | 5 | 6 | 7 |
| Relative age (1 = oldest) | 4? | 3 | 2 | 5? | 1 | 6? | 7 | 8 |

TABLE 7–14. DOMINANCE INTERACTIONS FOR ADULT MALES (KAUKORI)

| | | | | Dominated | | | | | | |
|---|---|---|---|---|---|---|---|---|---|---|
| Domi- nator | A | B | C | D | E | F | G | H | Uniden- tified Male | Total |
| A | — | 16 | 2 | 6 | 4 | 5 | 6 | 1 | 8 | 48 |
| B | 4 | — | 8 | 19 | 3 | 3 | 9 | 4 | 7 | 57 |
| C | 0 | 0 | — | 4 | 9 | 0 | 5 | 1 | 1 | 20 |
| D | 0 | 0 | 0 | — | 0 | 1 | 1 | 0 | 2 | 4 |
| E | 0 | 0 | 0 | 2 | — | 1 | 2 | 1 | 0 | 6 |
| F | 0 | 0 | 0 | 0 | 0 | — | 1 | 0 | 0 | 1 |
| G | 0 | 0 | 0 | 0 | 0 | 1 | — | 0 | 0 | 1 |
| H | 0 | 0 | 0 | 0 | 0 | 1 | 0 | — | 0 | 1 |
| Total | 4 | 16 | 10 | 31 | 16 | 12 | 24 | 7 | 18 | 138 |

When individual interactions are analyzed it is clear that the crucial measure of dominance is not the total number of times a male dominates or is dominated but which males do the dominating. For example, $B$ is responsible for all dominations of $A$, and $A$ is the only adult male to have dominated $B$.

The number of completed copulations does not always correspond to the dominance rank of the male as illustrated in Table 7–12. Male $G$, a subadult, was not successful in competition for estrous females; estrous females solicited him only when no other male responded. Male $D$ was a preferred sexual partner by almost every female in the group.

Presenting and grooming among males reflects dominance rank. A subordinate male presents to a dominant male, which usually responds by grooming him for two or three seconds. In a typical sequence the subordinate male approaches a male of high status, presents, and is groomed for a few seconds. The dominant male places his hand on the lower-status male and the tension decreases and both males relax. The subordinate usually moves a short distance away.

Only one major shift in a male dominance hierarchy was observed in 16 months of observation. Male $A$ in the Kaukori group was replaced by male $B$, $A$ moving down to the $B$ position. Exceptionally little aggressive fighting occurred in the two-and-one-half weeks during which these two males changed places in the dominance hierarchy. The first sign of tension between them was constant belching whenever they were within 50 feet of one another. The following are typical interactions between the two males, and of these males with other group members, during the first week of the change.

January 20. Rip (originally male $A$) moved past male $D$ and belched two times. Male $D$ ran off; then Rip moved to male $C$. At this, male $C$ swung his hindquarters to Rip in a gesture of subordination, and Rip groomed male $C$ for three seconds. $C$ walked away, sat, and Rip once more moved close to $C$. Again, $C$ walked away, this time grimacing, and sat 10 feet away from Rip. Rip belched once, and $C$ stood and walked farther. Rip again belched toward $C$, but the latter remained seated 25 feet from Rip.

Rip approached $C$, but $C$ turned his back and shook his head toward Rip. Then Rip groomed $C$. All the nearby adults had tensed but not moved when Rip approached $C$, but when he put his hand on $C$, they all relaxed and continued eating or resting.

Rip then moved to male $F$, then being groomed by female $D$. Rip gave two very slight shakes of his head; $F$ jerked aside, and the female groomed Rip.

January 21. Slate (originally male $B$) moved to Rip. Rip stood and walked off 10 feet and sat by a female. The female immediately started to groom Rip. Slate belched two times directly to the female grooming Rip and she stopped grooming, presented, and moved to groom Slate.

Rip came down a tree, belched two times and walked past male $E$. $E$ was being groomed and stood when Rip hesitated but Rip moved on, deliberately passing within 10 inches of him. $E$ did not volunteer to move from Rip and Rip did not assert his dominance.

Slate walked to within 4 feet of Rip and sat. Slate tossed his head once but Rip did not move. One minute later Rip walked slowly away. Neither male vocalized.

Rip was tearing about whooping. Monkeys were scattering in all directions. Several juvenile males and male $H$ ran after Rip squealing and tried to mount but could not catch up with him. When Rip initiated this running and vocalizing, Slate, at the other end of the mango grove, did the same. When the monkeys calmed down after 20 minutes of very active interaction, Rip sat quietly. Slate dashed down from a tree with one final whoop but Rip remained sitting. Both males sat belching.

Slate walked out onto a large branch where Rip was sitting. Rip got up slowly and moved 5 feet away and sat quietly. Slate sat where Rip had been sitting.

One striking characteristic of langur dominance emerged from this major change in the dominance hierarchy. Violent aggressive fighting rarely occurs. No single battle resulted in the replacement of the former alpha male. Instead, a gradual process with no single fight but a constant pressuring of $A$ by $B$ eventually resulted in $A$'s dropping in status. The percentage of dominant responses by the former $A$ male decreased while the percentage of dominant responses by the former $B$ male increased. As soon as the new ranks were established these males seldom threatened each other or other adults. The new $A$ male engaged in fewer dominance interactions than did other adult males, a characteristic of very dominant males.

## CONCLUSIONS

A langur's life is spent either in or very near trees. It is an essentially arboreal way of life, in which forms of social behavior are emphasized that are different from those forms most characteristic of ground-living monkeys. To be sure there are variations in behavior even among related kinds of langurs but they are not great. Additional field studies will undoubtedly demonstrate that the social behavior of all langurs is basically very similar and that variations among the different kinds of langurs are the result not so much of truly diverse forms of behavior as of different degrees of emphasis on patterns of behavior common to most langurs. Several kinds of southeast Asian langurs are exclusively arboreal, but the common langur of both north and south India is at home in trees and on the ground. The north Indian langur may spend as much as 80 percent of the day on the ground, but never more than a few seconds from the safety of trees. In contrast to this, the black Nilgiri langur of south India (*johni*) is a form that spends much less time on the ground, and the several varieties of purple-faced leaf-eating monkeys in Ceylon rarely come to the ground. In spite of these differences in the amount of time spent out of trees, all the kinds of langurs listed above are more like each other behaviorally and morphologically than any are like the macaques, with which they share the countryside.

The subfamily Colobinae, which includes the Asian langurs, is represented in Africa by the arboreal colobus monkeys. On the basis of Ullrich's (1961) brief six-month study of the African black-and-white colobus (*Colobus guereza caudatus*) on the eastern part of the Mount Meru forests, Tanganyika, there appear to be many similarities in the behavior of these colobus and the Asian langurs. Ullrich reports that colobus live in groups of approximately 13 animals. Home-range size is very small, averaging only .06 square miles for each group. Relationships within the group, like those of langurs, are peaceful with very rare displays of aggression. Ullrich was not able to delineate a dominance hierarchy among the group members. Group location was advertised by "shouting" and when two groups came within sight of each other the colobus shook branches and called attention to their presence by jumping up and down in what Ullrich describes as a visual display showing off their highly contrasting black and white fur.

Booth (1957) provides a brief description of the olive colobus monkey (*Colobus verus*), a leaf-eating monkey that lives in the low levels of the stratified High Forest Zone of West Africa. Groups are small and lack any obvious leadership or dominance structure. Unique to these African colobus is the mother's habit of carrying her infant in her mouth.

Thorough, systematic field studies of these primates are necessary before detailed comparisons may be made, but it is clear that the lack of aggression, dominance hierarchies that are not obvious, and the general pattern of colobus life are more like langur patterns than those of the baboon-macaques of the other subfamily of the Old-World monkeys.

Social relations in a north Indian langur group are not oriented primarily to protection of the individual by group action. Unlike macaques or baboons, a langur protects himself as an individual most effectively by dashing up into the nearest tree, instead of depending for protection on large adult males with well-developed fighting prowess. Sexual dimorphism is not pronounced among the north Indian langurs, but adult males can be distinguished from adult females by the male's slightly larger size and more robust body build. Relations among adult male langurs are relaxed. Dominance is relatively unimportant in langur daily life and most of the activities which occupy an individual's time are unrelated to dominance status. Aggressive threats and fighting are exceedingly uncommon.

This relaxed nature of langur life is one of the first characteristics an observer notices. The daily pattern of activity of a langur group is in rather sharp contrast to the more boisterous, noisy interactions of a rhesus group, a contrast easily discerned since throughout India langurs are frequently found side by side with macaques. Often the two different kinds of monkeys live together in the same area and use many of the same food and sleeping trees as well as the same sources of water. When they are observed mingled together in trees or fields differences are even more striking. Rhesus are more intense, quicker moving, more easily provoked to threat, more aggressive, and more vocal than are the relaxed langurs. The stocky, short, muscular rhesus moves slowly and cautiously in trees, whereas the slim, greyhoundlike langur takes long graceful jumps with apparent ease. Dominance interactions among langurs are infrequent and subtle, while among rhesus interactions are frequent and the fighting is often severe. As a consequence rhesus bear many scars of past fights, whereas langurs rarely show signs of any serious wounds. Even though these two different kinds of monkeys share the same over-all environment, rhesus have adapted to life on the ground and the langurs to life in or near the trees. Their behavior and morphology reflect these variations in adaptation.

Rhesus groups interact with langur groups but they normally remain completely distinct from them. However, instances are recorded of individual rhesus monkeys living within langur groups. In two examples adult rhesus macaques were observed to live with a langur group rather than alone or to return to a rhesus group. An adult male and adult female rhesus lived with the Kaukori group and an adult male rhesus with the Halwapura langur group. Both males had been severely wounded and perhaps driven from rhesus groups. The two adult rhesus macaques living with the Kaukori langur group assumed a dominant role over all the langurs in the group. Even the female rhesus could break up any fight among the adult male langurs if she were irritated. The adult male rhesus was easily irritated by noise and fighting among the langurs, and he was just as dominant as the female rhesus over all the langurs. With members of these two different kinds of monkeys living side by side within one group, observations on the great contrasts in their behavior were inescapable.

Among African baboons as among Indian rhesus macaques there is strong selective advantage for powerful aggressive adult males with large canines, and for forms of social behavior that produce constant alertness and increase the ability of the group to react quickly to danger. These are essential factors in the effective defense of plains-living baboons (see Hall and DeVore, Chap. 3, this volume). For a baboon, life in a group is necessary to survival. This is not so for a langur, as is evident from the small proportion of adult males that can and do live apart from a bisexual social group.

When field studies now in progress in south India and Ceylon are completed, we shall be able to present a far more comprehensive analysis of the variations in behavior that characterize this diverse group of Asian monkeys.

CLARENCE RAY CARPENTER

8

◆ The Howlers of Barro Colorado Island

INTRODUCTION

The description of howler monkey behavior and ecology in this chapter will be closely based on observational data. Generalizations and comparisons with other nonhuman primates will be limited, and theoretical constructs will be subordinated. Descriptions will represent the observations in condensed form as direct records of observations from field notebooks and other original sources that cannot be reprinted here. Generally, descriptions will be based on adequate and repeated observations and confirmation. Also, in special areas, estimates will be made of possible observational errors and of observational limits. In brief, this chapter is intended to be a factual and fairly systematic report or case study of howlers based on information that can be accepted with reasonable confidence.

Major Subjects of a Systematic Field Study

There are many possible options for making and organizing observations and descriptions of field studies of primates, and the reports on the different species of primates in this volume exemplify some of these possibilities. However, if the study is to be relatively complete and systematic, the following major subjects must be included: geographic distribution, ecology, taxonomy and characteristics, population structure and dynamics, behavior, complex group characteristics, and general deductions consisting

The author's first studies were supported by the National Research Council, Committee for Research in Problems of Sex, through the Yale University Institute of Human Relations, and Professor Robert M. Yerkes' Department of Psychobiology. His 1935 study was financed by the Social Science Research Council, Columbia University, through Bard College. The 1959 study by the author with Mason and Southwick *et al.* was financed by the National Science Foundation through the Pennsylvania State University.

of abstracted concepts, theories, generalizations, and inferences. These are the major subjects developed in this chapter.

### Sources of Information

Fortunately, the howlers of Barro Colorado have been observed extensively by different observers using somewhat comparable methods. Thus, the sample of observations is relatively large, and different investigators have confirmed, questioned, and refined those observations. The studies have not been regularly spaced over the years, making it impossible to describe long-term trends and changes—for example, consistent population fluctuations and changes of structure. It is noteworthy, however, that these studies are unique in that they have been made at irregular intervals over a period of about thirty years. Studies by the author in 1932, 1933 (Carpenter 1934), and 1935 (Carpenter 1953) were followed by those of Collias and Southwick (1952), of Altmann in 1955 (1959), and the study by the author with Mason, Southwick, and student assistants in 1959 (Carpenter 1962). These special studies of howlers were supplemented by occasional and incidental observations and reports of other observers. In all, howlers have been observed for an estimated total of 24 man-months. Most of the observations were made from late December through August (the dry season and first months of the usually rainy season). Altmann's study sampled the period in the rainy season during the month of November. Ideally, field studies should have been scheduled and conducted at regular intervals over the years. Furthermore, comparable studies should have been made throughout the entire year in order to chart any seasonal variations that may occur.

A list of the field studies of howlers on Barro Colorado Island is given in tabular form below. Generally where the source material in this chapter is that of the author, bibliographic references will be omitted. The reports of other observers will be cited where significant new information resulted and where observations and interpretations differ importantly from those of the author.

It should be recognized that the basic conditions making it possible to study howlers as they have been studied were those of the reservation, protection, and administration of the Barro Colorado Island Biological Laboratory, formerly of the Institute for Research in Tropical America, and now of the Smithsonian Institution of Washington. Another necessary condition of these studies was the sponsorship and grants provided by men and organizations supporting work in the field.

### Brief Historical Sketch of Barro Colorado Island

Barro Colorado Island (Fig. 8-1) was formed by the creation of Gatun Lake, made by damming the Chagres River, in the Isthmus of Panama, and

TABLE 8–1. FIELD STUDIES OF HOWLERS ON BARRO COLORADO ISLAND

| Investigator | Period of Study | Census | Other Observations | Publications |
|---|---|---|---|---|
| C. R. Carpenter | Dec. 25, 1931 to May 26, 1932 | Complete in April 1932 | General coverage of behavior and ecology | Carpenter 1934 |
| | Dec. 23, 1932 to Feb. 12, 1933 April 1, 1933 to May 12, 1933 | Complete in April 1933 | | |
| C. R. Carpenter | January 1935 | Incomplete — 15 groups | | Carpenter 1953 |
| N. Collias & C. Southwick | January to May 1951 | Complete — March and April 1951 | Ecology | Collias and Southwick 1952 |
| S. Altmann | October 29 to December 1, 1955 | Incomplete — 5 groups | Communication, maternal behavior | Altmann 1959 |
| C. R. Carpenter et al. | June to August 1959 | Complete | Film making | Carpenter 1962 |

a large section of the Panama Canal runs through the lake. The present island was formerly the Loma de Palenquilla ridge, which rose between the valley of Rio Gigante and Laguna de Peña Blanca. The geology of the island is mainly of Bohio conglomerate and Caimito formations, of late Eocene and early Oligocene and of late Oligocene periods respectively (Woodring 1958).

Gatun Lake was filled and the rugged hilltops became Barro Colorado Island in 1914. The island was a hunting area for Canal Zone people and nearby mainland residents until 1923, when it was made a protected reservation of the Institute for Research in Tropical America under the auspices of the National Research Council. Since 1946 the island has been administered and protected by the Smithsonian Institution as part of the Canal Zone Biological Area.

The isolating lake waters and the protective measures taken in 1923 by the island Laboratory Staff have prevented all but occasional poaching, and that principally for peccaries. There is no evidence that the howlers of the island have been hunted or the population affected by the usual world-wide encroachments by man on the habitats of nonhuman primates.

In the 1920s the Institute for Research in Tropical America provided

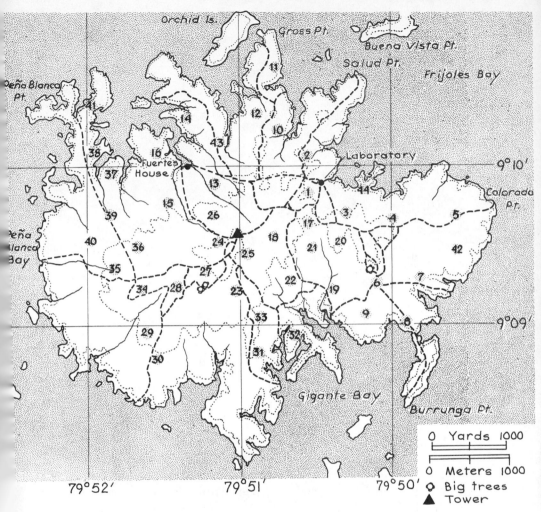

Fig. 8–1. Contour map of Barro Colorado Island in Gatum Lake, Isthmus of Panama. Numbers show location of howler groups in 1959 census.

arrangements and facilities on the island that greatly facilitated the principal studies basic to the content of this chapter. A field laboratory and living quarters were built and basic services provided. A network of named and numbered trails was laid out along the ridges of the rugged island and was maintained and progressively extended. One-room houses were built at the ends of five trails on the lake shore where observers could sleep while studying howlers in adjacent areas. These facilities, together with limited launch and canoe ("dugout") services, greatly improved conditions of work for the field investigator compared with temporary camp living. The trails opened

Fig. 8–2. Aerial view of Barro Colorado Island showing bay and research station. (*Courtesy Smithsonian Institution*)

up the forest and aided the location, relocation, and following of groups of howlers. The advantages of the end-of-trail houses were clearly realized in 1959 when the demanding census work had to be done without any such houses except the one at the end of Fuertes Trail. The persisting and greatest lack on the island for many years has been the unavailability of adequate boat services for field investigators. Especially is this a difficulty since the trail houses have now fallen and decayed.

Investigators on the island have profited from an interesting succession of visiting scientists and guests. Also important has been the small but carefully selected library of natural history books and journals and of basic reference sources relevant to the ecology, flora, and fauna of the island.

The interest, foresight, and efforts of such men as James Zetek, Frank M. Chapman, Thomas Barbour, and Leonard Carmichael have thus resulted in unusually favorable conditions for the relatively long and periodically repeated studies of scientific problems on Barro Colorado Island and specifically of the howlers.

254

## FIELD METHODS

### Approaches and Viewpoints

The author's early principal study of howlers was characterized by attempts to find answers to hundreds of questions. The questions were formulated during extensive reading of literature in natural history, anthropology, animal behavior, physiology, and especially in the literature on non-human primates written on the basis of both laboratory research and field observations. The writings of Yerkes, especially *The Great Apes* (1929), the reports of field studies of Bingham (1932) and of Nissen (1931) on the gorilla and chimpanzee, and the works of Pavlov, Sherrington, Mead, Malinowski, Darwin, Kropotkin, Heap, and Tolman were rich sources of questions that may be, at least descriptively, answered or illuminated by field observations of primates living in an undisturbed environment. Later, in 1932, when the howler field studies were in progress, the author read Zuckerman's *Social Life of Monkeys and Apes* (1932), which yielded additional hundreds of questions.

The next step was to collect enough pertinent observations on undisturbed howlers living in their natural habitat to provide answers—some tentative, others perhaps conclusive within the limitations of field methodologies and macroscopic observations.

The main purpose of the field studies was to collect complete and systematic information on all possible characteristics of the selected population of a primate living in an undisturbed habitat. Hopefully, field observations would suggest problems for laboratory investigation and would assist students of behavior to interpret and, in a sense, to validate the results of laboratory research. Finally, it was hoped that field studies might eventually lead to comparative behavioral studies of nonhuman and human primates and contribute to studies of primate evolution.

### Observational Methods and Procedures

Standards and methods for observing primates in their natural habitats are set forth in detail in the section on Field Procedures in the appendix of this volume. Those that served as guide lines for the study of howlers can be stated briefly as follows:

1. Basically the collection of evidence in the field depends on the macroscopic observational capacities of the observer, which in turn depend on his education, training, skills, interests, and motivation. The characteristics of the observer influence results more in naturalistic than in laboratory studies, where observational demands are limited and instruments can be

used to greater advantage to aid and check the accuracy of observations.

2. The amounts and kinds of observations must be adequate to answer the questions being asked and the problems being studied.

3. Observations must be repeated and confirmed to establish their validity, preferably by different and well-trained observers, either working simultaneously or successively on the same sample population living in the same environment. Observations can also be checked for reliability by the use of photography, sound recordings, and the like.

4. Observations must adequately sample normal, usual, and frequently occurring behavior as well as unusual and infrequently occurring events. Norms as well as variations must be reported so as to permit evaluation of their relative importance in the total behavioral systems of the primate. In brief, norms should be emphasized and care taken not to overemphasize unusual dramatic incidents.

5. Ideally, the observer should make his observations of a primate in its native habitat without disturbing or modifying the behavior. The realistic requirement in the study of most primates, however, is to reduce the observer disturbance to the lowest possible minimum.

6. For some purposes active skillful intrusion into the group is necessary; a group may be driven so that a census of its composition can be made, the observer may test the reactions of animals to observer "tolerance distances," and close approaches may be necessary in photography and sound recordings.

7. Observations must be accurately recorded by means of shorthand or brief notes made *in the field* and transcribed and expanded the same day, while memory of the events is clear. It is helpful, also, to categorize field notes and records so that the observer can know which categories are being studied sufficiently and which need further study, and can watch the development of significant trends and the emergence of new questions requiring further observations.

8. Finally, all methods, procedures, and techniques must be adapted and modified for different species, their general characteristics, and their environment. Even among the New-World platyrrhines, and those indigenous to Barro Colorado Island, very different procedures are required for studying the howler, capuchin, night monkeys, and marmosets. Arboreal and terrestrial primates require even greater differences in field methods. These procedural differences yield differences in kind and quantity of information, making it difficult to compare the results of studies of different primates living under different conditions.

The problem of the reliability of field observations deserves special attention. Often single or even several observations of an event may be unreliable. In the howler studies repetition of observations was used to increase reliability, two or more observers being used in the later studies. Repeated studies by different but qualified observers contribute to the re-

Fig. 8–3. An adult male howler takes a midday nap astraddle a cecropia limb. (*Photograph by John H. Kaufmann*)

liability of evaluation, since the *consistency* of information can be used as a criterion. The problem of reliability is complicated and perhaps impossible to solve completely with qualitative descriptive data such as that yielded by most field studies.

The question must be asked: Who made the observations, reports, and inferences and what were his qualifications for making them?

In summary, field studies of primates require special combinations of broad and advanced scientific training, special observational abilities and skills, intellectual curiosity and honesty, and the endurance and patience of a pack mule.

## TAXONOMY AND CHARACTERISTICS

The howlers of Barro Colorado belong taxonomically to the Order Primates, suborder anthropoidea. They belong to the family, Cebidae, the subfamily, Alouattinae, and the genus *Alouatta*, and the species classification is *A. palliata*. These howlers are believed to be representative taxonomically of the subfamily Alouattinae, and limited samplings of field studies on other genera and species suggest that observations made on the Barro Colorado population apply to other genera and species of Alouattinae but not to other subfamilies of the Cebidae. The behavior of the cebus and spider monkeys is very different, and each differs markedly from howlers. Behavioral variations in different species of howlers are most probably the results of different environmental rather than genetic and evolutionary factors.

257

Male and female adult howlers differ in size; adult males are estimated to weigh from 16 to 20 pounds and adult females from perhaps 12 to 18 pounds. The average length in a sample of 15 males was $1146 \pm 57$ mm. and 16 females averaged $1111 \pm 39$ mm. (Carpenter 1934).

The anatomical configurations of fully adult howlers can be discriminated by a field observer on the basis of differences of gross size, the size and shape of the heads (the male's head being larger and squarish), the larger beards of the males, the longer and more extensive ochreous-colored mantles of the males, and especially the large, yellowish-whitish scrotum of the male. The same color characterizes the labia of the female. The genitalia and sex characteristics of immature male and female howlers cannot be reliably discriminated.

Color variations of the usually black howler consist of differences in the amount of brownish, reddish, or ochreous mantle hair. These color variations exist within a group and the amounts of reddish color may be greater in individuals of some groups than of others. Yellowish white areas and bands on the tails of both males and females are observed infrequently. This color variation was seen more often during the 1959 studies than during the studies made in the 1930s. The same tail markings were seen in a few of the howlers of Coiba Island (*A. coibenses*).

Some age differences can be observed, principally size changes, but color, facial, and behavioral changes occur as well. For example, the bare faces of old animals are more wrinkled than those of prime adults, showing loose folds of skin and sometimes drooping lips and eyelids. It is uncertain whether there is a trend toward grayness or increases in light-colored hair as animals become aged.

As howlers mature, their activity reflects their age change, and behavior supplements anatomical differences to aid the observer in identifying the ages and sexes of the animals. Differences in reproductive behavior of males and females provide a basis for identifying the sexes. Maternal behavior aids in the identification of females with dependent or semi-dependent young, and adult males exhibit conspicuously different vocal behavior from that of adult females. Sex differences are not discriminable for young in the field.

One of the early and important questions asked about primates in their natural habitat was: "What kinds and numbers of individuals exist in groups?" The answers to this question can be learned only by counting and classifying the individuals into sex-age classes. Early in 1932 a classification scheme was developed by the author and used fairly consistently in all later work.

Previous descriptions show the clarity and obviousness of the identifying characteristics of fully adult males, which preclude confusion with fully adult females. Adult females were put into two categories: those without and those with dependent or closely associated young. Under some condi-

Fig. 8–4. A young adult female howler rests in a tree.
(*Life Magazine*)

tions it is difficult to distinguish between adult females without young and late juvenile or very early adult males before their testes have descended and the scrota have become extended. It is not yet known when this occurs during the maturation of male howlers. This, then, is an area of possible error. The young were classified fairly reliably as infants and juveniles, in accordance with criteria listed in Table 8–2.

In the absence of records on growth and age of howlers in captivity and of long-term, continuous field studies of identified and marked individuals in the field, it is only possible to guess or estimate crudely the age of the different classes and subclasses.

The age of reproductive maturity for howlers is estimated to be from four to five years old for females and from six to eight years old for males. When young females come into estrus, that is, when they are sexually receptive and ovulate, the probabilities are high for fertilization, and with the birth of young they would be classed with adult females. Males not only require several more years to mature to the time when they produce viable sperm and get most of their adult physical growth, but in order to reproduce they must also gain social status in mixed groups and thus have access to receptive females. It is suggested that this latter delay in *social maturation* may require several additional years.

TABLE 8-2. CLASSIFICATION AND DESCRIPTION OF HOWLER YOUNG

| Classification | Estimated Size (grams) | Color | Relation to Mother and Social Behavior | Tendency to Play | Estimated Age |
|---|---|---|---|---|---|
| Infant-one | 600 | Grayish brown | Almost constantly carried on mother's belly. | + | From birth to 5–6 months. |
| Infant-two | 900 | Brownish black | Closely associated with mother—carried on her back. | ++ | From 5–6 to 10–12 months. |
| Infant-three | 1500 | Black | Occasionally travels alone during group movement. | +++ | From 10–12 to 18–20 months. |
| Juvenile-one | 2500 | Black | Weaning period; relatively independent of mother but occasionally assisted by her over difficult crossings. Often with play group. | ++++ | From 20 to 30 months. |
| Juvenile-two | 4000 | Black with reddish mantle. | Usually with other young. Occasionally seen with mother and younger sibling. | ++ | From 30 to 40 months. |
| Juvenile-three | 6000 | Black with distinctly red mantle. | Entirely independent. Dominates play groups. Some avoidance of adult males. | + | From 40 to 50 months. |

These facts on classes of animals will be important to the descriptions of the compositions of groups and population structures.

## GEOGRAPHIC DISTRIBUTION AND ECOLOGY

It is customary to report geographic distribution of primates as that region from which museum specimens have been collected and identified. On this basis howlers have a distribution ranging from southern Mexico throughout Central America, including some large islands like Coiba and Trinidad, and throughout northern South America to southern Brazil and Argentina. The boundaries of the geographic distribution are not well defined. Distribution is not yet correlated with climatic zones nor are there even estimates of population densities for different habitats. Since howlers are forest dwellers, it can be assumed that populations of howlers exist where there are suitable forests. However, there are no systematic

Fig. 8–5. A juvenile howler hangs by its tail and hind feet as it picks a cecropia leaf with its hands. (*Photograph by John H. Kaufmann*)

studies of the adaptability of howlers to different kinds of forests, and in addition howlers could be eliminated from some areas of suitable forests by hunting or diseases. Therefore the information on the geographic distribution of howlers is inadequate.

### Ecology of the Study Area

Barro Colorado Island lies slightly more than 9 degrees north of the equator. Thus a tropical climate prevails, and owing to the shifts of trade winds there is an annual dry season from December to May and a wet season from May to November. The average annual rainfall for 35 years is 107.4 inches (Kaufmann 1962).

Field studies of howlers and of their gross behavior are affected by weather. Beginning with the dry season, usually in late December or early January, the weather is clear, the days sunny, and temperature rises into the high 80s F.; observations are not interfered with by rain.

261

Beginning usually in late April and May field work is periodically interrupted by rain. Frequent rains from June through October limit observations. Late in October, on the average, and on through November into December periods of heavy and continuous rain may make observations extremely difficult.

Howlers react to rain by reducing their activity and by assuming protective postures; they do not build nests or seek protected places in trees. They often give roars in response to the approach and during the first part of heavy downpours, thus aiding field observers to locate groups. During heavy rain and strong winds, howlers become silent or at least any sounds they make cannot be heard, and the observer is well advised to seek protection from the rain, falling limbs, and trees.

There is little additional that can be said with confidence about the direct effects of macroclimate on the behavior of howlers. Speculations about the effects of climate on the incidence of births and breeding seasons usually point to possible chain effects operating through foods.

### The Flora of the Island

The forests of Barro Colorado are usually described as a tropical rain forest that in many parts of the island has reached the climax stage. However, the geology and soils, rugged topography and drainage, erosion and landslides, and other conditions have resulted in great variations in the forest. In 1959, in contrast to the 1930s, howlers were found in all parts of the island, although in different densities. The most conspicuous changes from 1930 to 1959 were occurring in climax areas, where many great tree falls interrupted the forest canopy and permitted sunlight to reach the forest floor, creating interesting ecological islands in which there were new successions of plant and animal communities.

In areas where there were many treefalls the arboreal trails of howlers were interrupted and detours occurred. The treefalls may have caused some groups to change their territorial ranges, both because of interrupted treeways and because of changes in the location of food and preferred lodge trees.

To summarize, the forest of Barro Colorado is a very heterogeneous tropical rain forest that has been continuing to change while studies of howlers have been going on. Over the island the forest varies greatly in composition; there are many different kinds of trees and dense undergrowth, and the height of the trees varies considerably.

### Food of Howlers

Howlers are herbivorous and frugivorous. They eat relatively large quantities of succulent leaves, buds, and flowers from many kinds of trees, and a wide range of fruits, as well as the succulent shells or cortex of some nuts—for example, the Almendro nut shell and the red cortex of wild nutmeg. Lists of plants eaten by howlers have been published (Carpenter 1934). Wild figs of many varieties that ripen throughout most of the year grow all over the island and are a principal food of howlers. The ubiquitous espavé trees are sources of succulent leaves, and the Almendro nut when ripe is a favorite food for howlers, as it is for most other animals of the island. Few of the succulent fruits of the island are rejected by howlers.

In brief, foods suitable for howlers occur in abundance and great variety on the island. It is difficult to imagine that either the amount or kinds of food would be factors limiting the howler population until there are many thousands of the animals on the island. The dispersion of foods permits groups to spread all over the island. However, competition between groups is stimulated by the location in overlapping ranges of highly *preferred* foods like figs, plums, Almendro nuts, and cecropia. Howlers may also compete for preferred arboreal pathways, lodge trees, and preferred localized forest complexes.

### Fauna: Macroscopic and Microscopic

The fauna of Barro Colorado has been studied extensively (Enders 1935; Goldman 1920). The concern here is with those organisms of the island's association that may interact importantly with the population of howlers and affect their behavior.

There is no conclusive evidence that any of the island's mammals or birds act as predators of howlers. The puma is mainly a ground dweller. The more arboreal ocelot may occasionally attack young group-living howlers and become, in turn, the object of aggression of the adult males. Ocelots would have a better chance of success preying on young animals that become separated from the protection of groups. Sick animals may become food for ocelots, but it is unlikely that this cat significantly affects the howler population or their behavior. The tyra is an unlikely predator also. There is no evidence to show that eagles and hawks attack howlers.

Man is not a predator of howlers on Barro Colorado Island and this contrasts sharply with the situation on the mainland of Panama, where howlers may be hunted and where successive deforestation destroys the howler population. On the mainland, in Panama and Costa Rica, out of stretches of permanent forest, howlers are found in small, wild, and elusive groups. It can be inferred that of all the macroscopic fauna, man is the howler's most serious predator, directly or indirectly.

The effects of diseases, parasites, and viruses on howler populations and behavior are not well known. Observable botflies in the larval stage infect and apparently annoy howlers seriously, and some young individuals appear to be sick from botfly larval infections. Yet there is no direct evidence that howlers are killed by them. Filarial infections are known to occur and when infections are heavy in the peritoneal cavity the parasites may be transformed to scar tissue of the ovarian cortex and this may prevent

264 - Monkeys and Prosimians

ovulation in heavily infected female howlers (Collias and Southwick 1952).

Diseases and viruses are probably the most important regulators of howler populations, which are otherwise not seriously affected by adverse factors. Collias and Southwick (1952) have presented evidence suggesting an epidemic of yellow fever as the possible cause of the drastic reduction in the Barro Colorado Island howler population around 1949 or 1950. Other viruses may also importantly affect primate populations. For example, in the mid-1950s the Russian spring virus (summer encephalitis) killed many macaques and langurs in India (Rockefeller Virus Research Center, personal communication). It would seem important for field investigators to study more thoroughly the diseases of primates in their natural habitats.

## THE POPULATION STRUCTURE ON BARRO COLORADO ISLAND

The Barro Colorado howler population is a sample of the total population of the species *A. palliata* in Panama. The limitations and possibilities of evidence for generalizations to other population samples of the species and genus should be understood in this context.

The particular ecological conditions of Barro Colorado, its protection, its climate, and special complexes of flora and fauna, which have been briefly described, further affect the generalizations that can be made from the available evidence.

To illustrate the importance of sampling, if the only study of the Barro Colorado Island howlers had been made in 1950–1951 when, as Collias and Southwick (1952) found, the population consisted of about 237 animals living in about 30 groups — only 6 of which had two males, the rest having one — a very distorted picture of that population would have been drawn. However, when these observations are added to the evidence from studies undertaken at other times a most illuminating natural experiment is reported, showing what happens to a primate population when it is greatly reduced by an epidemic.

The importance of sampling types of primates and of ecological areas, and the importance of the length of time involved, is demonstrated in this case study of the howlers of Barro Colorado Island. In addition, there is the further sampling of the sample which will be discussed later.

### Censuses of Howlers and Number of Groups

The first attempt to develop procedures for a complete census of the island's howler population was made in 1932. The census of that year could not be highly reliable because the observer worked alone; he was becoming familiar with the island and was developing the necessary skills and endurance for making censuses of groups and their composition. In that census the reliability of classifications of animals, and especially adult males and females with infants, was probably greater than that of estimates for the total number of groups and for the critical figure of the total number of animals on the island. The 1932 census, then, should be considered a sample of the sample, with fairly large probable errors.

Three censuses have been done thoroughly enough to be considered complete: the April 1933 census by the author, working persistently but alone; the March and April 1951 census conducted by Collias and Southwick (1952) with the assistance of two woodsmen (including Silvester Aviles, untrained formally but an experienced naturalist); and the June to August 1959 census conducted by the author, Mason, Southwick, and three student assistants: Lane Carpenter, Alan Elms, and Dan Peterman.

No other isolated nonhuman primate population sample, living in protected natural conditions of forest and feeding, has been analyzed so completely and so frequently. It is regrettable from the viewpoint of population dynamics that the censuses have not been made on a regular basis and that frequent checks are not now being made on a group sampling basis of this population's trends and changes.

The 1933 census counted 28 groups and these contained a total of about 489 animals of all classes. The Collias and Southwick census of 1951 counted 30 groups, which had a total of about 237 animals. An epidemic, perhaps of yellow fever, had reduced the population possibly as recently as the previous year or two. Following the publication of these results in 1952, I predicted, on the basis of my 1932–1933 studies that the population would be greatly increased by 1960 and that the norms for group composition would be reestablished.

A team that included Mason and Southwick attempted a complete census during rainy months of late June, July, and early August 1959. During this census 44 main island groups were counted and they contained a total of about 814 howlers of all classes. (The two groups found by Collias and Southwick on Orchid Island and an unnamed small island near the west coast of Barro Colorado Island proper are excluded here to make the results more comparable with those of the 1951 census.)

The methods used in the different censuses, although similar in approach and techniques, were not strictly comparable. It is certain that the participation of teams of qualified observers, rather than a single observer, increased accuracy, especially of group counts and hence of totals. The well-manned observer team of 1959 worked during the rainy months and could not live on trails at night as did Collias, Southwick, and their assistants. Only the Fuertes trail house remained in 1959 and adequate boat transport could not be arranged. The author believes that the field methods used by Collias and Southwick (1952) most closely approximated the ideal model for making censuses of the Barro Colorado Island howlers.

However, even under the best conditions, complete censuses have a margin of error. This is true even for slow-moving howlers, which often travel linearly from tree to tree, and it is most difficult to determine or even estimate the magnitude of such errors.

Two specific examples will illustrate the problems confronting the field observer as he attempts to contact, identify, and determine the composition of howler groups.

During the 1959 census the observer teams had been surveying consecutively the groups living in the areas of the Fairchild, Lathrop, and Miller trails. The decision was made to relocate groups previously studied near the Laboratory and then proceed clockwise around the island.

Early on the afternoon of June 28 a group was located on the Snyder-Molino trail at the intersection with Shannon trail. The group was feeding in a cluster of trees. After three hours of difficult observations the group, which was moderately wild, moved in a somewhat scattered pattern along Shannon trail. A count was made: the total number of animals was 20 or 21, including 3 or 4 males, a female carrying an infant-one and another with an infant classed as infant-two.

Previously Group 1 had been studied and found to have about the same number of animals: 4 males, an infant-one, and late infants or early juveniles that might under some conditions be classed as infant-twos.

Thus, the problem: Was this Group 1 or another group? After several days of studying adjacent groups and recounts of Group 1, it was decided to consider this a count of Group 1.

The second example of the problem of discriminating groups involved the largest group surveyed during the 1959 census. The team was scouting for howlers around the central area of the island. At 4:30 P.M. the sound of howling led to the location of a group, the 24th in order, 50 yards northwest of Armour 3. Soon after being located the group streamed from the fig trees in which they had been feeding. The clear and fairly orderly count showed that there were 45 animals, including 9 adult males. The team maintained contact with this group for three days and plotted its locations for two additional days, but, owing to its scatter, size, and irregular progression, it was not possible to repeat a count and classification accurately enough to be acceptable. Although Group 24 was kept under observation, it was impossible to be absolutely sure whether the large group counted on July 1 was a single cohesive group or a temporary association of two groups attracted to the same food trees. On the basis of all possible observations, however, the observers considered it an additional separate group and this added 45 animals to the total population count.

These examples illustrate the complex problems involved in making censuses of nonhuman primate populations. An additional problem is that of how to represent and report the variations and uncertainties in the number of discrete groups and their composition, as well as in the total population of animals. Published tables of accepted counts do not usually show these variations and uncertainties. Checks and rechecks and the immediate agreement of two or more of the observers making the complex observations are practical ways of insuring reasonable accuracy. These procedures were used in the 1951 and 1959 censuses.

## Samples of Population

For some purposes a complete census of a population segment need not be made. The population can be sampled in order to collect evidence on the sizes of groups, group composition, and distribution, and even to estimate population trends and totals.

Such a sampling procedure was used in 1935 when, from all the groups on the island, 15 were counted and their composition determined. The main problems in this sampling method are those of making accurate counts and in particular of using *the same bases* for classifying the animals. This latter is difficult to do even by the same observers, especially for the older infants or early juveniles and for the young males or adult females without young. Nevertheless, group and area sampling provides reasonably accurate data for estimating group sizes and the numbers and proportions of the different classes of individuals.

Table 8–3 shows the proportions or percentages of the classes of animals found in the three acceptable "complete" censuses and the two group sampling procedures.

TABLE 8–3. GROUP NUMBERS, POPULATIONS, AND COMPOSITION OF HOWLERS ON BARRO COLORADO ISLAND, AS REPORTED IN FIVE CENSUSES

| Year | Number of Groups | Total Individuals | Fully Adult Males (percent) | Females without Young (percent) | Females with Young (percent) | Infants (percent) | Juveniles (percent) |
|---|---|---|---|---|---|---|---|
| 1932 | 23 | 398 | 16 | 27 | 16 | 18 | 23 |
| 1933 | 28 | 489 | 17 | 19 | 20 | 20 | 24 |
| 1935 | 15 | 273 | 18 | 24 | 14 | 14 | 30 |
| 1951 | 30 | 239 | 15 | 42 | 15 | 15 | 13 |
| 1959 | 44 | 814 | 18 | 33 | 16 | 16 | 17 |
| Averages . . . . . . . . . . . . | | | 16.8 | 29 | 16.2 | 16.6 | 21.4 |

The consistencies of these results indicate that considerable confidence can be put in the results of group analyses. However, it cannot be known whether variations are due to differences that actually existed or to observational errors. It is believed that most confidence can be put in the data for adult males, females with young, and infants. The numbers of infants may reflect the reproduction rate and slight variations for the time of year when studies were made. There is no known way of assessing *constant* errors of all observations on, for example, the difficult problem of discriminating between young preadult males and females without infants. Within the limitations clearly outlined, we have for a *naturalistic* population of howlers a unique body of information which can be analyzed in many ways and for different purposes.

## Group Size

The size of all groups counted from 1932 to 1959 ranged from 2 to 45 and the average size was 15.81 individuals. These figures *included* the data on the depressed population, and correspondingly small groups, of the 1951 census. The average size of 30 groups for that census was 7.97, while the average for all other censuses was 17.95; the average for the other censuses in chronological order was 17.30, 17.46, 18.20, and 18.50. Again, these latter data are very consistent, the range being 1.20 or slightly more than one animal. It is suggested, therefore, that the *normal* average group size of Barro Colorado howlers is, and will be found by future censuses to be, about 18 animals.

This fact of the established average group size makes possible a new method of estimating the total howler population of the island. Since howler groups within 800–1000 yards away from an observer can be located dependably by the early morning roars, the number of groups in successive areas of the island can be counted. The total number of groups, thus located, times the average group size might give as accurate an estimate of the total population as the extraordinarily demanding methods which have been used to make a complete census.

It is believed that the variations in group sizes will consistently fall within the range that has been established.

## Group Composition

Approximately a third of the animals classified as adult females carry infants or are closely associated with them. This serves as an estimate of the reproductive rate and is comparable to data collected during the dry season and first months of the wet season. Altmann's (1959) observations on the "laboratory group," with supplementary observation of five other groups during the height of the wet season, October to December 1955, supplement these data. Apparently howlers do not have discrete breeding seasons, although variations in the frequency of births may occur—a variation that must be established.

There are more animals classified as juveniles than as infants—perhaps because of the greater age range covered by the category of juvenile than of infant. Animals classified as adult females, both with and without young, represent about 45 percent of the total number of group-living individuals.

Even if the error of classing young males as females accounted for 5 percent of the total, the adult female component would be 40 percent of group-living animals.

The number of fully adult and socially established males almost exactly equals the number of females with infants. There is little possibility of error in making these two classifications.

Using the conservative figure for the percentage of adult females, 40 percent, it seems well established that in normal howler groups there are about 2.5 females on the average to one fully adult male. This has been named the *socionomic sex ratio*. This disparity between the number of adult females and adult males living in organized groups is a very important characteristic of howler groupings and apparently the same disparity is found in many other nonhuman primates.

Full and satisfactory explanations of the socionomic sex ratios found in howler groups and other primates have not been made. The following are possible factors, any of which might operate to result in the greater number of females than males living in groups: (1) The rate of maturity, or age to reproduction, may be about one third longer for males than females. (2) There may be a different mortality rate for males, especially young males attempting to establish their statuses in groups, than for the more protected and socially accepted females. (3) Some howler males leave groups, live for periods of time (some may live permanently) outside any group or in transition among groups. (4) Male howlers, after maturing physically, must gain social maturity to become reproductively effective.

### Extragroup Males

In each of the five census studies, observers found male howlers living alone or ranging remotely from cohesive, organized groups. Observations also show that these extragroup males range in stages of maturity from late juveniles or young adults to old animals, with more of the former being observed than the latter. Five extragroup males were counted in the census of 1932 and six in 1933. Two of these animals were quite old whereas two others were clearly young adults. Two extragroup males were observed by Collias and Southwick (1952) in 1951 at a time when the total population of the island was greatly reduced. One was a juvenile and the other a young adult male. Repeatedly, also, single males have been observed as the source of disturbance of group-living animals. Single males have been seen to follow groups over long periods, progressively becoming more and more closely associated with them and eventually becoming accepted as members of the groups. This behavior and the associated interactions led to these extragroup males being described as peripheral, transitional, and complemental males. They are *not permanently isolated*; they certainly came from groups and some of them return to join groups; some may remain separated from groups spatially, but even so they continue to interact with them, to exchange howls and roars, to approach, harass, and be harassed.

No howler females have been seen separated from cohesive groups, except very temporarily and for a limited space. All females apparently grow up, live, and die within groups.

The fact that some howler males leave or are driven from their parental groups, live for varied periods of time separately from groups, and eventually may join different groups, provides a behavioral mechanism for interbreeding among semiclosed groups and reduces group inbreeding. This affects the population's "gene pool," and hence genetic and evolutionary trends.

It has been theorized that dynamics of groupings of howlers operate around "homeostatic" or *sociostatic* equilibrations and that the socionomic sex ratio is one such trend toward a balance between the summed male-with-female sexual drives, needs, or hungers. Further, groups are conceived to be permeable (open) or stable in varied degrees, depending on the balanced network of social drives and incentives within them. Some unbalanced groups vary in their probabilities of admitting extragroup males; others may extrude excess males; some may divide as males polarize the group and one male pulls away with a subgroup. These theories are not proven but they provide ways of conceptualizing the dynamics of primate groupings.

### Factors Producing Variations in Group Composition

Obviously births and deaths most importantly affect the composition of groups. It is surmised that healthy fertile females may produce on the average an infant about every two or three years; it is known that roughly one third of the females have dependent infants.

Little is known about upper age limits and deaths. All observers have been surprised to find little evidence for deaths; few carcasses or skeletal parts are found in the field. Yet the population must have a complete turnover every twenty years or less. Epidemics of diseases reduce the length of this cycle. The data of Collias and Southwick (1952) show conclusively, when comparisons are made with other census data, that when the total population is reduced by more than 50 percent, groups become smaller, about one half the normal; smaller groups have only one male; and home ranges are greatly reduced. The fact that most groups have only one male suggests that the population of males available after the epidemic is redistributed, for it seems improbable that any epidemic would kill off males selectively, leaving one and not more than two males in each group throughout the island.

It is reasonably certain that groups divide, usually when they grow toward the upper limits of normal size. It seems most probable that cohesive subgroups, led by one male, separate gradually from the main group and thus change its composition, reduce its size, and form a new group. Groups that are polarized between one male and the remaining males are most likely to divide.

The probabilities are that groups that have divided from each other may have some degree of tolerance for reassociation. Groups 1 and 2 in 1959 seemed to reflect a bit of this relationship.

Also, groups frequently coming into contact in overlapping territorial ranges may develop tolerances that permit closer association than groups that never or rarely come into contact and are recognized as strangers.

Then there is the possibility that specific conflict and antagonism may differentially increase hostility between some groups.

It appears highly improbable that distinct cohesive groups ever merge and fuse permanently unless two such groups are very imbalanced and distorted in their composition. In general howler groups tend to react antagonistically to each other and, at least during the months of observations, tended to maintain their identity and composition except as previously described.

The population density varies over different areas of the island. The Lutz ravine is an area of unusual density and so also is the area in the center of the island.

Variations in density relate to several circumstances: (1) There are local habitats on the island that are favored by howlers because they have more or preferred foods, are protected, have preferred lodge trees, and the like. (2) Since howler groups do not range widely, high productivity may result in greater densities in some areas than in others. (3) Young groups tend to stay near their parental group's range. (4) Familiar areas and arboreal trails tend to hold their populations and hence contribute to varied densities.

Where there is localized dense population with large numbers of groups in close association conflicts are frequent, aggressions occur (mainly expressed by vocal exchanges), and often "tensions" are high. In such areas, and especially in the large groups reported in the 1959 census, the data suggest that the number of infants, that is, the birth rate, may be reduced. Some peripheral and widely separated groups like those along Armour and Barbour trails appeared to have more infants than those groups that were crowded in other areas of the island. This hypothesis deserves additional study and, if possible, proof or disproof.

## INTERGROUP RELATIONS AND HOME RANGES

Field studies in undisturbed habitats are uniquely appropriate for observing patterns of group movements in nonhuman primates.

The data about group movements and home ranges for the arboreal howlers of Barro Colorado are relatively abundant and form a clear picture unless confused by preconceptions, diverse terminologies, incomparable evidence from other animals (especially rodents and birds), and incomplete studies of other nonhuman primates.

Let us describe the simplest case of two groups of howlers and their movements throughout a month. One group was followed daily and almost hourly, the other was located repeatedly and its locations estimated and plotted on a map. The two groups were about the same size.

The group that was followed moved an average of about 200 yards each day, but the distances covered varied from less than 50 yards to 1000 yards of travel. The average daily travel distance, with a four-day exception, was greatest in areas peripheral to the area where the group was located most frequently. Several days of limited travel were periodically followed by unusually long and fairly continuous marches. The map does not indicate that lodge trees and food trees were often used repeatedly for several days and then the group would move away. The plotted locations of the second group overlapped the followed and plotted movements of the first group.

Extensive observations have confirmed and filled in details of the behavior illustrated by these examples. Collias and Southwick found what may have been the historic "Laboratory Clan" of Chapman (1938), also noted as Group 1 of the 1932 census notes, reduced in size and its range restricted to a more limited area around the laboratory buildings and clearing. In 1955 Altmann (1959), plotted the movements of a group in the same area for one month and found that the group had a range which did not extend beyond 480 square meters.

Experienced field observers find it possible to locate and relocate the same identified group in the same *general* area over periods of several months.

The observed limits of Group 1 of the 1959 census study was from the Laboratory to Fairchild 3 or 4, to Lathrop 5, to Shannon 2, along the south side of the ridge along which runs Barbour Trail to marker 6 and along Donato Trail back to the boat dock and clearing. Within this area Group 1 ranged for about two months.

Group 2 ranged during the same period over the Fairchild Peninsula, to the Laboratory clearing on the north and along Lathrop to marker 3 or 4. Whereas Group 1 ranged on the Fairchild Peninsula, Group 2 never came into the area near the Laboratory on the west, along Snyder-Molino, or into the Lutz ravine. However, several other groups frequented the Lutz ravine in areas immediately adjacent to the Laboratory but not along Snyder-Molino to marker 3 or between that trail and Lathrop to marker 3. In brief, howlers range over areas that are relatively limited.

Since the howlers are arboreal, their ranges have cubic dimensions that vary with the height, density, and type of forest. Howler groups frequent some locations in their total ranges more often than others. Thus plots of frequencies of locations over time result in complex topographic maps of their ranges.

Generally the ranges of neighboring groups overlap. For some groups in some areas the mosaic of the ranges of several groups may overlap completely, but with other groups like Group 1 of the 1932 and 1959 censuses, there are areas into which other groups do not go. It appears that this area need not be the one most frequently visited by the resident group. Periods of limited or sedentary activity may be followed by bursts of travel over unusually great distances either away from or back to the foci of intensive occupation.

### Home Range and Territoriality

In a familiar part of the range howlers behave differently, and observably so, from the way they do in less familiar peripheral range areas. In the latter they are more active, restless, and excitable, and appear to be on the defensive. In familiar areas, by comparison, they are calmer, less excitable, and take the offensive only if approached by another group or groups.

It is a distortion of facts to draw boundary lines around howler ranges, because such lines convey the impression that the limits of ranges are sharp and distinct, closed rather than open, constant rather than fluid and variable. Howlers do not defend *boundaries* or whole territories; *they defend the place where they are*, and since they are most frequently in the familiar parts of their total ranges, these areas are most frequently defended — typically by interchanges of roaring at approaching or approached animals. In such frequently defended areas resident groups seem to have priority rights to movement, as can be inferred from the directions of movements and countermovements of the interacting groups.

When howler ranges are described in terms of patterns of movement in space over time and the frequencies with which a group is found in different places, then some general characteristics of such ranges can be described. The area covered is localized, but shifts seasonally because of responses to ripening fruits or preferred leaf trees, like espavé and cecropia. Occasionally a group will move for unusually long distances. Finally, there are the possibilities of home-range *drift*, when a group gradually changes its range area and pattern.

It can be seen that the "territory" concept holding that an animal, or bird, or a group of them, defends an exclusive space, den, or nest does not describe accurately the behavior of howler groups.

Howler groups are spaced with varied distances between them. And when two or more groups come within a few hundred yards of each other, as happened several times in Lutz ravine in 1959, they become disturbed,

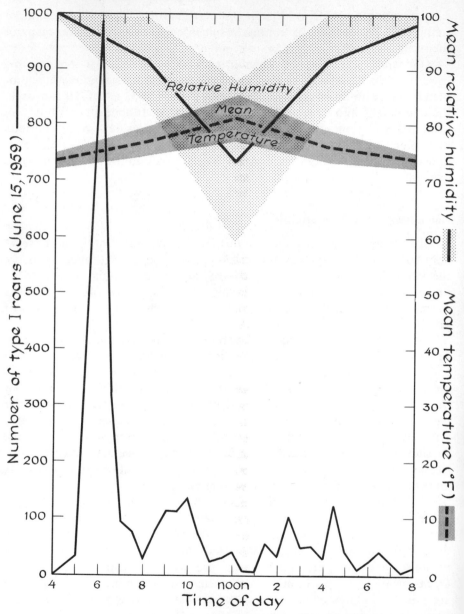

Fig. 8–6. Frequencies of roaring throughout the day.

howl and roar in bursts that may last at the extreme for several hours. Thus it would seem that the "howls" of howlers are functionally a kind of spacing behavior. They may be either offensive or defensive depending on the prevailing situation.

From an extended study of the frequencies of roaring throughout the day, but with special attention to the early morning roars occurring between 5 and 6 A.M. (see Fig. 8–6), it appears reasonable to hypothesize that these vocalizations function also as locational signs. All groups in hearing distance roar repeatedly and interchangeably. The roars and replies build to a peak of frequencies and then subside. It is also possible that some hours later the movements of groups are affected by the early morning locational roars. This interpretation could possibly be checked by plotting the initial directions of movements of the interacting groups later in the morning. However, some groups may move toward others offensively and some move away. Movements, then, will be difficult to interpret relative to the theories of roars being location signs with persevering effects on behavior.

## BEHAVIOR: INDIVIDUAL

All complex activities such as responses to ecological factors, the processes of population dynamics, the forces that regulate and control the composition of groups, and the interactional behavior that determines the general characteristics of groups—all are shaped and limited by the anatomical, physiological, and behavioral characteristics of individual howlers.

### Postures and Locomotion

Howlers exhibit typical pronograde postures and locomotion. Generally they lie and move with the main axis of their trunks parallel to limbs, vines, and tree trunks. When the howler sits, its trunk is usually flexed forward with the weight on the feet, legs, and haunches. The hands and arms are free for a variety of actions and the long prehensile tail usually anchors the animal to supports. The rate of changes in postures, locomotion, and general activity is slow and "deliberate." Faster rates of action than normal occur during the play of young and when the animals are excited in particular stimulus situations. These behavioral characteristics are best shown by motion and still pictures of howlers (Carpenter, "Howler Monkeys of Barro Colorado," Pennsylvania State University Film Library).

The limits of group movements and perhaps the compact spacing of groups reflect, in part, the slow locomotor and general behavioral characteristics of howlers.

Howlers are well adapted for the arboreal life and the environment of tropical trees. They climb expertly up trees of small to moderate size and descend such trees and vines head foremost, constantly using their prehensile tails. While moving from one tree to another over intersecting terminal branches they maintain contact with their tails and bridge spaces with a minimum of jumping. They are tree-bound and, in continuous stands of forests, range mainly through the mid-altitudes where the most continuous networks of intersecting branches are found. Howlers are strictly arboreal on Barro Colorado Island. Observers have very infrequently seen an animal come to the ground and move over it. When on the ground they walk and run on all four feet and hold their tails off the ground but not curved over the back as in the manner of spider monkeys.

## Manipulation

Howlers are said to have opposing thumbs. This statement is misleading. The thumb is atrophic, small and inefficient, and thus never *opposes* the long slender fingers. There is a division of the hand between the first and second digit. As the animal travels along limbs and in grasping and feeding, this division can be seen as the first finger and small receded thumb used together and the other three fingers acting as another, opposing segment of the hand. Fine prehensory acts such as removing scales or opening fruits and nuts cannot be performed by howlers, so that such manipulatory behavior requires the use of the mouth and teeth. When scratching themselves they make gross hooklike movements with hands and arms.

This general pattern of manipulation and the structure of the hands is seen in the newborn infant. Infants have efficient grasping reflexes of all appendages including the tail, and those of all ages are capable of clinging securely to the mother's coat, often with the tail wrapped around the base of the mother's tail, when being carried on the belly of the mother. The female does not assist the infant in clinging to her body.

## Feeding and Drinking

Howlers go to the terminal leaf, fruit, and flower twigs and eat directly from them, often finding it necessary to swing by their tails while feeding. Foods are pulled in and eaten directly from the stems where they grow. Rarely is food picked, held in the hands, and eaten, but large cecropia leaves, clusters of espavé buds, and young leaves may be broken off and eaten while they are being held. Howlers drop a large proportion of the foods they handle either while still on the stems or after it is picked. Infants and young juveniles sometimes eat food after it has been picked and is being held by the females; this sharing of food has never been observed between adult males and young howlers.

The main source of water is in the content of foods. There is no evidence that howlers come down from trees regularly and drink from the streams of the island, even during the dry season. Following heavy rain, when the trees are soaked and streamlets run down the branches and trunks of trees, howlers may lick water from leaves or collect it on their hands and then lick it off. Nursing infants, of course, get needed water from their mothers.

**Activity Cycles, Resting, and Sleeping**

During the diurnal cycle adult howlers spend much more time in rest and sleep than in activity. Following the dawn roars, which usually occur between 5 and 6 A.M., the animals rest, sleep, and feed a little in the tree or trees where they have spent the night. About midmorning they move out to food trees. This movement is usually accompanied by distance vocalizations (a tabulation of howler vocalizations and their probable functions is presented below). After a period of active feeding there generally follows a relatively inactive period that lasts until midafternoon. There is another period of travel and vocalization as the groups move to lodge trees and settle down for the night. Generally the time from between 7 or 8 P.M. until 5 or 6 A.M. is a period of resting and sleeping.

There are, to be sure, variations in this cycle of generalized daily activity. Weather, especially wind and rains, may cause protective inactivity. Disturbances like the movements and calls of neighboring groups and the activities of observers may affect the general behavior rhythms. Groups under some internal stresses vary their behavior. When there are females in estrus, female-male consorts do not follow the general cycles of resting, feeding, and sleeping. Finally, late infants and all juveniles play most of the time during the daylight hours, except while feeding, while adults rest and sleep.

An observer gets the impression that the energy expenditures of howlers are low as evidenced by low levels of general activity.

## BEHAVIOR: SOCIAL INTERACTIONS

Methodological approaches to the formidable problem of making both analytical and systematic studies of complex primate groupings were undeveloped in the early 1930s. In the first persistent studies of the howlers of Barro Colorado Island, in 1932, three methodological advances were made:

1. Techniques were developed for describing in considerable detail the composition of groups. The results of this approach have been given earlier in this chapter.

2. This accomplished, the next step was to make interactional analyses of the behavior of paired classes of animals of different sexes and ages. This method required systematic descriptions of the reciprocal interactional behavior of males with males, males with females, males with young, and so forth, class by class, until all interactional possibilities were exhausted. The scheme, which later came to be termed *dyadic analysis*, could be general between different classes or specific to all particular individuals living in a studied group.

3. The final tasks were to describe the patterns and characteristics of

TABLE 8–4. HOWLER VOCALIZATIONS AND THEIR PROBABLE
FUNCTIONS (AFTER CARPENTER 1934)

| Description of Vocalization | Situation | Probable Function |
|---|---|---|
| Voluminous barking roar, low-pitched and sonorous (males); Terrierlike bark (female). | In response to a disturbance. Animals show anticipation of aggressive or defensive action. | Warning of possible danger; threatening display. |
| Deep cluck repeated at irregular intervals. | Before and during group movement by leading animal. | Coordinates movement of group. |
| Series of gurgling grunts or crackling sounds produced by inhaling through constricted pharynx. | Given by an adult male in mildly disturbing situation. | Warning of possible danger. Coordinates adult males in group defense. |
| Wailing ending with a grunt or groan. | Given by a mother whose young has been separated from her or fallen. | Coordinates group toward retrieving of young. |
| Series of cries usually consisting of three notes. | Given by lost or separated young one. | Location and retrieving of lost young. |
| Purr of several seconds duration. | Given by infant or early juvenile when satiated and in warm and undisturbed affective state. | Facilitation of the mother-young relation. Stimulates coddling. |
| Little chirping squeal. | Young in play group. | Coordination of play activity. |
| Grunting sound. | Given by adult male when play-fighting of young becomes very vigorous. | Control of activity of young by adult male. |
| Rapid grunting similar to who! who! who! | Adult male in strange situation. Attracts attention of group. | Directs behavior of group. |

entire groups and the interactions between or among them.

The application of these methods of study to howlers has shown that it is possible to describe fairly adequately, systematically, and completely most of the important aspects of the behavior of primates living in their natural habitats. These approaches yield a great deal of information about the organisms and their behavior that summate to produce "gregariousness" and complex social behavior, including the derived general characteristics such as the way groups are regulated and controlled ("leadership"), coordinated, and integrated.

Two other approaches influenced the early field research. One was the attempts to observe and understand the *determinants* and *conditions* that affected, "caused," or influenced complex social behavior. The other was to observe and understand the effects of social behavior on broader adaptations and adjustments of howlers in context of groups, the sample study population, and habitat.

A supplementary or alternative approach involves the description of different kinds of modalities of behavior, for example, sexual behavior, maternal behavior, agonistic behavior, play. Here the emphasis is more on descriptions of activity and less on the characteristics of the actors. However, for some reporting purposes it is necessary to generalize descriptions, to describe kinds and modalities of behavior and generalize these descriptions to genera and species.

### Male-Female Interactions

Male-female interactions can be classed as (a) general or diffuse and (b) specific. Each male of the normally multimale group has general interactions with all group females. The male component of the group exercises controls over the females, intervenes when conflicts occur, and regulates to some degree the behavior of females. Occasionally females give right of way when a male approaches and passes them. No attacks of males on females have been observed, nor have females been seen with injuries or scars that might have resulted from fighting. Some females appear to be more compatible than others with specific males, as indicated by spatial separations among them.

#### Sexual Behavior

Special interactions occur between a male and a female when she is in estrus. Estrus in female howlers was identified and described by the author in 1932, at a time when the problem of the periodicity of sexual receptiveness was debated and unsettled.

Typically, when a howler female's endocrines make her receptive, she approaches a male. The approaches themselves constitute the first general signs of estrus because they are unusual; normally a female does not approach a male persistently and repeatedly. It is not clear whether receptive postures also signal estrus. Like other platyrrhines a howler female in estrus does not have genital swelling.

The first male approached may or may not respond. If he does not, the female repeats the approach to other males of multimale groups until one does respond. Whether or not there is preferential selection or responses by males remains to be determined. The level of sexual motivation would seem to determine whether a particular male responds. When he does, the female forms an unusually close spatial association with him. The pairs of animals thus closely associated are termed consorts. As the strength of the sex drives and excitement increases, the female and male may exchange rhythmic tongue movements with their mouths partly opened. When these species-specific gestures occur, copulation is likely to follow in a short time.

During copulation the male only partially mounts the female. Most of his weight is borne on his feet while he may anchor himself to branches by his tail. The female raises her rump, lowers the forward part of her body, and accepts the male. During copulation she may look back at the male, touch him, if a hand can be freed, and sometimes continues to exhibit rhythmic tongue movements during copulation. The pelvic thrusts of the male can be observed and counted; his knees move outward and inward rhythmically with each thrust. These copulatory patterns and mountings may be repeated in series, perhaps sometimes without ejaculation — in fact, it is difficult to be sure when insemination does occur.

It is inferred, but uncertainly, that estrous females during their three-or-four-day period may satiate one male and then form consort relations with one or more additional group males. Thus, it is thought that successional mateships occur in howlers, as is certainly true for the rhesus monkey (Carpenter 1942a, 1942b).

### Female-Young Interactions

Estrous behavior, characterized by many copulations with one or more group males, usually results in pregnancy and the birth of an infant. During parturition the female may become the focus of attention of several other females. She emits vocalizations expressive of pain, and she may become separated from the group if it is moving during the birth of the infant. Under this condition the wailing cries may function to maintain contact at a distance with the group. Limited observations suggest that howler females eat the placenta and umbilicus. The amneotic fluids are licked from the infant and it is cleaned. The female becomes relatively inactive, spends much time flexed forward with the infant on her belly and chest and between her legs — a protected and warm location for the infant.

Typically, several other females, especially those without infants, are attracted by the newborn. Thus an observer may see a cluster of females near one that has recently given birth. The attraction is to the infant and not to the mother; the females explore the infant, touching it with their muzzles and hands. Mild avoidance behavior may be shown by the mother. When awake, the newborn infant squirms and climbs up the body of the mother, and she reacts by pulling it onto her chest.

Generally, it would seem that after a period of several days or a week the infant-mother complex is less stimulating and attractive for other females. This is particularly characteristic of the behavior of females in groups where there are many infants. However, in groups where there are few infants (as was the case in Group 1 during the 1959 studies) females without infants may be closely and fairly constantly associated with the infant-mother dyad. The females appear to have a compulsive attraction to the infant, to muzzle and touch it and occasionally to encourage it to crawl on them. However, they have not been observed to take the infant and carry it away from the mother, as has been observed in langur monkeys (Jay 1962).

What are the physiological states, needs, social statuses, and conditions that result in some female howlers without infants being attracted to the young infants of other females? Are they pregnant? Have they lost their young? Are infants generally attractive to females and, if so, do infants exercise a cohesive influence on the group structure? More information is required than is available to answer these questions.

Infants are completely dependent for care and survival on their mothers for at least six months. Young infants are in constant contact with their mothers and do not move away from them, or if they do the females reach out and pull them toward them. Thus the infants' spheres of activity are restricted by the mothers. During this period control by force is exercised, but signs, signals, and cues of movements soon begin to operate to coordinate the behavior of the two animals. We learned by raising an infant howler from the age of a few weeks to 24 months that howler infants purr. The sound is very like the purr of kittens and expresses comfort, warmth, and affective states. These sounds probably act as cues for the mothers.

The signals and gestures given by the mother that invite the infant to mount need further close study, but they do occur as infants grow older and move short distances from the females. When the female begins to move it shows approach behavior, looking toward the infant, perhaps using facial expressions and sound signals; all of these coordinate the infant's actions of mounting to be carried. Later still, when infants begin playing with others and become separated from their mothers, they produce repeated patterns of distress cries to which the mothers respond. These exchanges of cries and low calls while the female waits or meets the approaching infant help bring the animals back together.

As infants reach the late stages of this class and the intensity of playing increases, females become less occupied with them. However, they do watch young playing and if disturbances occur, or if the infants get trapped on branches or vines over which they move, females may retrieve them.

Young howlers seem to be less disturbed by an observer than adults are. Females have been observed to retrieve their young ones when they have wandered close to the observer, risking closer approaches to the observer than their normal tolerance distance.

Early infants, of course, depend for food entirely on the milk of the lactating females. Later infants nibble the food, leaves, and fruits being eaten by the females, and this is a perfect naturalistic learning situation. Before the next infant of a female is born the young howler gets and eats his own foods.

Infant-three young continue to associate with their mothers even after the birth of a sibling. Therefore, one of the most frequently observed sub-groupings, or clusters, is that of a female, an infant-one, and a late infant or early juvenile. Rapidly, however, the second infant completely displaces the first and it, in turn, becomes an independent member of the group.

## Young-Young Interactions

As young howlers mature through the infant and into the juvenile stages of development, the constant interactions and dependencies with the mothers are phased out as further interactions with peers, mainly in play groups, develop. Thus the dependency on the mother is replaced by competitive play interactions with other young howlers. They associate in clusters of from six to eight individuals ranging from infant-twos through late juveniles or even young adults.

The play behavior of young howlers, in the amount of time spent and the intensity, variety, and complexity of activities, has a most prominent place in the howler's life history. Except when sleeping at night, or feeding and traveling with their groups during the day, young howlers are playing. Probably 80 percent of their waking time is spent playing. The patterns of activity are varied and complex. They wrestle on branches or swing by their tails, sometimes more than two together. They chase each other and appear to bite each other—at least, both hands and mouths are used in the encounters. The older ones engage in play-fighting and these struggles result in mild distress cries. The play is not organized, but rather chaotic, with each animal playing a changing role, and the scores and goals are not easily evident to an observer. The play of howlers is intense and it seems to be competitive. There are suggestions of "ganging-up" of several smaller animals on a large individual. "Harassment" types of actions can be observed both among the young animals and, occasionally, by the young toward adults, which may nip or slap back but usually just appear annoyed and move away from the young.

During the play of howlers transient mountings occur, but these action patterns do not consist of distinct components of copulatory behavior like those seen in rhesus young.

Adequate systematic observations give a sufficient basis for the generalization that play in these young primates, involving as it does so much intensive and extensive interaction with group peers, ranks second only to interactions with the mothers in importance to their normal development. The effects of play on the maturation development and social learning ("socialization") can be inferred to be of the greatest importance in the howler's life history. In play they not only practice actively and hourly the perceptual-motor skills that are necessary for their future adjustments and survival in a tropical forest environment, but also they learn the complex social behavior that characterizes their life in compact groups, where each individual must interact appropriately with most of the other animals in a group. Thus in play each young howler learns to know each other young of the group and also learns the roles and statuses as these become functionally established. In other words, during play each young howler learns its group niche and how to live in it. Unless this occurs for an individual, it confronts two options: to be "maladjusted" within the group or to be excluded from the group.

The young-young interactions and their effects on the behavior of individuals may relate to the different paths of social maturation that males follow and, also, they relate to the differences between males and females. These are speculations; the behavioral characteristics may also result from differences in the interactions of adult females and of adult males.

### Female-Female Interactions

Females of howler groups are conspicuously compatible. They behave in concert and act in parallel as they feed, move over arboreal highways, and settle compactly in trees for rest and sleep. They rarely are observed to come into conflict within groups, and when conflicts do occur, they are sharply but quickly resolved. In conflict two females confront each other and signal aggression with partly opened mouths and contracted lips, thus partially baring their teeth. Collias and Southwick (1952) report having heard "cackling" or "clacking" sounds uttered by females in conflict. Similar sounds are believed to characterize conflict in males also, and perhaps in young animals. It is important to remember that an observer may spend hundreds of hours studying howlers without seeing strongly overt aggression between howler females in a group.

An observer does form the impression that females have differentiated roles and statuses, but the differences are not easily observed or described, especially in natural groups where it is impossible to distinguish individual animals. Undoubtedly this lack of identification operates over time to create impressions of more uniformity and similarity of behavior in classes of animals (for example, adult males and females, young of different classes and grades) than would be the case if each individual could be repeatedly identified and known. Techniques for marking all black arboreal howlers of a group have not been developed and applied. Many groups do have individuals that can be identified, and this fact is extremely useful in identifying groups. Once known reliably, such counts as the number of males, females with infants, and the like also help to identify groups.

Generally the females of a group constitute a kind of majority control. Common responses of the females may, in many kinds of situations, interact with actions of the males, which might be called "leadership," in determining the over-all group actions, that is, to move or not to move, to travel in one or another direction, as well as other group options.

Females respond in concert to disturbances, and during the male roars in intergroup offense or defense the whines and cries of the females can be heard in the background.

During group movements females occupy positions of all orders in the line of march through trees, with females carrying young usually slightly clustered toward the rear of the line. Sometimes females are in forward positions, particularly when the trail is well known by frequent use, but the spacing and order of behavior has general reference to the center of gravity of the actions and locations of the adult males.

The best estimate that can now be made is that the females of a howler group order themselves along a dominance-subordinance gradient of low slope. At the extremes older mature females may have more control and "rights" than young females at the other extreme. However, in field observations where food is abundant and dispersed, space extensive, and frustrations minimized, the behavioral indices of dominance and subordinance are difficult to make.

### Male-Male Interactions

Adult howler males are easily distinguished from females and, being relatively large, they form a conspicuous class. Thus they invite a proportionately large amount of observational time and attention. Most of the males can be identified in a group with as many as five or six males, if it is studied intensively for a sufficiently long period of time. Size, coloring, facial configurations, botfly larva, and sometimes scars or other markings aid identification. For example, a principal male in Group 1 of the 1959 study had a broken finger, a botfly larva on his head, and his lower lip drooped asymmetrically. A male may be identified also by his behavior with reference to the group. One may be consistently on the periphery of the area of the group and another may be seen regularly in or near the center of a group or forward in group progressions. Typically, however, in a multimale group several act together and often range or rest near one another.

The vocalizations of males added to their distinctive appearance make them very conspicuous. The early morning roars, the barks, hoots, and grunts with which they usually respond to an observer (unless they are very wild, in which case they hide and become silent) and the deep clucks they use in regulating the movements of the group—all these make male howlers conspicuous.

In many situations males in a group act together or coordinately. This occurs daily in exploring for travel routes and in leading the group over them. In defensive and offensive "vocal battles" with other groups such males act together and in concert. The series of howling roars are produced usually by all the males of a group, with each contributing to the volume of sound. Some males may initiate these roaring series of sounds more frequently than others. Disturbances in the group may stimulate simultaneous actions by several males. For example, when an infant fell from a tree to the ground, the group's males roared together, possibly creating a protective shield of sound; they approached the fallen infant and thus aided in its recovery by the female. Again, when an ocelot attacked a juvenile, all the adult males in the group rushed back along the line of progression and came to the defense of the bleeding juvenile.

It has already been seen that the males of multimale groups form successional consort relations with estrous females. Depending on the strength of the sexual drives, there may be mild competition for females, but after the consort pairing is formed by a male and female, the other males do not aggressively interfere with the consort's behavior.

The limited amount and kinds of aggressive interactions, and particularly of fighting, requires explanation. First, it would seem that in cohesive groups the roles and statuses and interactional probabilities are so well learned and established that each male tends to respond appropriately to the other males, thus removing the necessity for overt fighting. Second, postures, gestures, and vocal signals are highly developed systems of communicative interactions, which, when operating effectively, reduce conflict and fighting.

It is inferred on the basis of very limited observations that the greatest incidence of conflicts occurs between adult males and late juveniles or young adult males. Sharp conflicts and momentary attacks of males on late juvenile animals have been observed. Collias and Southwick (1952) report seeing a male bite into the tail of a juvenile. Other occurrences of aggression involving a male and juvenile, possibly a male, were seen in 1959. The agonistic behavior of adult males may be one vector of force that results in some males leaving groups, and hence these interactions may serve to regulate the number of males in groups.

It is certain that group males resist the approaches of peripheral males into groups. Single males that approach groups have often been identified as the immediate cause of series of howling roars of group males, which act toward a single male during his early approaches much as they do to other groups. Persistent following of the group by a peripheral male reduces the resistance of the group males, and group membership may be attained eventually as the strange male becomes a familiar one. Thus it is reasonable to assume here too that the interactions of the group with peripheral males is a factor in selectively determining the male composition of groups.

The howler males' dominance-subordinance order in groups is similar to that described for females, the difference being that the individual difference gradient is of steeper slope. A range can be observed between a young male that has recently gained tentative acceptance in the group up to a principal male that has the highest status and the most control potential. However, among the principal howler males there would seem to be far fewer differences in dominance statuses than are observable in comparable rhesus monkeys or baboons (this volume).

The limited observed aggression, conflict, and, particularly, fighting among howler males reflect both the characteristics of the animals and the naturalistic conditions in which they have been observed. These conditions, including the group contexts, provide regulators for overt aggression that tend to reduce it to an appropriate functional level in the total bioeconomy of the howlers.

There is another factor that should not be overlooked and that may operate in all field studies of primates. The reactions of males to the observer, and to other animals too, include persistent attention and actions that may suppress intragroup conflicts. It would seem to be a general behavioral principle that external threat or disturbance has stronger stimulus values for organized groups than internal threat. Hence suppression of normal aggression owing to the presence of the observer may introduce a bias that operates constantly to affect observations and impressions about aggression in free-ranging primates.

In this section brief generalized descriptions have been given of typical interactions and of some variants, of the dyads of male-female, female-young, young-young, female-female, and male-male. It is clear that for some subjects more and different observations are needed.

## The Application of Dyadic Analyses

Detailed descriptions of the web of dyadic interactions between classes of howlers in naturalistic groupings should give a systematic and generalized picture of their social behavioral characteristics within groups. More specific descriptions could be made if *each* animal were identified and if the interactions of each individual of an organized group with every other individual could be described. Such an intensive analysis would reveal individual differences, in addition to class and grade differences. The individual-marking technique introduced by the author and Michael Tomilin in 1938 with the Santiago Rhesus Colony in Puerto Rico was an attempt to make such analyses possible (see Koford, Chap. 5, this volume).

The web of interactional possibilities is large and varied. The $\dfrac{N(N-1)}{2}$

formula gives the number of such interactions that could be described. Thus for a group of 17 howlers there would be 136 different interactional possibilities. For most descriptive purposes the class (that is, male, female, and so on) interactions yield results that characterize group behavior fairly accurately and congruently. However, when this is done there are some general characteristics of groups that must be described at a level of generality and abstraction above the level of individual behavior, for example, interactions of clusters of animals.

## SOME GENERAL CHARACTERISTICS OF HOWLER GROUPS

Howler groups seem to show a high degree of *closure* or lack of permeability, but they are not completely closed or impermeable. Complemental males leave groups, live "interstitially" among groups for unknown periods of time, and then regain membership in a group by persistent close approaches, by following the group, and by gradually conditioning the group to their presence. Surely selective processes operate here to determine what specific males are ejected or leave the parental group, the duration of living away from the group, and the male-group interactions that lead to the complemental male's again becoming a member of a particular group.

Groups divide or split, usually unequally, perhaps as a result of cleavages, the unequal cohesion of clusters or subgroups, and the development of polarized antagonisms between the principal males. New groups are apparently formed by a kind of gradual or sudden budding-off process.

The evidence is against strange howler groups joining together or coalescing. Possibly groups come together temporarily; when this occurs, however, the groups are not strangers to each other, but have probably had frequent contacts and, indeed, may be divisions of the same parental groups. There are no observations to show that the male members of one group form consorts and reproduce with females of another group. Thus group membership would seem to be a necessary precondition for reproduction.

The semiclosed or semipermeable character of howler groups is made effective by protective-defensive behavior of group members, especially by the adult males. The aggressive behavior toward sources of disturbances or threatening situations is marked and contrasts sharply with the lack of observable overt aggression among animals within the group. The stimulus situations that provoke aggression are predominantly the presence of other howler groups, approaches of complemental males, and disturbances such as an approaching storm, thunder, aeroplanes, or observers. The responses are primarily vocal. The howling roars are protective and defensive in function and may represent a type of adaptive mechanism that replaces or substitutes for direct fighting. Howlers, and particularly the adult males, may approach sources of disturbance as they roar together. During extreme excitement the males may shake branches and sometimes dislodge broken ones and let them drop to the ground. However, very wild animals may retreat or climb to the tops of the trees and become silent when pressed by an observer.

The observations have been confirmed by independent observers that howlers will move to positions over an observer and drop fecal matter and urine. The intent of these *instrumental aggressive acts* can only be inferred but that the behavior is defensive in function seems to be clear.

In conclusion, the protective-defensive behavior of howlers affects group cohesion, provides a selective mechanism for group permeability and composition, and creates an envelope of security wherein young and defenseless animals live.

## Group Interactions

The high degree of autonomy that characterizes howler groups operates to make them relatively separate social units. Although the interactions of different groups vary, there is no evidence that several groups form *supergroup organizations* or communities. Typically the interactions between groups are antagonistic. When groups come near each other all animals become disturbed to some degree; typically, the males roar, the females whine, the young cease to play, and the groups become compact. This behavior tends to separate groups and contributes to the types of range adjustments that have been previously described. The early morning roars also affect the subsequent movements, and hence the dispersal of howler groups.

## Integration and Coordination of Groups

Learning in primates in a natural setting has been neglected as a subject of study, and therefore as an explanation for much complex behavior of free-ranging primates. Learning surely plays an important role in producing what might be termed the *integration* of groups of animals. It is also possible that before coordinative behavior can function properly, and with economy of effort, the processes and effects of integration must have already occurred. Group coordination is dependent on group integration.

### Integration of the Group

Intensive study of a howler group leads to the unproven conviction that each adult animal has learned to discriminate (to know) each other adult animal in a group. This discrimination learning is thought to be a basic condition in order for each animal to make specific and fitting reactions to others. Furthermore, it is reasonable to assume that the statuses occupied by each animal in the group structure and the behavioral roles it takes have been importantly determined by learning. Membership in a group is only possible when an animal is discriminated as a "familiar" and not a "strange" animal. The first kind of discrimination leads to neutral accepting or positive responses; the second kind to negative, resistant, or aggressive behavior.

All the necessary requirements and conditions for complex social learning are present in close-living, interactive howler groups in a natural habitat. The operations of conditioned stimulus-response principles, once known, can be observed and need not be merely inferred. Infants learn to discriminate their mothers and they, in turn, learn to discriminate their infants. Contact and warmth, support and protection, as well as nourishment, reward the needs and drives of infants and *positively condition* them to their mothers. Controls and restrictions imposed by the females shape and orient the behavior of infants to them. As infants mature affinitive play among peers rewards social learning and reinforces the discrimination learning of all interactive individuals.

Behavioral patterns that have stimulus values are also learned; the postures, approaches, gestures, facial expressions, and vocalizations. Thus, the appropriateness of actions and reactions is increased by naturalistic learning as the young mature toward adulthood.

The constant close association of group members while resting, feeding, and moving can be thought of as leading to positive conditioning and to the elimination of some individual-group responses.

The rotational consort pattern previously described is a positive conditioning in which the estrous female periodically reinforces interactions with the adult males of the group.

Thus groups become integrated and high levels of accommodated behavior are maintained. This integrated group state is a necessary condition for the effective functioning of what is termed *group coordination.*

### Group Coordination

Processes of group coordination and interactional behavior are conceived as regulating the actions of individuals in a howler group toward a high degree of unity and cohesiveness. These regulatory interactions can be described as stimulus-response communication networks. They counteract centrifugal movements of individuals and clusters away from the central mass of the group and in general support the centripetal movements that result in the relatively compact cohesiveness typical of howler groups.

### Communicative Behavior

The communication network of an established, integrated howler group is very complex. There are many patterns of stimulation and reaction, but two kinds are prominent, those which are positive and attract and those which are negative and repel. All these patterns function in a context that affects their biotic significance or the degree stimulus of *valences.* The key to understanding the biotic significance is to observe the pattern of the communication behavior, to know the specifically correlated or resulting responses of integrated animals, and to record the kind of situation in which the communicative interactions occur. Thus the significance of a posture, movement, gesture, or vocalization is inferred from the immediate responses of preconditioned individuals of the group.

There are two additional generalizations: (1) Communicative stimulus patterns vary along a continuum of specificity to generality. For example, the wailing cry of a lost or separated young and the orienting vocal calls of its mother, produced alternately as the two animals rejoin each other, appears to be highly specific to these two animals. There is little, if any, observable effect on other associated animals. Similarly, the rhythmic tongue movements exchanged between a consort pair are specific to these animals and their motivational states and are followed by specific copulatory behavior. Here, too, other animals appear not to be affected, although the signals may have an inhibitory effect on other males. At the other extreme, the deep clucks, usually of males but perhaps also of females, that function to initiate and guide group movements or progression have general effects on all members of the group (except perhaps the infants) within the stimulus range of the sounds. The roars of howlers and other howler protective-defensive behavior may affect in varying degrees the behavior of all group members. (2) The group status of individual animals interacts with the communication pattern and determines its stimulus value for other animals. For example, the communicative postures, movements, and vocalizations of the principal male have an observable, different, and stronger effect on group members than do the same gross behavior patterns produced by a low-order male, such as one that has recently joined the group. Thus communicative behavior varies in the *spread of effects* to other animals. The statuses and characteristics of the individual affect the responses of other group members.

The signal and cue *referents* are generally those of the immediate situation; referents in the past or future are extremely limited, if indeed they exist at all. It is in this connection that the possibility that early morning roars have an effect on later morning movements of groups poses a problem deserving careful study.

Clearly, signal and cue behavior is of many kinds. The characteristics of the stimulus animal, its location in the space and social structure of the group, its posturing, gross movements, facial expressions, gestures, and vocalizations all may function as communicative signals and signs or stimulus cues for regulating the behavior of responsive group animals.

Only a limited purpose would be served by further categorizing the communicative behavioral patterns ranging from gross movements to specific patterns of gestures and vocalizations. It is especially difficult to describe accurately the repertoires of gestures and vocalizations of primates and for different observers to agree on them. In the basic references of the chapter attempts have been made to describe a few patterns of the complete repertoire in terms of (1) the animal giving the stimulus, (2) its behavior on emitting the stimulus, (3) the responding animal or animals, and (4) the biotic functions served or the significance of the interactions in the chains or series of resulting responses. What seems to be needed are detailed photographic recordings of gestures and related behavior, sound recordings and the spectrographic analysis of their patterns in order to advance understanding of the complex coordination systems characterizing the behavior of individuals in established howler groups.

## CONCLUDING STATEMENT

An attempt has been made in this chapter to give a generalized description of the howlers of Barro Colorado Island. This is done with the hope that some appropriate comparisons can be made with the other species described in this volume.

Studies of the Barro Colorado Island howlers in 1931–1933 preceded by about twenty years the greatly increased interest in the naturalistic behavior of primates displayed in the 1950s. It is hoped that the chapter will be viewed in its historical context.

The emphasis in this chapter, determined in part by the available data, has been on the population organization in its natural context. This emphasis is also justified, however, because in the field of population dynamics there have not yet been comparable studies of a primate population, its dispersion, grouping patterns, and composition over a period of almost 28 years. The Barro Colorado Island howler population is important as one sample, which should be studied regularly and analytically in order to gain new knowledge and understanding of the determinants and regulators of nonhuman primate populations. The world-wide importance of problems of regulating human populations justifies intensive and thorough basic research on nonhuman populations.

Generally this chapter has minimized consideration of theories and hypotheses. This has been done to make the chapter consistent with others of this volume. Systematic theoretical formulations should soon be undertaken in order to derive hypotheses and broad conceptual understanding of the naturalistic behavior of nonhuman primates and in order to define more precisely than is now possible new problems for investigation. This is a necessary stage for building theoretical constructs from the level of nonhuman to human primates.

JEAN JACQUES PETTER

9

# ◆ The Lemurs of Madagascar

## INTRODUCTION

The uniqueness of the lemurs has been recognized for a long time. As early as 1758 Linnæus made them a distinct subgroup of the primates, and this opinion was later confirmed by the work of Blainville, Cuvier, Mivart, Illiger, and their successors. In the present classification the Lemuriformes are divided into three superfamilies: the Tupaioidea, the Lemuroidea, and the Daubentonioidea. Only the Lemuroidea and the Daubentonioidea are native to Madagascar, and it is with these that this chapter is concerned.

Until recently the characteristics used in taxonomy have been essentially morphological. Without minimizing the importance of these criteria, which have the advantage of lending themselves to a quantitative study and which permit comparison with fossil forms, it seems worthwhile to reconsider the classification of the Madagascar species in the light of our study of the animals in the wild as well as in captivity and to see whether the ecology and ethology of this group can be related to their taxonomy.

Before attempting to draw conclusions I want first to point out the similarities and differences among the species of each group by following the present classification, which is given below. Several modifications of this classification will then be proposed.

PRESENT CLASSIFICATION OF THE MADAGASCAR LEMURS
(after Schwarz 1931 and Hill 1953)

1. Family of the Lemuridae
   A. Subfamily of the Cheirogaleinae
      Genus *Microcebus*
         *M. murinus* with two subspecies: *murinus* and *smithii*
         *M. coquereli*

    Genus *Cheirogaleus*
      *C. major* with two subspecies: *major* and *crossleyi*
      *C. medius* with two subspecies: *medius* and *samati*
      *C. trichotis*
    Genus *Phaner*
      *P. furcifer*
  B. Subfamily of the Lemurinae
    Genus *Lepilemur*
      *L. mustelinus*
      *L. ruficaudatus* with two subspecies: *ruficaudatus* and *leucopus*
    Genus *Lemur*
      *L. variegatus* with four subspecies:
        *variegatus, ruber, subcintus,* and *editorum*
      *L. macaco*
      *L. fulvus* with seven subspecies: *flavifrons, sanfordi,*
        *albifrons, fulvus, collaris, rufus, mayottensis*
      *L. mongoz* with two subspecies: *mongoz* and *coronatus*
      *L. catta*
      *L. rubriventer*
    Genus *Hapalemur*
      *H. griseus* with two subspecies: *griseus* and *olivaceus*
      *H. simus*

2. Family of the Indridae
    Genus *Indri*
      *I. indri*
    Genus *Propithecus*
      *P. verreauxi* with five subspecies: *verreauxi, majori,*
        *deckenii, coronatus, coquereli*
      *P. diadema* with five subspecies: *diadema, edwardsi,*
        *holomelas, candidus, perrieri.*
    Genus *Avahi*
      *A. laniger* with two subspecies: *laniger* and *occidentalis*

3. Family of the Daubentonidae
    Genus *Daubentonia*
      *D. madagascariensis*

## ACTIVITY RHYTHMS

The lemurs of Madagascar include both nocturnal and diurnal species. In the Lemuridae, among the subfamily Cheirogaleinae the genera *Microcebus, Cheirogaleus,* and *Phaner* are strictly nocturnal. After nightfall these animals emerge from cover, which may be a hole in a tree or a nest in foliage, where they have spent the day, and they do not return until the first light of day.

The Cheirogaleinae exhibit a somewhat incomplete temperature-regulating mechanism (Bourlière, Petter, and Petter-Rousseaux 1956b); this is particularly clear in the genus *Cheirogaleus*, which shows a regular alternation of periods of activity and of lethargy. In *Cheirogaleus major*, in captivity, the phases of torpor are always very short—from two to three days at the maximum. In *Cheirogaleus medius*, on the other hand, the phases can be very long. These animals become very fat, their tails loaded with reserves, and they remain torpid for a week or more. Their rectal temperature falls and follows the fluctuations of the temperature of the surrounding environment (for instance, a body temperature of 17.5° C. on the third and fourth of January 1954 reflected an external temperature of 16° C.). In a captive *Cheirogaleus medius* such a phase of lethargy lasted for more than a month and had been preceded by other long periods of lethargy, although the laboratory in which we maintained this animal was kept at a constant temperature.

Apart from these long periods of torpor, *C. medius*—and to a lesser degree *C. major*—exhibits diurnal variations in activity and in body temperature, varying from temporary virtual lethargy during the day to constant activity during the night. The long periods of lethargy of *C. medius* seem to be related to the presence of two well-defined seasons in western Madagascar where they live—a dry season and a wet season.

In certain regions of the eastern forest, according to the reports of natives, *C. major* also spends periods buried or hidden in a rotten trunk. We have seen some of our *C. major* captives bury themselves in the burrows of tenrecs, which were kept in the same enclosure.

We have not observed prolonged periods of lethargy among *Microcebus murinus*, although when the exterior temperature falls below 18° C. this animal becomes less active and, especially if it is fat, may exhibit a phase of torpor with lowering of body temperature during the day. It is probable that an analogous rhythm exists also in *Microcebus coquereli* and *Phaner furcifer*, but we have not been able to verify this.

The subfamily of Lemurinae, less homogeneous in activity rhythms, includes the genera *Lemur, Hapalemur*, and *Lepilemur*. The first two are comprised of animals having periods of half-light activity, which sleep for the most part during the night and spend the day resting in the midst of foliage. They are not really active except in the early morning and in the evening. However, in the forest we have seen bands of *Lemur* move in full daylight on overcast days. Also, if they are disturbed at night they can immediately become active (Petter and Petter-Rousseaux 1956). *Lemur variegatus*, on the other hand, tends to be more nocturnal than other *Lemur*, whereas *Lemur catta* seems to be more clearly diurnal. The genus *Lepilemur* is unlike other Lemurinae in its strictly nocturnal character; it leaves cover only when night has fallen and returns to it just before daybreak. The *Lepilemur* of east and west Madagascar all seem to have the habit of searching for holes in trees to spend the day. This is true, for example, of *Lepilemur*

Fig. 9–1. *Lepilemur mustelinus ruficaudatus* near the entrance of its hole.

Fig. 9–2. A group of *Avahi laniger occidentalis* sleeping at the end of a branch.

*mustelinus ruficaudatus* in the forest of Ankarafantsika where the animals are easily found by systematically observing old, half-dead tree trunks (see Fig. 9–1).

The subspecies of the island of Nosy-Bé, contrary to other *Lepilemur*, has never been found in a hole in a tree, but simply passes the day rolled into a ball in the middle of foliage. This difference in habits is interesting to note for there seem to be as many habitable holes in the forests of Nosy-Bé as in Madagascar. This subspecies when kept in captivity with other subspecies of *Lepilemur* did not immediately try to hide in the breeding cages, but the younger ones gradually become accustomed to the cages and by the end of a month usually took up the habit. Perhaps this modification of behavior was caused by the colder climate of Tananarive or simply by imitation. It is interesting to note, in connection with this observation, that Nosy-Bé, unlike Madagascar, has no mammalian predators that pose a threat to *Lepilemur*.

The Indridae include two strictly diurnal genera, *Indri* and *Propithecus* (*Propithecus* prefers to begin to move toward the middle of the day), and one strictly nocturnal genus, *Avahi*, which is found rolled into a ball in the middle of foliage during the day and becomes active only after nightfall (see Fig. 9–2).

*Daubentonia*, the only genus of the family Daubentonidae, is strictly nocturnal and spends the day in a thick nest of leaves.

## LOCOMOTION

All the lemurs are arboreal, but in comparing genera two main types of locomotion may be distinguished: (1) A generalized type in which the

Figs. 9–3a & b. Microcebus murinus in characteristic postures.

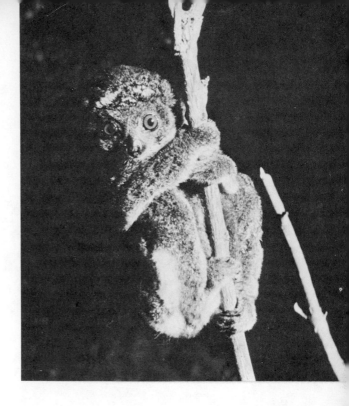

Fig. 9–4. A young *Avahi laniger orientalis* in characteristic vertical posture.

body remains almost horizontal when the animal walks, runs, or jumps from one branch to another (Fig. 9–3). (2) A specialized type in which the body remains generally vertical and the animal moves almost exclusively by jumping from one vertical support to another (see Figs. 9–1, 9–4, and 9–5).

Among the Lemuridae all the Cheirogaleinae are characterized by the generalized type of locomotion. *Microcebus* moves chiefly on small branches and on the dense foliage in the large trees (see Figs. 9–3*a* & *b*). Cheirogaleus mainly utilizes the large branches as pathways and jumps only rarely. *Phaner* has the same means of locomotion but jumps more frequently.

All the Lemurinae, with the exception of *Lepilemur*, use almost the same means of locomotion. They move on middle-sized and large branches and jump from the extremity of one branch to another. Their jumps are sometimes considerable; we have frequently seen *Lemur macaco* leap more than eight meters from the end of one branch to another. Before jumping the tail is held erect above the body; during the jump it is at first horizontal and then raised rapidly at the moment of landing, while the paws reach out to secure a better grip on the branches. The landing is broken by the flexibility of the foliage on which the animal falls with a great impact and to which it clings with determination. The flexible branches may then sag several meters, and their slackening at the top certainly aids the animal by giving it impetus to progress toward the heavier branches and toward the trunk (Petter 1962b).

297

Fig. 9–5. *Propithecus ver-reauxi coquereli* gripping a vertical tree trunk.

In contrast to the other Lemurinae the *Lepilemur* has a specialized type of locomotion. Its body is almost always vertical and its movements are made by jumps from one vertical support to another (Fig. 9–1).

The Indridae exhibit the same type of specialized locomotion. At rest the body is constantly vertical (see Figs. 9–4 and 9–5); during jumps, which may be of considerable length, the body becomes horizontal, describing a sort of glide; and on landing the vertical position is always reestablished. Unlike the *Lemur*, these animals do not use the tail as a balance, and it is probably of no use to them during the jump, since *Indri*, which is virtually tailless, is one of the best jumpers.

*Propithecus* will sometimes descend to the ground, although rarely. In August of 1956 we saw a band of four cross a small road in this way in the forest of Ankarafantsika. They jumped in a series of leaps, one after another, in a bipedal position with arms lightly flexed and raised, the hands at the level of the head. We have also seen this posture adopted by two *Propithecus diadema* crossing a road in east Madagascar, and we have often observed it in captive animals. Nevertheless, *Propithecus* appears to leave the trees reluctantly. Thus, in our long-term observations of certain groups in the north of the Ankarafantsika reserve, a region where the forest is very sparse, we have seen *Propithecus* make detours of more than 100 meters from their route of the day to look for tamarind seeds, although a few leaps on the ground would have allowed them to shorten their route considerably (Petter 1962).

*Daubentonia* uses almost the same mode of locomotion as *Lemur* (Figs. 9–6*a* & *b*). It is slower, however, and its powerful claws permit more varied postures, in keeping with its peculiar mode of feeding.

## MANIPULATION

Because of the importance of the hands, among the primates generally, in locomotion and manipulation, some notes on the dexterity of various lemurs have been included. Like other features of their morphology, considerable variety is evident. Detailed analyses of manipulation require laboratory conditions, see, for example, Bishop (1962).

In *Microcebus* the hand is relatively unspecialized and is morphologically comparable to the human hand, although the thumb is less well developed and less opposable to the other fingers. The hands are frequently used to manipulate food, a large piece of fruit often being held in the hands while the animal eats. Insects such as butterflies and crickets are generally caught with the two hands. The hands are also used for grooming, both hands being used together.

The hand of *Cheirogaleus* is quite similar to that of *Microcebus*, but the elongation of the body in *Cheirogaleus*, which requires that the hands be used to support the body, prevents the frequent use of the hands for

Figs. 9–6*a* & *b*. *Daubentonia madagascariensis* in the forests of eastern Madagascar.

handling food. *Cheirogaleus* has never been observed to clean the face with two hands, as does *Microcebus*, and the hands are not obviously used in mutual grooming.

In *Lepilemur* the hands are more specialized than those of the animals previously discussed. The palm and fingers are elongated and therefore the thumb is more obviously separate from the rest of the hand. This results in less manual dexterity, and fine movements are poorly coordinated. Small objects are generally held between the fingers and palm. The *Lepilemur* defends itself by slapping or boxing with its hands.

The hands of the Indridae are similar to those of *Lepilemur* but the specialized elongation is even more extreme.

During movement along tree branches *Daubentonia* use their hands as do the other lemurs, the thumb opposing the other fingers, which are quite elongated.

In 1964, during an expedition made specifically for the study of Aye-Ayes, I was able to observe the manner in which the third digit was used. In the cases observed the animal did not try to "extract" the larva with its digit, but turned its finger several times inside the hole, apparently in order to crush the larva. Following this, he licked the finger several times.

## DIET

The lemurs may be grouped according to their dietary preferences into species with a varied diet and species with a specialized diet. Among the Lemuridae all the Cheirogaleinae have a considerably varied diet. In captivity all accept a great diversity of foods, including fruits, insects, and rice. None, however, accept leaves or bark.

The Cheirogaleinae, then, are more or less homogeneous with respect to diet. One can discern, however, a more clearly insectivorous tendency in *Phaner furcifer* and especially in *Microcebus murinus* which in the wild consumes a great deal of animal prey. And a somewhat more frugivorous tendency is discernible among the Cheirogaleinae.

The Lemurinae, except for *Lepilemur*, also have a varied diet, but, in contrast to the Cheirogaleinae, these related forms only rarely eat animal prey. In our many hours of observation in the wild, we have never seen any *Lemur* eat an insect or a small vertebrate, although they frequently had the opportunity to do so. In further contrast to the Cheirogaleinae, *Lemur* eats leaves more frequently and more fruit.

*Lepilemur*, in contrast to other Lemurinae, has a specialized diet, and they are difficult to keep in captivity since they accept only certain kinds of leafage. In the wild for the most part they eat leaves, fruits, bark, and buds.

The Indridae also have a specialized diet, and their feeding habits are in this respect quite comparable to those of *Lepilemur*.

*Daubentonia*, although it may accept a rather large variety of food in captivity, has a predominantly insectivorous diet in the wild. Further indications of its adaptation to this diet are the specialization of its incisors, which permit it to remove the bark from branches, and the specialization of its long and slender third digit.

In 1964 I was also able to observe Aye-Ayes collecting minuscule larva from the interior of the pits of the *Terminalia* fruit by the hour. The fruit and then the very hard pit were rapidly gnawed off at one end with the incisors, and the third digit was then thrust several times in rapid succession into the hole made in the almond and finally licked.

I have also observed *Daubentonia* eating mangos and coconuts near the villages. The coconut is eaten on the tree. The animal rapidly tears away the fibers on one side of the nut, and then he makes a small round hole three or four centimeters in diameter in the shell. Through this hole he drinks the liquid and scrapes all the pulp that he can reach with his third finger.

## COMMUNICATION

### Vocalization

The means of communication, particularly vocalization and techniques of marking, vary widely among the lemurs, and sometimes it is even difficult to find analogies between different genera within the same subfamily.

Among the Lemuridae, the Cheirogaleinae, except for the *Phaner*, emit auditory signals that are in general discrete, composed chiefly of tones of a very high frequency, which are difficult for the human ear to perceive. At night in the forest it is often very difficult to distinguish the calls of *Microcebus murinus*, for instance, from those of insects. *Phaner furcifer*, unlike the other Cheirogaleinae, is very vocal, but its calls are not much varied. At regular intervals it emits a series of short signals with a frequency of about 2 kilocycles.

The Lemurinae exhibit a rather large variety of different, clear vocalizations, and in this respect *Lemur macaco, fulvus, mongoz*, and *rubriventer* may be grouped in the same category. Essentially they emit several characteristic kinds of grunts and sharp calls. The differences among them are in detail.

These vocalizations are grouped in three main categories below, although, in addition, there are numerous intermediate or less typical calls that can be heard in various more or less rare situations and are difficult to interpret.

1. Individuals in a rapidly moving group continuously utter a sort of weak grunt. The rhythm of these grunts is variable and often without seeing the animals but simply by hearing the grunts one can get an idea of their speed of movement or of the difficulty of a crossing. This grunting is gen-

erally begun by an individual which is giving some sort of alarm and is usually immediately imitated by the others, even if they have not seen the cause of the disturbance or if they are already accustomed to it. A mother makes her young come to her immediately by giving this same grunting sound. There are also similar grunts made by *Lemurs* who have been disturbed by the observer.

2. When a group is disturbed, even though the danger is not urgent, if the cause persists the animals at first work themselves up by grunts, which become louder and louder, and then suddenly the group all together utters a loud cry, a sort of "crou-crou-cou-crouou-crouiiiiiii," which becomes still louder toward the end. This call is repeated, according to the degree of the disturbance, from every two to five seconds. Between times the animals grunt without stopping. In fact, only the end of the cry is perfectly in unison; the beginning apparently serves to prepare all the animals to call together, and it is the most excited among them which begin and are imitated by the others. The climax of the sequence is not always reached.

3. Another sort of call, peculiar to *Lemur macaco*, consists of a series of deep, loud, and prolonged grunts, which, although deeper, occasionally resemble the call of a drake. This call is rather variable in intensity and tone and can be heard frequently. It is most commonly uttered by a lone individual, generally by a male but occasionally by a female.

Other species of the Lemurinae, *Hapalemur griseus, L. catta* (Brandes-Hall 1909), and *L. Variegatus*, each has its own particular repertoire of clear signals.

HAPALEMUR GRISEUS: For the most part the grunts of *Hapalemur griseus* resemble those made by *Lemurs*. They emit a sort of double grunt, to which other individuals may respond with a faint bleat.

LEMUR CATTA: The cries of *Lemur catta* are also similar to those of the other *Lemurs*, occasionally they emit small, trembling groans which have been compared with miaows.

LEMUR VARIEGATUS: These seem to have a repertoire which is less varied, but their cries are by far the most powerful of all those uttered by the *Lemurs*. This animal emits a series of intense roars which rise progressively, generally for the duration of several seconds. These cries may be followed by varied clucks, which are also intense, and are very surprising in the silence of the forest. This is also true for *Lepilemur*, which is equally exceptional in this respect and which emits a great variety of calls in the forest, heard only at night. These calls begin often with great intensity as early as sunset and are correlated with the first movement of the animals. Later on their vocalizations are very irregular and probably are elicited by encounters with individuals or by various disturbances. These vocalizations are extremely variable in volume and in pitch, and range from faint grating noises to sharp, loud calls.

The Indridae have a repertoire of vocalizations that have relatively little variation. *Indri*, however, is famous for the long, modulated wailing, comparable to the calls of gibbons, which it emits in the forest. We have noted in *Indri* two other types of clear signals, grunts and uniform calls resembling the noise of a Klaxon horn.

*Propithecus* appears to have only two types of call: (1) a characteristic click-grunt, which is the origin of the Malagasy name, pronounced by the natives "Sifak," and (2) a series of barks that are emitted in unison by the group. These calls may be uttered during nearly all parts of the day, principally early in the morning, a few in the middle of the afternoon, and some also at dusk. They seem to have a clear enough relationship to the presence of a predator bird (Petter 1962).

Among the *Avahi laniger* we have recognized two principal categories of signals: an almost inaudible whistling of a very high frequency and a short, clear call.

In *Daubentonia* we have also recognized two distinct types of calls: (1) a kind of grinding resembling the sound of two metal sheets being rubbed together, which is answered periodically by a similar cry from another animal in the distance; (2) a cry of anger emitted when an animal is approached by an observer or when a light is shone on one — a cry that might be translated "Rron-Tsit" repeated rapidly many times in succession.

**Marking Behavior**

Marking behavior seems to be rather rudimentary among the Cheirogaleinae, and none seems to possess a specialized gland for this purpose.

Fig. 9–7. A male *Hapalemur griseus* showing the marking glands of the armpit and forearm.

Fig. 9–8. A female *Lemur catta* "marking" the wall with her clitoris, with the male waiting to smell it.

In *Microcebus murinus* we have observed a type of marking with urine during a period of sexual excitement, similar to that observed among the *Galago* (Eibl-Eibesfeldt 1953). *Cheirogaleus* smears branches with excrement.

Among the Lemurinae certain species are very specialized for marking. This is so for *Lemur catta* (Brandes-Hall 1909) and *Hapalemur griseus* (Affolter 1937, Archbold 1932, Breddard 1884), which have glands on the forearms and at the level of the armpit. The animals have behavioral patterns that are particularly suited to these anatomical characteristics (see Figs. 9–7, 9–8, and 9–9). *Lemur catta* rubs the end of its tail on the cornified area on its forearm after a series of rhythmic movements of the tail. It may also rub its forearms on branches that it wants to mark, after having momentarily touched the glands of its forearm and armpit together by flexing its arm. *Hapalemur griseus* also often exhibits this behavior pattern. In *Lemur catta* the female also marks objects with her clitoris.

*Lemur macaco*, which does not have such glands, does, however, exhibit very similar behavior, occurring usually during moments of sexual excitement or anger. It often rubs its forearms and hands on branches. Most of the other species may mark with urine or excrement, either by moistening their hands or by using the tops of their heads. Most interaction among adult animals is limited to marking behavior and the frequency of such behavior is variable. In November it was rare for us to see a male sleeping with a female or rubbing a branch near her with his forearm. In April and May the males were far more active, and this type of marking behavior was much more frequently observed. Marking generally occurred very early in the morning or very late in the evening when the group reassembled for the night or when groups met each other during the day. A male and female were very frequently seen sleeping together, and often in the daytime we saw males actively marking branches or rubbing their genito-anal region on females. In April and May, when more than one male approached the same female, the first male tried to mark the second male and usually a short quarrel and pursuit followed. In general the more dominant male succeeded in rubbing his genito-anal region on the less dominant male (most often a young or an old

Fig. 9–9. Male *Lemur catta* rubbing the tip of his tail against the cornified area of his forearm.

individual). The female frequently marks objects with her clitoris, as we noted for *Lemur catta*, and at the height of excitement a male may rub the top of his head in his urine or his excrement and seek to mark the animals he encounters. This behavior is very easy to observe in captive animals and also in the forest. At Nosy-Bé we filmed a male who had an actual tonsure as the result of marking in this fashion.

The following field notes give examples of marking behavior.

NOSY-KOMBA, MAY 8, 1956

A very excited male is next to a female on a horizontal branch. Another animal approaches. The first animal becomes more nervous, rubbing his anal-genital region on the back of the female and then facing the other animal and rubbing his hands rapidly on the branch.

NOSY-KOMBA, MAY 13, 1956

Two groups meet at the boundaries of their territories. Fighting and chasing ensue. A male rubs the palms of his hands on a branch and jumps. Another appears and rubs the top of his head on this same spot.

NOSY-KOMBA, NOVEMBER 10, 1956

Two groups of animals are present. Chasing and cries are followed by numerous grunts. The males, which are very excited, rub their palms on the branches constantly.

In *Lepilemur* no marking behavior has been observed. However, the male has a glandular area on the scrotum.

No glands nor specific marking behavior has been observed in *Lemur variegatus*.

Some of the Indridae have specializations for marking. *Propithecus* males have a gland at the base of the neck that they rub frequently against tree trunks. Urination can also serve as a means of marking, as the following example of frequently observed behavior illustrates. The adult female in a family group that was moving through the forest was seen to stop for a moment and grip a tree branch. After having urinated at length against the branch she leapt to a neighboring branch. The male who followed her, having approached and sniffed the damp spot a long time, then rubbed the glandular zone of his neck back and forth repeatedly in it, urinated in his turn, and bounded off to follow the female.

Similar observations have also been made on a small family group of four individuals in captivity that we were able to observe at Tananarive. We noted the special behavior of the adult female in this group; in contrast to the young and the adult male, which urinate in various places, the adult female habitually urinates on a door of the cage, her belly against it. This spot was visited from time to time by the adult male and even by a young two-year-old male who came to rub their neck glands in it. Often these animals also rubbed their necks on the cage at a spot probably also marked by the female.

In both sexes of *Avahi laniger* there are pairs of glands situated on the head at the level of the angle of the mandible (Bourlière, Petter, Petter-Rousseau 1956).

Among the *Daubentonia*, there is no cutaneous gland which can be used for marking, but we have on several occasions observed Aye-Ayes rubbing their anal regions upon the branch on which they were traveling.

### Summary

As one can see from these examples, the Madagascar lemurs present a great variety of forms of intercommunication. Although we have spoken here chiefly of communication that is dependent upon hearing and smelling, sight is apparently as well developed as the other senses. The tail, in particular, plays a significant role in the various positions it assumes and has an important place in signaling behavior.

It is interesting to observe—and this is particularly clear for marking—that a variety of devices or kinds of behavior have developed to the same end in the course of the evolution of this group.

## TERRITORY AND HOME RANGE

Observations of behavior were made on many species, but during this general survey it was not possible to study any one species long enough to collect detailed, long-term data on home range and territorial activities. The presence of marking behavior suggests a greater degree of territoriality than in most primates, and the following observations are pertinent to this question.

Among the three groups of *Lemur macaco* that were extensively studied, numerous territorial disputes were observed. The following excerpts from field notes illustrate some of these.

14:00, at the eastern limit of the common sleeping area. A male from Group 2 leaves the others and slowly crosses the sleeping area uttering a long grunting cry and joins a male from Group 3 which has come forward to meet him. The two approach each other hesitantly. They lick each other for a long time. . . . Both animals are very calm. They remain near each other until 14:50.

16:20. Groups 2 and 3 are in their respective home ranges. The author appears near Group 3. The adult male of this group gives a long grunting noise, and the other animals in his group give the same cry, repeating it for about five minutes.

16:35. Grunts and the sound of leaping animals are heard from the east, and Group 1 arrives. The animals in Group 2 begin grunting again. The two groups rest immobile for a moment near the boundary of the small wood which comprises the home range of Group 3. A female in Group 1 becomes very excited and rubs the top of her head on a branch and grunts. The three others leap around among the branches.

15:40. A female from Group 1 jumps from a rock onto a branch near Group 3. Three females from Group 3 rush toward her threateningly and force her to return to the rock. The three females then return to their branch. . . .

Suddenly a male and a female of Group 1 bound toward the three members of Group 3, who go up to the top of a tree. A desperate chase follows. The younger male from Group 3 is attacked by a female. A female from his group comes to his rescue. A male attacks a female, pulling the hair on the top of her head. Leaping and chasing and, from time to time, rapid grunting follow. (During all this the adult male of Group 3 sits by himself and does not move). . . .

Little by little the animals calm down and they all move toward the common sleeping area, which they reach about 17:20.

I was not able to determine the exact territories occupied by the *Lepi-lemurs*, but I gained the impression that they moved independently, each one in its own restricted area, during their periods of nocturnal activity. The animals uttered a great many cries, which have been interpreted as cries of defense, pointing to typical territorial behavior.

Among the *Propithecus* it was also difficult to determine whether defended territories exist. In areas where the forest is sparse the population is less dense than it is in the more heavily wooded regions. Home ranges were observed, but no furious battles such as have been reported were seen. However, all the males more than two years of age and some of the females that we observed had their ears torn to some degree; of course, this is not proof of territoriality, for the ears could have been torn in quarrels over estrous females. The following field notes record observations indicating the existence of home range or territoriality.

Along the shores of Lake Ampijoroa the author made several attempts to drive animals out of their habitual zones of occupation, but without success. As soon as the animals came to a certain point they stopped; intense grunting was heard and the animals leaped up into the higher branches and passed to the rear of the observer.

JANUARY 23, 1957
Two groups, each composed of four individuals and each in a mango tree, are in full view of each other. A male from one group indicates that he is about to move forward. One or two members of the other group immediately face him and their action prompts him to leave. No cries or grunts are heard.

I have also observed groups encroaching upon the home range of other groups during the absence of the latter, but the trespassers always moved with hesitancy.

The *Indri* inhabit a rather hilly area, and it appears that each group inhabits its own hill, the animals generally being found in a tree near the crest of the hill. Exact home ranges could not be determined, but each group seemed to remain in its own particular area of the forest, and it is possible that their howls are related to some defense or signaling mechanism.

Territorial behavior has not been observed among the *Avahi*, but this may be owing to the sparseness of the population.

Sufficient observations have not been made to determine territoriality among the *Daubentonia*, but it is possible that the vocal signals that are frequently emitted by these animals are of territorial significance.

## GROUP COMPOSITION AND INTRAGROUP BEHAVIOR

There are several types of social groupings among the Madagascar lemurs. In spite of the great difficulty of behavioral observation, particularly for the nocturnal species, we may divide the different species into three categories according to living habits: (1) those living mostly alone, (2) those living in family groups, and (3) those living in more complex social groups.

Among the Lemuridae the members of the subfamily Cheirogaleinae are rather similar in living habits. All the Cheirogaleinae seem to be solitary; they are usually encountered alone in the forest. However, in *Microcebus murinus* we have observed sleeping groups that we are still unable to interpret, and it is possible that a slight amount of gregariousness is present in this animal at least under certain circumstances.

Except for *Lepilemur* all the Lemurinae are gregarious. The groups they form are not large and in *Lemur variegatus* and *Hapalemur griseus* they are probably of the family type. In the other *Lemur* the groups are much more complex, particularly in *Lemur fulvus*, *Lemur macaco*, and *Lemur catta*. Groups of these species each contain several adult males and several adult females. The number of members of such a group is variable but almost always exceeds a simple family group. It seems certain to us that in an average group several males are sexually active at the same time. On the island of Nosy-Komba we were able to distinguish in *Lemur macaco* quite large nocturnal groups formed every evening at the same place by the reunion of two or three elementary groups, each of which was generally composed of from ten to fifteen animals. We have observed two or three young in each elementary group. For the most part social behavior between adults is limited to marking behavior. Pairs consisting of a male and a female are sometimes seen sleeping together, especially in the breeding season. In captivity caged pairs frequently sleep huddled together on a branch. They often lick each other, especially on the head—around the eyes and ears. However, prolonged mutual grooming such as that seen among monkeys has never been observed.

Unlike the other Lemurinae, *Lepilemur* seems to be solitary. They live in the forest in small "population centers," where the animals live a short distance from one another but remain continually separated (except, of course, for the mother and her young).

The Indridae all live in small family groups, composed usually of a male, an adult female, and one or two young. During periods of eating and resting there is generally a distance of at least one meter between individuals. They come into contact for mutual grooming sessions only occasionally, and then only briefly. Animals sometimes touch or approach each other in the course of marking behavior. A male often approaches a female as she urinates, the female generally appearing indifferent to his approach—although she sometimes chases the male away. Play, which is frequent in captivity, has never been observed in the course of the many hours of field observation. The animals merely rest, move about, and eat. Nor has fighting over food been observed between animals of the same group when the same piece of food attracts a certain number of individuals. Often food is quietly divided, or the possessor of a piece of fruit moves a few meters away with it and no one follows him.

*Daubentonia* is a solitary species. Apart from the female and her young, no grouping has ever been observed by us or by the natives.

It is interesting to note the role of the female in group progression. Among *L. macaco* the females are generally at the head of the group during group movement, with the males usually bringing up the rear. Females also appear to assume the lead among *L. fulvus*; during observations in the Ankarafantsika forest, one of the females, carrying an infant under her belly, was frequently seen to lead the group. The situation seems to be similar among the *Propithecus*, with a female usually in the lead. Group movement is generally very slow and the animals move less than an average of 500 meters a day.

In summary, as these examples show, there is a great variety of social systems among the lemurs. The Lemurinae have the most highly evolved system, and although our observations are still not sufficiently numerous and precise, it seems that groups are stable throughout the entire year in spite of the strictly seasonal character of reproduction.

## REPRODUCTION AND SEXUAL BEHAVIOR

Much is still unknown concerning the reproduction of the Madagascar lemurs. Among all lemurs sexual activity appears to be seasonal, as the table on the following page illustrates.

It was noted earlier with reference to *L. macaco* that observations of marking activity and of pairs of animals sleeping huddled together are particularly frequent in the breeding season. Mutual licking behavior also seems to be associated with periods of sexual excitement. During the breeding season females have often been observed to approach and to excite the males, occasionally approaching and licking a sleeping animal. Females have also been observed displaying another curious behavior pattern: the female approaches a sleeping male and stands motionless with her legs stiff and her tail arched over his.

Sexual activity as described in field notes has already been cited in

| Genus or Species | Mating Season (inclusive dates) | Gestation Period (in months) | Number of Young |
|---|---|---|---|
| Microcebus | September–January | 2 | 2 or 3 |
| L. macaco | | | |
| L. catta | April–June | 4½ | 1 |
| L. mongoz | | | |
| L. rubriventer | | | |
| Lepilemur | May–July | 4½ | 1 |
| Propithecus | January–March | 5 | 1 |

According to the natives, *Daubentonia* gives birth to one infant between early February and late March.

connection with the discussion of marking activity above. Despite many long hours of observation, however, copulation has never been observed in the field.

It is probable that mating takes place at dawn when observation is difficult. A copulation in captivity was observed on April 27, 1957. An adult female and a very old male were placed in a cage containing an adult male which was at least four years old and another male which was two and a half years old. Excerpts from notes follow:

At first the old male is the most enterprising; he follows the female and sniffs at her. Little by little the adult male begins to follow the female and finally sits next to her. Each time the old male approaches to within two meters the adult male leaves the female and chases the old male away with threatening screams. Then he sits on a branch and rubs his palms on the end of a branch; his penis becomes erect.

The adult male remains as close as possible to the female and frequently rubs his palms on the branches. At one point in his excitement he rubs his anal-genital region on the back of the young male, who shows no immediate reaction, but soon the adult male returns to his harassment of the old male.

8:30 The adult male sits next to the female on a branch. Suddenly he approaches her from the rear and holds on to her, wrapping his arms around her waist and giving pelvic thrusts. Meanwhile the female holds her tail between her legs and protests, pulling the hair on his head. He persists and a short battle ensues. Then he remains next to her, his penis erect and about 5 cm. long. He licks the end of his penis for some time, holding it in his left hand and then taking half of it in his mouth and licking it. A dozen more attempts at copulation are observed, but the female either resists or remains passive, keeping her tail between her legs.

Observations were continued until 10:00. The female did not give birth to an infant that year.

We have been able to observe the mating of *Cheirogaleus major* in captivity. The male holds the female between his hands, and, briskly licking her flanks and neck without biting her, he emits a sort of twitter; with his hind feet, he grips the ankles of the female; his tail is animated by rapid, undulating movements. The female is either in a "normal" position, the hind quarters stretched out on the ground, or lying on her side (as is the male), or holding onto the mesh of the cage or to any object.

Mating occurred seven times in the afternoon. Each time the duration was of two or three minutes, and each act was separated by an interval of five or ten minutes. The male threw himself upon the female each time she passed near him as she moved about the cage.

## MOTHER-INFANT RELATIONSHIPS

### The Newborn

The relations between mother and young at birth vary according to species. Among the Lemuridae the Cheirogaleinae have two or three young that are little developed at birth and are placed in a nest. The mother takes them in her mouth when transporting them.

In the Lemurinae there is generally only one young per litter. Among them, also, the state of development of the young at birth and mother-infant behavior vary according to the species.

In *Hapalemur griseus* and *Lemur variegatus* the young are born in an undeveloped state and are placed in the fork of a tree or an epiphytic plant. We observed a female (*L. variegatus*) in captivity which pulled fur from her side in order to line the bottom of a breeding box in which she had placed her infant. In both these species the mother takes the young in her mouth to carry it.

Among other *Lemur* the young is much more developed at birth and is capable of grasping the hair on the mother's belly, where it stays securely during the movements of the group. On these moves the mother is not at all hindered and leaps with the same ease as the others.

Among *Lemur catta* the young after a few days hold on more and more often to the back of the female, an ability which is rather rare among the other species.

The newborn *Lepilemur, mustelinus dorsalis* of the island of Nosy-Bé, is even more developed; it can progress unassisted on the branches. The mother generally allows it to grasp one of the branches while she moves during feeding. When she wants to carry it she seizes it in her mouth.

The young of the Indridae, like those of the *Lemur*, are able to grasp the mother's fur from birth and are carried in this way during group movements. For some days after the birth of the young the mother exhibits a special behavior. When she is resting she attempts to form a sort of cradle with her body, the trunk slightly inclined backward and the thighs folded. The young can rest there and can even lean over the edge to look below. Keeping the same position, the female is also able to eat.

When the mother wishes to move, with a quick pat of her hand she helps the infant take up a perpendicular position beneath her, clinging tightly to the fur of her belly. When the female moves with the others it is often difficult to see if she has a young one with her; only the top of the infant's head is visible in the fold of the mother's thigh.

Shortly after the birth of the infant the mother, when the group rests, usually stays a few meters from the others, whom she prevents from approaching. Then little by little she lets herself be licked by the male, then by the other individuals of the group, all much attracted by the newborn, which they also try to lick.

When it is two weeks old the infant more and more often holds onto the mother's back, a position that it maintains until it is much older. The infant grips the mother's fur and holds its body parallel to hers. We have even observed young that have attained two thirds of their adult size in this position on their mothers' backs.

According to the reports of natives, *Daubentonia* seem to have comparable habits, the young being able to grasp the mother's coat at birth.


## The Developing Infant

The infant *Microcebus* begins to feed on its own at around one month of age, and becomes independent at about four months. As soon as the young are capable of walking they begin playing together; they run and bite at each other and at their mothers. The infant reaches physical maturity at seven or eight months and is then capable of reproducing.

At birth all the *L. macaco* are dark in color and their sex is difficult to determine. Observations were made at Nosy-Bé at the end of October, when all but one of the infants had been born. The infants were carried under their mothers' bellies during group movement, but were allowed to play a meter or so away from their mothers during rests. Other females were allowed to approach and to lick infants, and males frequently licked or played with young infants, but sometimes were chased away by a brief threatening motion of the mother.

Observations were made again in April, when the infants were six months old. The young females were a very light red-brown whereas the males were a dull black. The young animals were about one-third of their adult size and their fur was longer than that of the adults. The young were often alone but returned frequently to their mothers, who licked them vigorously at each return. During group movements they often followed in their mothers' steps and at difficult crossings the infants occasionally clung beneath their mothers.

Observations made on *L. macaco* and *L. catta* in captivity indicate that the young begin to feed by themselves at about one month old, but continue to nurse until about the age of five months. By six months of age they are completely independent and are thereafter frequently chased away by their mothers.

## TAXONOMIC IMPLICATIONS OF THESE OBSERVATIONS

Using as a basis the ecological and ethological information that has just been summarized, it is possible to reconsider the customary classification of Madagascar lemurs and to propose some modifications. Two other factors, the vegetation zones and topographic divisions of the country, also warrant consideration here.

The island of Madagascar has a great variety of different habitats, largely as a result of topography and climate. This fact was first emphasized by M. M. Perrier de la Bathie (1921, 1931) and Humbert (1954), who defined the principal vegetation zones of the island and described the peculiar characteristics of each.

All the lemurs are very intimately connected with the forest, and the existence of these vegetation zones, which not only differ in climate (Ravet 1952) and flora but also are often separated from one another by natural barriers, has constituted a powerful agent of speciation. In addition, in the middle of these different habitats there exists a virtual compartmentalization of habitats, due to the presence of large rivers that many species cannot cross, and to discontinuities in the forest. Thus the populations of lemurs are found fragmented in the midst of their range of distribution and this contributes to an increase in the degree of subspeciation (probably through genetic drift). Intraspecific variations exist among all the lemurs to varying degrees. This is particularly clear among the *Lemurs* and the Indridae, but we have also found it, although less evident, in *Lepilemur, Cheirogaleus,* and *Microcebus.* All the forest massifs have yet to be completely explored in detail, and thus it is still possible that new forms remain to be discovered in Madagascar. Such a new form (*Lemur sanfordi*) was discovered in 1932 by Archbold (1932).

### Cheirogaleinae

As we mentioned at the beginning of this chapter, the subfamily Cheirogaleinae appears to be very homogeneous as a whole. The animals that compose this group are very different from *Lemur*, however, and to the ecologist and ethologist their being grouped in the same family with these latter forms appears scarcely justified. Several of the taxonomic details of this group deserve to be discussed.

*Genus Microcebus*

According to the present classification *Microcebus murinus* is differentiated into two forms that have the rank of subspecies: *M.m. murinus* and *M.m. smithii*. After our observations in the wild it seems to us that the genus *Microcebus* should be phenotypically divided into three taxonomic entities.

The first, living in the east of Madagascar, is smaller than the others, has a slightly shorter tail, a dull reddish brown coat (except for the belly, which is yellowish), and short ears almost hidden in the fur.

The second and third types coexist in the west. We have obtained living animals of these two forms from the same forest at Ankarafantsika. They have certain characteristics in common that separate them from the eastern race—a slightly larger stature; a longer tail; a brighter coat; large, erect, membranous ears standing well above the fur. One of these two latter forms, by far the most common, has a gray coat more or less tinted with red, sometimes completely gray with a very white belly. These animals are gentle and not aggressive in captivity. Representatives of other rarer forms have a bright red coat that is more or less tinted with yellow and a pale yellow belly. They do not grow fat in captivity and are very active and very aggressive. The differences between the two western forms are scarcely visible in dead specimens, but are clearly apparent in the living animals. Their coexistence in the same environment, however, makes us hesitate to name them as subspecies.

We have seen but have been unable to capture *Microcebus murinus* on the island of Nosy-Bé. We do not know whether this form is strictly comparable to one of the mainland forms or whether it constitutes a separate subspecies.

*Microcebus coquereli* is larger than *Microcebus murinus*. It is a rare species and probably very localized.

*Genus Cheirogaleus*

Three species of the genus *Cheirogaleus* may be distinguished.

*Cheirogaleus major*, the largest member of the genus, is a little larger than a rat in size. It lives only in the eastern forest, where it seems to be represented by two forms that are slightly different in color. One is reddish and has a more pointed muzzle and very marked brownish black eye-rings. The other is grayer with a more rounded muzzle and is slightly larger. However, the results of our recent breeding program (June 1964) have shown us that these two forms can be crossed.

In the western and southern regions *Cheirogaleus major* is replaced by a smaller species, *Cheirogaleus medius*, which is grayer in color and has a white belly. Although we have observed a great number of these living animals and have also studied specimens in collections, we have not been able to distinguish differences sufficient to justify the usual separation of this species into two subspecies, *C. medius medius* and *C. medius samati*.

*Cheirogaleus trichotis*, a form of about the same size as *Microcebus murinus*, has up to now been represented by a single specimen in the collection of the British Museum of Natural History. We were able to find two other old specimens in the collection of the Paris Natural History Museum (Petter and Petter-Rousseaux 1956). Unfortunately we have not been able to get any more information concerning the distribution of this animal, which is apparently very rare. The three specimens were probably collected in the eastern forest, but no other information is available on the collectors' labels.

## Genus Phaner

*Phaner furcifer* represents the only species of this genus. The distribution of this species is little known. It is found in the north and the west of the island. We have observed it near the coast in the Bay of Ampasindava and in the southwest near Tulear. Within this species there do not seem to be any distinct subspecies.

### Lemurinae

The subfamily Lemurinae seems, as we have already noted, much less homogeneous in its ecology and ethology. *Lemur variegatus* differs from the other *Lemurs* in numerous characteristics; it is larger in size and has a different skull form. Gray, in 1863, proposed the creation of a special genus for this animal: Genus *Varecia*. We think that this generic distinction is justified. In our opinion there are as many if not more differences between *Varecia variegatus* and *Lemur* as there are between this group and *Hapalemur griseus*. The important color variations in *Lemur variegatus* have long been known. Six varieties have been discriminated in the literature, but more recent revisions, appropriately we feel, have reduced this number to three.

1. A black-and-white form in which the black coloration of the back is limited to the upper part and is cut longitudinally by a white band. This form is *Lemur variegatus variegatus* of Kerr (1792) or *Varecia varia* (Variety 1) of Gray (1870).

2. A form in which almost all the white parts are replaced by brownish red and in which the black parts are reduced in area. This is *Lemur variegatus ruber* of E. Geoffroy (1812), or *Varecia rubra* of Gray (1870).

3. An entirely black-backed form, except for the base of the tail, but with a transverse belt of white in the middle. This is *Lemur variegatus subcinctus* of Smith (1833) or *Varecia varia* (Variety 2) of Gray (1870).

Hill (1953) recognized a fourth form which he proposed to call *L. variegatus editorum*. This form is characterized by the absence of the longitudinal white line on the upper part of the back and corresponds to *Varecia varia* (Variety 3) of Gray (1870).

An examination of the collection in the British Museum of Natural History in London might make one believe in the existence of this last form, but in the collection of the Muséum National d'Histoire Naturelle of Paris there is a series of intermediates between the typical form with the longitudinal white band across the upper part of the back and the form in which the white band is absent. Therefore, we do not believe that this form should be considered as distinct.

### Genus Hapalemur

The genus *Hapalemur* consists of two species, *H. griseus* and *H. simus*. We have not been able to find this latter form, which is probably very localized in the eastern part of the island (Petter 1962b).

According to current classification, *Hapalemur griseus* is divided into two subspecies, *H. g. griseus* and *H. g. olivaceus*. Neither the examination of the type specimens (both in Paris) and of the collections in Paris and London, nor the observation of living animals found in Madagascar, has enabled us clearly to distinguish these two subspecies, both of which, in addition, are native to the eastern part of the island.

### Genus Lepilemur

As we have already noted, the genus *Lepilemur* is very different from the other Lemurinae. In their ecology and ethology they have almost nothing in common. Many of the characteristics of *Lepilemur* appear to be closer to those of the Indridae than of the Lemuridae and in our opinion its inclusion in the subfamily of the Lemurinae is not justified.

In a recent revision of the genus (Petter 1960), we have lumped all the described forms in the species *Lepilemur mustelinus*. On the basis of external morphological characteristics, cranial characteristics, behavior, and geographical distribution, we have distinguished five distinct populations corresponding to the following subspecies: *Lepilemur mustelinus mustelinus* (L. Geoffroy) in the east, *Lepilemur mustelinus microdon* (Forsyth Major) in the southeast, *Lepilemur mustelinus ruficaudatus* (Grandidier) in the west, *Lepilemur mustelinus leucopus* (Forsyth Major) in the south, and *Lepilemur mustelinus dorsalis* (Gray) on the island of Nosy-Bé.

Apart from *Lemur variegatus*, which we are inclined to exclude from the genus, the different species of *Lemur* form a rather homogeneous group. However, the problems posed by their detailed taxonomy are quite complex. The presence of these animals in all the wooded regions of Madagascar and the frequency of a more or less clear sexual difference in coloration has inclined authors to describe numerous subspecies without taking into account morphological variations due to age or sex, or even ecological or ethological particularities.

The classification generally used divides the *Lemur* into five species. However, as Schwarz has already noted (1936), *Lemur fulvus* does not seem to be sufficiently different from *Lemur macaco* to be specifically separated. In fact, two intermediate forms exist between these extreme types; one, *Lemur fulvus flavifrons* (Gray), has a similar distribution to that of *Lemur macaco* and exhibits a sexual difference in coloration which is even more pronounced. It is relatively easy to imagine that *Lemur macaco* derives from *Lemur fulvus* by the simple acquisition of tufts of hair on the ears and intensification of the coat color. Moreover, the presence of long brushes of hair on the ears is frequent among the lemurs; it is found in *Lemur macaco, Lemur fulvus sanfordi, Lemur fulvus collaris*, and also in *Cheirogaleus trichotis*.

The other intermediate form, *Lemur fulvus sanfordi* (Archbold 1932), lives in a region situated between the Sambirano forest, which is the habitat of *Lemur macaco*, and the forest of the northeast coast of Madagascar, the area where *Lemur fulvus albifrons* is found. The coloration of *Lemur fulvus sanfordi* in the two sexes is close to that of *Lemur fulvus albifrons*, although paler, but the male of the species (*L. f. sanfordi*) has tufts of long hairs on the ears, similar to *Lemur macaco*. This subspecies may therefore be a transitional form between *Lemur macaco* and *Lemur fulvus albifrons*.

There do not seem to be important differences in skull form between various species of *Lemur*. Their behavior also appears to be very similar in a number of aspects, and several forms have produced hybrids. A. P. Gray (1954), who raised hybrids born in zoological gardens, mentions several offspring of males of *Lemur macaco* and females of the different subspecies of *Lemur fulvus*.

All this inclines us to agree with Schwarz that it is preferable to unite these two species, *Lemur macaco* and *Lemur fulvus*, into a single species, and *macaco* having priority the four species ought to be named as follows:

*Lemur macaco*, with eight subspecies: *macaco, flavifrons, sanfordi, albifrons, fulvus, collaris, rufus,* and *mayottensis.*
*Lemur mongoz*, with two subspecies: *mongoz* and *coronatus.*
*Lemur catta.*
*Lemur rubriventer.*

### Indridae

As we have noted, the Indridae form a rather homogeneous group. The only species of the genus *Indri*, which is localized in the northeast of the island, shows little variation. Except where the color of the coat is concerned this is true also for the two species of the genus *Propithecus*, which has been studied in detail by Kaudern (1915). Only attempts at hybridization can demonstrate whether the existence of two species of *Propithecus* is real, or if it is only a question of subspecies.

*Avahi laniger*, although it is nocturnal and smaller, is very distantly related to the other Indridae, and it has two well-defined subspecies that we have observed in the east and west respectively.

### Daubentonidae

Although *Daubentonia* is very clearly separated from the other lemurs, it seems ecologically and ethologically to be closer to *Lemur* than to the other Malagasy prosimians.

## CONCLUSIONS

In conclusion, our ecological and ethological preliminary survey of the Malagasy lemurs has led us to reconsider somewhat the taxonomy of this group.

Basing our judgments purely on ecological and ethological criteria, we have attempted to propose some modifications, and it would be interesting to see these evaluated in the light of other considerations, particularly cytogenetics. It seems to us, for instance, that the rather similar homogeneous group called Cheirogaleinae in the present classification has very little in common with the Lemurinae and should be elevated to the rank of a distinct family.

The Lemurinae themselves are composed of two completely different types, *Lemur* and *Lepilemur*; and the combination of these in the same family in our opinion ought to be reconsidered.

Although the species *Lemur variegatus* is close to the typical *Lemurs* in certain characteristics, it is distinguished from them by numerous ecological and ethological particularities, and it seems to us merits separation in a special genus (*Varecia*).

In reconsidering the geographic division of the various species, we have been inclined to separate three forms of *Microcebus murinus*, to group all forms described as *Lepilemur* into five subspecies of a single species, *Lepilemur mustelinus*, and lastly to consider, according to the laws of nominal priority, all the subspecies of *Lemur fulvus* in the present classification as subspecies of *Lemur macaco*.

# PART II

 Apes

M an's nearest relatives are the anthropoid apes: the gibbon and orangutan, which live in Southeast Asia and the East Indies, and the gorilla
and chimpanzee, which are confined to equatorial Africa. The gibbon is
the smallest of the apes, standing less than three feet high and weighing
between 12 and 30 pounds. It does not resemble man as much as do the
other three apes, the great apes, being both more specialized in such
characteristics as brachiation and more primitive in the retention of ischial
callosities (Chap. 1). Gibbons are heavily furred and come in many colors,
including light gray, black, and reddish brown. But it is for their aerial
acrobatics that gibbons are justly famous. They seem to skim through the
forest scarcely touching the branches as they pass. Some idea of their
agility is contained in the following observation by Carpenter (1940:76):

> The buff female of group 3 swung quickly through an open tree and out
> on a limb. As she was preparing to swing into an adjacent tree, the limb broke,
> leaving a stub which was about six inches long. As the limb broke and fell the
> gibbon recovered by turning almost in mid-air and catching the remaining stub
> of the branch. With extreme rapidity she swung around under and then on top
> of the limb and then, with only a slight loss of time and momentum, jumped
> outward and downward 30 feet to an adjacent tree top.

The orangutan, the rarest of the apes, is confined to Borneo and Sumatra; there are probably no more than 5000 alive today. The male orang
is large, weighing as much as a heavy man. In zoos orang males have a
tendency to become very obese, they are virtually mountains of rolling fat,
and this condition emphasizes the large, fleshy pads on the sides of the
face and the pouch of skin under the jaw. Instead of the short, thick fur of
the gibbon, the orange-red hair of the orang is long and relatively sparse.
The orang is as deliberate in its movements as the gibbon is agile. His
legs and feet resemble arms and hands, in the human sense, more than is
true of any of the other apes; he is literally quadrumanual. These armlike
legs are almost as mobile as arms. Adapted for life in the tall trees of
tropical jungles, the orang is able to support his heavy weight by distribut-
ing it over many limbs, but the specializations that make this way of life
possible mean that adult orangs are very clumsy on the ground.

The chimpanzee and gorilla are closer to man in many respects than
they are to the Asian apes (Chap. 1). They are so similar to each other that
Simpson (1963) has recently suggested that they should be considered
only two species of the genus *Pan*. One of the major differences between
them is size—chimpanzee males are smaller than a man, weighing around
100 pounds, whereas gorilla males weigh as much as 375 pounds in the
wild (but, like the orang, may become much fatter and heavier in captivity).

The following three chapters describe recent field studies on the gorilla
by George Schaller and on two populations of chimpanzees, one in Uganda
(Vernon and Frances Reynolds) and one in Tanganyika (Jane Goodall).

It should be pointed out that both of these studies were made on the common chimpanzee, and refer to the same species, but the Reynolds prefer the specific name *troglodytes*, a name that is synonymous with the name *satyrus*, which Goodall prefers. The inclusion of two field studies of chimpanzees in this book reflects the fact that man is most interested in this most manlike of the apes, and is further justified because the two studies were made in very different parts of the chimpanzee's range. The two studies reveal broad similarities as well as some interesting contrasts. Social behavior and group organization, for example, seem much the same in both areas, with groups of about the same size and composition observed with comparable frequency. In both studies a core population seems to remain in, or return constantly to, the same area, and visitors from beyond this central area mix freely with the resident population.

One of the most interesting differences between the two studies is probably related to the two different habitats. Chimpanzees are basically tropical forest animals, and in the Budongo Forest the Reynolds found a population density of about 10 chimpanzees per square mile whereas Goodall estimated a maximum of only 3.3 per square mile (even when only the commonly used portions of the Reserve are included in the calculation). This difference in population density can be assumed to be due at least in part to the food resources available to the two populations. In the Budongo study area there is a more or less year-round abundance of fruit; heavily laden fig trees may be ignored in favor of other foods. The Gombe Stream Reserve, however, occurs at the edge of chimpanzee distribution. Not only is there a smaller proportion of fruit in the diet of the Gombe Reserve chimpanzees, but the inventory of food items eaten there is much larger. In expanding their diet, the Gombe Reserve chimpanzees employ tools and kill other animals, and the demands of this harsher environment may be such that the potential abilities of this species are more challenged, more fully developed than they ordinarily are in the forest. In this respect their behavior may more nearly approach that of chimpanzees in laboratory test situations. Although no tool use is involved, the baboons of South-West Africa, by comparison, exploit a wider variety of animal insect foods than do those on the Cape.

George Schaller was the only member of the Primate Project who had observed all four of the apes in the wild, and he consented to prepare a summary on the gibbon and orangutan, and a brief comparison of the behavior patterns of all the apes. His comparisons follow the three field reports.

GEORGE B. SCHALLER

10

◈ The Behavior of the Mountain Gorilla

Few animals have fired the imagination of man as much as the gorilla. Ever since this large ape was discovered in 1847 in West Africa, tales of the gorilla's ferocity and strength have stirred popular and scientific interest. The following excerpt from Owen (1859) provides an example of this literature:

> Negroes when stealing through the shades of the tropical forest become sometimes aware of the proximity of one of these frightfully formidable apes by the sudden disappearance of one of their companions, who is hoisted up into the tree, uttering, perhaps, a short choking cry. In a few minutes he falls to the ground a strangled corpse.

In spite of this considerable interest little factual information about the habits of the gorilla in nature became known, as Yerkes and Yerkes (1929) clearly illustrated in summarizing the available literature. The lowland gorilla (*Gorilla gorilla gorilla*), which inhabits the forests of southern Nigeria, Gabon, Cameroun, Rio Muni, and elsewhere in West Africa, still remains unstudied, although such authors as Merfield and Miller (1956) and Sabater Pi (1960) present useful local notes. The mountain gorilla (*Gorilla gorilla beringei*), separated by 650 miles of forest from the lowland gorilla, was discovered in 1902 in the eastern Congo and western Uganda. It closely resembles the lowland gorilla, the primary difference between the two subspecies being minor physical characters such as the length of the palate and the length of hair (Schultz 1934). Prominent among the previous studies of the mountain gorilla are those of Bingham (1932), Donisthorpe (1958), and Kawai and Mizuhara (1959).

The study was financed by the National Science Foundation and the New York Zoological Society, and the latter institution also acted as sponsor. Local sponsors were the Institute of the Parks of the Congo, and Makerere College, Uganda. I am extremely grateful to the University of Chicago Press for permission to quote and to reproduce the tables and figures from my earlier report. Dr. J. T. Emlen kindly read this manuscript critically.

This chapter is based on data which were collected between February 1959 and October 1960 on an expedition under the leadership of Dr. John T. Emlen, professor of zoology, University of Wisconsin. The main purposes of the expedition included: (1) a general six-month survey of mountain gorilla range with emphasis on distribution and ecological diversity (Emlen and Schaller February–July 1959), and (2) sustained observations into the life history of the mountain gorilla in a selected area for at least one year (Schaller August 1959–September 1960).

The first phase of the project involved long journeys by car and considerable hiking through various types of forests. We usually asked the local population about the presence or absence of gorillas, and whenever possible checked the information by personal inspection. In addition, we took detailed notes on the vegetation types and food plants that the gorillas used, and obtained comparative data on the ape's relative abundance in various parts of its range.

Fig. 10–1. View of the Kabara study area in the Mts. Mikeno-Karisimbi saddle, Virunga Volcanoes, Congo. (Courtesy Institut Géographique, République du Congo)

| | | |
|---|---|---|
| M = Mt. Mikeno | 1 = Bamboo | 4 = Heath |
| C = Mt. Karisimbi | 2 = Hagenia woodland | 5 = Giant senecio |
| K = Kabara (altitude 10,200 feet) | 3 = Grass meadow (altitude 11,400 feet) | |

Most of the observations of gorilla behavior were made on ten groups, comprising nearly 200 animals, in the Virunga Volcanoes of Albert National Park, Congo. My wife and I camped at an altitude of 10,200 feet in the saddle between Mts. Mikeno and Karisimbi, two dormant volcanoes both nearly 15,000 feet high. This main study area, called Kabara, included about 25 square miles of *Hagenia* woodland growing on the precipitous slopes of the two volcanoes (Fig. 10–1).

The purpose of this chapter is to present a brief summary of those aspects of the gorilla's behavior which are of greatest interest as they relate to comparative primate studies. For a detailed account of behavior and for full documentation see Schaller (1963).


## STUDY METHODS

Gorillas are usually not difficult to locate, for if a fresh trail is found the trampled vegetation, food remnants, dung, and other spoor aid in leading the tracker to the animals. In most areas, however, gorillas inhabit such dense vegetation that prolonged daily observations are difficult, if not impossible. The habitat with the best visibility was the Hagenia woodland in the Virunga Volcanoes, primarily because a shrub stratum was almost absent.

Two methods were used in observing gorillas. They were viewed from the cover of a tree trunk, with the observer remaining undetected by the animals; or they were approached by the observer slowly, alone, and in full view, to within about 150 feet, with the hope that after repeated contacts they would become habituated to his presence. The former method had only limited value, for the gorillas, with senses comparable to those of man, frequently detected me. The value of the latter method was shown by the fact that after from 10 to 15 prolonged contact periods some groups became so well habituated that their daily routine was little affected. Animals occasionally approached to within 15 feet of me, and once climbed into the same tree in which I was sitting. An excerpt from my field notes illustrates the casual manner in which group VII responded to my close proximity after 78 observation periods.

> 08:30 I advance inadvertently to within 30 feet of a foraging group. After I have settled myself on a low branch 5 feet above ground, a female with an infant on her back spots me, looks intently, and then continues to feed. A juvenile backs into the vegetation upon seeing me, and when the silver-backed male glances over from a distance of 45 feet he emits an annoyed grunt. However, the animals continue to sit and feed leisurely in the sun within 25 to 60 feet of my observation post.
>
> 09:30 Foraging slows down and ceases entirely as the animals rest in the sun within 40 to 60 feet of me.

10:30 Two animals begin to snack, and 10 minutes later the silver-backed male rises, looks at me seemingly startled and roars three times. He begins to feed and the whole group joins him. During the following 25 minutes the group moves some 500 feet and then settles into another rest area.

A group was usually observed daily for from one to four weeks until it moved outside the main study area, perhaps to reappear a few weeks later. I was always able to find at least one of the ten groups which intermittently frequented the forest around camp. In more than 300 encounters and 466 hours of direct observation, six groups became habituated to me. All members of these six groups (II, IV, V, VI, VII, VIII), as well as several gorillas in each of the other four groups and seven lone males, were recognized individually.

In spite of the excellent possibilities for observing gorillas at Kabara, the dense vegetation and the wandering habits of the animals made it difficult at times to see clearly and to obtain continuous observations on one group for more than a few successive hours. Once a group had voluntarily moved out of sight it was rarely pursued for this tended to frighten the animals and increase the chance of attacks. Most observation periods ranged from one to three hours, with a few as long as seven hours.

## DISTRIBUTION AND ECOLOGY

### Distribution

The range of the mountain gorilla extends over an area of about 35,000 square miles from the equator southward to 4°20′ S. latitude, a distance of some 300 miles, and from longitude 26°30′ E. to the eastern escarpment of the western Rift Valley (29°45′ E.), a distance of some 220 miles. Gorillas are not randomly distributed through the forest, but are concentrated in isolated population units in about 8000 square miles of terrain (Fig. 10–2). The boundaries of some of these units coincide with such natural barriers to the forest-dwelling gorilla as extensive grasslands, cultivation, or broad rivers, but frequently the forest continues unchanged at the boundary of an inhabited area. Stragglers, lone males or small groups, are sometimes found 20 or more miles from the nearest gorilla population. The erratic wanderings of such animals may be a means of colonizing new territory, accounting for some of the isolated population units.

Local concentrations of animals also exist within larger population units, especially in the lowland rain forest of the Congo basin. Populations of gorillas probably drift or are pushed about as local conditions change. The most important disturbance to the region during the past 200 or more years has been the repeated clearing of the forest for cultivation in small patches. Fields are worked by the Africans for three or four years

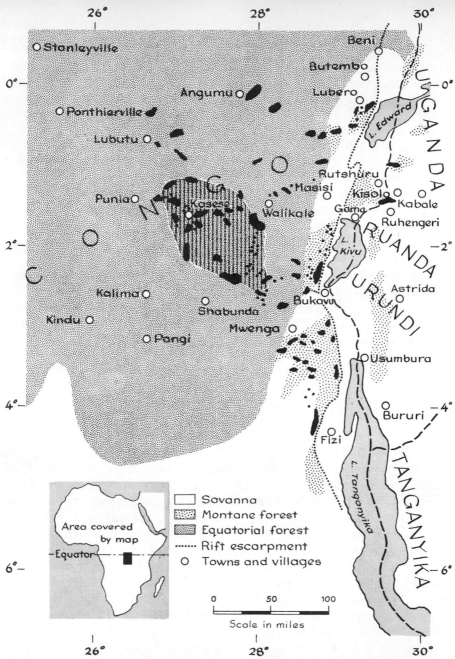

Fig. 10–2. The distribution of the mountain gorilla with respect to vegetation types. Mountain rain forest and bamboo are lumped under montane forest. The black areas indicate the location and approximate shape of isolated gorilla populations or gorilla concentrations in areas of continuous distribution. The small dots represent records of gorillas outside these areas. The hatching marks a central region of continuous but sparse distribution. The Virunga Volcanoes are represented by the black area near the village of Kisolo; the Kayonza Forest lies just north of the Virunga Volcanoes.

328

and then abandoned for at least ten years, allowing the forest to regenerate. Gorillas favor the dense secondary growth, where forage in the form of herbs, shrubs, and vines is plentiful, over primary forest, which supports only a sparse ground cover in its shadowy interior. Many gorilla concentrations occur near roads and around villages where disturbance to the forest has been most recent (Emlen and Schaller 1960).

## Ecology

The range of the mountain gorilla, although small, has considerable ecological diversity. The animals inhabit three major forest types which are stratified altitudinally from the Congo basin eastward to the summits bordering the Rift Valley.

About three-fourths of the gorillas are found, not in the mountains as their common name implies, but in lowland or equatorial rain forest at an altitude of from 1500 to 5000 feet (Fig. 10–2). A seemingly endless expanse of forest covers the flat to undulating terrain, broken here and there by a road, a village, or some ephemeral native fields (Fig. 10–3). The evergreen trees are from 120 to 180 feet high and the canopy is almost continuous. Lianas entwine the branches and epiphytes are common. Although sunlight filters to the ground in places, it is usually insufficient to support a herba-

Fig. 10–3. A typical view of the lowland rain forest region, showing a village of mud huts surrounded by stands of bananas, some young secondary forest, and in the distance the mature forest.

Fig. 10–4. Mountain rain forest covers the chaotic jumble of ridges and valleys of the rift escarpment. This photograph was taken in the highlands west of Lake Tanganyika.

ceous understory. Only where the canopy is broken—along rivers, at the edge of fields, and where a large tree has crashed to the ground—is there the tangle of low vegetation that the gorillas favor. The climate is enervating with high humidity and temperatures that tend to remain above 20° C. throughout the day.

Along the eastern edge of the Congo basin, the mountains become rugged, reaching a height of over 10,000 feet. Much of the area between 5000 and 8000 feet is covered with mountain rain forest (Fig. 10–4). This rain forest differs from that in the lowlands primarily in the somewhat smaller size of the trees and in the presence of gymnosperms. Gorillas are usually found in the lush valleys among tree ferns and vines rather than on the more open ridges. The climate in the highlands is temperate with temperatures rarely far above 20° C. and occasionally down to near the freezing point.

Gorillas are also found in bamboo (*Arundinaria alpina*) which occurs

330

as a definite vegetation zone between 8000 and 10,000 feet (Fig. 10–5). This grass forms a somewhat translucent and usually continuous canopy of some 20 to 35 feet high over miles of rolling uplands. Ground cover is sparse or absent except along trails and clearings. Because of its limited distribution, bamboo is of relatively minor importance in the total ecology of the gorilla. The main food of gorillas in this zone consists of bamboo shoots, which are abundant only during the rainy periods of the year. In the absence of shoots the apes have to seek other forage.

In addition to these three major forest types, there are minor local ones. The Hagenia woodland, a subtype of mountain rain forest in which the major part of the study was conducted, is found only in the Virunga Volcanoes (Figs. 10–5 and 10–6). The Hagenia forest resembles a parkland, with gnarled trees widely spaced and averaging only about 60 feet in height, and with a dense herbaceous understory consisting of *Senecio*, *Lobelia*, and other succulent plants. Above 11,500 feet the forest ceases and the open slopes are covered with scattered groves of giant lobelias and senecios (Fig. 10–5). Gorillas penetrate into this zone to an altitude of 13,500 feet, where temperatures drop to or below freezing nightly.

Though the climate and vegetation in the range of the mountain gorilla vary from tropical to temperate, the habitats are similar in being lush and damp throughout the year. Gorillas show considerable ecological adaptability, but they have remained entirely within the humid forests.

Fig. 10–5. A view of the Virunga Volcanoes, looking east from an altitude of 12,000 feet. The two distant peaks, Mts. Sabinio and Muhavura, lie on the Uganda border. The main part of the gorilla study was done in the Virunga chain.

## AGE AND SEX CLASSES

The development of one infant was traced in the wild from birth to the age of one and one-half years, and that of others of various ages for from 10 to 12 consecutive months. This enabled me to compare the sizes and behavior of infants and provided a fairly accurate means of estimating age. For further comparison, weight and size data of captive gorillas of approximately known age were obtained and compared to those of wild ones — another method for deriving a crude age scale. The following age and sex criteria are used in this chapter:

| Age and Sex Class | Approximate Age (in years) | Definition and Distinguishing Field Marks |
|---|---|---|
| Infant | 0–3 | Any animal carried by a female for prolonged periods and weighing less than about 50 to 60 pounds (Fig. 10–11). |
| Juvenile | 3–6 | Any small animal not carried by a female and weighing 60 to 120 pounds (Fig. 10–6). |
| Subadult and adult | 6+ | Any animal larger than a juvenile. |
| Female | 6+ | Any animal that carries an infant for prolonged periods; any large gorilla (weighing 150 to 250 pounds) with sagging breasts and long nipples (Figs. 10–6, 10–11). |
| Black-backed male | 6–10 | Any gorilla weighing 150 to 250 pounds with angular, muscular body, and with few or no gray hairs in its saddle (Fig. 10–14). |
| Silver-backed male | 10+ | Any very large gorilla (300 to 450 pounds) with prominent sagittal crest and with a gray or silver back (Figs. 10–6, 10–11). |

## POPULATION AND GROUP DYNAMICS

### Population Density

Population estimates are by necessity tentative, for accurate counts of gorillas in their forest environment are difficult to make. Two areas were sampled intensively, and the following figures obtained:

| Area | Approximate Number Square Miles | Estimated Gorilla Population | Number Gorillas Per Square Mile |
|------|------|------|------|
| Virunga Volcanoes | 155 | 450 | 2.9 |
| Kayonza Forest, Uganda | 96 | 150 | 1.5 |

Gorillas or their spoor were encountered more often in these two isolated and protected areas than in the other forests sampled, suggesting that the population density for the mountain-gorilla range as a whole does not exceed one animal per square mile. If this estimate is accurate, about 8000 gorillas exist in the 8000 or so square miles of forest inhabited by the subspecies. However, until further work amplifies the population data in more regions, a figure of from 5000 to 15,000 is suggested.

## Population Dynamics

We know very little about the factors that govern the dynamics of gorilla populations. For certain information, such as age at sexual maturity and longevity, only a few records from zoological gardens are available, and these may not be entirely applicable to free-living animals. The data I was able to obtain on wild gorillas reflect only the characteristics of the study population during a one-year period.

### Age at Sexual Maturity

Three pairs of lowland gorillas have reproduced in zoos (at Columbus, Basel, and Washington), and several females have shown behavior indicating their sexual maturity. Two of the males were about 9 to 9½ years old when they impregnated the females, but a third male was only about 7 years old. The 3 females were about 7, 7¼, and 10 years old at the time of conception; two other females first showed cyclic sexual receptivity between the ages of 6 and 7 years. This evidence suggests that females reach sexual maturity between 6 and 7 years of age, and males usually at about 9.

### Birth Rates

Infants remain with their mothers for about 3 years, and at least that amount of time elapses between births. Some juveniles about 4 years old occasionally associated with infantless females which were presumably their mothers. These observations suggest that females give birth every 3½ to 4½ years unless the infant dies. Of 27 females in 4 groups whose status was traced for more than 8 months, only 2 females lacked an infant or failed to give birth to one. Both these females seemed elderly and physically below par, one having a scabby skin, the other a blind eye.

*Mortality Factors*

Injury, predation, and disease were three general causes of mortality observed. Fourteen injuries were noted during the study. Most of these were minor, probably caused by collisions with branches or falls from trees. One female appeared to have a broken jaw, the only bone injury noted. Two of the wounds seemed to be bites; one of the bitten animals was an infant and the wound was so severe that it probably died.

Interactions between gorillas and most other large mammals in the forest, such as the elephant (*Loxodonta africana*) and buffalo (*Syncerus caffer*), appeared to be peaceful. One lone bull buffalo was observed to flee when a female gorilla approached to within 30 feet. Golden monkeys (*Cercopithecus mitis kandti*) were twice seen within 10 feet of gorillas, but the two species did not visibly respond to each other. Although gorillas and chimpanzees (*Pan troglodytes schweinfurthi*) inhabit the same forests in several areas, no interactions were seen. I found no evidence that leopards preyed on gorillas in my study area, but there is one reliable account from Uganda which indicates that they may occasionally do so. Some Bantu tribes persistently snare, spear, shoot, or net gorillas for food and to protect their crops, making man the only major predator on the apes.

Diseases are probably the chief cause of death in the mountain gorilla. Microfilaria have been collected from its blood, and such helminths as *Anaplocephala, Ascaris*, and *Anaglostoma* from its intestine. One adult male, autopsied by a veterinarian, died of gastro enteritis. Several of my study animals showed symptoms resembling those of the common cold. I found nematode ova, similar to those of the human hookworm, in 53.3 percent of 45 dung samples collected. Even minor ailments, such as the nematode infestation, can lower the resistance of the animal and make it susceptible to more serious disorders.

*Longevity*

At least five lowland gorillas have lived longer than 20 years in captivity. One of these died at the age of 34½ years and looked definitely old at that time. Very old-appearing animals are uncommon in the wild, indicating that longevity there perhaps rarely exceeds from 25 to 30 years.

*Population Structure*

Only the ten groups in the main study area were known sufficiently well to permit an analysis of population structure. Males, silver-backed and black-backed combined, constituted 18.9 percent of these groups, and females 36.7 percent (Table 10–1, A)—a ratio of approximately 2 females to 1 male. However, if all males, including the lone individuals, are considered, the ratio changes to about 1½ females to 1 male (Table 10–1, B). Although additional lone males undoubtedly existed in the area, their num-

TABLE 10-1. SEX AND AGE CLASS COMPOSITION
OF THE KABARA GORILLA POPULATION

| | A | | B | |
| | Animals in Groups at the Beginning of the Study* | | Total Kabara Population Including All Known Lone Males, Births, and Animals Who Have Left Groups or Joined Them by the End of the Study | |
| Sex and Age Class | Number of Animals | Percent | Number of Animals | Percent |
|---|---|---|---|---|
| Silver-backed male | 17 | 10.0 | 25 | 13.1 |
| Black-backed male | 15 | 8.9 | 18 | 9.4 |
| Female | 62 | 36.7 | 65 | 34.1 |
| Juvenile | 29 | 17.2 | 31 | 16.2 |
| Infant | 46 | 27.2 | 52** | 27.2 |
| Total | 169 | 100.0 | 191 | 100.0 |

\* Indicates animals present at the time of the first complete count of each group.
\*\* Two infants that died soon after birth are not included.

ber was not sufficient to raise the total to the expected 1 : 1 ratio. Juveniles were difficult to sex accurately in the wild, but their sex ratio seemed to me roughly equal. It is possible that males have a higher postjuvenile mortality rate than females.

About 45 percent of the population was juvenile or infant. Infants outnumbered juveniles 52 (27.2 percent) to 31 (16.2 percent), or by about 30 percent. The 54 infants which were present at one or another time in the population indicate a yearly birthrate of 17/193 or 90/1000.

### Infant and Juvenile Mortality Rates

Of 13 infants born between August 1959 and August 1960, one died, one disappeared, and one was so seriously wounded that it probably died — a mortality rate of 23 percent in the first year of life. Given the birth rate and the population figures in Table 10-1, B, it can be deduced that, assuming a 50 : 50 sex ratio at birth, the number of males declines about 47 percent between birth and the age of 6 years. Because it was impossible to differentiate two age classes in adult females, it could not be determined if their mortality rate was of similar magnitude.

## Group Dynamics

### Group Size

Gorilla groups varied in size from 2 to about 30 animals. C. Cordier, an animal dealer, has trapped or seen groups of 4, 13, 14, 15, 19, and 25 animals in the lowland rain forests near Utu. In the Kayonza Forest, a mountain rain forest, I obtained counts of about 2, 5, 5, 7, 14, and 15 animals per group. In my main study area the smallest group consisted of 5 animals, the largest of 27 (Table 10–2), but changes occurred in one group which brought its number temporarily up to 30. Although there appeared to be no difference in the size of groups in the various vegetation types, the average size of groups varied from region to region. Around Kabara average group size was 16.9 animals; in the Uganda portion of the Virunga Volcanoes and in the Kayonza Forest it was only from 7 to 8 animals. It is possible that in the absence of predation by man such factors as availability and type of forage influence the size of groups.

TABLE 10–2. THE COMPOSITION OF GORILLA GROUPS AT KABARA

| Group | Silver-backed Male | Black-backed Male | Female | Juvenile | Infant | Total |
|-------|------|------|--------|----------|--------|-------|
| I | 1 | 0 | 3 | 2 | 2 | 8 |
| II | 1 | 3 | 6 | 5 | 4 | 19 |
| III | 1 | 0 | 2 | 1 | 1 | 5 |
| IV | 4 | 1 | 10 | 3 | 6 | 24 |
| V | 2 | 2 | 3 | 2 | 2 | 11 |
| VI | 1 | 1 | 9 | 2 | 7 | 20 |
| VII | 1 | 2 | 6 | 4 | 5 | 18 |
| VIII | 1 | 2 | 8 | 3 | 7 | 21 |
| IX | 4 | 3 | 9 | 5 | 6 | 27 |
| XI | 1 | 1 | 6 | 2 | 6 | 16 |
| Total | 17 | 15 | 62 | 29 | 46 | 169 |
| Percent | 10.0 | 8.9 | 36.7 | 17.2 | 27.2 | 100 |

### Group Composition

The composition of the 10 study groups at the time of the first accurate count of each group is presented in Table 10–2. All groups contained at least 1 silver-backed male, 1 or more females, and a variable number of young (Fig. 10–6). Average group composition was: 1.7 silver-backed males, 1.5 black-backed males, 6.2 females, 2.9 juveniles, and 4.6 infants.

### Changes in Group Composition

Changes in composition occurred with relative frequency in some groups, but only rarely in others. Three examples illustrate this.

Group VIII: This group was observed at intervals between November 1959 and May 1960. Its composition of November 19, 1959, was 1 silver-backed male, 2 black-backed males, 8 females, 3 juveniles, and 7 infants — a total of 21. No changes occurred in the composition of this group.

Fig. 10–6. A typical gorilla group in the rank ground cover of the Hagenia wood-land. Ten animals are visible. The silver-backed male is yawning, showing his black tartar-covered teeth. The animal in the right foreground is a female, be-hind her is a black-blacked male, and then another female. The small animal by the silver-backed male and facing the camera is a juvenile.

Group VII: I studied group VII in greater detail than any other group from October 1959 to September 1960. Its composition on October 10, 1959, was 1 silver-backed male, 2 black-backed males, 6 females, 4 juve-niles, and 5 infants—a total of 18. Between February 1 and 6 an infant was born. Between February 14 and March 16 an unknown female with infant joined the group, the only change of this type noted during the study.

Group IV: Detailed records of the composition of this group were ob-tained at intervals between March 1959 and August 1960. These records follow:

Composition on September 1, 1959: 4 silver-backed males, 1 black-backed male, 10 females, 3 juveniles, 6 infants—a total of 24.

March 12, 1959: An infant was born.

August 28 to August 30: A peripheral silver-backed male left; then rejoined the group.

September 9: A new silver-back joined the group. The peripheral male of August left again but rejoined it by September 22.

September 18–20: An infant was born.

Between October 2, 1959, and January 11, 1960: The peripheral male and the No. 2 male in the hierarchy left. A new silver-backed male and two females both with infants were added. They probably represented a small group which joined. An infant was born in late December.

April 24, 1960: A silver-backed male who had been with the group at least since August 1959 left.

April 25, 1960: An infant was born but died two days later.

Between May 1 and 15: A new silver-backed male joined the group and remained at least to May 24.

Between May 24 and August 12: The male who joined in early May left.

In the course of 17 months, 7 different silver-backed males were known to have associated with the group, but of the 4 present in August 1959 only the dominant male remained one year later. Figure 10–7 illustrates the coming and going of the males, and also indicates their dominance status and comparative size. Four infants were born, and 2 females with infants were added. At my last encounter, on August 13, 1960, the composition

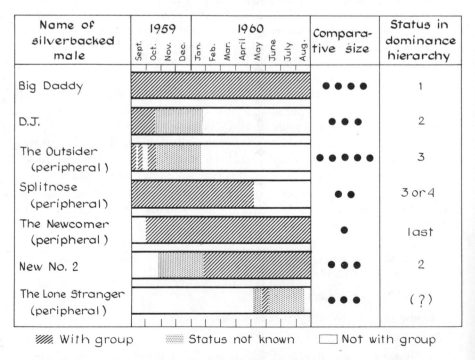

Fig. 10–7. The joining and parting of silver-backed males in group IV.

was 3 silver-backed males, 1 black-backed male, 12 females, 3 juveniles, and 10 infants, a total of 29.

In general, groups tended to remain quite stable in composition over many months. One group of 6 animals, which was repeatedly encountered by many different observers in the eastern part of the Virunga Volcanoes, showed no changes in two years except for the birth of one infant. Most changes in my study resulted from arrival and departure of males and the births and deaths of infants.

### Subgroups

Subgrouping, or the temporary splitting of one group into two distinct units, was infrequent. Once group IV split into two units in the morning, moving about 600 feet apart, but the subgroups joined again the same evening. Two juveniles and two silver-backed males apparently parted from group V for several days before rejoining, raising the total number of silver-backed males and juveniles in the group to four each (see Table 10–2).

### Lone Males

The term "lone male" was applied to animals which were not associated with a group at the time of observation. At least four silver-backed males and three black-backed males were lone animals all or most of the time in the study area. Lone females were not encountered.

The most detailed observations on the behavior of males were made on group IV (Fig. 10–7). Males which tended to remain at the outer edge of the group were designated as "peripheral." Only the dominant male remained with the group the whole year; one male joined and left twice within about 20 days; others remained for several months before departing. Between November and May, one of the lone males, "The Lone Stranger," was seen repeatedly and usually alone. Once I encountered him at the periphery of group VI, but he left it the same day. Six months later he joined group IV, where he remained for at least one week.

The response of groups to lone males was observed three times. Once a silver-backed male merely walked into group IV without eliciting a reaction. In another instance, the dominant male of group VI stared threateningly at an approaching lone silver-backed male, and the latter made no further attempt to join the group. Again, two "lone" males, a silver-back and a black-back, approached and remained at the periphery of group VI one day; they were seen in the group the following day and had both left by the third day.

Lone males fell into several age classes. The three black-backed males in the study area were small, medium, and large. Most of the silver-backed males appeared to be in the prime of life, and only one seemed old.

Lone males associated with some groups but not with others. Of the six groups which were studied intensively, they were seen only with groups IV and VI, suggesting that the lone males exercised some form of selectiveness. It is possible that through previous contacts they have learned which group will accept them and which will not.

It is a popular supposition that lone males have been forcibly thrown from groups by rivals. I observed no strife between males in a group, and the readiness with which they left and joined some groups suggested that they did so quite freely.

### Intergroup Interactions

Several gorilla groups periodically occupied the same general section of the forest, and two or more sometimes wandered close to each other. On at least 12 occasions, one group heard but could not see another group in the distance yet the groups made no attempt to approach each other. However, sometimes groups met face to face. I took notes on the sequence of events at four such meetings, and close association eight more times was confirmed by evidence from trails and contact with the animals after the event. Most interactions involved only two groups, but once three groups (I, II, III) briefly occupied an area of about 300 feet in diameter.

The responses of groups to each other varied considerably. Group VII and another group approached each other to within 300 feet or less on two

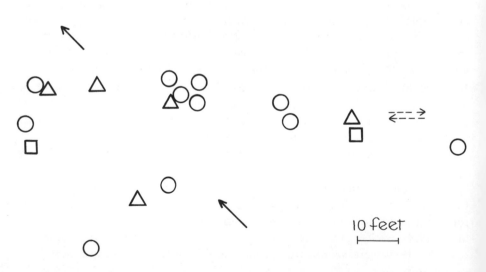

Fig. 10–8. A combined nest site of groups VII and III during the night of October 19–20, 1959. Squares represent nests of silver-backed males, circles of black-backed males or females, and triangles of juveniles. The solid arrow indicates the evening and morning direction of travel of group VII; the dashed arrow of group III.

occasions, but made no attempt to join as they foraged and rested in full view of one another for several hours. Groups VII and XI once sat in adjoining rest areas, and two members of group VII mingled for about two minutes with group XI. However, the dominant male of group VII charged several times silently and on all fours at the dominant male of group XI. The two males then stared at each other, sometimes with brow ridges almost touching. The two groups parted later in the day. In contrast, group VII and group III joined one afternoon, occupied a common nest site (Fig. 10–8), and parted the following morning. Groups VI and VIII once remained near each other for three days before I saw them mingle briefly. On the first day the groups were at one time only 35 feet apart, and that evening they nested near each other, with 30 feet separating the closest animals of the respective groups. On the second day the dominant male of group VIII approached to within 15 feet of a female of group VI before the latter moved away. The two groups nested 800 feet apart, but finally, on the third day, mingled for about five minutes before parting.

On the whole, interactions between groups were peaceful. Aggressive bluff charges were made by one male as noted above, and I once observed weak aggressiveness, in the form of incipient charges toward intruders from another group by a female, a juvenile, and an infant. Chest-beating displays were not prominent, except once, the animals giving the impression of being only slightly excited.

The most striking aspect of intergroup behavior was the highly variable response of a given group to the presence of others. Group VII, for example, joined one group, merely advanced toward another, and behaved antagonistically toward a third. It is likely that many neighboring groups in a local population such as at Kabara have repeated contacts with each other and that each encounter affects the nature of subsequent meetings.

### Group Ranges and Movements

#### Home Range

Groups restricted their activities to definite areas or home ranges on the order of from 10 to 15 square miles each. Group VI, for instance, was encountered repeatedly over 8 square miles of forest and group VII over 8½ square miles; however, both groups left the study area for varying periods. Although the range of each group was fairly large, groups occasionally spent many days in a restricted locality. Group VII once remained for 18 days in 1½ square miles of terrain, then switched its center of activity to another part of the forest.

Home ranges were not exclusively occupied by one group (Fig. 10–9). Sometimes the overlap between adjoining ranges was slight, but for several

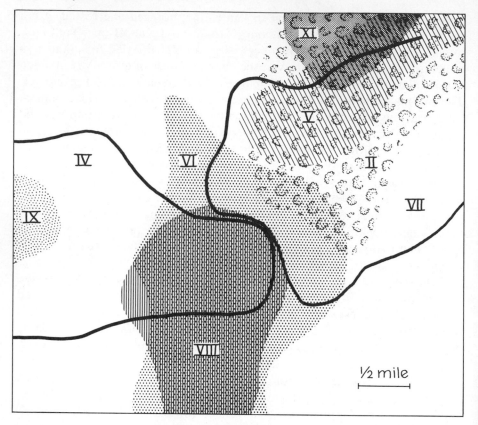

Fig. 10–9. A schematic diagram illustrating the extensive overlap of the home ranges of eight gorilla groups in the Kabara area of the Virunga Volcanoes. Two further groups, not indicated on the diagram, were encountered several times in the range of group VII. The scale of the diagram corresponds to the aerial photograph (Fig. 10–1).

groups it was quite extensive. Six groups intermittently used the same square mile of forest in one area, and three groups periodically occupied a slope by camp, once all at the same time.

The almost complete overlap of some ranges and observations on peaceful interactions between groups indicate that gorillas have no territory in the sense of an exclusive area defended against others of the same species.

### Seasonal Movement

Except for bamboo, the vegetation types frequented by gorillas show no conspicuous differences in the abundance of forage throughout the year. No evidence that gorillas move seasonally was obtained, although some groups used the bamboo below Kabara more during the periods of heavy rain, when shoots were present, than during the drier periods of the year.

### Patterns of Group Movement

The only generalization about movement which can safely be made is that groups travel continuously within the boundaries of their home range and that they frequent certain parts of this range at irregular intervals. Group VI, for example, made its appearance near our camp at intervals of about 40 days (from 24 to 57 days), and group VIII at intervals of about 60 days (from 52 to 78 days). Groups remained in a limited area anywhere from 1 day to 1 month before moving on to another part of the forest.

### Patterns and Distances of Daily Movement

That the direction and distance of travel by a group in the course of a day tends to be unpredictable is illustrated by Fig. 10–10, which shows the peregrinations of group IV over a 17-day period. I paced, or alternately paced and estimated, the complete daily trail of a group from night nest site to night nest site on 114 occasions. The distance of travel in this sample varied from 300 to 6000 feet with an average of 1742 feet. How-

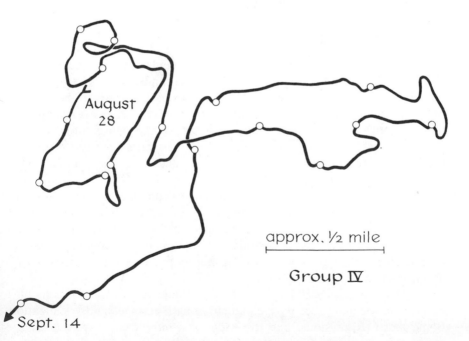

Fig. 10–10. The daily route of travel of group IV on the slopes of Mt. Mikeno between August 28 and September 14, 1959. Each circle represents one night nest site.

ever, the average distance varied somewhat from group to group. Group VI, for instance, averaged 1242 feet (S.D. 660) per day, and group VII averaged 2177 feet (S.D. 353) per day.

Groups tended to move farther in the afternoon than in the morning. After rising from the night nest, usually between 06:00 and 08:00 hours, the animals fed intensively for about 2 hours, moving very slowly. Between 09:00 and 10:00 hours activity slowed down as most gorillas snacked, sunbathed, and slept intermittently until about 14:00 hours. Thus, by noon the average distance of a group from its nest site of the previous night was only about 500 feet, and by midafternoon about 700 feet. Approximately half of the average daily distance was covered between 15:00 and 17:00 hours as the animals walked fairly steadily while feeding. After 17:00 hours activity tended to slow down and finally ceased at dusk, at 18:00 hours, when the gorillas bedded down for the night and remained in their nests during the hours of darkness.

Search for food did not account for all the movement observed. A wandering group at Kabara ate only a negligible amount of the available forage in its path. On several occasions, and for unknown reasons, a group moved without stopping some 5000 to 15,000 feet to another part of the forest before settling down again.

## SOCIAL BEHAVIOR

Gorilla groups are quite cohesive. The central core of each group is composed of the dominant male and all females and young. The extra males, both black-backed and silver-backed, tend to be peripheral. The diameter of a group at any given moment rarely exceeds 200 feet as every animal remains attentive to the movements of others in the dense forest environment. Except for extra males, single individuals rarely are more than 100 feet from other members of the group. The behavior of the group is coordinated by four means:

1. Postures and gestures are important in communication. A dominant male who stands motionless, facing in a certain direction, indicates that he is ready to leave and the other members of the group crowd around him (Fig. 10–11); an unexplained sudden run by an animal communicates danger; in order to be groomed a gorilla merely presents a part of its body to another animal.

2. How much facial expressions communicate emotions is difficult to determine, for many occur in conjunction with gestures and vocalizations. Some facial expressions, like the wide-open mouth and exposed teeth of angry animals, probably emphasize and elaborate information communicated by other means.

3. Vocalizations and other sounds are occasionally an important means

Fig. 10–11. A silver-backed male indicates his readiness to leave the rest area by standing motionless with his legs spread. A female with small infant on her back has joined him.

of communication in dense vegetation, for not until the animal has drawn attention to itself is further communication by means of gestures or facial expressions possible.

4. Physical control appears to be of importance only in females handling their infants. A female pulls her small infant back when it wanders too far from her side, and she regularly shifts it from her chest to her back and vice versa.

The small number of overt social interactions was a most striking aspect of intragroup behavior. The most frequently noted interactions were dominance (at .23 times per hour of observation), mutual grooming (at .28 times), and social play (at .11 times). The relative infrequency of interaction can probably be attributed to the following circumstances. Competition for food and mates provided little basis for strife since forage was abundant and sexual behavior not prominent. The members of a group were alert to the possibility of aggressive encounters, and subordinate animals tended to circumvent issues before they materialized. And, finally, the gorillas gave

345

one the impression of having an independent and self-dependent temperament, appearing stoic, aloof, and reserved in their affective behavior.

Though the members of a group spent most of the day very close to one another and were highly tolerant of each other, persistent aggregations of specific individuals were rare. Once two females in group VII consorted closely for several days. One juvenile tagged behind the sole black-backed male of group IV for more than one month. Various members of the group sometimes sought the vicinity of the dominant male for brief periods. In group IV as many as four silver-backed males occasionally rested within a diameter of 30 feet. Females now and then approached the dominant male to lie by his side, and on nine occasions rested their heads on his saddle or leaned against his body. Juveniles and infants were also attracted to the silver-backed male. At times as many as four youngsters climbed over the reclining male, slid down his rump, and pulled his hair without eliciting a response. Twice within the space of an hour, a large infant grabbed the rump hairs of the dominant male and hitched a ride for from 30 to 50 feet. However, the only persistent associations were between mothers and their young.

TABLE 10–3. DOMINANCE INTERACTIONS BETWEEN AGE AND SEX CLASSES

| Dominant Animal | Silver-backed Male | Black-backed Male | Female | Juvenile | Infant | Total |
|---|---|---|---|---|---|---|
| | | | Subordinate Animal | | | |
| Silver-backed male | 13 | 1 | 26 | 9 | 2 | 51 |
| Black-backed male | — | — | 2 | 3 | — | 5 |
| Female | — | 4 | 12 | 13 | 11* | 40 |
| Juvenile | — | — | — | 4 | 8 | 12 |
| Infant (One year or older) | — | — | — | — | 2 | 2 |
| Total | 13 | 5 | 40 | 29 | 23 | 110 |

* Tabulated only if infant was not in direct contact with its mother at the time.

### Dominance and Leadership

Definite dominance interactions were observed 110 times (Table 10–3). Dominance was most frequently asserted along narrow trails, when one animal claimed the right of way, or in the choice of sitting place, when the dominant animal supplanted the subordinate one. Gorillas showed their dominance with a minimum of actions. Usually an animal low in the rank order simply moved out of the way at the mere approach or brief stare of a high-ranking one. The most frequently noted gesture involving bodily contact was a light tap with the back of the hand of a dominant individual against the body of a subordinate one.

One example from my field notes illustrates a typical dominance interaction:

> A juvenile sits under the dry canopy of a leaning tree trunk during a heavy rain storm. A female walks toward the juvenile who rapidly vacates its seat, while she appropriates the dry spot. Shortly thereafter the silver-backed male arrives and pushes the female with the back of his hand on the lower part of her back until she is out in the rain and he is under cover.

Dominance was largely correlated with body size. Silver-backed males were dominant over all black-backed males, females, and young. If more than one silver-backed male was present in a group, they appeared to have a linear hierarchy (Fig. 10–7), seemingly based in part on age, with old and young males occupying subordinate positions. Black-backed males and females were dominant over all juveniles and infants not with their mothers. The relationship between black-backed males and females varied, perhaps being dependent on size and personal differences. As shown in Table 10–3, females were dominant over black-backed males four times and the reverse occurred twice. Females appeared to lack a stable hierarchy among themselves, for situations which resulted in dominance behavior between other group members frequently elicited no response among females. The 12 female-female interactions suggest that females have a changing hierarchy in which mothers with young infants are dominant over those with older infants or with none. Dominance among and between juveniles and infants seemed to be based on size.

The dominant silver-backed male was also the leader of the group. Every independent animal in the group appeared to be aware of the activity of the leader either directly or through the behavior of animals in his vicinity. Cues reflecting a changed pattern of activity were patterned after the leader. Thus, the entire daily routine—the distance of travel, the location of rest stops, and the time and place of nesting—was largely determined by the leader. In times of danger the leader also acted as protector of the group, frequently dropping behind the fleeing animals to face the intruder. Once, when I inadvertently surprised group IV at close range, the leader grabbed a juvenile around the waist and raced from 30 to 40 feet away before releasing it. Variations in the behavior of groups tended to reflect the individual idiosyncrasies of the leaders.

Groups moving rapidly tended to travel in single or double file with the leader at or near the front. One procession in group VII was typical: silver-backed male, female and infant, female and infant, juvenile, juvenile, black-backed male, female and infant, large infant, female and infant, 2 females (one with infant) and 2 juveniles together, female and infant, black-backed male. However, when movement was slow, the leader often traveled in the center or near the end of the group. The number-two silver-backed male in the group IV hierarchy assumed leadership of a subgroup until the two units rejoined.

TABLE 10–4. NUMBER OF OBSERVATIONS OF MUTUAL GROOMING IN THE VARIOUS AGE AND SEX CLASSES

| Animals Grooming | Animals Groomed | | | | | |
| --- | --- | --- | --- | --- | --- | --- |
| | Silver-backed Male | Black-backed Male | Female | Juvenile | Infant | Total |
| Silver-backed male | 0 | 0 | 0 | 0 | 3 | 3 |
| Black-backed male | 0 | 0 | 0 | 0 | 0 | 0 |
| Female | 0 | 1 | 5 | 13 | 76 | 95 |
| Juvenile | 1 | 1 | 9 | 10 | 12 | 33 |
| Infant | 0 | 0 | 2 | 0 | 1 | 3 |
| Total | 1 | 2 | 16 | 23 | 92 | 134 |

**Mutual Grooming**

The 134 observations of instances in which one animal groomed the pelage of another are summarized in Table 10–4. Gorillas did not often groom each other, and grooming was never reciprocal. No female was seen to groom the dominant male, and females groomed each other only five times. Nearly three-fourths of my observations were made on females grooming infants and juveniles, the activity being sometimes intense and prolonged. Juveniles groomed females on nine occasions, sometimes when the latter carried small infants. A 1¼-year-old infant groomed the back of its mother; it was the youngest animal observed to groom either itself or another.

The function of grooming in adult gorillas seems to be primarily utilitarian since they rarely groom each other and when they do, they concentrate on those parts of the body which the animal itself cannot reach with ease. However, the purpose of grooming appears to vary somewhat with age and sex class. At times juveniles seemed to employ grooming as a means of initiating social contact with females and with infants. Generally, animals groomed themselves, with females doing so proportionally twice as often as males, and juveniles another half as many times as females. Infants less than 2 years old were never seen to groom themselves.

## Play

I recorded as play any relatively unstereotyped behavior in which an animal was involved in vigorous actions seemingly without definite purpose. Of 156 gorillas involved in 96 observations of play, all but five were juvenile or infant. One female played with an infant by holding it down until it struggled free, the only interaction of this type noted. About half (43 percent) of the animals played alone, and this usually involved swinging and sliding on branches and lianas, batting vegetation, and turning somersaults down slopes. One infant placed a cushion of moss on its head like a cap and walked back and forth on a branch. Infants played alone twice as frequently as juveniles.

In social play infants had their first opportunity to interact closely with other youngsters in the group. Some 81 percent of the play groups consisted of only two animals, but a few contained three or four young. Playing youngsters rarely remained together for more than 15 minutes. Although a juvenile sometimes weighed five times as much as the infant with which it was wrestling vigorously, the disparity in weight never caused quarrels or injury, for the larger animal always contained its strength. Most social play included wrestling and chasing, and such games as follow the leader and king of the mountain.

The following two quotations from my field notes illustrate typical lone and social play sequences:

(1) A 9-month-old bumbles around by the reclining silver-backed male. With a wide overhand motion it swats the male on the nose, but he merely turns his head. The infant then runs downhill and turns a somersault over one shoulder and ends up on its back, kicking its legs in bicycle fashion and waving its arms above the head with great abandon. A 10-month-old infant watches these proceedings while propped against the rump of the male. Suddenly the ten-month-old infant rises, hurries to a sitting juvenile and pulls the hair on its crown with one hand. When this brings no response, the infant yanks at the hair with both hands, but the juvenile remains oblivious. The infant desists, sits briefly, suddenly rolls forward over one shoulder, and with arms and legs flailing like a windmill rolls over and over downhill and disappears in the vegetation.

(2) A juvenile and a 1¾-year-old infant sit about 4 feet apart. Suddenly the juvenile twists around and grabs for the infant, which rushes away hotly pursued by the juvenile. The juvenile catches the infant and covers it with his body, propped on elbows and knees. Twisting and turning, struggling and kicking, more and more of the infant emerges from beneath the juvenile. Freedom gained, the infant grabs an herb stalk at one end and the juvenile snatches the other end. They pull in opposite directions; the juvenile yanks hard and the infant is jerked

forward. They then sit facing each other, mouths open, and swing their arms at each other and grapple slowly. Another juvenile comes dashing up, and in passing swipes at the juvenile and all three disappear running into the undergrowth. (Schaller 1963).

### Female-Young Interactions

The relationship between the mother and her single offspring changes from the infant's complete dependence during the first few months of its life, through a period of gradual lessening of the physical and emotional bonds, to a stage when the youngster becomes integrated into the group.

#### Female-Infant Interactions

The ties between mothers and their infants remain close for about 3 years. Only females care for infants, feeding, transporting, and protecting them when they are small, and, after they are fairly self-sufficient, providing the social comfort which the young seem to derive from the female's proximity.

FEEDING: I observed only 5 instances of suckling in infants older than 1 year of age, indicating that the young were partly weaned by then. Twice females pushed away their young, 8 months and 1¼ years old respectively, when they attempted to suckle. One infant, 5 months old, suckled on a female who was not its mother. Infants ingested some solid food by the age of 2½ months, and by the age of 7 or 8 months the bulk of their diet probably consisted of forage.

Females rarely exerted direct control over the foraging of their young, who appeared to learn what to eat and what not to eat largely by observing their mothers and by trial and error. Once a female removed a leaf from the hands of her infant and threw it away, the only such instance noted. One infant took some food from the hands of its mother and ate it, and another picked a leaf from its mother's lip. On 5 occasions infants placed plants which adults did not eat into their mouths, but 3 times they spat them out.

TRANSPORT: Over long distances mothers carried only their own infants. Juveniles picked up infants 8 times but never transported them farther than 50 feet before the infant either struggled free or was retrieved by its mother. The method of transport varied with the infant's age. A newborn young appeared to lack the strength to clasp its mother's hair securely, and she supported it to her chest with one or both arms until it was nearly 3 months old. By the age of 1 month an infant was able to hang on by itself long enough to permit the female to use both hands briefly while ascending trees. By the age of 3 months infants began to ride regularly on the broad backs of their mothers. The characteristic position of the infant on the back of a walking female was to lie prostrate with the head near the shoulder region and with the hands grasping the mother's sides, shoulders, or neck.

Although the youngster was carried throughout the period of infancy, the female gave it the opportunity to travel on its own at an early age. One female placed her 3-month-old infant, barely able to crawl, on the ground and walked slowly along while her offspring attempted to follow. By 4 and 5 months of age, when infants assumed the quadrupedal gait of adults, they began to leave their mothers and to seek social contact with others in the group. By 6 and 7 months of age, infants were walking and climbing by themselves. Large infants, from 1 to 1¼ years old, spent much time sitting beside rather than upon their mothers. When infants reached the age of 1½ years and weighed some 25 pounds, females sometimes appeared unwilling to carry them. A frequent sight was a female walking slowly with an infant toddling at her heels. However, at the first sign of danger or the onset of rapid movement all infants up to the age of nearly 3 years rushed to their mothers and climbed aboard.

PROTECTION: The mother guarded the infant from harm during the average day-to-day existence. On two occasions mothers batted away the hands of other females when they attempted to touch a newborn. When younger than about 4 months old, the infant was rarely permitted to stray farther than 10 feet from its mother before being pulled back to her side. By the age of 8 months, young sometimes strayed more than 20 feet from their mothers, and by the age of 1 year they wandered through the resting group, sometimes out of their mothers' sight. One female retraced her steps 8 feet through a tree and pulled her 1½-year-old young across a gap in the branches. Another female showed strong concern for her infant, which had a large wound on its rump; the infant never rode on her back, but was cradled gently in her arm in such a way that no part of the injury was touched.

SOCIAL: The mother was the only object in the environment to which the infant turned readily at all times even after it had been weaned and was able to travel under its own power. Large infants retained their social ties with their mothers, remaining near them most of the day and all night until they became fully integrated into the group at the age of about 3 years.

Two infants were observed to have strong social bonds with females other than their mothers. One 6-month-old young repeatedly visited an infantless female and stayed with her for an hour or more. Another infant, 1½ years old, spent most of its time from November through May with a female and small infant, returning to its mother only intermittently during the day and apparently at night.

Strong social ties also appeared to bind females to their infants. Sometimes a female walked up to a large infant, sat beside it, and placed her arm over its shoulder, drawing it close. The infant of one female died 2 days after birth and was then carried by her for 4 days before being discarded on the trail.

*Female-Juvenile Interactions*

Although most females and juveniles interacted only in dominance and grooming, a few juveniles associated closely with certain females, presumably their mothers. One juvenile, about 3 or 3½ years old, was constantly near an infantless female; 1 year later the female still had no infant, but the juvenile associated with her only intermittently. Another juvenile, judged to be 3½ or 4 years old, was frequently seen with an infantless female, but when she gave birth the juvenile no longer stayed near her. Several juveniles approached females with small infants and rested near them. A close examination of dung in nests revealed that juveniles occasionally slept in the nest with a female or with a female and infant. Although females sometimes rebuffed juveniles mildly by swatting at them or by simply walking away from them, the social ties between some animals persisted until juveniles were about 4½ years old.

**Mating Behavior**

My work on free-living gorillas yielded remarkably few observations on sexual behavior. I witnessed only two copulation sequences and one invitation to copulate. Thus, most of my information is based on captive gorillas, whose behavior is not necessarily comparable to free-living ones. Captive males and females, for example, masturbate and display such eroticisms as fondling each other's genitalia, behavior never seen in the wild. In fact, I saw no instances of play mounting, homosexualism, or deviant sexual behavior in wild gorillas.

*Estrous Cycle*

The monthly cycle of the female is not readily discernible in nature, for gorillas lack a prominent genital swelling and their menstrual flow of blood is minute. However, captive females exhibit intermittent periods of sexual receptivity, lasting from three to four days, during which they initiate contact with other gorillas or with humans. Reports from several zoos indicate that the average length of this cycle is from about 30 to 31 days.

*Copulation*

I observed copulation in group IV on September 4 and 23, 1959. Two different silver-backed males were involved, and both were subordinate individuals. One occupied the number-two position in the hierarchy and the other was peripheral. On both occasions the dominant male was resting near the copulating animals and did not prevent them from completing the act. One copulation lasted 15 minutes as the male thrust intermittently while covering the back of the female, who rested on her knees, belly, and elbows. A female initiated the second copulation by mounting the male and thrusting about 20 times. The male then grabbed her by the hips and pulled her into his lap. They copulated first in a squatting position, with the female facing away from the male, and later with the female lying prone and the male squatting at her rump. The animals copulated three times in one hour, resting during the intervals. The male reached orgasm only during the third copulation, after a total of about 300 thrusts.

Copulation in wild gorillas was more direct than in captives, lacking the prolonged preliminary wrestling, chasing, and fondling which I observed in a pair of lowland gorillas at the Columbus zoo. Captive gorillas also copulated in a ventro-ventral position.

### Pregnancy, Parturition, and Gestation Period

The abdomen of wild females is ordinarily so distended that pregnancy cannot be detected with certainty. Captives tend to show edema of the ankles, a gain in weight, and a certain irascibility. Although I twice encountered females in the wild within a few hours after they had given birth, I never witnessed the event itself. However, six infants have been born in captivity. The birth itself occurs so rapidly that no trained observer has witnessed it. The native keepers at a stockade in the Congo saw a female mountain gorilla lie down, and within five minutes the head of the infant appeared; the mother pulled the infant out with her hands, but then killed it. Four of the captive females took little or no care of their first-born. However, two of these females gave birth a second time and cared for their infants.

The gestation period of four infant lowland gorillas born in zoos was 251–253, 252, about 266 (256–295), and 289 days, respectively.

### Breeding Season

In an effort to determine if gorilla young are born at certain seasons, I estimated the probable month of birth for all 54 infants in my study area. The 27 birth date estimates for 1959 and 1960 are listed below and suggest that gorillas lack a definite breeding season.

| Month | 1959 | 1960 | Month | 1959 | 1960 |
|---|---|---|---|---|---|
| January | 0 | 1 | July | 4 | |
| February | 2 | 1 | August | 3 | |
| March | 2 | 0 | September | 4 | |
| April | 2 | 1 | October | 1 | |
| May | 1 | | November | 0 | |
| June | 3 | | December | 2 | |

### Aggressive and Submissive Behavior

There was considerable variation in the intensity of aggressive behavior which gorillas exhibited toward each other and toward such intruders as man. In the order of increasing intensity, the responses included: (1) an unwavering but usually brief stare, sometimes with furrowed brow and slightly pursed lips; (2) a jerk of the head or a snap in the direction of the offending animal; (3) an incipient charge, indicated by a light forward lunge of the body, occasionally without moving the feet, but usually accompanied by one or two abrupt steps; (4) a quadrupedal bluff charge over a distance of from 10 to 80 feet; and (5) physical contact in the form of biting or wrestling.

Most intragroup aggressiveness was confined to staring and snapping. I saw incipient charges about 10 times, directed primarily at members of another group or at lone males. One dominant male charged in bluff at the dominant male of another group, the only such instance noted. Occasionally two members of a group ran at and slapped each other in passing, behavior which appeared to be redirected aggressiveness elicited by my presence. I have not witnessed serious aggressive contacts between gorillas. Although females sometimes quarreled, the grappling, screaming, and mock biting never resulted in a discernible injury. However, if a gorilla group is harassed by man, males, and occasionally females, may attack him and cause serious injury. According to several observers, such attacks usually consist of a lunge forward, brief contact during which the gorilla bites, and retreat.

The following excerpt from my field notes describes a typical quarrel between females:

A female walks leisurely past another one sitting by the trail. The latter slaps her on the back for a reason unknown to observer. She in turn wheels around and runs with open mouth straight at the female who swatted her. This female cowers down with legs and arms tucked under, but with head raised screaming loudly. Her lips are curled up and the teeth and gums show. The two females then grapple briefly and mock-bite each other's shoulder.

As the two fight, two other females run up and join the melee. All four then scream, grapple with each other, and run around with teeth bared. The rest of the group watches; that is, all but the silver-backed male who sits five feet from the nearest combatants and does not even turn his head toward them. After about 15 to 20 seconds three females cease fighting and walk away. Only one female remains in the battle area and emits short screams. Suddenly she takes two steps after one of the retreating females and slaps at her hind leg, whereupon the latter one turns and advances screaming. The former one backs away and collides with the silver-backed male, who gives an annoyed grunt.

The two females meet and wrestle briefly as a third female runs up to join the hassle. Finally all part after the whole sequence has lasted about one minute. (Schaller 1963)

Gorillas indicated their submissiveness during an aggressive encounter in three ways. Usually they simply averted their eyes by turning their heads to one side. When an animal was within 60 feet of me and presumably nervous, it sometimes shook its head rapidly back and forth, a gesture that appeared to mean, "I intend no harm." Occasionally when a male, excited by my presence, slapped at a female or youngster the latter cowered down on the abdomen, head lowered, and arms tucked under, presenting only the broad back.

## INDIVIDUAL BEHAVIOR

### Locomotion

Gorillas are primarily quadrupedal and terrestrial, walking with the soles of the feet flat on the ground and with the anterior part of the body supported on the middle phalanges of the fingers. Although gorillas spent much time on their hindlimbs with their hands freed for such tasks as grooming and feeding, bipedal locomotion was rare. The animals frequently took a step or two in a bipedal position, but only twice were they seen to walk farther than 20 feet in this manner.

Gorillas ascended trees with ease to sit, feed, rest, and nest, though they did so cautiously. Only young animals swung on lianas and ran along branches. No gorilla was ever seen to brachiate—that is, to swing from branch to branch by means of its arms alone. Proportionally females ascended trees to a height of 10 or more feet twice as often as silver-backed and black-backed males, and juveniles more than 4 times as often. Infants less than $1\frac{1}{4}$ years old usually hesitated to climb high into trees, but the infant class as a whole climbed with a frequency comparable to that of females.

### Feeding Behavior

Gorillas are herbivorous and subsist on a wide variety of vines, leaves, barks, roots, and some fruits. I obtained no evidence that they feed on animal matter. The apes usually foraged leisurely, alternately sitting and walking. Food was collected almost entirely manually, although a leaf was sometimes detached directly by mouth. The gorillas were highly selective feeders, consuming only certain parts of certain plants. They used hands and teeth equally to tear and shred a food item, with the hands prominent in manipulating, holding, and pulling, and the teeth in biting and gnawing. Food was rarely transported and never for more than 25 feet. No animal offered food to another and no gorilla was seen to use a tool to obtain its food.

The following quote from my field notes describes the leisurely feeding behavior of "Junior," a black-backed male:

> Junior sits and peers intently at the vegetation, reaches over, and bends the stalk of a *Senecio trichopterygius* to one side. He stretches far out and with a quick twist decapitates a *Helichrysum*. After stuffing the leafy top into his mouth, he looks around and spots two more plants of the same species which he also eats in similar fashion. He then yanks a *Peucedanum kerstenii*, including the root, from the ground, and with rapid sideways and backwards jerks of the head bites apart the stalk before gnawing out the pith. The sun appears briefly and Junior rolls onto his back. But soon the sun hides behind a cloud, and Junior changes to his side, holding the sole of his right foot with the right hand. After about 10 motionless minutes he suddenly sits up, reaches far out, slides his hand up the stalk of a *Carduus afromontanus*, thus collecting the leaves in a bouquet which he pushes with petioles first into his mouth. This is followed by a leafy thistle top, prickles and all, and a *Helichrysum*. He then leaves his seat, ambles 10 feet, and returns to his former place, carrying a thistle in one hand and a *Helichrysum* in the other. After eating the plants he sits hunched over for 15 minutes. The rest of the group feeds slightly uphill and Junior suddenly rises and moves toward the other members, plucking and eating a *Helichrysum* on the way. A *Senecio erici-rosenii* has been torn down by another gorilla, and Junior stops and rips off a leafy top. From the stem he bites large splinters until only a two-inch section of pith remains in his hand, which he eats. A strand of *Galium* follows, and just before he moves out of sight, a final *Helichrysum*. (Schaller 1963)

One hundred species of food plants were collected in various parts of the gorilla's range. This figure represents a minimum, for some plants were not identified below the generic level and thus are not included in the tabulation.

| Number of Species | Part of Plant Eaten | Type of Plant |
|---|---|---|
| 4 | shoot, base of stem | Grass-sedge |
| 5 | whole plant, pith of frond and stem, root | Fern |
| 29 | leaf, fruit, stem, bark, pith, flower, root | Herb |
| 22 | whole plant, leaf, stem, fruit, bark | Vine |
| 9 | leaf, fruit, flower, bark, pith | Shrub |
| 25 | leaf, fruit, bark, pith, rotten wood | Tree |
| 6 | fruit (maize, peas), pith (banana), root (taro, manioc, carrot) | Cultivated |

Gorillas have so well adjusted their food habits to the local vegetation types that I found, for example, no overlap between plants eaten in lowland rain forest and *Hagenia* woodland, although I collected 17 food plants in the former and 29 in the latter. Of the fairly large number of plants eaten in any one area, only a few provided the bulk of the forage. In the young secondary growth of lowland rain forest, the pith of the stem of the cultivated banana and the pith of the herb *Aframomum* were the plants most commonly consumed; around Kabara, 1 vine and 3 herbs (*Galium simense, Peucedanum linderi, Carduus afromontanus, Laportia alatipes*) furnished at least 80 percent of the daily food supply.

Several forage plants were widespread and tolerated considerable altitudinal variation. With these I attempted to determine if "cultural" differences in food habits existed from area to area. The vine *Urera hypselendron* and bamboo were eaten wherever they occurred. On the other hand, gorillas in the isolated Kayonza Forest of Uganda were not seen to eat five plants (*Galiniera coffeoides, Aframomum* sp. [stem], *Palisota* sp., *Marattia fraxinea*, and *Pennisetum purpureum*), although these plants were consumed by gorillas in other forests. Perhaps the animals ate them only sparingly, but my observations suggested qualitative rather than quantitative differences.

Gorillas were twice seen to feed on volcanic soil on the slopes of Mt. Mikeno. Analysis of the soil showed that it was high in sodium and potassium.

### Drinking Behavior

I never saw gorillas drink in the wild. In the Virunga Volcanoes, where permanent water was scarce, the animals probably obtained most of their moisture from the succulent forage.

### Nesting Behavior

Gorillas built crude platforms, either on the ground or in trees, to which the term "nest" was applied. Nests occasionally were built for resting at any time of the day, commonly between 0900 and 1300, and usually for sleeping at dusk. The animal stood or sat and broke and bent nearby branches, vines, and other vegetation from all sides, placing them around and under its body to form a roughly circular structure. There was no particular sequence in the placement of the vegetation, nor was there interlacing, knot-tying, or other involved manipulation. Gorillas never used the same nest two nights in succession.

The following quotation from my field notes describes a typical instance of nest construction:

> Group VII; April 1, 1960. A juvenile sits at the base of a tree and bends four to five handfuls of small herbs toward its left side with the right hand. It then stands on two legs, grabs the top of a mass of *Senecio trichopterygius* heavily overgrown with *Galium*, and pulls it in. It sits and breaks or bends the

tips of the herbs to fit in a semicircle around its body before pressing the mass down with both hands. Standing on three legs, it reaches far out and breaks two to three more *Senecio* stalks off at the base and pulls them in. After placing these individually along the edge of the nest, it breaks their protruding tops to fit the rim. It sits, turns around, and sits again. The time required for building was about one minute. (Schaller 1963)

Ground nests varied considerably in the care with which they were constructed. In the Hagenia woodland 10 percent of the animals bedded down for the night without constructing a definite nest. Numerous nests consisted merely of two or three handfuls of herbs pushed down to form a partial rim (Fig. 10–12). However, some nests had rims nearly two feet high and central cups a foot deep. There was no definite correlation between the age and sex of the animals and the complexity of the nests they constructed, although juveniles tended to build crude ones. Ground nests seemed to have little or no function. Most were so crude that they could offer but little comfort, or insulation from the bare soil. Nests did not protect the animal from rain and other adverse weather unless they were placed in a sheltered position. When it rained at bedtime, 18.5 percent of the animals built their nests under the leaning boles of trees and other shelters, as compared to 4.7 percent when it did not rain. In general, nest building on the

Fig. 10–12. A typical crude ground nest of herbs. Note that the emphasis of construction is on the nest rim rather than on the bottom. Dung lies on the rim and is squashed in the nest cup.

ground appeared to be vestigial behavior pointing to the ape's arboreal ancestry.

The principle of constructing tree nests was the same as that for ground nests, except that they were usually solidly built, and, in the absence of a firm substrate, considerable attention was given to the nest bottom. Nests in trees were functional in that they provided a platform on which the gorilla could recline without danger of falling.

TABLE 10–5. HEIGHT OF GORILLA NESTS ABOVE GROUND

| Location | Hagenia Woodland. Kabara, Virunga Volcanoes 2488 Nests (percent) | Mountain Woodland and Bamboo. Uganda Side, Virunga Volcanoes 106 Nests (percent) | Mountain Rain Forest. Kayonza Forest, Uganda 179 Nests (percent) | Lowland Rain Forest. Near Utu, Congo 110 Nests (percent) |
| --- | --- | --- | --- | --- |
| On ground | 97.1 | 45.3 | 53.5 | 21.8 |
| 2–10 feet above ground | 2.3 | 50.0 | 35.4 | 13.6 |
| 11–20 feet above ground | 0.3 | 4.7 | 8.9 | 26.4 |
| 21+ feet above ground | 0.3 | 0 | 2.2 | 38.2 |

Although gorillas nested both on the ground and in trees, the percentage of ground nests varied from area to area and seemed to be partly correlated with the availability of suitable trees. Table 10–5 shows that 97.1 percent of the nests in Hagenia woodland were on the ground as compared to only 21.8 percent in lowland rain forest. In the latter vegetation type, gorillas often nested from 20 to 60 feet above ground, a height rarely reached in the other areas. Analysis of dung in 50 nests above ground in Hagenia woodland showed that no silver-backed males nested in trees and that juveniles nested above ground twice as often as females and black-backed males combined. However, in the eastern portion of the Virunga Volcanoes, I saw nests of large males as high as 8 feet above ground.

Each juvenile and adult gorilla independently built its own nest for the night, although a juvenile occasionally slept with a female, or two juveniles occupied the same nest. Infants usually remained with their mothers, but sometimes a large one slept in its own nest adjacent to that of the female. Some infants built crude practice nests, both on the ground and in shrubs, but these were rarely used. The earliest age at which I observed nest-building behavior was 8 months.

On the 4 occasions when I watched the behavior of the whole group, the dominant male was the first animal to construct the night nest, and the other members then nested in his vicinity. Most bedding areas were compact (Fig. 10–13a), but occasionally some were split into 2 parts (Fig. 10–13b). Splitting occurred when a few members of the group continued to forage after the others had bedded down. Black-backed males sometimes nested

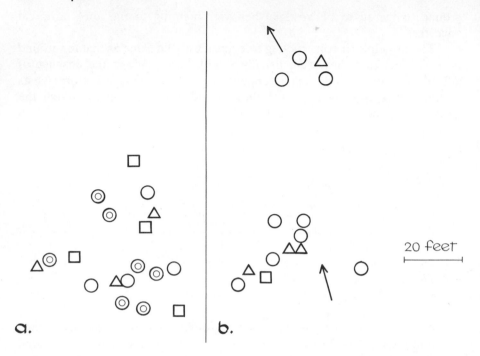

a.

b.

20 feet

Fig. 10–13. Two Kabara night nest sites—one compact, the other split. Squares represent nests of silver-backed males, circles of black-backed males or females, circles within a circle of females with infants (in Fig. 10–13a only), and triangles of juveniles. The arrow indicates the direction of travel.

    a. (*Left*) Group IV                 b. (*Right*) Group VII

60 or more feet from the main site. The distance to the nearest neighboring nests for the various age and sex classes was measured in 146 sites at Kabara, with the following results.

| Total Number Observations | Age and Sex Class | Mean Distance between the Nearest Nests (in feet) |
|---|---|---|
| 24 | Silver-backed male/silver-backed male | 34.0 |
| 103 | Silver-backed male/medium animal (female and black-backed male) | 13.4 |
| 81 | Silver-backed male/juvenile | 20.7 |
| 144 | Medium/medium | 5.4 |
| 120 | Medium/juvenile | 3.0 |
| 76 | Juvenile/juvenile | 12.0 |

The data suggest that most members of the group do not place their nests with reference to a certain sex class or particular animal but that medium-sized gorillas and juveniles may do so.

## Vocalizations

Undisturbed gorillas were generally quite silent. I noted 21 more or less distinct vocalizations in free-living gorillas, but four of these were heard only once and 7 fewer than 10 times each. Most sounds were abrupt and of low pitch and the most intense vocalizations were given in response to the presence of man. Table 10–6 presents a list of the 13 most common and easily recognizable vocalizations, as well as the situations which elicit them, the probable emotion underlying them, and their seeming function.

Although the number of basic vocalizations emitted by gorillas was fairly small, there was great variation in the pitch, pattern, and intensity of each sound. These variations broadened the scope of the gorilla's vocal repertoire, for the animals responded selectively to the sounds they heard. Their reaction depended not only on the condition under which a sound was given, but also on the member of the group that gave it. For example, harsh staccato grunts, signifying annoyance, emitted by a silver-backed male when females quarreled, caused them to subside. If, however, the male gave what appeared to be the same sound when the group was quietly resting and feeding, all members first looked at him and then in the direction which occupied his attention.

Infants were the least vocal members of the group. Soft, tremulous whines, with pursed lips and raised forehead, were noted three times. Screeches of distress were fairly common when infants thought themselves left behind by their mothers. Playing youngsters sometimes chuckled audibly with their mouths wide open and lips drawn back into a smile. Juveniles barked and grunted harshly in response to my presence, vocalizations not heard in free-living infants under similar conditions. Females emitted 12 different vocalizations, the largest number of any age and sex class; a panting ho-ho-ho during the chest-beating display appeared to be peculiar to them alone. Black-backed males were vocally at an awkward age; their voice seemed to be changing from one resembling the female's to that of silver-backed males. Thus young males screamed when angry, but larger ones produced a rather squeaky roar. Only large males emitted the hoot preceding the chest beat, the copulation call, and the full roar (Fig. 10–15b).

## The Chest-beating Display

The chest-beating display is the most striking behavior pattern of the gorilla, and one of the most complex and stereotyped displays among mammals. The display consists of nine more or less distinct acts, most of which

### TABLE 10–6. THE MOST CONSPICUOUS OR PREVALENT VOCALIZATIONS OF FREE-LIVING GORILLAS

| Description of Vocalization | Probable Emotion | Stimulating Situation | Probable Function |
|---|---|---|---|
| *Soft grunting | Content-ment | Feeding and resting peacefully | Indicates that all is well |
| *Series of abrupt grunts of low pitch | ? | Given primarily by male, but also by females and juveniles, when moving out of rest areas and when group is scattered | Aids in group cohesion—denotes "here I am" |
| *Series of rapid, high-pitched bo-bo-bo or similar sound | ? | Given when group is scattered widely | Probably aids in group cohesion |
| *Loud, clear, but low-pitched series of hoots ending in a growl | Excitement | Given by silver-backed males as part of chest-beating display in tension-producing situations: the presence of man, another group, etc. | Generates ex-citement; in-timidation as part of display |
| Rapid, loud, staccato series of ö-ö-ö-ö, with the first vowel more forceful than the others and separated from them by a brief pause | Excitement (?) | Given by silver-backed male during copulation | ? |
| *Harsh, staccato grunts (Fig. 10–15a) | Annoyance | Given by silver-backed male if females quarrel; given by quarreling animals | Warning of possible dan-danger |
| *Short, loud barks | Annoyance | Given by animals when quarreling; in response to presence of man | Warning of possible danger |
| Single, loud explosive roar (Fig. 10–15b) | Anger | Given by males in response to presence of man and, once, when swooped at by 2 ravens | Intimidation, warning of danger |
| *Harsh, fairly short screams | Anger | By quarreling females; in response to presence of man | Warning (sometimes contains ele-ments of fear) |

TABLE 10–6. THE MOST CONSPICUOUS OR PREVALENT VOCALIZATIONS OF FREE-LIVING GORILLAS — *Continued*

| Description of Vocalization | Probable Emotion | Stimulating Situation | Probable Function |
|---|---|---|---|
| Soft whine | Distress | Given by youngster when in danger of being abandoned or injured | Communicates distress |
| *One or two high-pitched screeches | Distress | Given by infant when in danger of being left behind by its mother | Communicates distress (sometimes contains elements of anger) |
| Intense screaming roar | Fear | Given by male to presence of man | Warning of danger; intimidation (usually contains elements of anger) |
| Loud, long, high-pitched screams | Fear | Given by females and juveniles to presence of man | Warning of danger |

* The most frequently heard vocalizations of undisturbed free-living gorillas.

may be given individually or in several combinations of two or more, with a tendency for some to precede others. The complete sequence is given infrequently and then only by silver-backed males. The entire display occurs typically as follows:

(1) At the start of the display the gorilla sits or stands as it emits a series of some 2 to 40 clear hoots, at first distinct, then more slurred as their tempo increases.

(2) The hoots may be interrupted as the animal plucks a leaf or branch from the surrounding vegetation and places it between its lips, seemingly a gesture of "symbolic feeding."

(3) Just before the climax of the display, the gorilla rises on its hind legs and remains bipedal for several seconds.

(4) As it rises, the animal often grabs a handful of vegetation and throws it upward, sideways, or downward.

Fig. 10–14. A black-backed male stands bipedally and beats his chest. A female with a large infant at her side sits behind him.

(5) The climax of the display is the chest beat, in which the gorilla raises its bent arms laterally and alternately slaps its chest with open, slightly cupped hands some 2 to 20 times (Fig. 10–14). The beats follow each other in rapid succession about .1 seconds apart (Fig. 10–15a). Gorillas may also beat their abdomens and thighs, as well as branches and tree trunks.

(6) A leg is sometimes kicked into the air while the chest is beaten.

(7) Immediately after, and occasionally during, the chest beat, the animal runs sideways, first a few steps bipedally then quadrupedally, for from 10 to 60 or more feet.

(8) While running, it sweeps one arm through the vegetation, swats the undergrowth, shakes branches, or breaks off trees in its path.

(9) In the final gesture of the display, the gorilla thumps the ground, usually with one but sometimes with both palms.

Infants displayed various acts in the sequence at an early age. Some rose shakily on their hindlegs and beat their chests at the age of 4 to 5 months. Infants were first seen to place a leaf between the lips and to throw vegetation at the age of 1½ years. Females showed all 9 acts in the display sequence except the hoot, but in them this behavior was less frequent, less intense, and the sequences shorter than those of males. The threshold of excitation also appeared to be lower in males than in females, which was perhaps correlated functionally to the male's being the protector of the group.

A variety of situations elicited the display, among them the presence of man, the presence of another group, displays by another member within the group, and play; sometimes the display occurred without apparent outside stimulus. The most general emotional term which encompasses these diverse manifestations is excitement. Thus, the primary causation of the chest-beating sequence appears to be the build-up of tension (excitement) above a certain threshold. The display itself serves to make the animal conspicuous, it advertises its presence, and probably functions in intimidation.

According to the concept of causation as developed by ethologists, a potentially dangerous situation arouses the impulses to flee and to attack. The conflicting tendencies generate tension, which finds release in some functionally inappropriate act, like the throwing of objects and the beating of the chest in gorillas. Behavior which is not actually relevant to the situation at hand has been termed a displacement activity. A displacement activity may become stereotyped, incorporated into a definite display, and achieve secondary functions, such as intimidation. In ethological terminology, it has become ritualized.

Several acts in the gorilla's display, especially the chest beating and the "symbolic feeding," appear to represent ritualized displacement activities. The displacement and ritualized elements are especially evident in "symbolic feeding." At the first sight of the observer, males occasionally began to feed very intensively, stuffing large handfuls of food into their mouths. This appeared to be displacement feeding. Sometimes, just before rising to beat his chest, a male pushed two or three handfuls of vegetation into his mouth, but at other times he placed only a single plant, branch, or leaf between his lips. This latter act probably represented ritualization of displacement feeding.

## CONCLUSION

Gorillas are rather amiable vegetarians, who, though primarily terrestrial, reveal their arboreal ancestry in their structure and in some aspects of their behavior. The arms and trunk of the gorilla are adapted more for climbing, hanging, and reaching in trees than for walking quadrupedally on

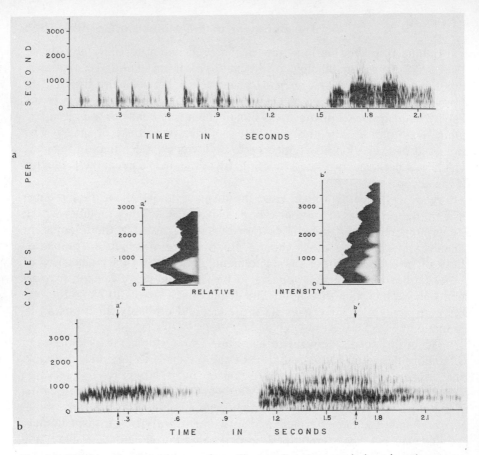

Fig. 10–15. Sound spectrograms of gorilla vocalizations and chest beating.

a. A female slaps her chest 11 times. The intermittent vertical lines of high frequency represent the impact of the hand against the chest. The sounds between
each beat apparently consist of resonance and of background noises. A three-
toned roar of low intensity by a silver-backed male is shown on the right of
the spectrogram.

b. Intensely roaring males. The first roar is that of a black-backed male, the
second that of a silver-backed male. The section above each roar represents
the relative amplitude of the sound at the instant of time a-a' or b-b'. The
instant of time is 1/24 seconds long. The sections show relative intensity throughout the entire spectrum of the sound, including overtones that did not register
on the spectrogram.

the ground, but the huge size and reduced agility of the ape have made a life
in trees impracticable. The gorilla has, however, retained the habit of building nests, behavior which appears to be of adaptive value in trees and which
on the ground seems to be an anachronism serving little or no function. On
the other hand, the elaborate chest-beating display probably evolved after
the gorilla assumed its terrestrial mode of life. Although single components
of the display such as beating, shaking, and throwing are seen in a variety

366

of arboreal primates, the full sequence of the gorilla's display, which includes rising up on the hindlegs while facing the opponent and running sideways, is unlikely to have adaptive significance in the forest canopy. Not only is the efficacy of the full display in such a situation questionable, but when gorillas attempt to display in trees they easily lose their balance and are in imminent danger of falling.

The social life of gorillas differs in some respects from that of the other primates studied so far. Groups are quite cohesive; they are led by the dominant adult male who by his actions and idiosyncrasies determines to a large extent the daily routine of the group and its response to other groups and to man. In spite of the continuous and usually peaceful contacts between the members of the group, overt interactions between adults are infrequent. For instance, grooming, which is often thought to strengthen the social bonds of primates, was never seen between adult males and females. The composition of many groups tends to remain stable over several months like that of the stable social groups of the monkey species described in this volume. However, some groups are fairly unstable, with certain males leaving freely to lead a lone life and others joining for a time. A further difference in the behavior of groups is apparent when groups, or groups and lone males, meet. Some join readily, others merely approach each other closely, and a few behave antagonistically toward each other. These individual responses are striking but not surprising if it is remembered that, because of the extensive overlap of ranges, each group undoubtedly contacts others fairly often. Many groups are probably well acquainted and may even be related to each other; they have had favorable or unfavorable meetings in the past, and this, together with the fact that gorillas are often highly individualistic in their behavior, may strongly influence the kind of interaction witnessed by the observer. The variable responses shown by gorillas in a given situation emphasize that the behavior of primates is highly adaptable and that generalizations based on a few observations in one area may be quite misleading.

# VERNON REYNOLDS and FRANCES REYNOLDS

### 11

# ◆ Chimpanzees of the Budongo Forest

## INTRODUCTION

Chimpanzees are familiar in circuses, zoos, and laboratories, and have served recently in space research, but until the last few years almost nothing was known of their way of life in their natural environment of equatorial Africa. Since 1960 three field studies, in three different habitats of East and Central Africa, have been made: those of Kortlandt in 1960, of Goodall in 1961–1963, and of Reynolds in 1962. There is now enough information, which will be presented in the following two chapters, for an understanding of many of the habits and capacities of the chimpanzee in nature, although many problems remain for further investigations.

Chimpanzees are large, the adult males weighing an average of 110 pounds, females 90 pounds. They are usually black-haired but occasionally chimpanzees with reddish or ginger hair have been observed or collected. Yerkes (1929:201) and Nissen (1931:22) report such individuals in West Africa, and in the present study in East Africa one ginger-haired juvenile was clearly seen at play with a black-haired juvenile. Chimpanzees are well adapted to both arboreal and terrestrial locomotion and are known to walk and run bipedally in some circumstances (Kortlandt 1962). One of their best-

We should like to extend our thanks to the following persons and institutions; without them our work would have been impossible or much more difficult: Dr. Adriaan Kortlandt, for his work on our behalf and his initial and continued advice, ideas, and encouragement; Professor Niels Bolwig, for invaluable negotiations at Makerere for our benefit before we arrived in Uganda; The University of London and The Wilkie Foundation of America for financial assistance. While we were preparing and equipping for the study and continually throughout our stay, help, both official and personal, was given freely by the Forest Department and the Game Department in Entebbe, Hoima, and Masindi. Especial thanks are due to Michael Philip, Henry Osmaston, Barry Cahusac, David Lyon, John Blower, John Heppes, and Marco Okenyi. At Makerere, the Institute of Social Research, in particular Dr. and Mrs. Derek Stenning and

Fig. 11–1. The plank buttresses of an ironwood tree (*Cynometra alexandri*) that are beaten by chimpanzees to produce a drumming sound.

known characteristics is the loud drumming they do on tree buttresses, which carries as far as two miles in the forest (Fig. 11–1). They are not normally dangerous to the human observer, most of them being shy and quick to run off when disturbed; reports of attacks by chimpanzees can usually be traced to attempts to catch or injure them. They are fascinating to watch, far more so in the wild than in captivity. A human observer cannot

Miss Grace Hunter, aided us in every way. While we were living in the forest invaluable assistance in many practical ways was rendered by Robin Knight and the other employees of the Budongo sawmills. The District Commissioner, David Arrowsmith, also gave us his support. Brief help with chimpanzee observations was given by Ralph and Penelope Tanner and Robert Wingfield. Help in identifying the samples of chimpanzee foods was given by Michael Philip in Entebbe, Collyer Dawkins at Oxford, Dr. Tallantyre at Makerere College, and by Kew Gardens. The manuscript was prepared at the Center for Advanced Studies in the Behavioral Sciences, where help and criticisms were received from George Schaller, Irven DeVore, Peter Marler, Charles Southwick, John Calhoun, Sherwood Washburn, William Mason, Richard Lee, and others. In the construction of the map showing the distribution of chimpanzees in Uganda, information provided by Allan Brooks, John Blower, and Alec Haddow was of great help. Finally, thanks are due to our forest guide and friend, Manueri, whose daily efforts on our behalf did more than anything else to make the study possible.

but feel a certain amount of understanding and sympathy with them because of the many gestures and habits they share with man.

## AIMS AND METHODS

The aim of this study was to observe as much as possible of chimpanzee behavior in natural circumstances, with particular emphasis on understanding their social organization.

First, in order to select a suitable site, we visited the major forests of western Uganda that contain chimpanzee populations. The Budongo Forest in Bunyoro was selected as the best place for our work for a number of reasons: The terrain is hilly but not mountainous and there are no deep gulleys or cliffs to delay progress; there is a European-owned sawmill that has been operating for more than 40 years; during this time tracks have been pushed through the forest, allowing the observer to penetrate many miles into the forest interior by Land Rover before he must cut through the forest undergrowth, and also, the forest is exceptionally well mapped by the Forest Department, at two inches to the mile, with the different types of forest clearly marked.

Of various methods of study that were tried four were successful and are discussed below.

1. Chimpanzees make loud calls that carry for more than a mile, and it was possible to take a compass bearing on the first calls heard at dawn and to push through the forest until the group was located at its early morning feeding. Close to the chimpanzees the use of the machete to cut undergrowth was not advisable and the last hundred yards had to be covered silently, if necessary crawling on all fours along a chimpanzee track. Observations were made as far as possible from hidden positions below a thick canopy of leaves or creepers, or from behind trunks of large trees. Chimpanzees were never disturbed by slight sounds, but if they saw a sharp movement they immediately became alert. When they did notice us, they either fled at once from the trees and made their way off silently along the ground, or they started hooting loudly and threateningly, stamping and branch-shaking, drawing the attention of all in the vicinity who would crowd closer to see better and then eventually leave. When a chimpanzee did notice our presence it was most often because of the reflection of sunlight from the lenses of the binoculars. If we wore a camouflage net over our faces and binoculars, this so impeded vision and so often caught on spiky undergrowth at the wrong moment that it was discarded. When the chimpanzees moved on to a new place, provided they had not been disturbed, they called as they went, and it was often possible to track and follow them to their next feeding place. As often as possible a group was followed until the animals made nests at dusk and then was relocated at dawn the following day. We plotted all followed movements of groups daily on large-scale maps.

2. When a tree with abundant fruit began to ripen, groups of chimpanzees came to visit it each day. It was possible for us to be in position at dawn in a carefully selected vantage point and to watch arrivals and departures. If the fruit lasted several days, we came to recognize individuals, and thus could obtain more detailed information on social relations and groupings than by following groups in the forest.

3. Inside the forest it was impossible to distinguish chimpanzees on the ground as they were merely black shadows in the undergrowth. After we had become familiar with the movement patterns of the groups followed, we could anticipate to some extent when a movement might be made that would require the crossing of a track through the forest. When this happened it enabled us to count the numbers of entire groups and to record the group compositions and, sometimes, to identify animals seen previously elsewhere.

4. All group movements were recorded in an attempt to keep a simultaneous check on the movements, whereabouts, and interactions of all groups at once within the study area (approximately 16 square miles), instead of just the particular group being followed at the time. For this a number of local men were employed for a three-month period, to patrol strategic known chimpanzee areas along the forest tracks, for three hours from dawn, and from 4:00 P.M. until dusk at 7:00 P.M. These men reported on whether chimpanzee calls had been heard, and, if so, from which direction and whether they were close or distant. If chimpanzees crossed or were seen in the trees, they counted the number. A small group of really reliable and interested chimp-spotters was marshaled and the resultant coverage of the area helped to build up a fairly complete picture of group movements in relation to one another. In addition, the extra information coming in from all areas gave us more opportunities to witness large-scale movements and to notice fruiting trees. This turned out to be an invaluable field method for the particular situation in the Budongo Forest.

Several planned methods were tried and because of the conditions had to be abandoned. Attempts to habituate the chimpanzees to the observers were a failure, partly because of the forest conditions and partly because we rarely saw the same individuals from one day to the next. Construction of hides proved to be of no use, as the movements of chimpanzees were rather unpredictable and they kept away from hides. For one week we slept inside the forest near the chimpanzees, but this gained us little extra information.

We spent from 6 to 12 hours inside the Budongo Forest each day for a total of 170 days between February and October 1962. In addition, there were a few days of observation in the other major forests of Uganda. The Budongo data comprise a total of 300 observation hours, yielding an average of 1¾ hours per day. The rest of the time we spent tracking, following, or waiting—often very close to chimpanzees but unable to see them.

## SPECIES, DISTRIBUTION, AND HABITAT

The classification of chimpanzees presents numerous problems. Inter-individual differences within a single population are considerable, making it difficult to find clear-cut taxonomic characters. Following Yerkes (1943) and Fiedler (1956) we may distinguish four types. Three of these, *Pan troglodytes troglodytes* Blumenbach, *Pan troglodytes verus* Schwarz, and *Pan troglodytes schweinfurthii* Giglioli, are generally distinguished at the subspecific level, while the fourth may be a distinct species, *Pan paniscus* Schwarz, or another subspecies, *Pan troglodytes paniscus* Schwarz.

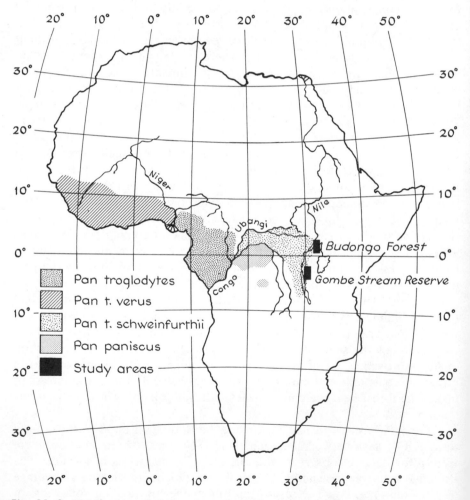

Fig. 11–2. Distribution of chimpanzees in Africa (after Yerkes 1943).

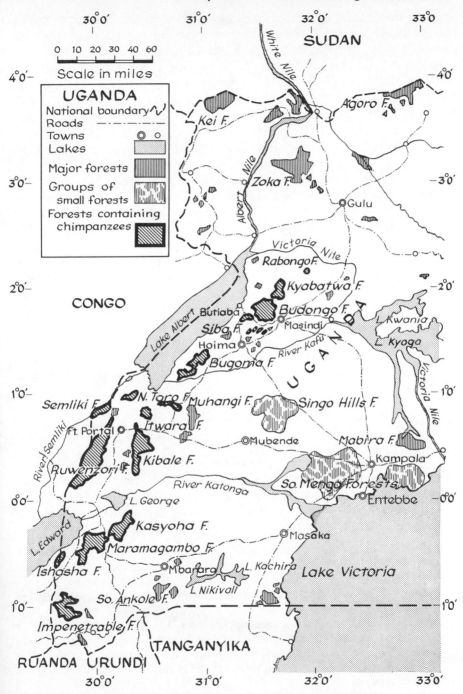

Fig. 11-3. Distribution of *Pan troglodytes schweinfurthii* in Uganda.

The distribution of chimpanzees in Africa is shown in Fig. 11–2. The various types are separated by the great African rivers, the Niger, the Congo, and the Ubangi, their total range being from longitude 15° W. to longitude 32° E., and latitude 12° N. to latitude 8° S. Within Uganda distribution of *Pan troglodytes schweinfurthii* is shown in Fig. 11–3. Chimpanzees occur in all the major forests along the eastern edge of the Rift Valley in Uganda, south of latitude 2° N. Formerly their range may have extended east as far as the forests of central Uganda. Sir Harry Johnston (1902) reported that according to local traditions chimpanzees occurred earlier in the Mabira Forest, Kiagwe County, central Uganda.

Several chimpanzee habitats have been described. Nissen (1931) studied chimpanzees in French Guinea in a hilly area with many forested streams and woodland, grass, or bamboo cover on the higher ground. Kortlandt (1962) observed chimpanzees at a plantation site bordering on rain forest in east Congo. The Gombe Stream Chimpanzee Reserve habitat in Tanganyika, studied by Goodall (Chap. 12, this volume), is hilly, with fairly open Brachystegia woodland and grass cover on the hills, and dense vegetation with trees of medium height in the valleys. Chimpanzees also occur on the lower slopes of the Ruwenzori Mountains, up to 10,000 feet, in montane forest (personal observation). The Budongo Forest in Uganda, site of the present study, is typical rain forest. The total range of chimpanzees is roughly coincident with the vast African equatorial rain forest zone. Outside this zone, they occur in neighboring areas of forest-savanna mosaic and woodland.

## ECOLOGY

### The Budongo Forest

Figure 11–4 shows the forest and the area of study. The Budongo Forest is a tropical rain forest; its ecology and that of its southwestern extension, the Siba Forest, is very well known, owing to the intensive studies of W. J. Eggeling (1947:21), from whom the following extract is taken:

> The Budongo Forest lies towards the north end of the lake [Lake Albert], on the gentle upper slopes of the watershed, with its western edge only two to four miles from the top of the escarpment. . . . The forest is situated between latitudes 1°35' and 1°55' N., and between longitudes 31°8' and 31°42' E. It has an average altitude of about 3600 feet.
>
> . . . Budongo proper is a solid mass of forest 136 square miles in area. The Siba Forest (32 square miles) consists of a more or less compact central portion some twelve square miles in extent, together with about twenty square miles of narrow strips of gallery forest on the banks of the Siba and Waki rivers and their tributaries.
>
> In the Budongo portion of the forest, the ground is undulating. The valley bottoms are generally soft, and many of the so-called streams are mere trickles through rattan (*Calamus*) swamp, with no apparent flow in dry weather. The

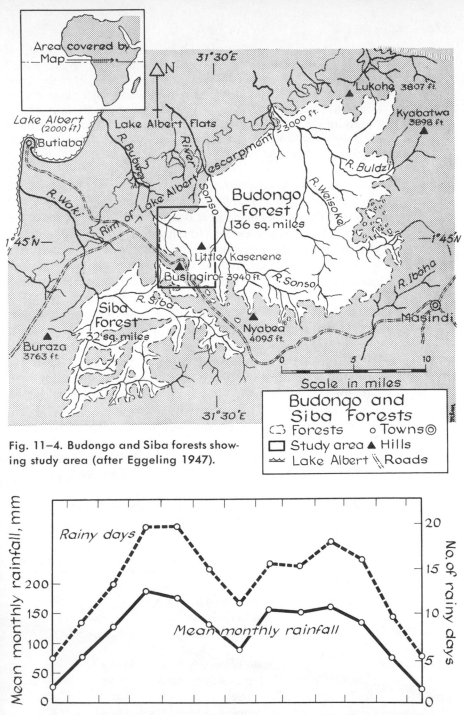

Fig. 11–4. Budongo and Siba forests showing study area (after Eggeling 1947).

Fig. 11–5. Rainfall at Busingiro for the period August 1933–July 1943 (after Eggeling 1947).

general direction of the numerous valleys is from south-east to north-west, but not infrequently the streams turn for short distances at right angles along small fault lines or joint planes. As they approach the western margin of the forest the majority of the watercourses join to form two rivers which run in slightly deeper valleys, the Sonso and Weisoke. In the wet season these rivers may be up to 4 feet deep. In the dry season the Sonso often dries up completely. The whole area is well weathered, slopes are with few exceptions gradual, and the intervening ridges are rounded.

Figure 11–5 shows the mean monthly rainfall and number of rainy days over a ten-year period. There is a short dry season from mid-December to mid-February. These data were collected at Busingiro Hill on the edge of the forest. As Eggeling (*loc. cit.*) points out, "the mean annual precipitation of 1495 mm. (58.8 inches) at Busingiro is without doubt well below that over the forest. . . . The average annual rainfall over Budongo probably lies between 1780 and 1900 mm. (70–75 inches), but actual measurements are necessary." In 1945, the only year for which published figures are available, actual rainfall was 1842 mm. (69.53 inches) in the middle of the forest.

There is very little variation in the monthly temperature means at Busingiro (see Fig. 11–6). Total temperature range averages from 14° C. (57° F.) to 28° C. (82° F.). Percentages of humidity are illustrated in this figure for nearby township Masindi, which is situated some 25 miles to the southeast of Budongo. The humidity is not unduly high, the most humid month being July and the least humid February.

The forest is completely surrounded by grassland, into which it is slowly advancing. The chief factors limiting the forest's advance are the annual dry-season grassland fires and continual browsing by elephants on saplings at the forest edge. The chief types of forest are shown below:

TABLE 11–1. BUDONGO FOREST – MAJOR FOREST TYPES
(EGGELING 1947)

| Type | Description | Percentage of Entire Forest |
|---|---|---|
| 1. Colonizing forest | | 6 |
|   a) Colonizing (*Maesopsis*) forest | Dominant large tree is *Maesopsis eminii* | |
|   b) Colonizing (woodland) forest | *Maesopsis* is absent or scarce | |
| 2. Mixed forest | Midway stage between (1) and (3); canopy composed of many species | 60 |
| 3. Ironwood forest | *Cynometra alexandri* is dominant | 32 |
| 4. Swamp forest | Variety of swamp species, e.g., *Pseudospondias microcarpa* | 2 |

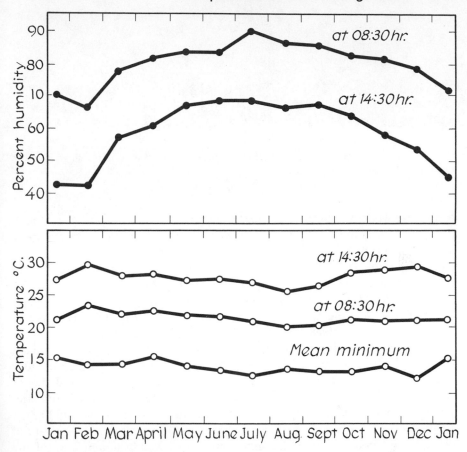

Fig. 11–6. Mean maximum, minimum, and air temperatures at Busingiro (1942); and mean percentage humidity of the air at Masindi over a period of years (after Eggeling 1947).

Each forest type has its own distinctive appearance and stratification. Woodland forest is two-storied, with an almost closed, dense bottom story, and a very irregular emergent top story of larger trees. *Maesopsis* forest also has two stories, but the top story is remarkably even in height and forms a practically closed upper canopy. Mixed forest has four stories, of which the two lower form a closed (lower) canopy and the two upper form a closed (upper) canopy, 140 feet high on average. Ironwood forest resembles mixed forest except that in place of the two upper stories of the latter it has a single upper story consisting solely of ironwood trees.

Beneath the trees there is a shrub stratum and beneath this an herb stratum. These are least dense in ironwood forest, and densest in swamp

Fig. 11–7. The northwest corner of the Budongo Forest looking toward Little Kasenene hill from Busingiro.

forest and woodland forest. Where these strata are thick, walking is difficult for humans and the machete is essential; in parts of the forest where there are almost no herbs and few shrubs a clearing knife is not necessary. The canopy is bound together, and the remaining spots of sunlight are utilized by numerous lianas, woody climbers, and herbaceous climbers.

The present study concentrated on an area of approximately 16 square miles of forest on the north, east, and south sides of Busingiro Hill, where the observers were based (see Figs. 11–4 and 11–7). This area consists primarily of colonizing forest (both *Maesopsis* and woodland) and mixed forest with some swamp forest but very little ironwood forest. It includes some gallery forest in the Siba. This entire area was selectively felled over some 20 or 30 years ago, and, apart from certain limited areas, where large-scale tree poisoning by the Forest Department is having a profound effect on the forest flora and fauna, it is regenerating peacefully under the care of the Forest Department, whose aim is to ensure a subsequent crop of the valuable timber species that have been removed. Felling does not radically alter the composition of the forest but promotes a dense growth of saplings and climbers in spots where the canopy has been opened by the falling of a giant tree.

### TABLE 11–2. FOOD PLANTS COLLECTED IN STUDY AREA

| Species | Type of Plant | Part Eaten |
| --- | --- | --- |
| *Aframomum sp* | shrub | fruits |
| *Aningeria altissima* | tree | fruits |
| *Antiaris toxicaria* | tree | fruits |
| *Calamus sp.* | climber | pith (stem)* |
| *Celtis brownii* | tree | leaves |
| *Celtis durandii* | tree | leaves |

TABLE 11-2. FOOD PLANTS COLLECTED IN STUDY AREA — *Continued*

| Species | Type of Plant | Part Eaten |
|---|---|---|
| Celtis mildbraedii | tree | fruits, leaves |
| Chlorophora excelsa | tree | fruits |
| Cola gigantea | tree | bark |
| Chrysophyllum sp. nov. | tree | fruits |
| Cordia millenii | tree | fruits |
| Cynometra alexandri | tree | fruits, bark, leaves |
| Ficus brachypoda | tree | fruits |
| Ficus capensis | tree | fruits |
| Ficus congensis | tree | fruits |
| Ficus dawei | tree | fruits |
| Ficus depauperata | epiphyte | fruits |
| Ficus mucuso | tree | fruits, leaves |
| Ficus namalalensis | epiphyte | fruits |
| Ficus natalensis | tree | fruits |
| Ficus polita | tree | fruits |
| Ficus urceolaris | shrub | fruits |
| Funtumia elastica | tree | fruits |
| Khaya anthotheca | tree | leaves |
| Maesopsis eminii | tree | fruits |
| Mammea africana | tree | fruits |
| Marantochloa leucantha | shrub | pith (stem) |
| Melanodiscus sp. nov. | tree | fruits |
| Mildbraediodendron excelsum | tree | fruits |
| Morus lactea | tree | fruits, leaves |
| Piper guineense | climber | fruits |
| Platycerium angolense | epiphyte | leaves |
| Pseudospondias microcarpa | tree | fruits |
| Setaria sp. | grass | leaf tips |
| Zanha golungensis | tree | fruits |

**Diet, Food Habits, and Excretion**

Table 11-2 lists the plant species that we observed chimpanzees eating and that we identified. Chimpanzees are primarily frugivorous, supplementing their diet with leaves, bark, and pith. In addition, chimpanzees were seen on rare occasions eating insects; as the latter crawled along branches or up a tree trunk they were picked off directly with the lips. The dietary breakdown is as follows:

COMPOSITION OF DIET

| Food Type | Number of Species | Percentage of Total Bulk (Estimated) |
|---|---|---|
| Fruits | 27 | 90 |
| Leaves | 9 | 5 |
| Bark, stem | 4 | 4 |
| Insects | ? | 1 |

No evidence that these chimpanzees eat meat or birds' eggs was obtained, and it is doubtful that meat eating is at all usual in this forest environment. Kortlandt (personal communication) placed hen eggs in imitated nests along chimpanzee paths, and found that only one chimpanzee took the eggs without breaking them and consumed the eggs in the forest. The others did not seem to regard eggs as food. Nor did any chimpanzees kill and eat the chickens or goat kids fastened by Kortlandt in their tracks. Nor was there any evidence of the use of tools to obtain food. Beatty (1951) has reported that chimpanzees use rocks to break open palm nuts, but in the Budongo Forest rocks are rare, and there appear to be no large hard foods which have to be split open. Merfield and Miller report on the use of stick tools by chimpanzees to obtain honey: "Each ape held a long twig, poked it down the hole and withdrew it coated with honey" (1956:44). In the Budongo Forest there are numerous bees' nests, but we never saw signs of interference with such a nest. Goodall (Chap. 12, this volume) describes a method by which chimpanzees obtain termites, but we found no evidence of interference with the termite heaps in chimpanzee localities.

Certain species of food trees are found in particular environments in different forest types. For example, many species of figs occur in sunny spots, such as by the roadside or at the edge of a valley in mixed forest, single trees being well separated from each other. *Pseudospondias microcarpa*, which bears a fruit like a small bitter plum, smelling like turpentine, occurs in groups of several trees in certain areas of swamp forest and along the sides of streams. *Maesopsis eminii*, the ripe fruits of which look like black olives, is found at the edges of the forest where conditions for its growth are favorable and inside the forest in certain places that may formerly have been cleared. This species occurs in clusters and may form stands of several acres. *Melanodiscus sp. nov.*, an understory tree with a fruit looking like a small double apricot when ripe, is widely scattered in mixed forest.

The fruits of each species of food tree ripen over a particular period of the year. Figure 11–8 shows the period of ripening of those fruiting species that constituted a major source of nourishment at some time between March and October 1962.

Chimpanzee movement and distribution through the study area was markedly affected by the ripening of fruit trees at different times and in

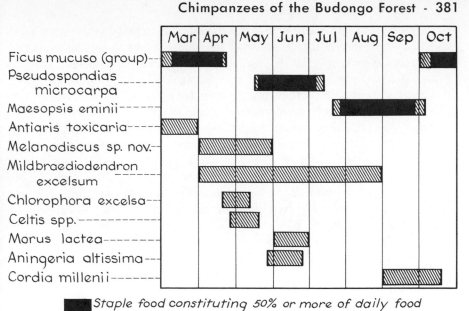

Fig. 11–8. Major foods and some other foods in study area March–October 1962.

different places (see also below). Chimpanzees are large primates and in order to subsist on a predominantly fruit diet they must spend from six to eight hours per day feeding or foraging. When food was scattered widely, as when *Melanodiscus* was the chief fruit source, chimpanzees were very mobile and ranged over several square miles each day. When figs or *Pseudospondias* were ripe, they tended to move less frequently, from patch to patch over distances of a mile or so only. During the fruiting of *Maesopsis*, some groups did not move more than a few hundred yards in a day. In early May fruit was scarce, and chimpanzees were observed eating leaves (young leaves of *Celtis spp.* preferred) and this continued until the ripening of *Pseudospondias*.

On four occasions chimpanzees were observed to leave a tree carrying in one hand a small branch with fruit on it. On another occasion a subadult male was seen leaving a tree with a piece of prepared rattan pith 12 inches long carried in his mouth (chimpanzees prepare rattan stalk by peeling off the hard outer layer revealing the pith inside, which is chewed) and an unprepared stalk, somewhat longer, in his left foot. Once a female was observed sitting in a mahogany tree feeding on a branch of *Pseudospondias* fruits, which she must have carried there. Figure 11–9 shows a male chimpanzee crossing the road with a food object clutched in his right hand.

We tested briefly the response of the chimpanzees to certain fruits that do not occur naturally in the forest: bananas, mangoes, maize, avocado pears, and paw-paws. A bunch of ripe bananas was hung up under a food tree they were visiting. Next day the bunch had been bitten into and individual bananas roughly torn off at the middle of the fruit. None of the bananas was picked off whole, and there was no evidence of peeling. Apparently the portion removed had been eaten. The same thing happened again each of the next two days, then the chimpanzees did not return. Mangoes left on the ground and put in trees were not touched and were left to rot. Of two avocado pears, one was eaten by ants and the other was moved 17 yards, probably by chimpanzees. The maize cobs were eaten by baboons. Of two unripe paw-paws, one was ignored throughout, and the other was ignored until it ripened; it was then carried some 50 yards along a chimpanzee track, peeled, and the inside eaten.

Nissen (1931:61) reports twice observing chimpanzees drinking: "Crouching at the bank of a tiny stream, hands and feet on solid ground, the ape lowered his head until his lips were in contact with the water. The water was apparently sucked, rather than lapped up." No similar observations were made in the Budongo, probably because of the difficulty of seeing

Fig. 11–9. An adult male crosses the road with a food object, probably rattan, in his right hand.

anything on the ground. However, drinking was observed on one occasion in a *Maesopsis* tree. A fault in one of the branches at about 70 feet had led to the formation of a natural bowl in which rain water had collected. During the space of half an hour in the early afternoon an adult male chimpanzee drank twice. Each time the method was the same: sitting, facing the bowl, he repeatedly put his right hand into the bowl, pulled it out, and, holding it in front of him, licked and sucked the water off his fingers. At various times nine other chimpanzees were in the tree with him, but none drank from the bowl. It is interesting to note that this method of drinking appears to be common to all the apes: it is reported for the gibbon (Carpenter 1940), the orangutan (Harrisson 1962:79), and is shown in the film sequence of mountain gorillas in "Lords of the Forest."

Excretion was observed during the daytime. Defecation and urination occurred both in the trees and on the ground. On the ground, 30 percent of a random sample of feces were by the side of fallen branches. On branches in trees, urination and defecation occurred in a sitting posture, and the animal would pause from feeding while it excreted. A juvenile was observed to urinate accidentally on its own hand, which it then shook and wiped against the branch. Dark red urine color was sometimes found spattered on leaves below trees where chimpanzees had been feeding, as reported by Nissen (1931:72). Chimpanzees did not soil their nests. On waking up, they excreted over the edge. "Panic diarrhea," or rapid discharge of very fluid feces, was observed on occasions of stress when the animal suddenly found itself close to the observers.

## Locomotion

Table 11–3 lists the forms of locomotion observed during the study. The characteristics of certain forms of locomotion indicate the independence of the forelimbs relative to hindlimbs (Fig. 11–10). The forelimbs sometimes do not swing in time with the hindlimbs, as is evident when they hang down loosely during bipedal walking. However, Elftman (1944) has clearly demonstrated that bipedal walking sometimes involves arm swinging in the chimpanzee.

Chimpanzees were both arboreal and terrestrial, the amount of time they spent in the trees or on the ground being dependent on such factors as the time of day and local food resources. At a very rough estimate, chimpanzees in the Budongo Forest spent an average of from 50 to 75 percent of the daylight hours in trees. To travel over distances of more than 50 yards they usually came down to the ground; they fled on the ground; and they had a network of tracks at ground level throughout the forest. When going from one tree to an adjacent one, they often moved at canopy level.

## TABLE 11–3. FORMS OF LOCOMOTION

| Name | Frequency | Characteristics | Ground Trees | Distance Covered |
|---|---|---|---|---|
| 1. Quadrupedal walk (Fig. 11–10) | Common | Quadrupedal limb movements, the weight of the forepart of the body being supported on the knuckles and the hind feet being placed flat on the ground. Very relaxed in confident animals. | Both | Any |
| 2. Quadrupedal run | Common | Quadrupedal movements. At one stage all feet are off the ground. | Both | Any |
| 3. Rapid run | Common | Legs move forward alternately, while arms move forward together. | Ground | 30 feet |
| 4. Gallop | Occasional | The fastest run of the chimpanzee when it is in a hurry to catch up with others or is scared. Limb movements unclear. | Ground | 30 feet, plus |
| 5. Vertical climb | Common | The arms and long hands are used to hold the chimpanzee against the tree, while the legs provide the upward thrust, the feet being placed on the side of the tree nearest the chimpanzee, toes one side, hallux the other. | Trees | 10–100 feet |
| 6. Bipedal walk | Rare | The arms are sometimes not swung in time with the legs, but hang loosely down. | Ground | Maximum seen, 9 paces |
| 7. Bipedal walk on legs with use of arms | Occasional | Independent movements of arms and legs, the arms supporting the body from branches above, while the legs walk along a branch. | Trees | 15 feet |
| 8. Ground leap | Occasional | The legs are swung forward under the chimpanzee and land first, before the arms, e.g., over ditches. | Ground | 6 feet |
| 9. Vertical leap | Rare | The animal uses its limbs merely to check its fall as it flings itself downwards from branch to branch. | Trees | 30-foot leaps |
| 10. Swing | Occasional | Arms are extended forward to grasp a branch and whole body is then swung across. Method used for moving from tree to tree. | Trees | 10 feet |
| 11. Brachiation | Common | Hanging from a branch, the animal moves along by means of alternate arm movements, swinging its body forwards, backwards, and to each side in turn. | Trees | 20 feet |

Fig. 11–10. An adult male, with balding rump, walks quadrupedally along a branch.

When several chimpanzees moved through the treetops, they tended to follow one another, well spaced out, along the same route, repeating each other's locomotor patterns. Climbing or descending trees with large trunks, they made their way up or down climbers or nearby saplings. In one observed method of descent from a tree the chimpanzee would grasp the top of a sapling with one arm and one leg and then allow the sapling to sway beneath the weight of the animal until it bent to the ground, when the chimpanzee stepped off. Nissen (1931:34) also observed this.

### Nesting Behavior

Most adolescent or older chimpanzees observed at dusk made a nest to sleep in. The youngest animal we saw building and using its own nest was a juvenile-two (see Table 11–4 below). This nest was small, and was built close beside the mother's, and we frequently found similar small nests that had been built beside a large one. Infants and juvenile-ones slept with their mothers in a nest constructed by her. Nest-sharing, other than by mother and offspring, is reported by Haddow (1958). He observed a female constructing a large platformlike nest in an oil palm; she was then joined in the nest by two other chimpanzees, and a fourth was rejected. It is probable

385

that some chimpanzees did not make nests to sleep in, either all or some of the time. At dusk on one occasion we watched an adult male (which was totally unaware of our presence); as night fell he stopped feeding and moved into a crotch of a tree, where he stayed until it was too dark for us to see anything. Next morning at dawn he was in the same crotch. Kortlandt (personal communication) considers that chimpanzees quite often do not build a new nest each night, as the number of nests was insufficient to account for the number of chimpanzees that habitually slept in the area he studied. One nest, the construction of which we observed, was still recognizable though withered after three months.

The period between sunset (6:30 P.M.) and darkness (7:15 P.M.) was the time for nest-building. Chimpanzees took from one to five minutes to make a nest, pulling in and intertwining branches at the site, collecting others from nearby and laying them on top, and finally adding leafy twiglets, sometimes from neighboring trees. Then followed a settling down period of from five to ten minutes while the chimpanzee made final adjustments from inside the nest, and finally all was quiet. On cloudy wet days nesting occurred early, whereas on sunny evenings it was delayed until the sun completely disappeared behind the horizon.

Details of nests and the behavior associated with them are to be found in Nissen (1931), Bolwig (1959b), and Goodall (1962). Certain additional points arising from the Budongo study are discussed here.

1. Two ground nests were found in the period of study. One was constructed primarily of the shrub *Marantochloa leucantha* with a covering of branches taken from nearby saplings. The other was a big nest made entirely of a broadleafed grass (*Setaria sp.*) collected from an area of ten yards in diameter around the nest. This nest was very well pressed down. These findings may be compared with the roughly improvised "day beds" with canopies observed on the ground by Nissen and may be contrasted with the absence of ground nests in the area studied by Goodall. Kortlandt (personal communication) observed 20 ground nests in his study area, indicating wide regional variations in the frequency with which these are constructed. The nests he found were not day nests, since they were on the "sleeping hill," an area occupied by the chimpanzees only at night.

Nissen, who was working in the dry season only, never observed chimpanzees in normally constructed tree nests during the daytime. Goodall observed the construction of day nests in trees often during the wet season but not during the dry season. In the Budongo, chimpanzees were observed in day nests in trees only on a few occasions, all during the long wet period of the year. But whereas Nissen's day beds were made in shady spots and Goodall's day nests were made in dry spots, the Budongo nests seemed to be made in sunny spots in trees. On occasion we saw chimpanzees breaking over a small leafy branch or two across a larger branch to sit on while feeding: these "daytime cushions" had nothing to do with sleeping and seemed to be made for comfort.

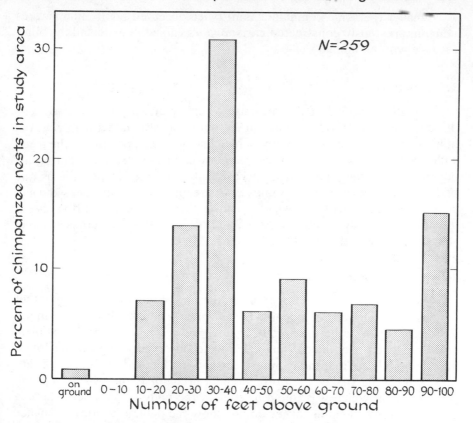

Fig. 11–11. Height of chimpanzee nests in study area.

2. The height of the trees influences the chimpanzees' behavior. In Nissen's area there were few trees more than 100 feet high, and only 7 percent of the nests were above 75 feet. In Goodall's area maximum tree height was 80 feet, and 25 percent of the nests were above 60 feet. In the Budongo Forest canopy height in mixed forest is typically 140 feet (Eggeling 1947), and 32.5 percent of the nests were above 60 feet, about 20 percent above 75 feet, and some 10 percent over 100 feet (see Fig. 11–11).

The use of nests for hiding when disturbed, previously reported for the chimpanzee (Christy 1915) and for the orangutan (Harrisson 1962), was observed clearly only once during the Budongo study. On this occasion a mother and her infant-two remained at the top of a tree after having seen the observers. The mother disappeared from view and sounds of nest-building were heard; later she was seen in a full-sized nest with the infant. She remained in this nest for four hours, during which time she defecated frequently over the edge. Finally, at a noise from the observers, she suddenly left the tree with a loud vocalization, the infant clinging below her.

Schaller (personal communication) twice observed adult chimpanzees hiding in previously constructed nests; one was an adult male and the other a female with an infant.

### Response to Water

Our observations of the response of chimpanzees to rain agree with those of Goodall (1962). Light rain did not noticeably affect behavior, but in heavy rain the animals adopted a hunched up sitting posture in the trees, with head resting on folded arms, face down. Feeding stopped during the downpour, and the chimpanzees occasionally vocalized, especially as rain first hit them. In crossing swamps and streams the chimpanzees did not come into contact with the water. Instead, they utilized fallen branches if possible, leaped over small streams, and occasionally they crossed larger streams along an arboreal route.

### Relations with Other Species

We obtained no evidence of predation on chimpanzees by other species. The chief diet of leopards (*Felis pardus*), which are common in the Budongo Forest, is the duikers (*Cephalophus spp.*). The fact that adolescents and even occasionally juveniles were observed alone on the forest floor may indicate that the chimpanzees had not learned any need for caution. Among the snakes the only potential predator is the python (*Python sebae*), one of which was found to contain the body of a duiker. There is evidence that wild chimpanzees do not show the panic reactions to snakes that are shown by captive chimpanzees. Kortlandt (personal communication) fastened a large living viper on the track of a group and the chimpanzees merely stepped aside a few feet. On one occasion we observed a female chimpanzee vocalize loudly as a buffalo charged past.

Birds of various species fed alongside the chimpanzees without interaction.

Chimpanzees share this forest with four species of monkeys, all of which are common. These are the blue monkey (*Cercopithecus mitis stuhlmanni*), the redtail monkey (*C. ascanius*), the black-and-white colobus monkey (*Colobus abyssinicus*), and the olive baboon (*Papio cynocephalus*). As pointed out by Haddow (1952:338), the first three of these species of monkeys mix freely with each other but not with baboons or chimpanzees. Redtail and blue monkeys share to some extent the diet of chimpanzees (for diet of redtail see Haddow 1952:342) and are sometimes found near them, occasionally feeding in the same tree. Single adult male blue monkeys were frequently seen feeding among groups of chimpanzees. On only one occasion was an interaction observed: A blue monkey approached within three yards of an adult male chimpanzee feeding in a tree, and the chimpanzee gave a sudden jerk toward it, at which the blue monkey ran off. *Colobus* were only once observed in the same tree with chimpanzees. Frequently *Colobus* moved out of trees as chimpanzees climbed up nearby and returned when the chimpanzees left. Baboons were never seen in the same trees as chimpanzees. On one observed occasion a group of baboons suddenly moved into a cluster of *Maesopsis* trees where a band of four adult male chimpanzees were feeding. There was no overt interaction or noise, but the chimpanzees swung away into neighboring trees. The two species continued feeding in proximity but not in the same trees for an hour that evening until dusk, and again for the first hour or so after dawn next day.

Relations between chimpanzee and man are complex. There is no hunting or persecution by the local Africans, who do not eat chimpanzees. Although the Budongo Forest is not a game reserve, chimpanzees are wholly protected throughout Uganda, that is, hunting of them is not allowed. On the roads and human tracks through the forest, especially where humans pass frequently, chimpanzees showed no fear of man. They fed placidly at the roadside watching people go by, and crossed the road frequently. When crossing the road, females, youngsters, and some males ran across, while certain males crossed at a leisurely walk, even when people were only 30 yards away. Inside the forest man is the object of intense suspicion, and the normal response of chimpanzees to seeing the observers was to flee instantly. Sometimes adult males stayed behind to watch or threaten with angry vocalizations.

Twice we were charged by chimpanzees, once by an adult male and the next day by an adult female, both in the same area. On the first occasion the group of chimpanzees we wanted to observe was about 100 yards ahead and we were approaching silently. The guide climbed a tree to see where they were, and when he jumped down his feet landed with a thud. Immediately an adult male broke cover about 12 yards away, running straight toward us. We shouted and raised the machete menacingly, from a distance of nine feet, at which the chimpanzee turned and fled.

The next day we were again silently approaching the chimpanzees when an infant was heard screaming close by, a short way up a tree. Immediately afterwards an adult female appeared running toward us through the undergrowth. We responded as before, and five yards from us she fled back to the tree, where she collected the infant and made her way across a tree-bridge over the Siba River with the infant on her back.

## POPULATION DYNAMICS

### Sex and Age Classification

1. In adolescent and adult chimpanzees the sex of the animal was clearly indicated by its perineal area, which consists of an expanse of pink or gray skin in the female and in the male is mostly covered by hair. Juveniles and infants could only be sexed by direct observation of the genitalia.

2. The problem of age determination was difficult. The estimates in Table 11–4 are based on captive specimens and should not be regarded as exactly applicable to the field data, which were less precise. In the field a size fraction was used for young animals, based on the average size of full-grown adults that were usually available for comparison. Adult females tended to be somewhat smaller than adult males (Schultz 1940; Yerkes 1943), but individual differences were very great.

TABLE 11–4. AGE CLASSIFICATION

| Designation | Description | Estimated Age* |
|---|---|---|
| Infant-one | Tiny, clings continuously to mother's belly. White tail tuft, pink face. | Up to 6 months |
| Infant-two | Tiny, active at short distances from mother, swinging, playing, etc. White tail tuft, pink face. | Average one year Range 6 months to 2 years |
| Juvenile-one | One quarter of adult size. Independent of mother for hours at a time, plays with other juveniles. Usually carried by mother on back or belly when on the move. White tail tuft, pink face. | Average 3 years Range 2 to 4 years |
| Juvenile-two | One third of adult size. Still plays, may be carried on mother's back, but more frequently walks behind her or may travel alone. Pink face. | Average 5 years Range 4 to 6 years |
| Adolescent | One half of adult size. May still follow mother, but usually on own, often with other adolescents. Face darkening, tail tuft of white hair usually gone. Older females in this group show sexual swellings. | Average 7 years Range 6 to 8 years |
| Subadult | Three quarters of adult size. Face is usually dark, females are mostly mature and older ones may have infants. | Average 9 years Range 8 to 10 years |
| Adult-one | Fully grown, has black hair all over including rump, face as a rule dark, may have gray beard. | Range 10 to 15 years |
| Adult-two | Differs from adult-one in having a bald rump (see Fig. 11–10). Rest of coat may be black, or there may be gray hair on back, or hair on back may be white. Head may be bald. | Older than 15 years |

* The ages have been estimated on the basis of Yerkes (1943), Fig. 2, page 57.

## Maturation, Sexual and Reproductive Cycles

Yerkes (1943:56) states: "It is indicated that our male subjects have reached puberty at seven to eight years. . . . The age of first menstruation . . . is from seven years and four months to ten years and two months, while the average for our seven cases is eight years and eleven months." Gavan (1953) found that the average age at menarche was eight years nine months in a sample of 21 females. Sexual maturity also involves behavioral criteria, for example, readiness to copulate, so that it may be some time before physically mature individuals have young. It should also be noted that there may be a time lag of as much as two years between the time of first sexual swelling and first menstruation (Zuckerman and Fulton 1934), so the adolescent females exhibiting sexual swellings, which we observed in the Budongo Forest, could not be assumed to be sexually mature.

The average length of the estrous cycle in captivity is now well established as $37 \pm 0.14$ days (Young and Yerkes 1943). Maximal swelling (when ovulation is known to occur) was the time of most frequent copulation, as is true in captivity (Elder and Yerkes 1936).

Gavan (1953) gives the average gestation period in a sample of 85 pregnancies as 227.2 days, range = 196–260 days. The period of lactation is very variable. Yerkes (1943:244) states: "In captivity nursing may continue indefinitely if mother and infant are kept together and lactation does not cease. We have records of its continuance into the third year." In the wild, infant-twos supplemented their diet with leaves even while continuing to suckle.

## Birth Intervals

Two sets of data are relevant: (1) the stage of development of youngest offspring, the mothers of which are sexually receptive, and (2) the relative stages of development of offspring of a single mother.

(1) Of the 88 occasions when females in estrus were observed, on 47 occasions they were accompanied by offspring. The developmental stage of these 47 offspring is shown below:

| Developmental stage | Inf.-One | Inf.-Two | Juv.-One | Juv.-Two | Adol. |
|---|---|---|---|---|---|
| Frequency of observations | — | 7 | 23 | 13 | 4 |

If we assume that a female in estrus was able to conceive, and if we accept the rough age scale in Table 11–4, these data indicate that the birth interval was most often three years, but was commonly four years, and could be anything from one year upward.

(2) Females were observed without offspring on 119 occasions, with one offspring on 199 occasions, and with more than one offspring on 54

## TABLE 11–5. RELATIVE AGE CLASSES OF OFFSPRING OF ONE MOTHER

| Frequency of Observations of Mothers with Two or More Young | Age Classes | | | | | Number of Offspring Per Mother. |
|---|---|---|---|---|---|---|
| | Inf.-One | Inf.-Two | Juv.-One | Juv.-Two | Adol. | |
| 1 | x | | x | | x | 3 |
| 1 | x | | x | | | 2 |
| 1 | x | | | x | | 2 |
| 1 | x | | | | x | 2 |
| 4 | | x | x | | | 2 |
| 1 | | x | | x | | 2 |
| 2 | | x | | x | x | 3 |
| 14 | | x | | | x | 2 |
| 1 | | | x | x | x | 3 |
| 3 | | | x | x | | 2 |
| 23 | | | x | | x | 2 |
| 2* | | | x | | x | 2 |

54

* pregnant at time of observation.

occasions. The relative age classes of the young in these 54 observations are shown in Table 11–5. The most frequent sibling relationship was juvenile-one with an adolescent (23); the next most frequent, infant-two and an adolescent (14). This again indicates that the commonest breeding rate among fertile females was one infant every three years, but that one every four or five years was also common. The remaining 17 sibling relationships show that every combination of age classes was observed, except that of infant-one and infant-two. Of the two mothers with the combination infant-two, juvenile-two, and adolescent, one was in estrous at the time she was observed, carrying the infant-two under her belly and the juvenile on her back, closely followed by the adolescent. Assuming all these were her own offspring and that she was ready to conceive, her breeding rate is seen to be one offspring every two to three years. It must not be overlooked, however, that on a few occasions females may have been seen carrying offspring that were not their own. Kortlandt frequently observed one particular mother with two juveniles of exactly the same size. He considered that either the juveniles were twins, or that the mother had "adopted" one of them.

### Birth Peak

Sufficient observations of mating and of newborn infants were not made to allow any conclusions regarding the possibility of a birth peak in the Budongo chimpanzees. Females in estrus were observed throughout the study period from March to October inclusive. The four observed copulations occurred on March 7, April 19, June 27, and October 11. Very young infants were observed in March, April, June (one definitely newborn), and October. Clearly pregnant females (that is, probably within two months of birth) were seen in each month from March to October.

## Mortality Factors and Longevity

Schultz (1940) has drawn attention to the high frequency of fractured and repaired bones in old wild chimpanzees. We saw a chimpanzee with a broken wrist which nevertheless could climb trees. Twice we saw chimpanzees fall, both times because the branch supporting them broke. On the first occasion an adult fell about 70 feet; during the fall it held out all four limbs stretched downwards and after landing in the undergrowth it ran off. The second time a small chimpanzee fell about 30 feet.

Once, prolonged coughing, of a kind suggesting a serious chest ailment, was heard from an adult female. One male had a glassy eye that appeared to be blind.

Yerkes (1943) includes a photograph of a male that died in captivity at 34 years of age, and this animal is not markedly different in appearance from many of the old males we saw. Mason (personal communication) observed that a male at the Yerkes Laboratories was still in fine condition at the age of 35, when he died from accidental causes. Riopelle and Daumy (1962) state that the oldest female at the Yerkes Laboratories is 42 years old. The extent to which baldness and the distribution of white hairs can be taken as a measure of old age in the Budongo chimpanzees is not known. We saw one large female that showed signs of what may have been great senility: she had a very bald head, her facial skeleton was visible under the skin, her skin showed in large bare patches over her limbs, her movements were labored, and she rested in nests during the morning. She was accompanied by a young adult female who groomed her and left the tree with her. Many times old animals were seen, but senile infirmity was rare.

## Population Structure

Chimpanzee groups in the Budongo Forest were constantly fluctuating in membership (see below), and it was impossible to determine accurately the structure of the total population in terms of the number of males, females, juveniles, and others. An estimate of the composition of the population in certain regions in the study area is given later during the discussion of social organization.

## Density and Range

From our data it was estimated that 60–80 chimpanzees (40–50 adults) habitually used approximately eight square miles of forest, giving a density of just less than ten chimpanzees to the square mile. These data were based on our observations of the chimpanzees living in the study area and may not apply to other areas of forest. Assuming they are typical, there would be somewhat less than 1700 chimpanzees living in the Budongo and Siba forests, but in view of the probable errors in this rough calculation, it seems safer to state that the population of these forests is between 1000 and 2000.

## SOCIAL ORGANIZATION

### Historical Review

Many hunters, explorers, and naturalists who traveled in equatorial Africa in the last century and this brought back accounts of free-living chimpanzees from personal knowledge and observation. Excerpts from their accounts are given here in chronological order, as are the observations of the chief scientists who have reported on chimpanzees more recently.

In 1844 Thomas Savage, a missionary in Cape Palmas, West Africa, reported on a chimpanzee specimen to the Boston Natural History Society. He described what he knew of the way of life of these animals, including what he had heard from the hunter who shot the specimen. "[Chimpanzees are] more often in pairs than in gangs. They are more numerous in the months of September, October, and November . . . when the greatest number of fruits come to maturity. . . . [Although] seldom more than 5 or 10 at most [are] found together . . . they occasionally assemble in large numbers in gambols . . . not less than 50 engaged in hooting, screaming and drumming with sticks on old logs." (p. 385)

In 1861 Paul du Chaillu, an explorer and hunter in the West African interior, reported that chimpanzees were "not gregarious. The young consort in small companies, but the adults go in pairs or singly." (p. 464) Similarly in 1873, another explorer and hunter, this time in Central Africa, Georg Schweinfurth, wrote: "They are not found in herds, but either in pairs or quite alone, and it is only the young which occasionally may be seen in groups." (p. 522) In 1884, P. Reichart, a scientist and hunter in Tanganyika, described some personal observations of a large band of 20 chimpanzees, which appeared to be composed of adult animals only.

In 1896 R. L. Garner, who appears from his book to have been a very enterprising character, reported on what was almost certainly the first attempted field study of gorillas and chimpanzees. Garner set up a strong cage for himself a short way inside the West African forest which both chimpanzees and gorillas frequented, and was able occasionally to observe passing apes, unaware of his presence until they came face to face with him. Garner wrote:

> While the chimpanzee is mostly found in large family groups, as I have reason to believe from *native accounts of them* [emphasis supplied] . . . I have never

been able to see a family of them together, but each of these I have mentioned was so far as I could tell quite alone. Whether the others were scattered through the forest in like manner hunting for food, and all came together after this or not, I can only say that every chimp I saw was alone at the time. (p. 160)

Garner had seen on the occasions to which he refers an adult male, an adult female, and several adolescents. In 1918–1919, Garner was still interested in observing chimpanzees, and reported to the New York Zoological Society on a site in West Africa where he had been able to watch groups of chimpanzees crossing an open space from one patch of forest to another. He reports the composition of the groups seen crossing on five days: Day 1, ten chimpanzees in a mixed group including juveniles; Day 2, three adults; Day 3, two mothers with young; Day 4, one large adult male alone; Day 5, a large movement through the day in bands of seven, five, one, and two chimpanzees.

In 1921 E. Reichenow, a hunter in West Africa, who studied chimpanzee nests, reported that the animals were usually found in large companies of 20–30 individuals, but that they split up over a wide area for sleeping, never more than two nests being found in one tree. The hunter J. L. Buck in 1927 reported some of his personal encounters with chimpanzee groups while attempting to capture them. One group contained seven or eight animals, including an old male, two females, and some juveniles; but on another occasion he captured a mother and juvenile which he had observed alone in one area for several days.

In 1931 H. Nissen, from the Yerkes laboratory, made a valuable contribution by his report on a field study he made in West Africa in the neighborhood of the Pasteur Institute. His observations were good and accurate, but his study was relatively short (49 days of actual observation) and the conditions of his study were difficult. He was unwilling to make any definite conclusions about chimpanzee social organization, but he estimated that he saw approximately 25 groups, varying in size from 4 to 14 chimpanzees, and that there were two or three groups at a time in his area. He observed groups meet, and, on two occasions, mingle. From his descriptions it is plain that none of these groups remained spatially compact for long, as individuals left trees singly or in pairs over time. There was no evidence of permanent groupings.

From Nissen's study, until the field studies of the 1960s, there were only a few individual observations reported in the literature. Captain Pitman, then a game warden in Uganda, reported in 1942 on his observations of a nesting group of a dozen chimpanzees. H. Beatty in West Africa in 1951 reported a group of 15 chimpanzees feeding on palm nuts. B. Grzimek, also in West Africa, watched a feeding group of 8–12 chimpanzees including adult males, mothers, and juveniles. N. Bolwig in 1955 made a study of chimpanzee nests, and found that "clusters of 3–5" were most common; he observed one mother and juvenile alone. A. Haddow wrote in Uganda in

1958, "They generally occur in small bands, often about 10, including juveniles, although solitary individuals are occasionally met."

It seems clear from the accounts given above that there has never been any worthwhile evidence that chimpanzees live in "family groups" or "harem groups," and that all such assumptions derive from the native population. Even Yerkes and Yerkes (1929:246) accepted the family group theory, although the only first-hand evidence available before 1929 pointed to looser fluctuating groupings, with every variation from single individuals of all ages and either sex (Garner 1896) to huge noisy gatherings at certain places at times of the ripening of the fruit trees (Savage 1844). Nevertheless, the idea that chimpanzees live in family groups is still very much alive today.

In 1960 Adriaan Kortlandt spent some months on a Congo plantation bordering on the rain forest that was regularly visited by numerous groups of chimpanzees, and where he had unusually good visibility for observations and identifications of individual animals. His study yielded reliable data on social organization, which are discussed below. Following Kortlandt's study came the studies of Goodall and of Reynolds, both reported in this volume.

### Group Dynamics

Chimpanzee groups in the Budongo Forest were not closed social groups. Groups were constantly changing membership, splitting apart, meeting others and joining them, congregating or dispersing. The term "band" will be used in the text to refer to these loosely organized, unstable groups of chimpanzees; "group" will be retained as a more generalized term.

The following typical examples of observations illustrate the fluctuations in grouping described above:

One fruiting fig tree was observed daily from the 19th to the 26th of April. Each day the tree was visited by chimpanzees. Two mothers with juveniles were the only constant visitors to the tree and often remained longer than the others. A white-backed old male and a white-backed female fed on the tree on five of the eight observation days. Two black-haired males and one gray-backed male were also frequent visitors in the mornings, but usually left after an hour's feeding. Six other females, three with juveniles, fed on the tree on one or more days. The times of arrival and departure from the tree varied with the individual, and never did all the animals arrive or leave as a group. Once there was three hours' difference between the departure time of the first and the last individual. Four times one chimpanzee remained behind alone in the tree for as long as two hours, twice a mother with her juveniles, and twice the old male. Other chimpanzees were feeding in another place about three quarters of a mile north along the river, and it was in this direction that the individuals went when they left. About 15 animals nested below the fig tree one evening when the fruit was almost finished, and the next morning some went northward as usual, while others went eastward to feed on a new tree.

When a fruit tree ripened, individuals or small bands included it in a daily routine of visits. For example, on one patch of *Aningeria altissima* trees, observed daily from the 2d to the 28th of June, a small band of from two to six mothers with young of various ages arrived early and took up habitual positions in the trees. On most days a band of from two to five adult males arrived after the females, from an easterly direction, fed in adjoining trees, and moved on westward toward a large feeding group about one half mile to the west. When the mothers finished feeding they returned to the river, which was to the southeast, where they often nested. However, when the fruit on the trees was finished, the mothers and the adult males all moved westward.

When an individual or small band was sufficiently familiar to us so as to be easily recognized, it was possible to record changes in the groups associated with it. For example, one small band of four adult males was seen many times and seemed to be a relatively stable unit. These males were easy to distinguish both physically and behaviorally as a group (singly it would not have been possible to identify them for certain). Three were large gray-backed males. One was small and thin, but also gray-backed. A fifth adult male was sometimes with them; he was old, with some white hairs, and was bald-headed. In response to our presence they were noticeable for their confident, relaxed behavior, showing curiosity, never fear. The following data based on field notes describe their activities:

June 26, 1962, this band headed a large group of 23 adults and adolescents as they crossed the main road to a new feeding area.

June 27 and for the next few days they were seen several times in a large aggregation including mothers, juveniles, and other adults feeding on *Pseudospondias*.

August 4, the four, without the old male, were feeding on *Maesopsis* trees, apart from other bands which were feeding in the next valley half a mile away.

August 5, the next day the old male joined them and so did four other adults.

August 10, all five were observed on the same *Maesopsis* trees in company with a young female in estrus, who was grooming the old male. The female left alone. The old male left alone. The other four spent two hours in mutual grooming, then left within minutes of each other.

August 23, during a large movement of many bands over a period of two days to a new *Maesopsis* patch, the four males crossed together, approaching the observers for a closer look.

August 26, in the course of a return movement all five crossed the road together.

Between the end of August and the early part of September chimpanzees were dispersed as the *Maesopsis* failed, and this band of four or five males was seen several times, alone as a group, feeding on outlying *Maesopsis* patches.

October 11, all five joined a band of mothers, one of which was in estrus. Two of them groomed this female at different times and one of them copulated with her.

The preceding examples serve to illustrate the way in which chimpanzee groups change and merge, and indicate some of the possible factors (concentration of fruit supply, estrous females, habit, friendship) that bring them together at certain times.

### Size and Composition of Bands

In the Budongo Forest there were seasonal variations in the size of the groups located. Three chief fruit seasons occurred in the study period: the figs in March and April; the *Pseudospondias* in late May and June; the *Maesopsis* in August and September. During these periods, the groups gathered on a tree or in a patch of neighboring trees often numbered 15 or more individuals. In the periods between, unless a large tree happened to fruit in the area, bands of three or four, or single individuals, were the rule.

Although the composition of bands was unstable, certain *types* of grouping were frequent and may reflect an inherent structure of the social organization. The frequent types of composition were: (1) adult bands, containing adults of both sexes, and occasionally adolescents, but not including any mothers with dependent young; (2) male bands, containing only adult males; (3) mother bands, containing only mothers with young, and occasionally other females; (4) mixed bands, containing mothers with young, other females, adolescents, and adult males.

Table 11–6 shows the frequency with which bands of these different types were observed, both large and small, in two different circumstances — feeding on a tree and traveling on the ground to a new place.

The figures support the observational data that the large mixed groups found feeding on fruit trees tend to be temporary congregations of smaller bands that have come to places where food is concentrated. When they leave the tree and travel about the forest, chimpanzees split up into small bands of less than seven individuals, and it is these small bands that help to reveal the social structure. On 50 occasions these small traveling bands consisted of all adult males or adult males and adult childless females (these two groups have here been treated together, for some of the small bands of adults may in fact have been all males). Only 14 times were small mother bands traveling about, and if this figure is combined with the figure for small mixed bands this makes a total of 25 occasions when mothers were seen in small traveling groups, in comparison with the 50 times a group of adults only was seen. This supports the field impression gained that mothers do less moving about the forest than do other adults. Al-

TABLE 11-6. FREQUENCY OF TYPES OF BANDS
WHEN FEEDING AND TRAVELING

| Size of Band | Type of Band | Situation | | Total |
| | | Feeding | Traveling | |
|---|---|---|---|---|
| Large (7 or more | Adults | 5 | 21 | 26 |
| individuals) | Males | 1 | 0 | 1 |
| | Mothers | 2 | 2 | 4 |
| | Mixed | 46 | 5 | 51 |
| Total | | 54 | 28 | 82 |
| Small* (6 or fewer | Adults | 3 | 36 | 39 |
| individuals) | Males | 19 | 14 | 33 |
| | Mothers | 18 | 14 | 32 |
| | Mixed | 18 | 11 | 29 |
| Total | | 58 | 75 | 133 |
| Large and small | Adults | 8 | 57 | 65 |
| bands combined | Males | 20 | 14 | 34 |
| | Mothers | 20 | 16 | 36 |
| | Mixed | 64 | 16 | 80 |
| Total all bands | | 112 | 103 | 215 |

* The count of small bands does not include single individuals. Chimpanzees of both sexes and of any age above juvenile-two were seen alone on occasion, but were usually within hearing distance of the calls of a group. Nor are young carried by the mother counted as individuals for the purpose of this table.

most always when mother bands were seen traveling they were part of a large-scale movement of many groups to a new focus of activity, whereas adults often moved to and fro between such areas, independently of other group movements. This lesser degree of mobility on the part of mothers with young is also reflected in the high figure of 21 occasions when a large band consisting solely of adults and adolescents (type 1) was observed in a movement. The largest bands in these 21 examples consisted of 10, 15, 18, 23, 28, and 30 individuals.

These data are consistent with those of Goodall (Chap. 12, this volume) and of Kortlandt (1962). Kortlandt watched for two months daily the various bands of chimpanzees that visited a plantation of pawpaw trees bordering on the forest in east Congo and was the first to distinguish between "nursery groups" and "sexual groups." He saw bands of mothers and young visiting the plantation, each band consisting of from 2 to 11 mothers, each with 1 or 2 offspring, and occasionally other females. Sometimes such a band was accompanied by 1 or 2 adult males, which Kortlandt considered might possibly be mature sons of the mothers in the band. The sexual groups often numbered more than 20 animals, consisting chiefly of males and childless females, and were behaviorally quite different from the nursery groups. They visited the pawpaw plantation only every 2 or 3 days, and appeared to range over a much wider area for food in between visits. While on the plantation, the sexual groups were noisy, and less shy than the nursery groups. However, there was much mixing and changing among the groups. When bands arriving at different times met on the plantation there was no friction, and individuals were seen to change bands. Kortlandt wrote: "Participation in either kind of aggregation did not seem to be fixed or controlled in any way. Individuals were free to join or leave a group at will, and the groups themselves often merged or split up" (1962:132).

The composition of bands visiting from day to day was not consistent although many individuals were recognized again and again. Individuals frequently arrived at the plantation alone, among them single males, single females, and mothers carrying infants.

**Relations between Bands**

The smallest social unit of chimpanzee organization in the Budongo Forest seemed to be a small, rather unstable band of from two to six individuals, whose association was probably based on personality characteristics, or similar age, sex, status, or condition. In addition, familiarity through blood relationship may well be another factor in band formation.

These small bands constantly interacted because of recurrent social and physical needs. The chief factors which brought bands together were: (1) concentration of food; (2) sexual behavior and grooming; (3) attraction to calls and drumming of neighbors; (4) use of habitual routes and regions of activity; (5) large-scale movements to a new place (usually related to the decrease of food supply in one area).

After following band movements in the forest and plotting all known routes and movements on large-scale maps, we found it convenient to divide the study area into three "regions" of about 6–8 square miles each — the Bubwe River region, the Eastern Valleys-Siba region, and the Kamirambwa region. Over most of the nine months of observations taken as a whole, bands within each of these regions had a higher frequency of interactions among one another than with bands beyond. These regions of activity are marked on the map of the study area (Fig. 11–12a) and can be compared with the maps showing movements at different fruit seasons (Figs. 11–12b, c, and d). Bands located in the Eastern Valleys-Siba region, for example, tended to move along habitual and predictable routes to and fro between food sources in the region, and recognizable individuals were sometimes seen traveling routes traveled before. These regions cannot be considered "ranges" in the normal sense, but rather areas of concentration and a product to some extent of the distribution of fruit sources. During the early *Maesopsis* season bands from neighboring regions congregated and there were bands feeding on *Maesopsis* patches at Game, Kasenene, Busingiro, and Eastern Valleys (see Fig. 11–12*d*) with continual comings and goings among all these places. The Busingiro and Kasenene areas had been used at times by bands coming from the Bubwe River region and the Eastern Valleys region, and at this season it seemed they were being used by both. On six recorded occasions a band from Eastern Valleys traveled fast and noisily right up into the Bubwe River region, and at other times similar movements occurred in the opposite direction. Thus the regions of activity shifted according to the seasons, and there were congregations of chimpanzees from different areas at the common food sources, without hostility, and with no indications that bands were not free to come and go as they pleased.

On the other hand, on all except two nights during the early *Maesopsis* season, when bands from both regions had been feeding in the same area, groups tended to move apart at dusk, and nesting bands were heard calling from within the two regions, only to unite again early next morning. Unusual excitement seemed to be present while large numbers of chimpanzees were feeding in the same area. During this early *Maesopsis* season there was an extraordinary frequency and volume of calling and drumming throughout the day and sometimes at night. This region resounded with prolonged choruses and long-repeated rolls of drumming for two to three hours on end, with chimpanzees coming and going in all directions, some to and some from the centers of hubbub.

Later in August, when bands began to move off toward other *Maesopsis* patches along their usual routes, the amount of noise decreased. There were no boundaries within the study area where bands of chimpanzees were not known to cross in both directions. It seems likely, however, that habit, and knowledge of a particular stretch of forest and its amenities, would tend to maintain a certain constancy of movement in the chimpanzees inhabiting an area. The fact that we recognized certain individuals traveling the same routes several times over periods of months tends to confirm this hypothesis. But it is also evident from our data that chimpanzees have a wider compass of social interrelationships than do most other primates discussed in this volume.

## Population and Range of Bands in a Region

It was difficult to estimate the total population of the bands within each region, since they were never all together in one place at one time. The largest aggregation of bands feeding in one *Maesopsis* area, which over a period of two days crossed the road toward a new patch, contained the fol-

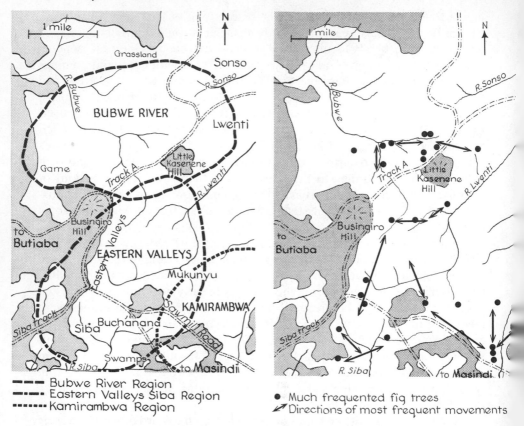

--- Bubwe River Region
---·--- Eastern Valleys Siba Region
········ Kamirambwa Region

● Much frequented fig trees
↗ Directions of most frequent movements

Fig. 11–12a. (*Left*) Regions of chimpanzee activity in study area. *b.* (*Right*) Most frequent movements during the height of the fig season.

lowing individuals: 17 mothers (one clearly pregnant) carrying infants or juveniles; 10 juvenile-twos and adolescents walking independently; 6 females (one clearly pregnant); 13 adult males. In addition to these animals, a few small bands had crossed unseen the day before, and prior to this a few calls from the new area had been heard. Most of these small bands of fore-runners were probably adult males, plus a few childless females. If this is taken to be so, the total population of this region at that time could be estimated to contain 17–20 mothers, each with a dependent youngster, 10–12 independent young approaching adolescence, 6–10 females without young, and perhaps 20 or more adult males, a total of 70–80 animals. In the other regions of this study, the total numbers were probably similar or some-what less. For example, in one other region a band of 30 adults and adoles-cents (without juveniles) was seen, which suggests a total population of 60

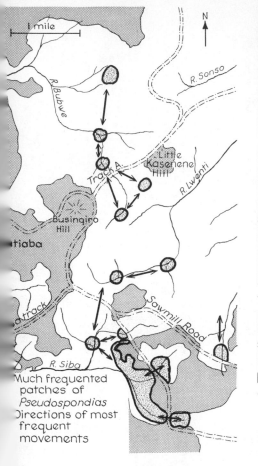

Much frequented patches of Pseudospondias
Directions of most frequent movements

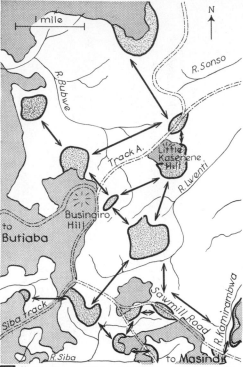

Much frequented patches of *Maesopsis*
Directions of most frequent movements

Fig. 11–12c. (Left) Most frequent movements during *Pseudospondias* season. d. (Right) Most frequent movements during *Maesopsis* season.

or more individuals when the estimated mothers and young are added.

Kortlandt estimated that a total population of 70–80 chimpanzees visited his plantation over his study period; the largest gathering he saw at one time consisted of 48 chimpanzees, nesting in one place.

The range of bands is certainly greater than the extent of the regions of activity specified. It is probable on the basis of our observations of traveling and feeding groups (see Table 11–6) that the bands of mothers and young tend to remain in the familiar places within each of the regions. But bands of males or adult bands often pass from one region into another, and the range of such bands is probably much greater than that of the mothers. Thus we estimate that whereas mothers may remain for long periods within a range of six square miles, adults, especially adult males, range over from eight to ten square miles or even much more.

**TABLE 11-7. CHIMPANZEE VOCALIZATIONS**

| Description of Sound | Facial Expression | Circumstances in Order of Frequency | Notes |
|---|---|---|---|
| 1. Grunts. | | Feeding in a group.<br>Feeding alone.<br>Traveling in a group.<br>Nest-building. | Single animals; probably contented or conversational. |
| 2. Gruff barks. (Fig. 11–13a). Low-intensity, low-pitched barks, often in a series. | | Feeding in a group.<br>Associated with other calls in minor excitements.<br>Traveling in a group.<br>Nesting and awakening. | Single animals. |
| 3. Panting barks. Low-pitched barks, followed by noisy intake of breath, often in a series ascending in pitch and intensity. | | Minor excitements such as:<br>Leaving a tree in response to calls from another band.<br>Traveling.<br>Feeding.<br>Seeing Observer. | Single animals often; but barks may be associated with other calls in a chorus. |
| 4. Waa barks. (Fig. 11–13b). Sudden sharp barks, with harsh grating in throat, single calls repeated. | Mouth half-open; lips not pouted, but tensed when barks at high intensity; teeth not bared. | Almost solely associated with seeing observer, on two occasions on seeing duiker or buffalo. | Single animal or chorus, indicating alarm or threat. Often associated with forms of display. |
| 5. Harsh and shrill barks. (Fig. 11–13c). High-pitched sometimes hoarse barks, often in ascending series, | | Restlessness and preparation for movement such as:<br>Swinging about in tree.<br>Descending from tree and moving off. | In choruses or associated with other calls. Often with display. |

rising to scream.

| | Mouth | Situations | Remarks |
|---|---|---|---|
| 6. Soft moans. | | Crossing a track. In quarrels. | Single animals; "worried." |
| 7. Moaning hoots. (Fig. 11–13d). Low-intensity form of panting or long hoots. One kind rises in pitch during each call, the other drops in pitch. | Mouth a little open, slight pout. | Always one animal which sees observer, in situations where animal is alone, or cannot see clearly, as on ground inside forest. Seeing observer. Starting off choruses. Following choruses. Response to choruses from another band. | Single animal, but others may join in with hoots. Excitement. |
| 8. Panting hoots and long hoots (Fig. 11–13e and f). Long whooping calls, starting at low pitch and intensity, with noisy breath-intake, rising to wild shrieking. | Mouth is usually half-open with slightly pouted tensed lips. At higher intensities lips go into round tight oo shape, sometimes very pouted. | (1) After feeding in preparation to move on. Traveling. In response to choruses from other bands. Meeting and splitting of large gatherings. Group sees observer. (2) Sometimes associated with delight or success such as: Seeing bunches of fruit. After dominating another animal. End of rain. Nesting or first dawn calls. | Nearly always in choruses, and very frequently accompanied by all forms of display. Great group excitement. Refers to occasional single hoots. |

## TABLE 11-7. CHIMPANZEE VOCALIZATIONS—Continued

| Description of Sound | Facial Expression | Circumstances in Order of Frequency | Notes |
|---|---|---|---|
| 9. Howls. (Fig. 11–3g) Long drawn-out singing call. | | | One animal goes on and on, either alone, or accompanied by other calls from other animals. |
| 10. Scream. (Fig. 11–13h) | Mouth wide open, all teeth especially canines showing. | In frustration or anger in variable situations. One animal in a quarrel. By deserted juveniles or threatened juveniles. Seeing observer. Rain comes, tree falls. Dissatisfaction with food or nesting site. One animal as others prepare to leave tree. | One animal screams usually while others make hooting calls. Sometimes one animal screams on own. Invariably accompanied by wildest forms of display. |
| 11. Squeal. (Fig. 11–13i) high-pitched short squealing sound. | Mouth drawn back over jaws showing teeth and gums, but jaws shut or only slightly open. | The threatened one in a quarrel or dominance encounter. Juveniles deserted by mothers. Often heard in choruses of other calls during traveling or feeding. | |
| 12. Roars and growls. Extreme form of scream, with grating of throat. High intensity. | | Only when one animal sees observer, on occasions when observer called back at animal. | Accompanied by extreme forms of display. |

TABLE 11-8. CHIMPANZEE FACIAL EXPRESSIONS AND GRIMACES

| Description | Circumstances in Which Observed |
| --- | --- |
| 1. Yawn | Animal sees observer but does not leave the tree. May indicate uncertainty. |
| 2. Gasp | An adolescent suddenly noticed the observer close by. |
| 3. Bared teeth and gums with jaws shut | Brief grimace of inferior towards superior in dominance interaction. |
| 4. Pursed lips | The animal notices the observer, becomes anxious, looks away, looks again. |
| 5. Mouth open occasionally accompanied by slight forward movement of head) | Immediate response to seeing observer; hearing alarm calls; to a truant juvenile; or any sudden disturbance. |
| 6. Pouted protruding lips | Made towards a bunch of fruit, or towards a small juvenile; once seen prior to kissing the backside of a juvenile. |
| 7. Scowl | An adult male charges towards the observers. |
| 8. Smile | Seen during the play of two juvenile-ones. |
| 9. Sticking out of tongue | Also seen while two juveniles were playing. |

## SOCIAL BEHAVIOR

### Expressive and Communicative Behavior

Expressive and communicative forms of behavior are summarized in Tables 11-7, 11-8, and 11-9, and sonograms of the chief calls are shown in Fig. 11-13. Chimpanzees are the most consistently noisy animals in the Budongo Forest. Except when food is in short supply, groups call from time to time throughout the day and also during the night. The farthest these calls were known to carry was just over two miles. Drumming was sometimes heard faintly when the accompanying vocalizations were out of range.

Occasionally, about eight times during nine months' observations but not at regular intervals, the chimpanzees in an area vocalized and drummed for several hours continuously, and these prolonged outbursts were memorable and exciting for us. Sometimes whole valleys along a stretch as much as a mile would resound and vibrate with the noise. These carnivals form part of the "mythology" of chimpanzees from the earliest reports. Savage and Wyman (1843–1844:385) wrote that chimpanzees occasionally gather in companies and engage in hooting, screaming, and drumming.

**TABLE 11–9. SOME CHIMPANZEE GESTURES AND FORMS OF DISPLAY**

| Description of Action | Circumstances in Which Observed |
|---|---|
| 1. Raising of one arm towards the rest of the band following behind. | Seen on two occasions when the leading animal noticed the observer, the chimpanzees following behind disappeared, while the leading chimpanzee remained to watch the observer. |
| 2. Reaching out one or both arms towards a juvenile. | Seen only in mothers. Juvenile always climbs aboard. |
| 3. Mounting of one male by another in which one male covers the back of the other and shakes whole body. | Dominance or greeting, when two males meet. |
| 4. Display:<br>Branch shaking<br>Branch breaking and throwing<br>Sapling shaking and wrenching<br>Stamping on branch or ground<br>Slapping ground<br>Hitting tree trunks with hands<br>Thumping on tree trunks with feet<br>Drumming on tree buttresses with hands or feet (Fig. 11–13*j*)<br>Jumping from branch to branch<br>Swinging in tree<br>Shaking of whole body while holding on to branches. | Occur in situations indicating threat or group excitement such as described for the panting hoot choruses. |

Garner (1896:59–60) wrote that, according to native hearsay, "one of the most remarkable habits of the chimpanzee is the *kanjo* as it is called in the native tongue. The word . . . implies more the idea of 'carnival.' It is believed that more than one family takes part in these festivities." He then went on to describe how the chimpanzees fashion a drum from damp clay and wait for it to dry. Then "the chimpanzees assemble by night in great numbers and then the carnival begins. One or two will beat violently on this dry clay, while others jump up and down in a wild grotesque manner. Some of them utter long rolling sounds as if trying to sing . . . and the festivities continue in this fashion for hours." Apart from the question of the drum, the account given above describes quite well what occurred in the Budongo Forest in its extreme form, as we heard it six times, once when we were very close to the chimpanzees. Only twice, however, did this happen at night; the four other times it lasted for a few hours during the daytime.

The "carnivals" consisted of prolonged noise for periods of hours, whereas ordinary outbursts of calling and drumming lasted a few minutes only. Although it was not possible to know the reason for this unusual behavior, twice (see below) it seemed to be associated with the meeting at a common food source of bands that may have been relatively unfamiliar to each other.

At the time of one of these six "carnivals" we were inside the forest close to the chimpanzees, while a third observer, a visiting European, was on a hill overlooking the area and reporting on all vocalizations and drummings and their directions. Inside the forest we were attempting to locate the chimpanzees to observe, if possible, the behavior associated with the tremendous uproar. Unfortunately this proved impossible. Calls were coming from all directions at once and all groups concerned seemed to be moving about rapidly. As we oriented toward the source of one outburst, another came from another direction. Stamping and fast-running feet were heard sometimes behind, sometimes in front, and howling outbursts and prolonged rolls of drums (as many as 13 rapid beats) shaking the ground surprised us every few yards. Conditions were impossible for observation and after a while the most intense source of the noise moved off southward.

Nissen, too, in 1931, was particularly impressed by "the almost unbelievable amount and intensity of sound production by free-living chimpanzees" (page 89). His experience with captive animals had not prepared him for this. "Although the cries and drumming presaged no danger to human listeners . . . their very intensity was sufficient to inspire something akin to excited wonderment . . . when drumming and vocalizing were close by, my guides and porters sometimes trembled in spite of themselves" (page 89). Nissen (page 33) wrote of what the natives referred to as "carnival nights," when chimpanzees vocalized all night long, and they associated this with the moonlight.

The normal outbursts of calls and drumming at Budongo were of one to three minutes duration and occurred at intervals throughout the day in association with circumstances of group excitement. They rarely occurred when chimpanzees were scattered in small groups over wide areas and food was scarce. The frequency of calls and drumming for one typical day, the cyclical nature of the outbursts, and their association with movement are shown in Table 11–10.

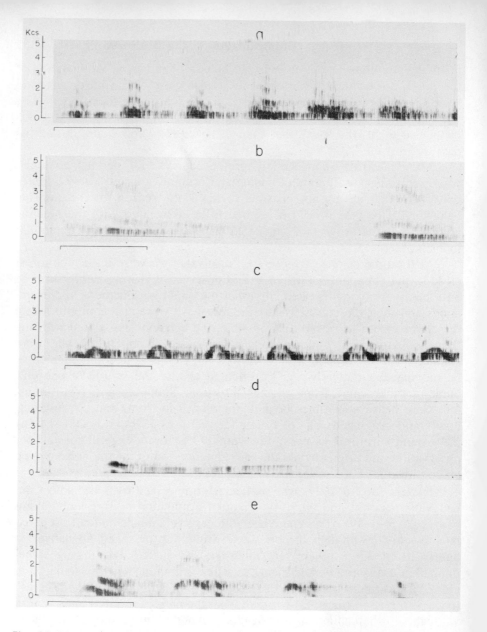

Fig. 11–13. Sonograms of some chimpanzee calls. *a.* A series of six gruff barks. *b.* Two waa barks. *c.* A series of six shrill barks. *d.* A moaning hoot which trails off. *e.* A series of four panting hoots by a single chimpanzee.

Between 20 and 30 chimpanzees were involved in these movements. Although each individual was not seen (they moved along many different tracks so that we were not able to cover them all), the youngest observed was a juvenile-two who walked independently. This suggests that these

410

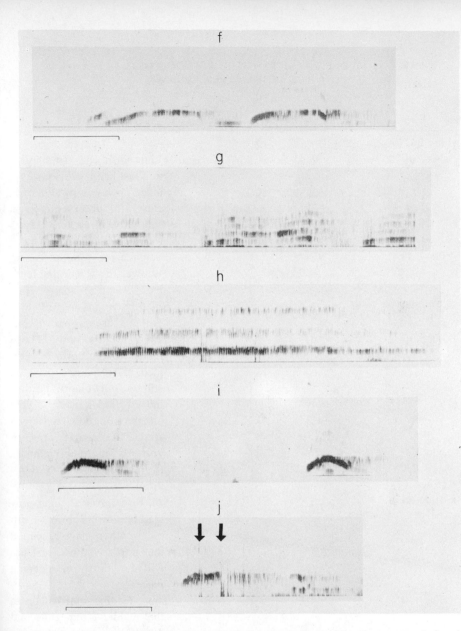

*f.* Two long hoots with panting breath-intake between the hoots. *g.* A howl. *h.* A scream. *i.* Two squeals. *j.* The termination of a hoot-drumming sequence; showing part of final scream and a two-beat drum, marked by arrows.

mobile groups were chiefly adults and adolescents and that the mothers remained in a central feeding area along the Bubwe River north.

The following circumstances were most noticeably associated with choruses:

### TABLE 11–10. ONE DAY DURING THE *PSEUDOSPONDIAS* SEASON IN THE BUBWE RIVER REGION

| Time | Number of Calling Outbursts | Number of Drummings | Behavior |
|---|---|---|---|
| (May 26, 1962) | | | |
| 6:30–7:00 | 2 | – | Faint north calls from position last heard previous evening. Then one party moves close to observers, in a southerly direction. Others remain feeding. |
| 7:00–7:30 | 2 | – | From large group north Bubwe. Early morning feeding. |
| 7:30–8:00 | 1 | 1 | Small party has moved close now, and drums on the move. |
| 8:00–8:30 | 6 | 2 | Three groups now. Those faintly calling north in early feeding trees, one party is still on Bubwe north but has moved closer now; a few chimps move down to Bubwe south to feeding area of yesterday morning, calling as they go. Those close north drum. |
| 8:30–9:00 | 6 | 2 | Still three groups, some now feeding on Bubwe south patch, others have remained just north of track, rest are still far north in sleeping place. |
| 9:00–9:30 | 4 | 1 | Those feeding south call once, the middle group calls and drums then settles down to feed. |
| 9:30–10:00 | No calls | | |
| 10:00–11:00 | 6 | 2 | The close north group moves around and drums. The south group also moves into new trees and drums. The far north group is silent. |

TABLE 11-10. ONE DAY DURING THE *PSEUDOSPONDIAS* SEASON IN
THE BUBWE RIVER REGION—*Continued*

| Time | Number of Calling Outbursts | Number of Drummings | Behavior |
|---|---|---|---|
| 11:00–11:30 | No calls | | |
| 11:30–12:30 p.m. | 3 | — | The close north group crosses southward and calls as arrives south. |
| 12:30–1:00 | No calls | | All feeding in trees. |
| 1:00–1:30 | 9 | 7 | The far north group has moved down southward toward the others. A small party crosses the track and calls on way to south feeding patch. |
| 1:30–2:00 | 8 | 2 | All calls and drums now come from Bubwe south. Several parties keep moving southwards from the Bubwe north to the Bubwe south. |
| 2:00–2:30 | 2 | — | A few more cross. No more call north all day. |
| 2:30–3:00 | 1 | — | From Bubwe south. In trees. |
| 3:00–3:30 | 4 | — | |
| 4:00–4:30 | 3 | 1 | |
| 4:30–5:00 | 1 | — | |
| 5:00–5:30 | 6 | — | Moving to final feeding trees. |
| 5:30–6:00 | 9 | — | Moving to final feeding trees. |
| 6:00–6:30 | 3 | — | Final feeding. |
| 6:30–7:00 | 1 | — | Nesting. |

1. Nesting and awakening, especially if it was a large group.

2. Meeting of two groups, or the arrival of new animals at a tree. In this situation the choruses were usually accompanied by swinging about in the tree, stamping, branch-shaking, and drumming.

3. Splitting up of a large group. As the two sections moved apart, there were crescendoes from either half, accompanied by prolonged drum rolls, and the continual coming and going between the two groups of some individuals.

4. When a group was about to move on to a new feeding area. A few

animals became restless and started shaking branches and calling. When these left the tree and descended to the ground, they drummed, shook saplings, slapped the ground, and made off along a track to a new place. Those left in the tree would answer the calls but might not leave immediately.

5. When a group was on the ground and on the move, these choruses were made, accompanied by ground slapping, sapling shaking and breaking, stamping, and drumming.

6. In answer to calls and drums heard elsewhere. Chimpanzees immediately looked up toward the calls and called in answer. This could lead to general excitement and the group would move off toward the calls.

7. At any time when large numbers of chimpanzees were congregated within limited areas, such as during the fig seasons, or when relatively unfamiliar bands were feeding on the same *Maesopsis* patches.

8. Before and during a large-scale movement of many groups of chimpanzees to a new food source when food in one place began to fail. The first group to move would make a great deal of noise and drumming, other groups started moving in the same direction, the excitement mounted, and a general movement of all chimpanzees in neighboring areas would begin. Groups and individuals tended to follow the direction of calls rather than any one route or track.

9. On occasion, the same kind of whooping choruses, accompanied by drumming, branch and sapling shaking, and stamping, occurred when a group of chimpanzees came upon us in circumstances where the observers were clearly seen to be humans. As they crowded round closer in low trees and saplings, the behavior seemed like anger or threat, although it was never followed up by attack, the chimpanzees eventually departing.

10. Finally, it was quite common for such outbursts to occur once or several times a night, but even when the observers spent the night close to the chimpanzees in the forest, no reason was apparent.

Although different groups no doubt "locate" each other by calling and answering over the forest, there was no evidence that this led to the spacing of groups; calls and drums from other chimpanzees appeared to be a source of attraction to others in the vicinity, a stimulus for the gathering rather than the spacing out of groups. At times of scarcest food, and thus maximal competition, very few calls were made.

These outbursts may be *communicative* to other bands in the following ways: First, the population of animals is not a cohesive unit that moves about together; chimpanzees may at times be widely scattered in small units or individuals. Second, bands of mothers travel and explore less than do adult males, and may be dependent upon information from the calling of the parties of males in order to know where the next food can be found. Third, drumming is done chiefly by the forerunners of a movement, and may act as a kind of "summons" to those behind. In large-scale movements, those animals following seem to orient to the call directions rather than to follow one track.

The loud calling in chorus and drumming displays of chimpanzees may thus be correlated with their loosely organized unstable society, which itself can be seen as an adaptation to the needs of large fruit eaters in a forest environment.

## Dominance and Leadership

Although there was some evidence of differences in status between individuals, dominance interactions formed a minute fraction of the observed chimpanzee behavior. There was no evidence of a linear hierarchy of dominance among males or females; there were no observations of exclusive rights to receptive females; and there were no permanent leaders of groups.

On 25 occasions one individual showed dominance over another individual or over a group of animals. On seven occasions one male moved to allow another to pass, or moved away as the dominant animal approached. Four times a small grooming group split up at the approach of a large male, and on one of these occasions a female which had been grooming two males moved up and groomed the more dominant intruder. On three occasions one male was the effective leader among a small band of adult males. They left the tree when he left, or followed him across the road. Six times the departure of one adult male caused the departure of a group. Only once was a female observed to show dominance over a male and never over a group.

One observed sequence of dominance behavior had an unusual feature. An adult male seemed to fall off a branch (at the approach of another adult male) on to the branch below. The dominant male then urinated above the subordinate; the subordinate bared his teeth and then proceeded to lick the urine off the branch.

When a large band was traveling, a group of graying adult males often went first, although this was by no means always true (reported also by Kortlandt 1962).

Some adult males showed a relaxed and confident bearing and an unhurried gait, which made them particularly noticeable. For example, on frequent occasions a white- or gray-backed male remained behind in a tree after the rest of the group had gone, often just sitting looking out from a high position. Such a male was not worried by the sight of the human observers, but would show merely a mild curiosity. This "look-out" behavior noticed in older adult males may be the same as that reported by Kortlandt, who found that in the group visiting the plantation one very old male acted as a "security inspector," although he was not an active leader in any way.

When crossing the main road through the forest, most chimpanzees, after cautiously peeping out to see that the way was clear, would speed across the open space and disappear into the forest beyond. In contrast, in each of the areas observed there were some adult males, or more often a small band of adult males, which walked on to the road slowly and confidently, looking around them, and if they happened to see us or the camera, they would show curiosity, often approaching for closer inspection. This type of behavior was limited to mature graying adult males, but by no means all gray-backed males behaved in this way.

### Aggressive Behavior

During 300 observation hours, 47 quarrels involving actual fighting or displays of threat or anger were seen, and none of these lasted more than a few seconds. Shaking of the body, or of branches, or stamping and hitting things may have indicated threat or frustrated anger but was never seen to lead to attack. Attacks, on the other hand, were sudden and occurred with no visible antecedents.

Four of these quarrels involved two adult males. Two took the form of short sudden scuffles, followed by mutual displays of branch shaking, stamping, barking, and squealing, with no clear sequel. In another, a male approached another male feeding in a nest and pushed him out of it; some mutual threats followed and then they moved a little apart. In the fourth, a male snatched a piece of bark away from another, after which there was some disturbance and a scuffle and then peace.

Four quarrels involved an adult and a juvenile. Once a female, with no evident provocation, chased away a juvenile-one which had been quietly playing with her infant-two; the victim fled and hung screaming from a neighboring tree, but ten minutes later it had returned and was again playing with the infant. On another occasion an adult was observed shaking all over, and looking toward an adolescent on the branch below.

Three of the quarrels involved two juveniles or two adolescents. Sometimes it seemed that the screams of the combatants set off barking by an adult; and once an adult male moved toward them and the fighting stopped.

On only one occasion was a male seen to threaten a female. She was quietly feeding when an adult male approached from behind and shook the branches behind her violently. She turned round to look at him and bared her teeth in a grimace, then started feeding again. The performance was repeated and then they both left the tree. Perhaps the male was trying to get the female to follow him; she was not in estrus. Also there was only one time when a female threatened a male; a large female in estrus approached a small patchy male who ran a little way screaming, at which she shook branches at him and barked. The only time two females were clearly in conflict occurred between a female and a mother with an infant; they had a short scuffle but soon settled down to feeding once more on the same branch.

## Grooming

Grooming was an activity carried on within small groups of chimpanzees, following an intense and satisfying bout of feeding, before the call came to move on to a new place. Fifty-seven clear examples of grooming behavior were observed, by far the most of them in the early part of the year when there were ripe fig trees and on the subsequent occasional ripenings of trees with abundant fruits. In the periods of scarcity of fruit there was so much moving about from place to place that there seemed little time for relaxed social activities.

**TABLE 11–11. FREQUENCY OF GROOMING BETWEEN DIFFERENT AGE AND SEX CATEGORIES**

| Age and Sex Class | Frequency | Number of Times a Female in Estrus Involved |
|---|---|---|
| Female grooming female | 7 | 2 |
| Mother grooming juvenile and/or other mother | 14 | 3 |
| Juvenile grooming mother | 4 | 2 |
| Male-female grooming* | 18 | 11 |
| Male-female grooming involving more than one male | 3 | 3 |
| Male grooming male | 5 | |
| Male grooming juvenile | 2 | |
| Unidentified adults | 4 | |
| Total observations | 57 | |

* Includes male grooming female, female grooming male, and mutual male-female grooming.

In two-thirds of the cases where there was male-female grooming, the female was in estrus. Three times a female was groomed by more than one male simultaneously, twice by two males, once by three. In the male-female grooming relations, there were several examples of "grooming promiscuity," where an estrous female groomed or was groomed by one male for a while, then was approached by another male and commenced grooming with him.

## Sexual Behavior

The behavior of a female in estrus was observed on 73 occasions and the composition of the group she was with recorded (Fig. 11–14). The frequency of observations of females in estrus, within different types of group composition, is shown on the following page.

Fig. 11–14. A female with large sexual swelling (top left) is seen with a group of adults in a fig tree.

| Group Composition Containing Female in Estrus | Frequency of Observations |
|---|---|
| With 1 adult male only | 8 |
| In group of 2–8 adult males | 10 |
| In mixed group but attended by 1 male | 14 |
| In mixed group containing males but none in attendance | 22 |
| In mothers' group | 5 |
| Alone | 4 |
| In group where presence of males not established (not all animals identified) | 10 |
| Total | 73 |

As 50 percent of the females observed in estrus were accompanied by off-spring, a higher percentage of estrous females would have been expected in mothers' groups than was actually found. This indicates that the mother in estrus tends to leave her group to join males, or that males join up with mother bands when one of them is in estrus.

Although the total observed social interactions are few in this study, there are indications that estrous females were involved in more of them than were other females. The high proportion of estrous females involved in heterosexual grooming relations has been mentioned in the previous section. Again, in the observed quarrels, the only instance of a female's threatening a male involved a female in estrus. Of the two quarrels involving a female and a juvenile, one of the females was in estrus. And of the three quarrels where both adults concerned were not identified, two certainly involved a female in estrus.

Four copulations were observed. These all took place in the trees during the midmorning, following intense early feeding. Details of the copulation most clearly observed can be given from the notes taken at the time:

> Three chimps sit in comfortable crotch of mahogany tree. Adult male sits placidly in fork about 50 feet up. He is all black, not bare on rump. Adult female with maximal swelling stands on branch with swelling toward male. She is small, adult, all black. A little up branch to right of male is a juvenile-one sitting, eating leaves, looking down at male and female. Male moves very casually toward female without really getting up. He grasps branch above with left hand, placing right hand on branch he is sitting on behind him as support, not moving position of legs but moving trunk toward rear of female, and giving slow thrusts approximately 1 per second for about 5 seconds, then goes back to sitting position looking about. Female continues to stand, made no visible movements during copulation, swelling still pointing at male. About 20 seconds later exact repetition of previous events, 30 seconds later another repetition. Very casual. No sounds, no excitement. After this male sits while female remains standing. He grooms her and examines swelling. Juvenile-one moves away. Female moves just below male, at which male lies down curled up in crotch and dozes.

> A few minutes later another male joined the two, and started grooming the female on her back and rump, and the first male resumed grooming the female. The female moved to present to the second male and he moved closer as though to copulate, but then the first male started grooming him and both males indulged in mutual grooming, ignoring the female. When the first male left the group temporarily, the second male looked at the female but did not mount. When the female left, both males, the juvenile, and another male followed her.

On another occasion, the relations of the males involved were somewhat similar: Four adult males and an estrous female (with juvenile-one) comprised the group. The female was grooming an adult male, and the male showed an erection. The male moved away a little, and the female followed him. She lay down on her belly on the branch in front of him and he copulated with her for a few seconds in a sitting position (from 10 to 15 thrusts), then sat a few yards off, picking off the ejaculate. A second male approached the female and groomed her, while a third manipulated his own erect penis. A little while later, three of the males were grooming each other and the female had moved off.

These observations, taken together with the data on composition of groups containing estrous females and the data on male-female grooming relations, indicate some degree of sexual promiscuity. However, there were no observations of more than one male copulating with a female within any observation period, even when opportunity seemed to present itself. On the other hand, there were no signs of jealousy, or aggression, between the males. The mutual grooming could have been caused by displaced aggressive tensions, but it was also observed between males in other situations where no source of tension was apparent.

It is not known whether dominance relations between the males were operating in these situations. In the copulation first described, the male and female were both young adults, and at least one older and seemingly more dominant male was present in the tree, but showed no interest in the female. The copulation observed by Kortlandt was on the ground, and an old male known to be bad-tempered and dominant watched the event without interfering or showing any aggression.

Homosexual mounting was seen only once, when an adult male, newly arrived at a fig tree where a band was feeding, approached one of the adult males already in the tree, covered the other's back and rump with his body, and shook all over. The shaking was not typical pelvic thrusts, but a general vibration of the whole body. The gesture was unclear, but in the circumstances it was taken to be either dominance or "greeting" behavior (see Goodall, Chap. 12, this volume). Kortlandt twice observed homosexual mounting that appeared to be displacement or appeasement behavior.

## RELATIONS BETWEEN MOTHER AND YOUNG

For the first months of life an infant chimpanzee remains with its mother, nursing, clinging, and holding on to her belly as she moves. Once a female was seen carrying in her mouth a limp, dark, furry shape that was probably a dead infant. Mothers were not seen to support young infants as they walked on the ground or climbed about in the trees. In captivity the infant's grasp appears to be weak (Mason, Chap. 15, this volume). Thus, either the grasp reflex in wild neonates is developed and strengthened through use and necessity to a greater extent than in captive-born neonates, or else the infant clings by holding on with its arms and legs round the mother's body, rather than merely grasping hair. This seems a possibility, as this is certainly the way older offspring may be carried. After a few weeks, the infant begins exploring its mother's body, but rarely leaves contact with the mother. As time goes by it explores farther afield. No mother was seen to instruct her infant in locomotion. From approximately six months to the age of four or five years, a young chimpanzee was usually found feeding in the same tree within a few yards of its mother.

Examples of maternal protective behavior are as follows. When a juvenile-one, which was walking independently, was unable to cross an arboreal gap to a neighboring tree the mother pulled a higher branch of the next tree toward her to make a connecting bridge for the juvenile to cross upon. A mother, spotting our cautious approach toward the main group ahead, charged toward us leaving her offspring behind in the tree and collecting it on her way back.

But there were also many observed occasions when it seemed that a juvenile was not attended to or protected. For example, several times a juvenile was seen or heard screaming for several minutes without distracting its mother from feeding or attracting any other adult. Sometimes adults barked when juveniles screamed, but did nothing actively. Twice the cause of the tantrums of the young chimpanzee was that it had noticed us, but high-pitched, rapid, continuous screams and stamping failed to bring the mother to investigate the cause. Twice a mother moved off without her juvenile, which then bared its teeth, screeched (on one occasion), and hurried after the female.

Most mothers tolerated a good deal of bother from the young without signs of aggression. Juveniles often swung from the mother's neck, moving round and round for several minutes, or, hanging from the branch above where the mother was sitting, they would dance on the mother's shoulder or head.

No instruction by a mother of her offspring was observed, nor was a mother ever seen to feed her juvenile with fruit or leaves.

Of interest here, however, are Kortlandt's observations of "begging" by a four-year-old juvenile, which stretched out a hand toward its mother who was eating a pawpaw. The mother gave the juvenile a piece of pawpaw. When the juvenile begged again, the mother turned her back, but eventually relented and gave it another piece. On another occasion, Kortlandt watched a juvenile beg from its own and another mother, receiving a piece of pawpaw from each female. Juveniles mostly received pawpaw from their mothers instead of picking it themselves. Goodall (Chap. 12, this volume) also describes begging.

Sometimes it was evident that a female other than the mother was looking after a juvenile. Once a juvenile-one was seen to leap on the back of an old female as she left the tree. This female had not previously been observed in the company of a juvenile and she was later seen without one. On another occasion a juvenile-one left a tree carried under the belly of an adolescent with which it had been playing. When a group of mothers regularly visited a fig tree for over a week, a particular female seemed to have one offspring on one day and on the next day she had two. This confusion may have been due to a certain amount of "swapping."

## Juvenile Play

Until adolescence young chimpanzees spend much of their time playing. As mothers tend to keep together in small groups, the offspring can play together, from the stage of infant-two upwards. Of 47 clear observations of juvenile play, 25 involved mock-fighting, chasing, or some kind of playful aggression between two juveniles, or between a juvenile and an adult, usually the mother. One favorite game was to hang by the arms from a branch and kick wildly at another juvenile. Wrestling or boxing was frequent. Five cases of play involving three young were seen. Once a chasing game between three youngsters varying in age from two to five continued for 30 minutes. Once a juvenile-one, chased up a tree by an older juvenile, repeatedly stamped on the hands of its pursuer reaching up below it. Another time a juvenile-one, clinging to a creeper, started it swinging to and fro, finally stretching out its legs and giving its playmate a kick. Only once was an adult male observed playing with a juvenile, whereas mothers often were, though never very actively. The male was pulling the juvenile around in a somewhat rough game, but the juvenile followed the male as he moved off.

Another large category of play activities involved acrobatics, usually occurring when a juvenile was playing alone. Seventeen cases of solo play were observed. A juvenile-one was watched for seven minutes while first he hung by two arms, then one, making bicycling movements with his legs. Then he swung his legs up and hung from his feet. Then he repeated all the performances.

Occasionally juveniles played at nest-building, pulling in small branches toward them in the typical manner and then sitting on them, but then leaving as something else distracted them. Once a juvenile was seen playing at nest-building, just after its mother had built a day nest. Play by an infant-two which could be termed "decoration of the body" was observed on one occasion, when the juvenile placed the feathery fronds of a lichen, hanging from the branch, on top of its head for a few minutes.

A final category of play activities observed could be described as the practicing of maternal or sexual behavior patterns. For example, hugging by youngsters, both front to front and dorso-ventrally, was often seen; sometimes they rolled over and over together. Twice a juvenile-two reached up to "kiss" the behind of a younger juvenile. Once a female juvenile played at "mother" with an infant-two for half an hour; she put out an arm and drew it toward her, letting it climb on her back, and placing it below her belly. Another time an adolescent carried off a juvenile, possibly a younger sibling, under its belly.

## DISCUSSION

From the data on chimpanzee social organization and behavior presented in this chapter, three features stand out as especially characteristic of chimpanzees and worthy of further thought. These are the loose unstable groupings and apparent lack of group social organization, the lack of dominance hierarchies as regulators of behavior, and the impressive choruses of hoots, screams, and drumming.

It is possible that the "looseness" and "instability" found in chimpanzee groups have been exaggerated, because of the obvious dissimilarity from the *spatially compact* type of group organization found in baboons. In fact, one may entertain the hypothesis that chimpanzees possess a social organization so highly developed that it can persist in the absence of immediate visual confirmation normally true for baboons. Certain insights relating to this hypothesis have been offered by J. B. Calhoun (in press, and personal communication). The central portion of the home range of an individual or a group tends to be utilized most intensely, and progressively less utilization is made of the habitat toward the periphery of the range. Equal usage of all portions of the habitat demands overlapping of adjoining home ranges to the extent that the range of any one group must extend beyond the center of the ranges of all adjoining groups. Of itself this concept only means that individuals inhabiting one range must have contact with individuals inhabiting the overlapping adjoining ranges. Thus it is to be expected that, if chimpanzees do possess a highly organized social group structure, members of two or more neighboring groups may be expected to assemble at some seasonally abundant source of food, such as represented by the *Maesopsis*.

Calhoun further points out that the physics of the use of space by socially primitive species, in which individuals maintain separate home ranges, is such that evolution toward a higher degree of social organization should lead to groups that on the average contain 12 adults. He points out, also, that the next expected stage in social evolution is a "double-12" group of adults in which there is a clear sex differentiation of roles encompassing more aspects of behavior than those pertaining directly to reproduction. Our estimate of 40–50 adults utilizing a 6–8 square mile region is at least consistent with the notion of a tract of this size being the primary range of one group, which is in part shared by individuals of adjoining groups.

Calhoun takes the stand that both increasing body size and increasing group size demand comparable increase in total range, but that the physical mobility of the group, particularly in a forested habitat, does not increase proportionally to the increase in range. This means a double-12 group, if it in fact exists, could not possibly move through the range as a compact group and locate adequate resources of food. They must split and search as individuals or as small groups. Survival of the group demands that when one individual or group locates food it must signal its associates of this fact. In accord with this concept, our observations show that vocalizations do increase upon the location of sources of food and chimpanzees do congregate when such sources are particularly abundant. With the increase in range to a diameter of three miles, Calhoun notes that vocalizations will be ineffective signals for reaching the more distant members; some effective means of signaling over greater distances than possible through vocalizations must be achieved. The drumming by chimpanzees may be an adaptation to this need, and it stands as the strongest circumstantial evidence that Calhoun's theories are correct in suggesting that the chimpanzees do have a highly organized social group structure. Final confirmation can come only through detailed study of a large number of marked individuals, a difficult task indeed!

JANE GOODALL

# 12
## ◈ Chimpanzees of the Gombe Stream Reserve

## INTRODUCTION

The chimpanzee was first described, in recognizable form, by Tulp in 1641, and in 1699 Tyson gave an accurate anatomical description of the species. The early literature is summarized by Yerkes and Yerkes (1929).[1] The genus *Pan*, with the widest distribution of any living great ape, is divided into two major species: *P. satyrus**  (the various races or subspecies of which differ only in minor details), which extends across equatorial Africa in a wide belt from the west coast to within a few hundred miles of the east coast, and *P. paniscus*, the Pygmy Chimpanzee, which occurs only in a relatively small area to the south of the Congo River.

Field studies of the chimpanzees have been carried out by Nissen (1932) in French Guinea, by Kortlandt (1962) in the Congo, and by Vernon and Frances Reynolds (Chap. 11, this volume) in Uganda. A team from the Japanese Monkey Center is undertaking a field study in Tanganyika at the time of writing.

The data on which this chapter is based were obtained during a total of 24 months (17 months between the end of June 1960 and the beginning of December 1961, and 7 months from the beginning of June 1962 to the end of December 1962) at the Gombe Stream Chimpanzee Reserve in Tan-

---

[1] See also the historical summary of field observations, pp. 394–396.

* Taxonomists disagree on the proper species name of the common chimpanzee. *P. satyrus* and *P. troglodytes* (Chap. 11) are equivalent — ed.

I should like to express my thanks to all those who made this field study possible: to Dr. L. S. B. Leaky, Hon. Director of the Coryndon Museum Center for Prehistory and Palaeontology, who initiated the expedition; to the Wilkie Foundation, which provided funds to launch the

Fig. 12–1. Part of the Gombe Stream Reserve seen from Lake Tanganyika, showing a thickly forested valley with more open deciduous woodland covering the upper slopes. (© *National Geographic Society*)

ganyika. This field study has not been completed as of this writing. A further 6 months between March and October 1963 was spent at the Reserve and a more detailed analysis of the data will be published.

### The Study Area

The Gombe Steam Reserve supports a semi-isolated population of *P. satyrus (= t. schweinfurthi)*, the eastern or long-haired chimpanzee (see Fig. 11–2). This area was selected for a field study because the country is not the closed rain forest habitat normal for chimpanzees and thus offers unusually favorable opportunities for observation. It consists of a narrow

project; to the National Geographic Society, which has subsequently financed my research; to the Tanganyika government officials in Kigoma and the Tanganyika Game Department for their cooperation and practical assistance; to my African staff and helpers; and to David Greybeard, for his unfailing cooperation and friendship. My thanks are also due to Dr. B. Verdcourt, Director of the East African Herbarium, for his identification of food-plant species; to Dr. E. Soulsby of the School of Veterinary Medicine, Cambridge University, for his parasitological examinations; and to my supervisor, Professor Robert Hinde of the Sub-Department of Animal Behaviour, Cambridge University, for his help and advice in the preparation of this manuscript.

426

mountainous strip stretching for some ten miles along the east shore of Lake Tanganyika, between Kigoma and Rwanda and Burundi, and running inland about three miles to the peaks of the mountains of the Rift escarpment, which rise steeply from the Lake (2334 feet) to heights of about 5000 feet. Numerous steep-sided valleys and ravines intersect the mountains, many of which support permanent streams. The dense gallery rain forests of the valleys and lower slopes give place to more open deciduous woodland on the upper slopes, and many of the peaks and ridges are covered only by grass (Figs. 12–1 and 12–2). In the valleys stands of trees reach a height of up to 80 feet, but the trees of the open woodlands seldom exceed 40 feet. During the rainy season, between October and May, the grass grows as high as 14 feet, but during the dry season grass fires usually sweep through the reserve, started by African farmers outside the boundary.

Temperatures in this area reach 115° in the day and drop below 60° in the night, and humidity is high during the rainy season. In normal years this area has about 50 inches of rain. During the wet season, from October to May, at least an hour's heavy rain fell on most days, and sometimes it rained for ten hours without stopping.

Fig. 12–2. Mature male and young female crossing an open space in the deciduous woodlands of the upper slopes. (© *National Geographic Society*)

### Field Study Methods and Equipment

A base camp was established near the lake shore at a central point in the reserve, and after all areas of the reserve had been investigated, a main study area of some 15 square miles was selected. I went to the north or south of this area when chimpanzee groups concentrated there.

From high vantage points in the reserve it is possible to watch chimpanzee movements over areas of up to two miles. The animals cannot be kept in sight all the time, but they can often be located from calls, the movement of branches, and the like. For the first three months of the study I concentrated on becoming familiar with general movements and basic behavior patterns, while also beginning to habituate the chimpanzees to my presence. An average of 12 hours per day was spent in the field, but the actual observation time varied from 0 to 8 hours a day. After the first three months it was unusual for an entire day to pass without my seeing at least one chimpanzee. Fifteen nights were spent near groups of sleeping chimpanzees and they could sometimes be observed in the moonlight.

It was decided from the start that for close-range study it would be necessary to habituate the chimpanzees to the presence of an observer. Observations from places of concealment (from behind tree trunks, tangles of undergrowth, and so on), proved impractical because the sharp eyesight of the chimpanzees normally detected my presence after the first few minutes. Habituation was a lengthy process. At first most of the chimpanzees ran off when they saw me as far away as 500 yards, but this distance gradually lessened, and after 8 months it was possible to approach to within 50 yards of them provided they were in fairly thick cover and up in a tree. (In the open or on the ground they were harder to approach, even at the end of the study.) After 10 months I could approach to within 100 feet of most individuals, and after 14 months the apes carried on their normal activities (feeding, mating, sleeping, and so on) when I was only from 30 to 50 feet away. Three mature males became "tame" and, after 18 months, took food from my hand, making it possible to observe relationships between mature males in detail. As chimpanzees became known individually they were named, and these 3 males were David Greybeard, Goliath, and William. Goliath was the largest and most powerfully built. William was the weakest and most timid (Fig. 12–3).

When a group moved away I never followed (except in the last few months), because the chimpanzees, even when no longer frightened, were usually shy of being observed. Every effort was made to conceal my interest in the activities of the chimpanzees. Often a group that had become uneasy at the proximity of a human was calmed if, for example, I ate leaves or dug a hole. On many occasions when chimpanzees were surprised in a tree they remained there if I walked past, but climbed down and moved away if I

Fig. 12–3. William, showing scars on upper lip. (© National Geographic Society)

stopped to look at them. This behavior was also reported in French Guinea (Nissen 1934).

After the initial three months of the study 7 × 32 binoculars were changed for 8 × 32 binoculars. During the last four months, long distance observations were greatly facilitated by the use of a 40 × 60 telescope mounted on a tripod on one of the high vantage points. No photography was attempted for the first half of the study, but during the latter part I always carried a Nikon 35 mm. camera with 200 mm. lens. I used 300 and 400 mm. lenses when it was known that chimpanzees would return to a particular feeding tree for several days running.

### Daily Behavior Pattern of Chimpanzees

Chimpanzees in the Gombe Stream area are nomadic in that they usually sleep in a different place each night, and although for the most part they keep within the same general area, they follow no regular circuit in their

429

daily search for food. The distance and direction of this daily wandering varies with the availability of food. Their diet is mainly vegetarian, but chimpanzees in this area have been observed feeding on insects and meat.

They move in small temporary groups, which may consist of any combination of age/sex classes. Lone males and, occasionally, lone females are also encountered. The only group that is stable over a period of months is a mother with her infant and older offspring.

Each night they construct new sleeping platforms or nests, which in this area are always made in trees and never on the ground at night. Individual animals sleep by themselves except for infants, which sleep with their mothers.

### Identification of Age and Sex Classes

No practical method for measuring the ages of chimpanzees in the field was found. However, there are certain physical and behavioral characteristics that typify the various life stages of the chimpanzees, summarized in Table 12–1, and these make it possible to place an animal seen in the field in its appropriate age class.

## ECOLOGY

### Population Density

It was not possible to make an accurate count of the chimpanzee population in the Gombe Stream Reserve, in part because the apes were not restricted to the reserve and in part because of the difficulty of recognizing all individuals encountered, particularly immature animals.

The lake forms a natural boundary to the west and chimpanzee penetration to the north is restricted by native cultivation, but there is nothing to prevent the apes from moving out of the reserve across the southern and eastern boundaries for ten miles or so. I saw five groups actually moving out of the reserve.

Fifteen mature males known individually were continually moving backward and forward across the main study area, and many of them were seen near both the northern and the southern boundaries of the reserve. Sixteen known mature females were encountered in various parts of the reserve.

Analysis of the data suggests that there were not less than 32 immature animals. The mature animals not known individually that were seen moving about with known animals were either temporary visitors from outside the reserve or animals which normally remained near the boundaries to the south and east.

At a rough estimate, then, there were no fewer than 60 and no more then 80 individuals normally to be found in the 30 square miles of the re serve. So there were, at a maximum, 2.6 animals per square mile. However, any estimate of the density of the population should take into account the fact that about 25 percent of the reserve is scarcely utilized since it offers little or no food to the chimpanzees. In relation to the area actually used the density of the population is about 3.3 percent.

## Population Dynamics

### Age at Puberty

Data from captive chimpanzees show that the female estrous cycle commences between six and ten years of age (Yerkes 1943). Adolescent females are not immediately fertile, and there is a time lag of from four months to two years after the first estrus before she conceives (Asdell 1946). In the wild adolescent females were observed with sexual swellings, though no swelling was seen comparable in size with the maximum swelling of a mature female. No adolescent female was seen copulating, or with an infant.

In captivity the male chimpanzee reaches puberty between seven and eight years of age (Yerkes 1943). In the wild adolescent males were observed copulating on four occasions.

### Birth Rate

Two infants which were born early in 1961 were still riding on their mothers' backs and sleeping with them at the end of 1962. It is estimated that infants, in the wild, are transported by their mothers for approximately from two and one-half to three years. No female was seen carrying two infants of different ages, so that the interval between births is probably about two and one-half to three years. No female with an infant-one or early infant-two was seen with a sexual swelling, but two females with late infant-twos showed sexual swellings, and one was seen to menstruate.

At the end of 1962 8 of the known population of 16 mature females in the reserve were without infants, which may have been because of infant mortality, although infertility is a possibility that cannot be overlooked.

### Mortality Factors and Longevity

AVAILABILITY OF FOOD: During the first twelve months of the present study there was no suggestion that food might be a limiting factor in the size of the chimpanzee population, for at all times of the year food was abundant. Data obtained the following year, however, suggested that annual seasonal fluctuations in the foods available might play some part in population control. During the dry season of 1960 the fruits of *Syzigium guineense* formed a major part of the chimpanzees' diet; in 1961 there was no fruit at all, and in 1962 the crop was blighted. Another fruit, not at present identified, also failed during 1961 and 1962. In 1961 the fruit of *Pseudospondias micro-carpa* failed to ripen. In 1962 the wild figs in one valley yielded only about 15 percent of their usual crop, and the *Pterocarpus angolensis* scarcely yielded a blossom. Despite this there was no apparent shortage of food and the chimpanzees remained fit and plump. The possibility cannot be over-looked, however, that a sudden failure of a greater number of foods in any one year might well have a damaging effect on the health of the chim-panzees.

DISEASES, PARASITES, AND INJURIES: Sneezing was heard on four sepa-rate occasions and three individuals were heard coughing. In addition, one male suffered for at least two weeks from what appeared to be a cold. His nose was continually running, he wheezed, coughed on an average of twice per day for one week, and was subjects to fits of violent and spasmodic shivering early in the morning. During the first five days when these symp-toms were observed he had diarrhea.

TABLE 12–1. AGE AND SEX CLASSES

| | |
|---|---|
| *1 to 4–6 months.* *Infant: Stage 1.* | Completely dependent on mother for food, transport, and pro-tection. Early Stage 1 clings to mother in ventral position only; later may lie along mother's back. Occasionally seen apart from mother when she has "hung it up" on a nearby branch. Towards end of Stage 1 it may sit beside mother on branch. Skin is pale pinky-yellow, hair is long, has long white rump tuft. |
| *4–6 months to* *1–1 1/2 years.* *Stage 2 (early).* | Still suckles, but beginning to eat solid foods. Travels about clinging to mother in ventral position or sitting up in "jockey" position. Gradually moves further away from mother but never out of sight: time spent not clinging to mother increases from about 5 percent to about 25 percent of the day. Social inter-actions with other early Stage 2 infants during play. Skin color still very pale; hair long—conspicuous rump tuft. |
| *1–1 1/2 to* *2 1/2–3 years.* *Stage 2 (late).* | Suckling may continue throughout this stage. Diet similar to that of adult. Rides about on mother jockey fashion except when she is moving fast when it reverts to ventral position. Still sleeps with mother. Time spent not touching mother in-creases to about 75 or 90 percent of day. Is very active. Social interactions with individuals of all age/sex classes except Stage 1 infants. Rump tuft smaller. |
| *2 1/2–3 to* *7–8 years.* *Juvenile.* | Small chimpanzee, independent of its mother for feeding, transport, and sleeping. During early juvenile stage invariably remains in close social contact with mother. Interactions mainly with other juveniles and mother. Patches of slightly darker skin may appear on face, especially under eyes. Rump tuft still obvious. May show first signs of baldness on forehead. |

TABLE 12-1. AGE AND SEX CLASSES—Continued

| | |
|---|---|
| *7–9 to 10–11 years. Adolescent Female.* | Smaller than mature chimpanzee. Menstruates and develops sexual swellings, but copulation is not observed. Less active and playful than juveniles. Still a few white hairs of rump tuft during early adolescence. May show marked forehead baldness. Cheek hair long. |
| *7–8 to 10–11 years. Adolescent Male.* | Smaller than mature male. Scrotum gradually increases in size. Copulation observed. Sometimes moves around alone. During late adolescence masculine behavior patterns appear. May have few white hairs of rump tuft. Cheek hair shorter than that of female. |
| *10–11 to 25–30 years. Mature Male and Female.* | Fully grown adult animal. Hair of cheeks not noticeably long. Hair in lumbar region gradually becomes shorter and may turn brown. Skin color of face, hands, and feet may be black, brown, mottled, or orangy. |
| *25–30 to ? years. Old Male and Female.* | Marked baldness of head and lumbar region. Animal appears thin. No signs of senility observed. |

The presence of a white beard and the degree of baldness cannot be used to assess the age of the individual. Some adolescents have white beards and marked forehead baldness: mature animals may have no white beard: two fully mature males show no signs of forehead baldness, though this was observed in all mature females.

Although a certain baldness in the region of the forehead and a thinning of hair in the lumbar region is normal for these chimpanzees (see Table 12-1), the baldness in one male that had no hair on the crown of his head or across his shoulders was definitely the result of some type of disease. Two old chimpanzees, a male and a female, also showed excessive baldness, having lost the hair from the sides of their faces and lower backs.

Parasitological examination of chimpanzee feces revealed a few eggs of *strongyle* in each of the four samples. These eggs indicate infection by either *Necator congolensis* (a hook worm) or *Oesophagostum pentigerum* (a common roundworm in primates).

One female with an infant-one had a lump, just smaller than a ping-pong ball, in a fold of skin on the left ventral surface of her neck. She was observed only once.

No chimpanzee with a serious injury was encountered. Three males had broken toe bones, and another had a broken finger. On six occasions chimpanzees were seen with small cuts or sores on their feet. One male had longitudinal scars down the right side of his upper lip. Another had a nick in his ear. It should not be inferred that only males have injuries; it was possible to work at much closer range to males than to females and consequently to identify injuries in males.

INFANT MORTALITY: During the period in the field two females were known to have lost early infant-ones. The dead infants were not found and there are no data as to the cause of death.

LONGEVITY: It is estimated that a chimpanzee in captivity may live for 60 or 70 years (Riopelle 1963). The oldest female at Yerkes laboratories is 41 at the time of writing. There are no data on the normal life span for a wild chimpanzee. Only four of the Gombe Stream population, two males and two females, were classified as old. One of the females gave birth to an infant in 1962. One of the males, which showed no signs of senility and was still active and fully integrated into the society, was not seen during the last six months of the research and may have died.

### Sex-Age Ratios

At the end of 1962 the "resident" adult population of known individuals comprised at least 15 males and 16 females. Eight of these females were accompanied by an infant and an older child; one had an older child only; and seven were without infants and not regularly accompanied by juveniles. Analysis of data shows that the number of juveniles was between 14 and 20 and the number of adolescents was between 10 and 20. So far as could be ascertained the proportion of males to females was about equal in both juveniles and adolescents.

Thus the male-to-female ratio is apparently fairly equal throughout all age groups of the "resident" population. If, however, temporary visitors are taken into consideration—and the possible role played by visiting males in breeding cannot be overlooked—available data suggest that visiting males outnumber visiting females by three to one. Certainly during the latter part of the study at least six strange males were seen and only two females. It is possible, therefore, that adult males may very slightly outnumber adult females in this area, even taking into consideration the fact that males travel more extensively and thus are counted more often. Nissen (1931) estimated that in French Guinea females considerably outnumbered males.

### Seasonal Effects on Movement and Behavior

Within the reserve some food plants are restricted to one or two valleys only, some are found mainly on the upper slopes, and others are found mostly along the lake shore. The seasonal ripening, flowering, or failure of these crops was observed to have a direct effect upon the movement patterns of the chimpanzees.

Chimpanzees tend to make their nests earlier and to leave them later in the morning in the rainy season then in the dry season. When a strong wind is blowing they may construct an atypical nest low in a tree where there is shelter, but they were never observed to attempt to construct any sort of roof over their nest, nor to attempt to take advantage of the shelter offered by an overhanging tree trunk (Goodall 1962).

During the rains chimpanzees are more active, generally, than during the dry season. Male ground-slapping and branch-waving displays are more common during the rains (see pages 457, 468).

In addition, arboreal locomotion was observed far more frequently during the rains. Mature chimpanzees were observed to travel distances of as much as 200 yards through the trees—behavior that was seldom seen in the dry season, when adults normally travel from place to place on the ground. A similar increase in arboreal locomotion during the rains was observed also in the baboons.

## Relations with Other Animals

### Predation

The role of the chimpanzee as a predator is described under feeding behavior below.

The only carnivore in this area that could be dangerous to an adult chimpanzee is the leopard (*Panthera pardos*). Once, when subsequent evidence showed that a leopard had been in the ravine below, a juvenile peered down and gave loud screams. Its mother, who had a small infant, glanced down once and then continued to feed. The juvenile screamed periodically for five minutes. On another occasion chimpanzees were under observation when a leopard "coughed" only a few hundred yards away and they paid no attention.

Other evidence also suggests that chimpanzees in this area are not normally afraid of attack. In the forests they often move about with a surprising lack of alertness. They often approached to within ten feet of me when I was in full view before being aware of my presence and sometimes they went past without seeing me at all. On four occasions, chimpanzees showed markedly delayed responses to visual stimuli; each time the animal sat down nearby, gazed round and past me without apparently seeing me, and then suddenly jerked its head round, stared, ran off for a few yards, and stopped to peer intently at me. (These incidents all occurred during the latter half of the field study when the chimpanzees were habituated to my presence.)

On one occasion a female showed a protective response to her infant-one, when a small hawk (Banded Harrier Hawk, *Polyborides typus*) flew past, although it is certain that this species would not attempt to seize a young chimpanzee. The only bird of prey in this area large enough to constitute a possible threat is the Martial Eagle (*Poleametus bellicosus*), but it was seen only twice.

### Relationship with Baboons

Interactions, other than those of predator and prey, were observed between chimpanzees and baboons (*Papio anubis*) (see Fig. 12–4). Nor-

mally the two species ignore each other and are often seen feeding together in the same tree. Occasionally, when a chimpanzee is feeding on some particularly attractive food, baboons approach very close. An adult female baboon went up to a male chimpanzee who was eating bananas (in camp), presented, looked toward him with a fear grimace, seized a skin, and ran off. On ten occasions the same male threatened baboons that approached while he was feeding, and once a male chimpanzee, which was eating meat, chased, hit, and briefly wrestled with a male baboon after it had approached three times to within a couple of feet.

On other occasions interactions between baboons and chimpanzees might be interpreted as play. Once an infant chimpanzee bounced five times toward young baboons, waving one hand at them; at the last moment the baboons leaped away and the chimpanzee scampered back to its mother. On six occasions, in the evenings just before the nest-making period for chimpanzees, young male baboons chased female and young chimpanzees, which ran off screaming; male chimpanzees then chased the baboons, which ran away. These interactions lasted from 5 to 20 minutes.

### Alarm Calls

Chimpanzees are alerted by the alarm calls of baboons, other species of monkey, bushbuck, and several species of bird. Upon hearing such a call, the chimpanzee peers round to ascertain the nature of the disturbance. When my presence elicited the continued barking of baboons, the chimpanzees might eventually become so uneasy that they moved away, even though the chimpanzees themselves were habituated to me.

## INDIVIDUAL BEHAVIOR

### Locomotion

Chimpanzees usually travel from place to place on the ground, normally in a leisurely fashion, the chimpanzees often helping themselves up steep slopes by hauling on tree trunks or low branches—behavior that I have not observed in other primates. In this area chimpanzees spend between 50 and 70 percent of the day in trees, either feeding or resting, but they seldom move from place to place through the trees, except for short distances during the rainy season. Infant-twos, juveniles, and young adolescents move easily and quickly in trees, but as they attain maturity arboreal locomotion becomes slow and careful unless the animals are frightened or excited.

Fig. 12–5. Mature male standing upright to look over grass. (© National Geographic Society)

*Bipedal Locomotion*

Chimpanzees frequently stand upright in order to look over long grass or other vegetation (see Fig. 12–5). Sometimes a branch or tree trunk is held with one hand, but often an erect posture is assumed with both arms hanging down at the animal's sides. In addition, they have been observed to walk or run bipedally for distances of as much as 30 yards.

Chimpanzees were observed to walk bipedally when moving through long grass for short distances while looking at an unusual object (such as the observer) or searching for a companion, and when carrying objects in both hands.

Bipedal running often occurs if males are socially excited, as during the branch-waving display, when they may run upright down a steep slope for a few yards before breaking off a branch or when chasing after and threatening baboons or the observer. It also occurs frequently during infant and juvenile play. Bipedal running is often accompanied by arm swinging, the arms being swung forward alternately with a circling movement.

Fig. 12–6. Mature male brachiating. (© *National Geographic Society*)

Fig. 12–7. Mature male feeding on leaf buds. (© *National Geographic Society*)

In addition, a ritualized form of bipedal locomotion may occur during greeting and courtship, when a male may stand upright and sway from foot to foot.

### Quadrupedal Locomotion

When running or walking on four limbs the chimpanzee places the backs of the flexed fingers and the soles of the feet on the ground. When descending a steep slope the arms may be used as crutches and the hind limbs swung through them, a type of locomotion frequently used by early infant-twos, even on level ground. Chimpanzees normally jump a stream quadrupedally, although I have also seen them jump across bipedally as reported by Kortlandt (1962).

When climbing a thick trunk the chimpanzee places its hands on either side with its feet in the normal walking position; it descends in the same way, backwards. When a chimpanzee moves about in a tree the fingers and toes are used for grasping the branches. In order to move from one tree to another, the chimpanzee usually walks out along a branch which bends under its weight until it can reach a lower branch of the other tree, keeping its hold on the original branch until it has secured firm hand and footholds on the new one.

439

### Swinging and Leaping

Brachiation for short distances is common (see Figs. 12–6 and 12–7). On these occasions, although the overhead branch is the only true support, the chimpanzee frequently grasps small twigs with its feet. It often swings through a tree in the upright position, with equal use of hands and feet (see also Avis 1962).

Young chimpanzees, in play, or adults when excited or frightened, sometimes leap from one branch to another. They may either take off and land quadrupedally or push off with the feet and reach out for another branch with the hands. On two occasions mature males, when excited, took off bipedally and appeared to "dive" down, catching a lower branch with their hands and swinging around under it.

## Feeding Behavior

### Vegetarian Feeding

The chimpanzee is primarily a vegetarian (see Goodall in press). Seventy-three different types of vegetable foods have been collected, consisting of 37 fruits, 21 leaves or leaf buds, 6 blossoms, 4 seeds, 3 stems, and 2 barks. (This list comprises a total number of 63 different species of plants and trees; a complete list will be published at a later date.)

In this area chimpanzees spend between six and seven hours a day in active feeding. About 90 percent of their food is found growing in trees and they seldom feed intensively on the ground.

They pick large fruits by hand, and usually use their lips to remove small fruits, buds, and blossoms from the stems. The fruits of *Strychnos*, which have hard rinds, are picked off, held in the hand, and banged against the trunk of a tree or against a rock until the rinds crack. Bark, which I saw eaten on only four occasions, was either pulled off in strips and the inner surface scraped with the incisors or the bark was left in place and scraped off directly from the trunk or branch, again with the incisors.

When a chimpanzee starts feeding early in the morning, or after traveling or resting, it eats ravenously, swallowing unripe food, and stones and skin. As hunger decreases it shows more discrimination, rejecting unripe foods and expressing the juice from a wad of stones and skin held in its lower lip, which it then spits out. When satiated the chimpanzee frequently sits or reclines, sucking a large wad of this kind for as long as 20 minutes.

### Insect Eating

In the Gombe Stream Reserve chimpanzees were seen feeding on two types of gall, on two species of ant, and on termites.

Between June and September the larvae of a species of gall fly form

Fig. 12-8. Two males working at a termite nest. (© *National Geographic Society*)

small white galls on the leaves of *Chlorophora excelsa*. Chimpanzees pick these off with their lips, and may spend as long as two hours at a stretch feeding in this way. They also eat galls formed by *Paracopium glabricorne* (a lace bug) in buds of *Clerodendrum schweinfurthii*.

Groups of chimpanzees were twice seen feeding on ants, once on a species of arboreal ant that makes a round nest in a tree and once on a species of *Dolaris* that makes an underground nest. The method of eating both species was similar; the chimpanzees poked sticks into the opened nests, left them there for a moment, and then withdrew them covered with ants that they removed with the lips and tongue. Eight sticks that had been used were found to be between 2 and 2½ feet in length, and another was 3½ feet. On three other occasions there was evidence that *Dolaris* ants had been eaten, when sticks with traces of earth adhering to one end were found beside freshly opened nests.

At the beginning of the rains, for a period of as long as nine weeks, the chimpanzees feed for one or two hours daily on a species of termite common

Fig. 12–9. A grass stalk is poked carefully into an opened passage in a termite nest. (© *National Geographic Society*)

in the area. At this time the fertile termites grow wings in preparation for leaving the nest to found new colonies, and their passages are extended to the surface of the termite hill and then sealed lightly over while the insects await good flying conditions. Chimpanzees were observed examining termite hills after a heavy rainstorm several weeks before the termite emigration actually started (see Fig. 12–8).

When a chimpanzee sees a sealed-up termite hole it scrapes away the thin layer of soil with index finger or thumb, picks a grass stalk, thin twig, or piece of vine, and pokes this carefully down the hole (see Fig. 12–9). It waits for a moment and then withdraws the tool, the end of which is coated with termites, hanging on with their mandibles, and these the chimpanzee picks off with the lips. Either hand may be used in the manipulation of the tool, and while picking off the insects the chimpanzee may support one end of the tool on the back of its other wrist (see Fig. 12–10).

The grass or other material selected is not normally longer than about 12 inches. When one end becomes bent the chimpanzee either turns it round and uses the other end or breaks off the bent part. When the tool becomes too short to be of use, a new tool is selected, and if this is too long, the chimpanzee usually breaks a piece off; if a leafy twig or vine is selected, the leaves are stripped off with the lips or fingers.

The chimpanzee also shows discrimination in its choice of materials.

A tangle of vines may be briefly examined and rejected if unsuitable (see Fig. 12–11). When working at an exceptionally deep hole, one male, after trying with several grasses of the usual length, looked round intently, got up, and went to pick a long piece of vine growing several yards away. An individual often showed a definite preference for one particular type of material for use as a tool on one particular day. Thus, one of the "tame" males picked and used grass stalks on one occasion and on the following day, working in the same place, he used only pieces of vine, even though this entailed climbing about ten feet up a tree to pick them.

On several occasions, when the nearest termite hill was at least 100 feet away and out of sight, a chimpanzee picked a grass stalk, carried it to the termite hill, and used it as a tool. One male carried a grass stalk (in his mouth) for half a mile, while he examined, one after the other, six termite hills, none of which was ready for working.

### Meat Eating

Chimpanzees were seen feeding on meat on nine occasions; three times the prey was identified as a monkey (twice the red colobus, *Colobus badius graueri*) and once as a young bushpig (*Potamochoerus koiropotamus sp.*).

Fig. 12–10. Mature male picking off the termites clinging to the end of a grass stalk. The end of a tool is often supported on one wrist in this way. (© *National Geographic Society*)

Fig. 12–11. A length of vine is subjected to careful scrutiny. A piece is broken off only if the material is suitable. (© *National Geographic Society*)

On four occasions the prey was not identified. Bones (once the toe bones of a monkey) were twice found in chimpanzee feces. On another occasion, the skin of the tail and part of the rump of a monkey was found on a termite hill where two male chimpanzees had been feeding; the skin was still damp and it was presumed that they had left it there. Hunting and killing was seen once only, when the prey was a red colobus. When the chimpanzees were eating the young bushpig referred to above, two adult pigs remained in the vicinity for an hour, chasing a juvenile chimpanzee that climbed to the ground. On one of the occasions when the flesh being eaten was not identified, a female bushbuck remained near the chimpanzees all night and was twice chased by an adult male; it is possible that the chimpanzees were eating its young.

When approached by a chimpanzee, bushbuck bark and run off. Four adult bushpig moved hurriedly away when surprised by a group of chimpanzees, and one pig bolted when a male chimpanzee disturbed it in a patch of long grass.

444

On the only occasion when hunting and killing were observed, the prey, a red colobus monkey, was sitting in a tree when an adolescent male chimpanzee climbed a neighboring tree, and remained very still as the monkey looked toward it. A second adolescent male chimpanzee then climbed the tree in which the colobus was sitting, ran quickly along the branch, leapt at the colobus, and caught it with its hands, presumably breaking its neck, as it did not struggle or call out. The other adolescent then leapt into the tree, and five other chimpanzees, including a mature male and a late infant-two, climbed up. The mature male pulled until he had half the carcass. Subsequently I observed that the mother of the infant had acquired a large piece of meat and afterward the other chimpanzees, with the exception of the infant, also managed to get small pieces or scraps. On the other occasions when I saw meat-eating, the prey was initially in the possession of a mature male. Each time the other chimpanzees in the group sat close to him, holding out their hands with the begging gesture (see p. 472).

Meat is eaten slowly, the chimpanzee pulling at the flesh with its incisors, and between each bite of meat a mouthful of leaves is always eaten. Small bones, apparently, are crunched up; large ones are gnawed for some time and then dropped.

Two reports from the Kigoma area of human infants being carried off by male chimpanzees are interesting when considered in relation to these observations on meat-eating. In 1957 a baby was seized from its mother's back and carried for some distance; it was already dead when the chimpanzee was driven away by natives. Subsequent medical examination showed that the child had definitely been gnawed by some animal. This incident occurred several miles to the east of the reserve. The second occurrence, however, took place in the reserve; a baby left alone for a few moments was seized by a mature chimpanzee, which was chased and ran off, dropping the child, who had been severely mutilated.

In addition to these two reports I have heard indirectly of a European who maintains that during his tour in the police force in West Africa five babies were carried off by chimpanzees.

### Other Observations on Feeding

Chimpanzees were not observed to eat wild birds' eggs, though one female climbed up a tree to feel carefully in a hollow, and Francolins (*Francolinus hildebrandti*) give the alarm call and fly off when chimpanzees approach. One male ate domestic hens' eggs without hesitation, stuffing several leaves into his mouth with the uncracked egg before eating it. Two other animals, however, persistently ignored eggs offered to them.

On five occasions chimpanzees were observed scraping and eating soil from a cliff face. This behavior was seen only in March and April, although I visited the area regularly throughout the year. Analysis of a sample of the soil showed that a small amount of halite (sodium chloride) was present.

During the field study a red block of mineral salts that had been put out disappeared, and the following day one of a group of chimpanzees was observed carrying the block of salt. For some 30 minutes it licked the salt while the others in the group sat close and held out their hands with the begging gesture.

A chimpanzee was observed drinking only once; it went to the edge of a stream, put its face down, and sucked up water with its lips for about 30 seconds.

Chimpanzees frequently carry food for short distances. For example, when one is partially satisfied it often makes a collection of fruits or picks a food-laden branch that it then carries, in one hand or in its mouth, to a comfortable branch or, occasionally, to the ground, where it eats at leisure. When a group is on the move one chimpanzee may pick and carry a food branch, pausing from time to time to eat. After feeding intensively on meat for some hours a chimpanzee often moves off with the remains of the carcass in its mouth; one male carried meat for at least half a mile. The block of mineral salts was transported for a distance of at least two miles. The three "tame" males frequently took cloth objects from camp in order to suck at the material. Blankets were either bundled under one arm or held in the hand or foot and dragged along; one heavy blanket was dragged for at least one and one-half miles up a steep mountain.

## Grooming and Nest Building

### Self-grooming

In captivity old chimpanzees spend more time grooming themselves than young ones do (Riopelle 1963), and the data suggest that this is also true in the wild. Infants were never observed grooming themselves, juveniles only on very few occasions, and adolescents during rest periods. Mature chimpanzees frequently groom themselves for as long as 15 minutes at a time. The areas most commonly groomed are the thighs, arms, chest, and abdomen. Sometimes the chimpanzee parts the hair with both hands and sometimes with one hand and its lips. Flakes of dried skin, grass seeds, and the like are removed with the lips or with the thumb and forefinger.

After rain the chimpanzee helps to dry its coat by shaking, by rubbing its back and shoulders against a tree trunk, or by stroking downward with its hand.

### Nest-making Behavior

Each chimpanzee builds a new nest every night, with the exception of those infants that sleep with their mothers. Chimpanzees usually sleep in small groups of from two to six individuals, but when two or three such groups are feeding in the same area at dusk they may unite and nest close together. Sometimes, however, a large group will split into two or three small groups at dusk, each nesting some distance from the others. Members of the same group usually construct their nests close together in the same tree or in a group of adjoining trees. One adolescent female left her completed nest when she found the rest of the group was nesting about 60 yards away and made a second one close to the others. A mature male, however, may sleep alone about 100 yards away from a group with which he has been associating, or even quite out of sight or earshot of other chimpanzees.

The area in which nests are made is related to the food available at the time, since chimpanzees normally sleep close to where they have been feeding at dusk. Nests were found in the thick forests and in the more open woodlands, but seldom above 4500 feet, where the vegetation is sparse and offers little or no food.

Chimpanzees in this area do not sleep on the ground at night. The lowest nests were 15 feet from the ground, and the average height was between 30 and 40 feet from the ground.

Almost any type of tree may be utilized, provided it is at least 20 feet high, has a fair amount of foliage and fairly strong branches. At the end of August 1961 a nest was observed in a palm tree (*Elaesis guineemsis*) for the first time. By the same month in the following year nests in palm trees were conspicuous in all parts of the reserve. Such nests apparently became a "fashion" among the chimpanzee population.

A nest usually takes between one and five minutes to construct, in the following manner. The chimpanzee takes up a central position on a suitable "foundation" (such as a horizontal fork or two adjacent parallel branches), takes hold of a fairly thick branch and bends it down across the foundation to form a crosspiece. This crosspiece is held in place with the feet, and a second branch is bent across it. From four to six main crosspieces are bent in, and then between six and ten smaller branches are bent across to form secondary crosspieces. The branches are bent so that their leafy ends form part of the main structure—if an end projects beyond this the chimpanzee bends it back across the nest. Finally all the small twigs projecting round the nest are bent in and normally a number of additional twigs are picked and laid loose on top of the nest. Occasionally a chimpanzee begins to make a nest, and, after bending in a few branches, abandons it because the material is insufficient or unsuitable.

A nest is usually used for one night only, but on three occasions chimpanzees reused nests that had been previously slept in. On each occasion fresh branches were bent over the existing structure.

In the rainy season nests are frequently made during a rest period in the daytime. Sometimes the chimpanzee simply bends a few leafy twigs across the branch on which it is lying. At other times it makes an elaborate structure, exactly similar to that made for the night (see Fig. 12–12). In the

Fig. 12–12. Mature male asleep in a day nest. (© *National Geographic Society*)

dry season when chimpanzees normally rest on the ground, the making of day nests was not observed.

There is evidence that experience gained during the first few years of the chimpanzee's life in the wilds is necessary for the development of nest-building behavior (Bernstein 1962). In the wild the infant has opportunity for watching nest-making, and infants still sleeping with their mothers sometimes make little nests during the day as a form of play activity. An early infant-two was observed to have difficulty in bending in two small twigs, but four infants, estimated at from six months to one year older, were already able to make nests using as many as ten branches.

### Sleeping and Resting

Data obtained during 15 nights spent within 20 yards of nesting chimpanzees suggest that they sleep fairly soundly during the night. Whenever they were observed in the moonlight there was little movement. Occasionally, however, when several groups are sleeping within earshot there may be intergroup calling during the night. When asleep the chimpanzee adopts various positions, the most normal being on the side with the knees drawn up close to the body. Sometimes the chimpanzee sleeps on its back with its legs stretched out and, occasionally, on its stomach. The infant sleeps with its head on its mother's shoulder or groin, cradled within one of her arms. The chimpanzee does not normally hold on to branches with hands or feet.

It has been noted that during the rainy season nests may be constructed earlier than they are during the dry season, often as early as two hours before darkness. On these occasions the chimpanzee may continue feeding if food is within reach or it may lie or sit gazing around, or immediately close its eyes and sleep. At dawn the chimpanzee normally urinates and defecates (over the side of the nest), after which it may lie down again relaxed or it may sleep.

Adult chimpanzees rest for at least two hours every day, generally at some time between 9:30 A.M. and 3:00 P.M. Whether they rest on the ground, on a comfortable branch, or on a "day nest," they usually sleep for at least 30 minutes of the rest period. For the remainder of the time they sit or sprawl in relaxed postures, or idly groom each other or themselves.

## SEXUAL BEHAVIOR

### The Female Estrous Cycle

Records for chimpanzees in captivity show that the female reaches puberty with her first menstrual period at an average of 8.8 years (Riopelle 1963). The female sexual cycle averages 35 days and is characterized by periodic swelling and deturgescence of the ano-genital region and by menstruation. In the field menstrual bleeding has been observed, and the sexual swelling is obvious. Although the period of estrus in not clearly defined, the gradual increase in genital swelling is associated with an increase in attraction and receptivity to the males culminating in a midcycle peak of from six to seven days and subsiding after ovulation.

During her period of sexual swelling the young female may become excitable and irritable and is likely to run off screaming when a male approaches. Occasionally she provokes aggressive behavior from females with no sexual swelling. On four occasions when "squabbling" between females was observed, females without swellings, for no reason that was apparent, ran after and hit at young females with sexual swellings.

### Courtship

Copulation may be initiated by the male or the female, although only 4 copulations, out of a total of 32 observed, were initiated entirely by the female. The soliciting female approached the male to within 6 feet and flattened herself in front of him in the "crouch" position, looking back at him, and on three occasions copulation took place immediately. Once the female was ignored; she backed toward the male, who got up and moved a few yards away, at which the female backed after him, looking over her shoulder, until she was almost touching him, when copulation took place. Twice a soliciting female was ignored by a male and the female moved away.

Nineteen of the copulations observed were preceded by a male courtship display. On 18 occasions the display was similar; the male, leaping into a tree after a female in estrus, swung vigorously from branch to branch in an upright position with the hair (particularly of head, shoulders, and arms) erect. This display never continued for more than a minute and terminated when the male approached the female. On most occasions the female at once adopted the crouch position, but three times the male touched the female lightly on her back with one hand before she did so.

Once an adolescent male walked up to a female in estrus, stood upright in front of her, and rocked rhythmically from foot to foot, his hair erect. The female turned away, crouched, and copulation occurred.

The female may scream when approached by a male at the end of a courtship display. Four times a female ran away, but when the male pursued, she stopped and crouched. Twice, when a female continued to run away screaming, the male stood upright, violently rocked branches of the tree, and finally moved away without having tried to force the female to copulate.

On nine occasions there was no courtship display; the male walked up to the female who crouched and copulation took place.

## Copulation

It has been demonstrated (Bingham 1928 and Nissen 1954) that young captive chimpanzees with no previous sexual experience are not immediately able to copulate successfully. On six occasions in the wild, late infant-twos watched carefully when their mothers were copulating. On one occasion an infant went close, peered intently underneath its mother, reached out one hand and felt in the region where the penis was inserted into the vagina. This behavior was also observed by Kortlandt (personal communication). An adolescent male, which had probably just attained puberty, had no difficulty in performing the sexual act.

When the female crouches the male normally places one hand on her back and adopts a "squatting" position, his buttocks scarcely more than an inch from the ground, and his other hand usually holding an overhead branch. On five occasions the position was very slightly different; once a male placed both hands on the back of the female; once the female stood quadrupedally on a branch with arms and legs only slightly bent and the male stood upright behind her, both hands holding an overhead branch.

Normally there were between four and eight slow and deliberate pelvic thrusts of the male (once 15 thrusts were counted). It was not possible to ascertain whether ejaculation took place.

During copulation slow rhythmic lip smacking was normally observed in the male. The female sometimes looked straight ahead, sometimes looked round at the male, and on eight occasions gave short high-pitched screams. After copulation the female either remained where she was, moved a few yards away, or rushed off screaming. On eight occasions mating was followed by brief grooming.

The chimpanzees in this area are promiscuous. Four times more than one male copulated with the same female; during one of these occasions seven males mounted one female, one after the other (one of them twice), with less than two minutes between each of the first five copulations.

A male chimpanzee was never seen to mount another male. Once a young female, after unsuccessfully soliciting a male, backed toward a mature female and crouched slightly; the older female mounted her for a moment.

## Mating Season

From the beginning of August until the end of November the Gombe Stream chimpanzees move about in large groups much of the time. It is not known whether these groups are formed as a result of a need for social contact stimulated by sexual excitement, or whether the increase in activity, due to the aggregation of a large number of chimpanzees, has a direct effect upon sexual behavior. Whatever the explanation, there appears to be a mating season during these four months. All copulations observed took place in this period and at a time when the animals concerned were part of a large group. Indeed, when a female with a sexual swelling solicited the only male in a small group she was twice ignored.

It cannot be assumed, however, that copulation occurs only during these months.[3] Females with sexual swellings have been observed at all times of the year; in addition an infant of only one or two months was seen in September, at the start of this apparent mating season, as was a female who appeared to be pregnant. At present there is insufficient data to permit any conclusion as to whether or not there is a breeding season for wild chimpanzees.

## GROUP BEHAVIOR

### Size and Composition of Groups

It has been stated above that there are no stable groups (other than mother/infant) in the Gombe Stream population. What is referred to in

---

[3] Since this chapter was written the author has observed three copulations in May 1963. These involved one female (in estrus) and two mature males. On each occasion the copulation was initiated by the female.

thi3 chapter as a "group" is no more than a temporary association of individuals that may be constant for a few hours or days.

Mature males frequently move about on their own, and each of the 15 males known individually was seen alone at least once. Two days was the longest period during which a male was known to be on his own. Mature females were seen alone on eight occasions; of these, two were feeding, two had lost their groups and were looking for the others, two were in estrus, and two appeared to be pregnant. There are no data on whether a female goes off alone to give birth although Nissen (1931) suggests that this might be so. Adolescent males may move about alone for a few hours at a time; adolescent females were seen on their own on three occasions.

### Size of Groups

A total of 498 temporary groups (including 64 solitary animals) was observed, and many other groups were encountered when it was not possible to make an accurate count of the animals forming them. The largest group seen (once only) consisted of 23 chimpanzees, and 3 groups of 20 were observed. On 44 occasions groups were seen consisting of between 10 and 23 animals. Of the total number of 498 groups, 91 percent consisted of groups of 9 animals or fewer; the number of animals constituting such groups and the percent of the total each such group represents is shown in the following tabulation.

| Number Per Group | Percent of Total |
| --- | --- |
| 3 | 20.5 |
| 2 | 18.5 |
| 4 | 16.0 |
| 5 | 13.0 |
| 6 | 9.0 |
| 7 | 3.0 |
| 8 | 3.0 |
| 9 | 3.0 |
| 1 | 14.0 |

### Composition of Groups

On 350 occasions it was possible to assess accurately the age and sex compositions of groups under observation. Of this total mixed groups (consisting of males, females, and young) formed 30 percent; groups of males and males on their own formed 28 percent (lone males formed 18 percent of the total); females and young formed 24 percent; and groups of mature or adolescent males with mature or adolescent females formed 18 percent.

The size and composition of a group may change at any moment when individual chimpanzees within a group move off in another direction or when two groups join. Mutual attraction between particular individuals is probably the most important factor determining the composition of a small group. Mother/infant ties may persist well into adult life and may form the main link in a group comprising a female with infant and older child, adolescent, and a young mature animal.

### Group Structure

#### Dominance

The temporary nature of chimpanzee groups results in a loose social structure within the community, and aggressive and submissive interactions between individuals are infrequent. This is in marked contrast to the rigid social structure found among some primates, such as baboons and macaques, in which each individual has its own rank in a "dominance hierarchy." However, although it is difficult to apply the dominance concept to the local chimpanzee population as a whole, it is useful when describing certain interactions between individuals. For instance, when two chimpanzees meet along a branch one of them normally gives way, and can be referred to as the subordinate animal; the subordinate chimpanzee may make a detour or may approach the other and either present or reach out to touch the dominant animal on the lips, thigh, or genital area. Again, if two individuals want the same piece of food they rarely fight; normally one gives way and allows the other to feed. Only 72 clear-cut dominance interactions were observed, involving either incidents of the sort described above or occasions when chimpanzees ran off screaming as an excited or angry male approached them; these interactions are summarized in Table 12–2.

TABLE 12–2. SUMMARY OF 73 DOMINANCE INTERACTIONS

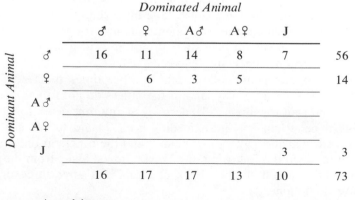

|  |  | Dominated Animal | | | | | |
|---|---|---|---|---|---|---|---|
|  |  | ♂ | ♀ | A♂ | A♀ | J |  |
| Dominant Animal | ♂ | 16 | 11 | 14 | 8 | 7 | 56 |
|  | ♀ |  | 6 | 3 | 5 |  | 14 |
|  | A♂ |  |  |  |  |  |  |
|  | A♀ |  |  |  |  |  |  |
|  | J |  |  |  |  | 3 | 3 |
|  |  | 16 | 17 | 17 | 13 | 10 | 73 |

A = adolescent
J = juvenile

The table shows that about 76 percent of all dominance interaction seen during this study was between mature males and that only about 8 percent was between mature females. Mature males were always dominant to females, adolescents, and juveniles, and mature females always dominated adolescents.

The stability of dominance relationships over a period of time is difficult to determine, partly because individuals seen together on one occasion may not thereafter be seen in each other's company for several months, and partly because even when two or more animals move about together for several days, dominance interactions of the type described above may not be observed during that period. Data obtained from a close study of interrelationships between the three "tame" males, however, suggest that although one particular individual may always appear dominant to another over an indefinite period, its dominance status with regard to other individuals may change according to the situation. Thus David Greybeard was dominant over William in all interactions observed between the two; he was dominant over Goliath in all situations except when the latter became particularly excited, when David ran away from him screaming. Goliath was always dominant over William when David was present; when David was absent the other two appeared to rank as equals. This was apparently due to a greater degree of mutual attraction between Goliath and David (who was the dominant male of the three except on rare occasions).

### Leadership

A chimpanzee can be termed the leader of a group when it initiates group movement and regulates its speed and direction. When one animal in a small group is known to be dominant (for example, a male in a group of females or a mature female in a group of adolescents and juveniles), that individual normally leads the group. The leader is not necessarily the chimpanzee moving in front of a group, although it normally takes up that position when the animals are traveling fairly fast between two main food sources. At other times the leader may take up a central or rear position while continuing to regulate the movements of the group—if it stops the others wait; when it moves on they start off again.

On many occasions when the leader leaves a feeding tree the others immediately climb down and follow, but at other times the leader may climb down, move off a little way, and, if the others do not follow, may sit down nearby and wait for them. A leader may at any time cease to lead the group. Thus once, when leaving a feeding area, David turned his head toward three other males, gave a low "huh," and the others at once got up and followed him. On the following day David moved away from the same three individuals, paused, looked back at them, and after three or four minutes moved off alone.

When chimpanzees are moving about in large mixed groups, or in bachelor groups, an obvious leader is not normally apparent. Part of the group may stop and climb into a feeding tree in one place while the others feed elsewhere. Males, alone or with other chimpanzees, sometimes move off in another direction without the rest of the group's paying any attention. Females or adolescents sometimes appear to initiate movement from one place to another. When leaving a feeding tree the chimpanzees in a large group normally climb down in ones and twos and wander off in a seemingly random manner, although occasionally they all follow one large male when he leaves the tree; he can then be said to be the leader.

### Tolerance

Chimpanzees normally show a good deal of tolerance in their behavior toward each other. This is especially true of males, less so with females. A typical instance of tolerance of a dominant to a subordinate animal occurred when an adolescent male was feeding from the only ripe cluster of fruits in a palm tree. A mature male climbed up but did not try to force the other away; he merely moved up beside the younger and the two fed side by side. Under similar circumstances a subordinate chimpanzee may move up to a dominant one, but before attempting to feed it normally reaches out to touch the other on the lips, thigh, or genital area.

Tolerance between males is particularly noticeable during the mating season, as for example on the occasion described above when seven males were observed copulating with one female with no signs of aggression between them; one of these males was an adolescent.

Tolerance of mature and adolescent chimpanzees toward infants is discussed on page 460.

## Group Range and Movements

It was established that all the individually recognized chimpanzees ranged regularly throughout the 15 square miles of the main study area. In addition, many individuals were encountered both at the northern boundary of the reserve and within 3 miles of the southern boundary. On 5 occasions small groups were seen leaving the reserve, crossing the eastern boundary; on only 1 of these occasions was I close enough to see that such a group consisted of known individuals. The small number of these observations is due to my having spent most of my time in the central area, away from the boundaries of the reserve.

Females with infants travel less extensively in general than do males and females without infants, but this depends in part upon the individual animal. Thus, although one mother was never encountered outside the main study area (and, in fact, was observed to leave groups which moved on farther), three other mothers with infants of similar age were frequently seen as far as two miles beyond the main study area on either side.

It is certain that mature chimpanzees in this area, with the exception of mothers with infants, have a range of at least 20 square miles and that some individuals may include as many as from 25 to 30 square miles in their range. No chimpanzee had a range of less than 6 square miles.

Since chimpanzee groups in the reserve freely unite from time to time without signs of aggression, they cannot be divided into separate communities. It seems likely that only a geographic barrier would constitute a limiting factor on the size of a community, although individuals living at opposite ends of the range might never come into contact.

Chimpanzees forming the static population of the reserve are nomadic only in the sense that they normally sleep in a different place each night — although some trees were found where a number of old nests, in varying stages of decay, showed that the site had been used on many occasions. Within their range individual chimpanzees also have their favorite trails across the mountains. Some trails, used frequently by a number of known individuals, are seldom if ever used by others.

The direction of the chimpanzees' daily wandering depends upon the availability of the food supply, which also affects the amount of distance traveled. However, the distance traveled depends as well on the number of chimpanzees in a group. Thus, although three or four individuals occasionally remain within an area of about three square miles for a whole day, this was never observed for a group of ten or more.

After feeding for two or three hours on one type of food, chimpanzees move off to another source, often returning to the former the following day. When traveling between food sources they sometimes move slowly, stopping frequently to feed or rest, or they may move rapidly with few, if any, pauses. Long journeys between food sources take place at any time during the day, but usually about two hours after leaving the nest, at midday, or two hours before nest making.

The daily pattern of movement for any group is irregular. Sometimes the chimpanzees leave their nests and immediately start feeding for as long as two hours in the vicinity; or they may move off early in the morning and travel as far as three miles before stopping to feed. A group normally rests for at least two hours during the morning and then wanders from place to place, pausing frequently to feed, during the afternoon. Nests are usually made close to the trees where the chimpanzees are feeding at dusk, but sometimes a group travels as far as a mile in order to sleep with another group or at a favored nesting site.

### Intergroup Interactions

When two temporary associations come together certain forms of behavior are observed that are not normally apparent in intragroup interactions, and this behavior varies in accordance with the age and sex composition of each group. If there is a mature male in each, there is normally a certain amount of excitement, which is greater when more males are present. Males may drum on tree trunks with their hands or feet, shake branches, run along slapping at the ground with their hands, or call loudly. Females and juveniles often rush out of the way screaming loudly. These displays may continue for as long as five minutes. Similar behavior is seen when a lone male joins a group.

When crossing open country toward a group which may be some distance away but within earshot, males frequently break into a run, slapping the ground, moving bipedally, hitting out at branches, and calling loudly.

On approaching a food tree in which another group containing one or more males is already feeding, each member of the arriving group usually pauses for about half a minute on a low branch and then climbs up and approaches and greets one or more of the chimpanzees in the tree, its place on the low branch being taken by the next newcomer. If the group established in the tree consists of females and juveniles only, the members of another group do not pause before climbing up.

### Intergroup Communication

When loud calls are given by members of one group they are apparently interpreted by members of another, which may be some distance away. For instance, when a large number of chimpanzees arrive at a feeding tree, or when one group joins another there, there is a good deal of calling that may persist for ten minutes or more. Other groups approaching the feeding area often respond to this calling by moving faster or calling out themselves each time they hear it.

Although calling often appears to help maintain contact between different groups, I often did not understand the exact significance of different calls. When a number of groups are within hearing distance of one another there is normally frequent intergroup calling. The reactions of chimpanzees to the calls of another group vary; they may ignore the sound; they may glance casually or stare fixedly toward the other group and call out themselves; or they may respond by actively leaping through the branches of a tree, or running along the ground and calling loudly.

### Behavior in Large Combined Groups

The behavior of a single chimpanzee, or of a group of from two to six individuals moving about together, is normally sedate. The adult chimpanzees climb up and down trees slowly, travel from place to place in a leisurely manner, and seldom call out. When ten or more are together, however, there is an increase in the tempo of most normal behavior; individuals tend to leap and swing more actively through the branches; more chasing is observed among adults; the distances covered during a day may be greater; and there is normally an increase in vocalizations. The possible effect of this social stimulation on reproductive behavior has been discussed above.

# INFANT, JUVENILE, AND ADOLESCENT DEVELOPMENT

## The Infant

### *Mother-Infant Relationships*

INFANT-ONE: Fewer observations of infant-one behavior have been obtained than of that of any other class. This is in part because not more than three infant-ones were observed at any one time and in part because females with small infants are shy of observation.

Throughout this stage the infant-one is completely dependent on its mother for transport, food, and protection. Initially it clings to her in the ventral position; while the mother is feeding or resting she may cradle the infant in her groin and if she moves only a few feet during the feeding she may carry it in this position, keeping her thigh flexed. Toward the end of the infant-one stage it may begin to ride on the mother's back, lying down with its head in the region of her shoulders.

Suckling was observed only five times; each time the mother apparently initiated feeding, holding the infant to her breast for about three minutes.

On three occasions an infant while patting at its mother's face took half-chewed fruit from her mouth and ate it. Toward the end of this stage the infant-one may take a piece of fruit from the mother's hand.

If the infant ventures more than about two feet from its mother, she pulls it back again, and if it shows signs of losing its balance, she is quick to reach out and catch hold of it. On the approach of a hawk, a mother which had been sitting in a relaxed position immediately responded by drawing the infant to her breast, encircling it with her arms, and pulling her knees up behind it. While she is feeding or making her nest, a mother may detach her infant and "hang it up" beside her for ten minutes or so—a procedure that is helpful in strengthening the muscles and that encourages locomotor development in the infant. Similar behavior is observed in captive chimpanzees (Yerkes 1943).

INFANT-TWO: The infant-two commences to ride sitting upright on its mother's back in the "jockey" position, holding onto hair on her back with its hands and onto hair in her flank region with its feet. When the mother of an early infant-two is about to move into thick undergrowth or climb a tree she usually reaches back and with a gentle push signals the child to move into the ventral position. Throughout the infant-two stage the ventral position is reverted to when the mother is moving rapidly through a tree or when there is a sudden alarm.

The mother of an infant-one warns it when she is about to move off by pressing it gently to her body. When it grows older and ventures away from its mother she signals her intention of moving by reaching out to touch it or simply gesturing toward it. The infant at once goes to her and holds on. If the infant has climbed up above her in a tree, she may look toward it and tap softly on the trunk with one hand; on the four occasions when this was seen the child climbed down at once.

As the infant becomes increasingly independent it ventures farther and farther from its mother and becomes more active. When leaving a tree the mother may climb to the lowest branch alone, but there she waits for the infant, holds out her hand, and settles it into the ventral position before swinging to the ground. Sometimes a mother of a late infant-two waits to carry it across a difficult gap. At other times a mother may sit and watch her infant trying to make a difficult leap, without making a move to assist it; the infant, after one or two attempts, may look toward its mother, bounce up and down, and scream. On three occasions this developed into a "temper tantrum" (Yerkes 1943); the infants screamed loudly and hit and rocked the branches on which they were standing. In no instance did such a display of temper elicit any response from a mother; the infants eventually calmed down and managed the jump or else made a detour.

A female was observed giving food to an infant-two on one occasion only, when the hard-shelled fruit of which she gave it a portion could not have been cracked by the infant itself. No chimpanzee was observed to take a preferred item of food from her infant, although I have observed this behavior in baboons and several other species of monkey.

Mothers frequently play with infant-twos, pushing them back and forth as they swing from a branch, tickling them, or sparring with them. I observed this behavior while the mother and infant were still in their nest in the morning, during rest periods, and at many other times when the mother was not traveling or actively feeding or grooming.

An early infant-two often interrupts a play session with another infant to run back to its mother and climb on her lap or sit beside her. A mother often reaches out, draws her infant toward her, and sits with her arm round it.

Although as it grows older the infant strays farther from its mother, playing with other infants or juveniles, it is seldom out of her sight during the early infant-two period. Once a juvenile was observed dragging an infant by one arm; the infant did not scream but its mother rushed to seize it and put her arms round it. Once two mothers of infant-twos ran up to them and gestured them to the ventral position when chimpanzees in a nearby group gave the "wraaah" call (see Table 12–3).

Even though the late infant-two feeds almost entirely on solid foods, suckling may continue throughout infancy. No weaning behavior was observed in wild chimpanzees; in fact, one mother of a late infant-two picked it up and placed it on her lap apparently to allow it to suckle. The antagonistic behavior of a mother toward her infant described in captive chimpanzees (Yerkes 1943) was not observed in the wild, where, instead, independence appeared to be initiated by the infant itself.

*Physical and Social Development of the Infant*

PHYSICAL DEVELOPMENT: The infant-two, although its diet is practically the same as that of an adult, may show slight differences in its feeding technique. While an adult puts the whole fruit in its mouth, the infant picks off the skin and then picks the flesh from the stone. The feces of adult chimpanzees sometimes consist largely of undigested food material—skins and stones, and the like—but this large proportion of roughage was never found in infant feces.

During the infant-two phase locomotor skill increases rapidly, and the late infant-two is extremely active, frequently swinging about through the tree while its mother rests or feeds, climbing into a tree beneath which its mother is walking, swinging through the branches, and then dropping down onto her back.

Individual play (as distinct from social play) gradually increases in activity throughout infancy. Infant-one play is limited to patting out at leaves, at its mother, or at its own toes as it hangs from a branch. Subsequently, as locomotor capabilities develop, playful activities include performing slow gymnastics on a branch, swinging through the branches, leaping from one branch down to another, and often executing a series of swings that may be repeated as many as eight times. Branches hanging by a piece of bark are pushed to and fro, twigs are broken off and played with, or carried about during swinging. All these forms of play are beneficial in aiding the muscular development of the young ape. The making of small nests as play activity has been discussed above.

RELATIONS WITH INDIVIDUALS OTHER THAN THE MOTHER: Most of the contacts of the early infant-two are with other infants of the same age. Play consists of gentle wrestling, patting out at each other, tugs-of-war with twigs, and so forth. During the late infant-two stage play becomes much more active and includes wrestling, chasing, and tickling.

Normally young chimpanzees play with their own age group, but occasionally an infant plays with juveniles. The latter are very gentle when playing with infants and are always quick to run and help them up or down a difficult climb.

No interactions between adolescents and infant-ones were seen. As the infant grows older, however, it seeks out adolescent company. On many occasions late infant-twos hurled themselves on to resting adolescents, of both sexes, pulled their hair, and bit and kicked them. Sometimes the adolescent sparred with the infant; at other times it merely patted at it from time to time. In one instance, an adolescent carried an infant-two into a tree; the infant at once ran and sat on its mother's lap.

Infant-twos frequently run to greet mature females. One infant lay for a few moments beside a female in her nest. On six occasions early infant-twos went up to examine the large sexual swellings of mature females.

### The Juvenile

#### Mother-Juvenile Relationship

The time at which an infant stops riding on its mother's back and sleeping with her may depend on the temperament of the infant, or of the mother, or on the birth of a new infant. Thus one female with an early infant-one was accompanied by an older offspring which, although classified as "juvenile," was in fact almost certainly younger than two animals that were classified as "infants," because they still rode on their mothers' backs and slept with them; of these two infants the smaller was by far the more independent.

The juvenile continues to associate closely with its mother for at least a year after the birth of another infant. After this it may leave her from time to time, sometimes to join a "nursery group," consisting of as many as 12 juveniles and adolescents, which is moving about with one or two mature females, and sometimes to join another mother/infant/juvenile group. Throughout the juvenile period, however, it continually returns to its mother to move about with her.

#### Social Interactions

Play is an important aspect of the social life of juveniles. They play mainly within their age group, although they may play with infants and sometimes with younger adolescents. Play is similar to that of the infant-twos, but it is rougher and chasing and wrestling continue for as long as 30 minutes at a time. Even when watching the wildest games I seldom heard a sound unless I was close enough to hear the soft panting that is the equivalent of human laughter. Most interactions of juveniles with mature chimpanzees (other than their mothers) were observed when juveniles ran or reached out to greet approaching males or females. One juvenile was gently cuffed on the head when it begged for meat from a mature male.

### The Adolescent

The playful activity of chimpanzees gradually decreases after they reach puberty. Young adolescents continue to chase and wrestle, but activities such as social grooming and resting increasingly occupy the hours of daylight.

Adolescents of both sexes often associate with mature males – the adolescent female whether or not she has a sexual swelling – and sometimes they are seen alone. Two chimpanzees, a male and a female, which reached adolescence in the course of the field study were frequently seen moving about with their mothers and siblings. They were also encountered on many occasions in other groups – without their mothers, and on their own.

## TABLE 12–3. CHIMPANZEE VOCALIZATIONS

| Description of Call | Situation in Which Normally Heard | Response of Other Chimpanzees |
|---|---|---|
| 1. Series of low panting grunts "ach-e-ach" or "ugh-e-ugh." | (a) When two chimpanzees are greeting.<br>(b) When two chimpanzees start to groom each other.<br>(c) When approaching and starting to eat desirable food. | (a) Makes similar sound.<br>(b) Makes similar sound.<br>(c) Hurries toward the food. |
| 2. Single low grunt repeated. On occasions may become a high-pitched squeaky grunt. | When eating desirable food. | |
| 3. Low panting,<br>(a) with lips pushed forward<br><br>(b) with mouth slightly open | (a) Made by subordinate when passing dominant with face near other's ear or genital area.<br>(b) Given by a dominant animal while using a reassuring gesture. | Usually no response. |
| 4. Series of very low "aach-e-aach." | Heard during play. | |
| 5. Series of low-pitched panting hoots. (Described by Nissen as "vocalized panting," 1934.) | (a) When chimpanzee peers toward another who is approaching.<br>(b) When a baboon or observer approaches. | (a) Looks toward sound. May give similar call.<br><br>(b) Others in group may join in. |
| 6. Series of loud panting hoots ending with panting screams. | When two groups join or a male joins group. | Another group may set off to join the calling groups if within earshot. |
| 7. Series of loud panting hoots ending with panting roars. | Given by male when crossing ridge accompanied by ground slapping or branch hitting. | Chimpanzees beyond ridge usually call out. |
| 8. Panting roars, rather like loud, rasping, but low-pitched screams. | During general excitement in a large group. | ? |

TABLE 12-3. CHIMPANZEE VOCALIZATIONS — *Continued*

| Description of Call | Situation in Which Normally Heard | Response of Other Chimpanzees |
|---|---|---|
| 9. Long drawn-out panting hoots sounding mournful. Last few in series particularly long drawn out. | Given by one or more in a group when another group is nearby. | Chimpanzees in another group usually look toward sound and may give panting hoots. |
| 10. Fairly loud low-pitched "hoo." | Given as male moves off and looks round at others. | Look toward male. Usually move off after him. |
| 11. Quiet high-pitched "hu." | Given after a short silence by startled chimpanzee. | Look toward chimpanzee who called, then peer round to see reason for call. |
| 12. Similar to 10, but much louder. | Heard when chimpanzees were uneasy at presence of observer. | |
| 13. Long drawn-out groan. | Heard when David Greybeard or William were refused bananas and turned to less desirable food. | |
| 14. Whimpering, similar to that of a dog. | ? Given by juveniles | ? |
| 15. Short, high-pitched scream. | Given by subordinate when approaching dominant with appeasement gesture. Given by subordinate when frustrated by dominant. | No obvious response. |
| 16. Louder screams, high-pitched with glottal cramps. | Given by a chimpanzee who has worked itself into a rage. | |
| 17. Single loud scream. | Given by male before chasing after another chimpanzee. | May rush away also screaming, or make appeasement gestures. |
| 18. Series of loud screams. | Given by chimpanzee fleeing from another. | |

TABLE 12–3. CHIMPANZEE VOCALIZATIONS—*Continued*

| Description of Call | Situation in Which Normally Heard | Response of Other Chimpanzees |
| --- | --- | --- |
| 19. Very loud screams which persist until the animal sounds hoarse. | Uncertain. | |
| 20. High-pitched bark. | Given by chimpanzee threatening baboons or humans. | May move toward animal calling to join in. |
| 21. Series of low-pitched panting barks. | Given by chimpanzee when threatening another chimpanzee, baboon, or the observer. Normally accompanied by the raising of one arm toward the threatened object. | Often screams with open mouth, teeth showing; may move away or else move toward the threatening animal and make an appeasement gesture. |
| 22. Loud barking calls, both low- and high-pitched. | Uncertain. Given during social excitement. | ? |
| 23. Loud savage "wraah," a long drawn-out pure sound, usually repeated several times. | Given by chimpanzee threatening observer. Occasionally heard when two groups meet. | Usually move toward animal calling to join in. |

## EXPRESSION AND COMMUNICATION

Chimpanzees express themselves and communicate by means of vocalizations, gestures, facial expressions, and body postures. Table 12–3 summarizes sounds or series of sounds that are easily distinguishable in the field. During further field research it is hoped to record and analyze these vocalizations in detail. It was not possible to make a detailed study of facial expressions in the field; such data as were obtained are in agreement with the descriptions of facial expressions in captive chimpanzees (Kohts 1935; van Hooff 1962).

In the following section these expressive movements and vocalizations are discussed in relation to the social or environmental situations that appear to elicit them.

### Relaxed and Attentive Postures

The chimpanzee in the wild normally appears relaxed. The most usual sitting position is with the legs bent up, the forearms resting on the knees, hands dangling, and back slightly hunched (see Fig. 12–13). When sitting in a tree it normally holds an overhead bough with one hand.

When a chimpanzee is interested in some object or situation it looks toward it intently, sometimes with slightly pouted lips. On observing this, another chimpanzee will look in the same direction until it sees the object.

### Threat and Attack

#### *Threat*

Threatening behavior was seen on four occasions when a subordinate male tried to take food before a dominant one. Three of these instances occurred under artificial conditions, when the observer threw a banana between the two. The threatening male moved bipedally toward the other,

465

giving high-pitched screams, his mouth half-open, lips drawn back from his teeth, and the hair of his shoulders, back, and arms erect.

Threatening gestures made toward baboons and humans included a rapid upward and backward movement of the forearm and "flapping" (that is, slapping movements made toward an object without hitting it). Both these gestures may be accompanied by low, panting barks with the lips pushed forward. Three times a male chimpanzee ran toward a baboon bipedally, swinging his arms round above his head.

Threatening behavior toward me increased as the chimpanzees became less afraid. Initially threatening movements such as ground-slapping, branch-shaking, or glaring were unaccompanied by vocalizations, but after the first nine months these displays became more violent and were accompanied by loud calling.

Males, females, adolescents, and occasionally juveniles took part in these threat displays, though males were usually more violent. Occasionally females and youngsters continued to feed peacefully during male threat displays.

### Attack

Instances of attack were seldom observed, and mature males were seen fighting on only one occasion, when William took a bite of fresh meat on which Huxley, an old male, was feeding. Huxley, with a scream, seized William and bit him on the shoulder, and J. B., a large and powerfully built mature male, chased him from the tree. After a few moments both males rejoined Huxley, who then reached out and hit William four or five times on the scrotum, while J. B. bit his shoulder. J. B. then hit and pulled at William's scrotum; the latter screamed loudly but did not try to escape or retaliate. No signs of injury were visible after the encounter.

Other instances of attack behavior are described elsewhere (see below).

On one occasion a mature male climbed a tree ten feet above me (I was lying down) and worked himself into a rage, screaming, hitting the trunk, and shaking the branches. After some five minutes he climbed down, moved behind me, paused, and then with a short yell hit my head, presumably with his hand. When I sat up he moved slowly away, still showing signs of excitement.

### Escape and Appeasement

### Submissive Behavior

When an excited male bounds toward a subordinate the latter sometimes runs off rapidly. It may hurl itself out of a tree, or leap into a tree if on the ground. Normally it screams loudly, glancing back over its shoulder at the male. Only on occasions when the fleeing chimpanzee was a female in estrus did the male pursue until he caught up with her; normally he chased for a short distance or not at all.

At other times the subordinate animal, instead of running away, remains where it is or moves toward the male, and makes an appeasement gesture (see below).

### Alarm and Avoidance

When chimpanzees are frightened by something in their environment, they normally run off silently with no alarm call. Baboons, and other animals living in groups, may also run off without a warning call, but in these other animals the structure of the group, in which each individual is continually aware of the others, ensures that the running off of one animal acts as an alarm signal to the group as a whole. The individuals in a chimpanzee group, even when moving along fairly close together, often seem to pay little attention to the other members of the group. As a consequence one chimpanzee may run off silently while the rest of the group remains quite unaware of the potential danger. It is difficult to explain this lack of coordination, which was observed on many occasions.

When chimpanzees were uneasy in my presence, they usually peered toward me, with tightly compressed lips, from a concealing tangle of foliage and were sometimes heard to tap gently on the trunk of a tree. This may serve as a signal.

When startled by a sudden noise or movement, a chimpanzee often flings one arm across its face, at the same time bowing its head and leaping away from the possible danger. This was also observed by Kortlandt in the Congo (personal communication). Habituated chimpanzees showed two "startle reactions" when they came across me unexpectedly. Sometimes, having stopped dead, they stared hard at me, often dropped open the lower jaw, and gave a soft high-pitched "hu" (see 11, Table 12–3). On other occasions they turned abruptly, and flinging one arm across the face ran off noisily for a short distance, stopped, and then looked back.

When a large insect flies close to a chimpanzee it jerks back its head and hits out at the insect with the back of the hand.

## Behavior in Uncertainty

When confronted by an unusual situation and apparently uncertain as to how to act, for instance when upset by my presence and/or when inclined both to flee and to attack, chimpanzees may show certain responses that will be summarized under the headings referred to as "displacement activities" and "redirection activities." These terms are classificatory devices only and apply to activities that appeared to me to be irrelevant to the situation and out of context (displacement activities) or else to be redirected on to an object or objects other than the initial eliciting stimulus.

DISPLACEMENT ACTIVITIES: In captivity a young chimpanzee when unable to obtain a desired object may start rocking its body from side to side. This behavior was seen on many occasions when William was prevented from getting bananas by his reluctance to approach me. Glaring at me, he rocked while sitting or standing upright, either in silence or giving loud panting hoots. Erections were observed of the hair on his back, shoulders, and arms, and of his penis. After rocking vigorously for a few minutes he sat and scratched his side or arm with slow downward movements of one hand while almost imperceptibly moving his head from side to side.

Chimpanzees sometimes yawned, while scratching as described above, in situations in which they were uneasy or frustrated.

On three occasions when chimpanzees were unable to share the meat of another they turned away and made rapid and ineffectual grooming movements on the shoulder of a chimpanzee nearby.

REDIRECTION ACTIVITIES: On two occasions aggression was redirected toward another chimpanzee—on both occasions the aggressor was the large male Goliath. Once, while shaking branches during a threat display directed at me, he caught hold of a mature female, bit, and wrestled with her. On another occasion, when a banana held out to Goliath was seized by a second male, the former, with his hair erect, rushed screaming toward a third male, but did not actually attack him.

During threat displays chimpanzees may shake branches, break them off, or hit tree trunks. When David Greybeard got more bananas than Goliath, the latter on four occasions seized a stick that he waved in the air and then dragged behind him as he ran backward and forward. Once, while charging toward a native, he picked up an axe and swung it over his head before dropping it.

Other examples of redirected activities are the drumming and branch-hitting displays of socially excited males. Either the hands or the feet are used in drumming on tree trunks; saplings or branches are seized and bent to the ground as the chimpanzee runs past. Both these actions are normally accompanied by loud panting roars (see 8, Table 12–3).

Sometimes an excited male rushes down a steep slope, often bipedally, calling, waving his arms, and tearing off a low branch that he drags behind him. On four occasions when six or more males were present, this developed into a "branch-waving display," during which the participants repeatedly ran down the mountainside, calling, tearing off and waving large branches, hurling themselves to the ground from trees. Some 50 yards down they paused and then walked back ready to rush down again. These displays continued for from 10 to 30 minutes. Females and juveniles did not take part in the displays but sat in trees and watched.

**Friendly Behavior**

There are a number of activities and gestures the main function of which is apparently to establish and maintain good relations between the individual chimpanzees of the community.

*Mutual Grooming*

Mutual grooming is an activity which plays an important part in the social life of the chimpanzee. During adolescence the proportion of time spent in social play slowly decreases while time spent in social grooming gradually increases. The 217 observations of mutual grooming when the age/sex classes of each of the chimpanzees could be determined are summarized in Table 12-4. This shows that about 45 percent of the total number of observations involved pairs of mature animals, about 24 percent involved pairs in which one was mature and the other adolescent, 8 percent involved adolescent pairs, and less than 3 percent involved juvenile pairs. Of the remaining, 17 percent were mothers grooming their infants or juveniles and 3 percent comprised juveniles grooming mature females and a single observation each of an adolescent grooming a juvenile and an infant grooming an infant. The table also shows that a mature male is most likely to groom and be groomed by another mature male; a female by another mature female. A female in estrus is more likely to be groomed by a male than is a nonreceptive female.

**TABLE 12-4. SUMMARY OF 217 OBSERVATIONS OF MUTUAL GROOMING**

|  |  | *Groomed Animal* | | | | | | |  |
|---|---|---|---|---|---|---|---|---|---|
|  |  | ♂ | ♀ | ♀E | A♀ | A♂ | J | I |  |
| | ♂ | 43 | 8 | 9 | 10 | 11 | 0 | 1 | 82 |
| *Grooming Animal* | ♀ | 15 | 14 | 1 | 1 | 0 | 12 | 24 | 67 |
| | ♀E | 7 | 1 | 0 | | | | | 8 |
| | A♀ | 11 | 2 | 0 | 9 | 2 | 0 | 0 | 24 |
| | A♂ | 14 | 0 | 3 | 2 | 5 | 1 | 0 | 25 |
| | J | 0 | 4 | 0 | 0 | 0 | 6 | 0 | 10 |
| | I | 0 | 1 | 0 | 0 | 0 | 0 | 0 | 1 |
| | | 90 | 30 | 13 | 22 | 18 | 19 | 25 | |

♀ E = female in estrus      A = adolescent      J = juvenile      I = infant

(On 71 occasions grooming was observed when the sex of one or both animals was not known.)

The table suggests that mature males groom each other more frequently than do mature females, but this is misleading and reflects the fact that males are less shy of observation. Thus, although two males in a mixed group may sit and groom in full view, the females often move out of sight. Often when I was able to move to where I could see the females, I found, as I had suspected, that they too were grooming each other.

The initiation of a grooming session may be mutual, as when two chimpanzees approach each other, sit down close to each other, and immediately start grooming. At other times one chimpanzee approaches another and solicits grooming, standing either facing or with its back to the other, and with its head bowed. Occasionally it lies down in front of the other. When one animal adopts a "grooming posture," a grooming response is normally elicited in the other. Sometimes a chimpanzee goes up to another and starts grooming it. If there is no response, it may stop after a few minutes and adopt a grooming posture in front of the other. If this is ignored, it may reach out and gently poke the other. If there is still no response, it usually goes away.

The chimpanzee grooms another animal in the same way it grooms itself. Often each of a grooming pair holds an overhead branch with one hand and grooms under the arm of its companion with the other. The chimpanzees take turns to groom each other's back. A grooming session may last as long as two hours, though juveniles were not observed to groom each other for longer than 20 minutes at a stretch. During a long session, periods of intense concentration, when grooming is invariably accompanied by slow lip-smacking, are interspersed with periods of slow and lazy grooming, when each chimpanzee sits with half-closed eyes idly running a forefinger, with a circular movement, through the hair of its partner.

More than half of the occasions on which one chimpanzee was groomed by another without responding involved a mother grooming her infant or her older child. (Only once was an infant—an early infant-two—observed to groom its mother, and juveniles were observed grooming their mothers on only four occasions.) On other such occasions mature males were groomed by other mature males, adolescents, or females. Chimpanzees were observed grooming in groups of as many as six individuals of any age and sex.

In addition to normal mutual grooming, the act of grooming occasionally appears to be significant in dominance or friendly interactions between individuals. For example:

After copulation either partner may briefly groom the other before moving away. This grooming was never mutual and never lasted more than two or three minutes.

When greeting another, a chimpanzee may make grooming movements on its shoulder with one hand.

A male frequently grooms the perineal hairs when a female with sexual swelling presents. This is not normally followed by copulation.

Fig. 12–14. Two males greeting. The one with back to the camera has his right hand between the arms of the other, his left hand reaching back to touch the other's scrotum. (© *National Geographic Society*)

### Greeting Behavior

There are several ways in which one chimpanzee may "greet" another, depending on the length of time they have been separated, the degree of mutual attraction, and their mood at the time.

The most common greeting occurs when one chimpanzee goes up to another and reaches out to touch it with the flat of the hand or with the back of the slightly flexed fingers (see Fig. 12–14). The top of the head, the shoulder, groin, thigh, or genital area may be touched in greeting. A female in estrus is normally touched on her sexual swelling in greeting; a male may also put his face to her genital area as though sniffing.

Greater mutual attraction is shown when two animals move toward each other with soft, panting grunts (see Table 12–3) and touch each other. Another form of greeting occurs when a male stands upright, one arm above his head, while another runs toward him. The two then fling

471

their arms around each other. In both forms of greeting described above a male normally has an erection of the penis.

Friendly behavior between juveniles and adults has been described above.

### Appeasement, Ingratiation, and Reassurance

There are a number of submissive actions with which a subordinate chimpanzee apparently shows its respect for or fear of a dominant animal in order to divert any possible aggression and help to insure the continued tolerance of its superiors. In addition, there are some gestures that appear to have a calming effect on uneasy chimpanzees.

When a mature male shows aggressiveness or social excitement, other chimpanzees may use gestures apparently intended to appease him and divert possible attack. Thus another male may move toward him with an "appeasement grin," the lower lip drawn down to show the teeth and gums, and may reach out to touch his lips or scrotum. A female in similar circumstances may move toward the male and "present," turning her buttocks toward him in a crouch position similar to that of a female soliciting copulation, with her limbs only slightly less flexed.

A subordinate chimpanzee, when it wants to pass a more dominant animal along a branch or sit beside it and share its food, shows behavior that can be termed "ingratiation." Most commonly the subordinate touches the other on its lips or scrotum, but instead of showing the appeasement grin its lips are normally slightly pouted. A female may present, but her posture is far less "tense" than in appeasement presenting, and the crouching less exaggerated. A chimpanzee which wants a share in another's food (such as meat) may use both of the gestures described above. In addition, it often reaches out its hand to touch the food (without taking any) and may use the "begging" gesture, holding out its hand palm uppermost. When begging behavior is successful, pieces of food are placed in the supplicator's outstretched hand.

This behavior was observed frequently during interactions between the three males David Greybeard, Goliath, and William. On many occasions when Goliath or William showed signs of nervousness, or jumped at a sudden noise, David went up to them, panted (3, Table 12–3) and laid one hand on their arm, shoulder, or, occasionally, scrotum. This gesture always had the effect of calming the chimpanzee on which it was used. On one occasion, when a baboon broke a branch with a sudden crack, David placed one hand on my arm.

## CONCLUSIONS

It is important to remember that the behavior described in this chapter applies specifically to a chimpanzee population in a rather atypical habitat. One noticeable difference between the Gombe Stream chimpanzees and those of the closed forest habitats described by Nissen (1931), Kortlandt (1962), and Reynolds (Chap. 11, this volume) is that the density of the population per square mile appears to be much greater in the latter type of habitat.

Two of the most interesting behavior patterns that were observed during this field study were, first, that these chimpanzees hunt and kill fairly large animals for food and, second, that tool-using is a relatively common practice.

Meat-eating has not, to my knowledge, been recorded from other parts of the chimpanzee's range in Africa, although if it is assumed that human infants are in fact taken for food, the report that five babies were carried off in West Africa suggests that carnivorous behavior may be widespread.

Although meat-eating cannot at present be regarded as common to the chimpanzee species as a whole, the ability to utilize natural objects as tools is undoubtedly a species characteristic of the chimpanzee throughout its range. Merfield (1954) describes a group of chimpanzees poking sticks into an underground bees' nest to obtain honey, and Beatty (1951) observed a chimpanzee using a stone to break open the kernel of a palm nut. Both these observations were made in West Africa. The Gombe Stream chimpanzees, however, in their ability to modify a twig or stick to make it suitable for a definite purpose, provide the first examples of free-ranging nonhuman primates actually *making* very crude tools.

Finally, I should like to stress that this chapter is based on data obtained in the course of a field study that has not yet been completed at this writing. I hope during the final months in the field not only to obtain many additional facts concerning such behavior as nest-making, feeding, grooming, and so on, but, in particular, to acquire more detailed information concerning the interrelationships between individuals in the complex chimpanzee society.

GEORGE B. SCHALLER

# 13
## ◈ Behavioral Comparisons of the Apes

## HISTORY OF DISCOVERY

Buffon described and pictured the gibbon as early as 1766; Cuvier distinguished between the chimpanzee and orangutan in 1798; and in 1847 two missionaries discovered the gorilla in the forests of Africa. Increasing knowledge of the existence of the apes gave a powerful impetus to theories of man's cultural evolution, and reports of travelers concerning these creatures were eagerly sought. For example, Auguste Comte, the founder of modern sociology, attempted to find out "by what necessary chain of successive transformations the human race, starting from a condition barely superior to that of a society of great apes, has been gradually led up to the present state of European civilization" (Comte quoted in Greene 1959). Yet familiarity with the ecology and behavior of free-living apes remained woefully inadequate, a fact clearly demonstrated by Yerkes and Yerkes (1929), who summarized the available literature.

## VARIETIES AND DISTRIBUTION

The African apes, the gorilla (*Gorilla*) and the chimpanzee (*Pan*), are largely confined to the equatorial rain forest belt, although by virtue of being to some extent terrestrial, both have also penetrated several adjoining areas of the vegetation type in which the trees are widely scattered and the habitat quite open. The one species of *Gorilla gorilla* is divided into two subspecies, one occurring in West Africa, the other in Central Africa (Coolidge 1929). Two species of chimpanzees are generally recognized; *Pan troglodytes* inhabits the forests north, west, and east of the Congo River, and *Pan paniscus*, the pygmy chimpanzee, is known only from south of the Congo River. The pioneer behavioral studies on the African apes include those of Bingham (1932) on the gorilla in the eastern Congo, and

474

Nissen (1931) on the chimpanzee in Guinea. The results of the first long-term studies of these two apes, and summaries of the pertinent literature regarding them, are included as separate chapters in this volume. Since the Asiatic apes are not so treated, a brief résumé of the extent of the knowledge concerning them is useful for comparison with the African apes.

## The Gibbon

The gibbons, which consist of two genera, are the smallest and geographically the most widespread of the apes. *Symphalangus syndactulus*, the siamang, possesses a laryngeal air sac and is about twice as large as the *Hylobates* gibbons (averaging 22 as against 13 pounds), which include from five to twelve species depending on the authority. The siamang is confined to Sumatra and Malaya, but *Hylobates* ranges from Assam and Burma through Thailand and Malaya to Sumatra and Borneo. Both types are usually found in the canopy of relatively undisturbed rain forest from sea level upward to an altitude of about 7000 feet. The behavior of the siamang is unknown, and the only detailed study of free-living gibbons was made by Carpenter (1940), who between March 23 and June 18, 1937, watched 21 groups of *Hylobates lar* at Doi Dao in northwestern Thailand. Some of the main points of his classic monograph are summarized below:

The 21 gibbon groups consisted of 93 individuals of which 21 were adult males, 21 adult females, 39 juveniles independent of their mothers and ranging in graded series to young adults, and 11 infants still being carried by their mothers. The size of groups ranged from two to six. "The mean grouping tendency in the gibbons of the species *Hylobates lar* is that of the family; a male, and a female with their young." The smallest group consisted of one adult male and one adult female. Two groups had two adult males each, but in both one male was aged; only one group had more than one adult female. Lone males were encountered several times. There were about 10 to 12 animals, or two or three groups, per square mile in one sample population. Although gibbon groups generally confined their activities to certain sections of the forest, clear instances of competition for food between groups were sometimes observed. Occasionally "neighboring groups actually intermingle for short periods of time." Three groups ranged over from 30 to 50 acres, from 60 to 75 acres, and from 60 to 100 acres, respectively. Shifts in the ranges of groups apparently were the result of pressures from surrounding groups, competition, group-splitting, and shifts in the supply of food.

The activity of groups begins at dawn when the animals move from the sleeping trees to the feeding area. Gibbons are primarily frugivorous (80 percent) and herbivorous (20 percent). "They were observed to eat insects and eggs, and skulls of nestling birds were found in stomachs of some shot specimens." At times the animals descend to or near the ground to drink by dipping the back of the hand into water and sucking the moisture from the hairs. After feeding for about two hours, the animals rest about three hours, and then feed and move until sundown, when they return to their "lodge trees" after having ranged from 600 to 6000 feet during the day. "In the forest, brachiating and walking occur in an estimated ratio of about 9:1."

Gibbon groups are relatively cohesive. The male and female are equal in leading, coordinating, and guarding the group, and they are about equally aggressive, fighting occasionally by biting with their canine teeth and by clawing with their fingers. Gibbons "show no striking sex differences in dominance." When two gibbons come together they display an elaborate greeting ceremony during which they embrace each other and squeal. "During hundreds of undisturbed hours of observation," only two copulations were seen, suggesting that gibbons "have a low degree of sexual drive." Members of the group readily groom each other, an activity that seems to enhance and strengthen the social bond. Nine distinct vocalizations are emitted by gibbons, usually when the group is moving and when excited by the presence of man or another group.

The focus of behavior for the infant is its mother. During the first six weeks of its life the newborn rarely leaves the female. It is carried over her pelvis and somewhat to one side, never on her back. Solid food supplements its milk diet after the first few weeks. Although infants lack age-mates in the group, play between the infants and juvenile siblings is common; mild play between a male and an infant is also quite frequent. Most social play consists of chasing, biting, and wrestling.

### The Orangutan

The orangutan (*Pongo pygmaeus*) is the rarest of the apes, being found only in northern Sumatra and in small sectors of Borneo (including Sarawak, North Borneo, and Indonesian Borneo). The animals are bulky, powerful creatures, with adult males averaging about 160 pounds in weight and females 80 pounds. They inhabit primary rain forest from sea level to an altitude of 3000 feet and, exceptionally, as high as 6000 feet. No studies of the orangutan have been made, and nearly all aspects of the ape's behavior remain unknown. Incidental observations can be found in, among others, Wallace (1869), Hornaday (1885), Beccari (1904), Carpenter (1939), Schaller (1961), and Harrisson (1962). These are summarized as follows:

The orangutan is rarely encountered in aggregations of more than two, three, or four animals, although one observer reported as many as six. The composition of these aggregations varies, the most frequent combinations being females with one or more subadults, one adult male and one adult female, and small groups of subadults. Lone males appear to be common. Nothing definite is known about the stability of groups, but one observa-

| Character | Gibbon (Hylobates lar) Carpenter 1940 | Orangutan (Pongo pygmaeus) Schaller 1961 | Chimpanzee (Pan troglodytes schweinfurthi) Reynolds and Reynolds, Chap. 11, this vol.; Goodall, Chap. 12, this vol. | Mountain Gorilla (Gorilla gorilla beringei) Schaller, Chap. 10, this vol. |
|---|---|---|---|---|
| Arboreal/ Terrestrial | Arboreal | Arboreal | Arboreal and terrestrial; amount of each varies with habitat | Terrestrial, although climbs readily into trees |
| Locomotion | Brachiation with some bipedal walking along branches | Quadrupedal with some brachiation | In trees: quadrupedal with some brachiation. On ground: quadrupedal, rarely bipedal over short distances | In trees: quadrupedal On ground: quadrupedal, rarely bipedal over short distances |
| Nest building | No | Yes, in trees | Yes, in trees, rarely on the ground | Yes, on the ground and in trees |
| Diet | Frugivorous (80%) and herbivorous (20%). May also eat insects, eggs and nestling birds | Primarily frugivorous, also herbivorous. Feeding on animal matter not conclusively determined | Primarily frugivorous, also herbivorous. Also eat insects, antelopes, monkeys (Goodall) | Primarily herbivorous, also frugivorous. Feeding on animal matter not reliably reported |
| Size of home range | 30–100 acres (group cohesive) | Unknown (group scattered widely over range) | 6–8 (Reynolds); up to 25 or 50 (Goodall) square miles (group scattered widely over range) | 10–15 square miles (group cohesive) |

**TABLE 13-1. SOME BEHAVIORAL COMPARISONS OF FREE-LIVING APES—Continued**

| Character | Gibbon (Hylobates lar) Carpenter 1940 | Orangutan (Pongo pygmaeus) Schaller 1961 | Chimpanzee (Pan troglodytes schweinfurthi) Reynolds and Reynolds, Chap. 11, this vol.; Goodall, Chap. 12, this vol. | Mountain Gorilla (Gorilla gorilla beringei) Schaller, Chap. 10, this vol. |
|---|---|---|---|---|
| Size of group | 2–6 (approx. mean 4.5) | Size of whole group unknown; size of subgroups is 2–6 (mean about 3.0) | Size of whole group is 65–75 (Reynolds) or 60–80 (Goodall), but whole group is rarely together. Subgroups number from 2–30 | 2–30 (mean 7–17 depending on area) |
| Composition of groups | Group consist usually of one adult male, one adult female, and young | Composition of whole group unknown; that of subgroups is variable and unstable: (1) adult female or females with one or more subadults, (2) one adult male and one adult female, (3) several subadults, (4) other combinations | Whole group consists of several males, females, and young; the group is highly unstable and readily breaks up into subgroups composed of: (1) several males, (2) several females with infants, (3) several males and females, (4) mixed | Groups consist of one or more adult males; one or more adult females; and young of various ages |

|  |  |  |  |  |
|---|---|---|---|---|
| *Stability of groups* | Stable over 3-month period of study | Appear to be unstable with animals joining and parting | Highly unstable—daily changes in composition as subgroups join and part | Most groups stable over periods of one year or more; some groups unstable with lone males joining and parting frequently |
| *Interactions between groups* | Frequent vocalizing near range boundaries; groups may mingle | Unknown | Constant peaceful mixing | Often ignore each other; sometimes approach each other closely and may mingle for several hours; rarely aggressive |
| *Adult dominance hierarchy* | "No striking sex difference in dominance" | Unknown | Males dominant over females; no clear hierarchy between males or between females | Males dominant over females. Males have linear hierarchy; females appear to lack stable hierarchy |
| *Grooming between adults* | Readily groom each other | Unknown | Males and females groom each other, especially when latter are in estrus; males readily groom each other, as do females | Males were never seen to groom females or vice versa. Males did not groom each other, and females did so rarely |

tion made by Schaller (1961) suggests that it may be unstable; during one night a male, a female with infant, and a juvenile nested in adjoining trees as revealed by their nests; another night the male slept 400 feet from the rest of the group; and a third night the male had apparently left the group entirely.

Orangutans are arboreal, rarely descending to the ground. In trees they progress quadrupedally, although they may brachiate along a branch on occasion. Toward dusk they construct nests of branches on which they lie during the hours of darkness. Of 228 nests sampled by Schaller (1961), 82 percent were located from 30 to 70 feet above ground. The apes seem to be primarily frugivorous.

## BEHAVIORAL COMPARISONS

In an attempt to assess similarities and differences between gibbons, orangutans, chimpanzees, and gorillas, and perhaps to make some generalizations about these apes, several aspects of their ecology and behavior are summarized in Table 13–1. At present, comparisons must by necessity be tentative. The behavior of several species and subspecies of apes, such as the siamang and pygmy chimpanzee, are unknown, and others, such as the orangutan and lowland gorilla, have not yet received detailed study. The fact that two kinds of primates are taxonomically closely related is no guarantee that their social structure is identical or even very similar, and extreme caution must be exercised in making generalizations about one kind on the basis of what is known of another. This is well exemplified by the difference in the social structure of *Papio hamadryas* and *Papio anubis* (Hall and DeVore, Chap. 3, this volume). Striking behavioral differences may even occur within the same species in different parts of its range. For instance, chimpanzees in open woodlands were occasionally seen to catch and eat monkeys and antelopes and they regularly used twigs as tools to extract termites from their mounds, (Goodall, Chap. 12, this volume), whereas those in the rain forest were never observed to behave in this fashion (Reynolds and Reynolds, Chap. 11, this volume).

All the apes are similar in being basically confined to the equatorial rain forest belt (although the chimpanzee, which appears to be more adaptable than the others in its habitat requirements, has also occupied open dry woodlands at the periphery of its range). However, apes have adapted to different modes of life within this ecologically similar vegetation zone. For example, the gibbon and orangutan are arboreal, with the former progressing to a large extent by brachiation and the latter by climbing quadrupedally through the forest canopy; chimpanzees are semiterrestrial, and gorilla almost wholly terrestrial.

One aspect of the study of apes that has so far received scant attention is the ecological and behavioral interactions between species that occupy the same area. Carpenter (1958) once observed gibbons and siamangs feeding together in the same tree in central Sumatra without overt sign of aggression, and Schaller (unpublished data) saw a group of gibbons less than 100 feet from two orangutans in Sarawak. Chimpanzees and gorillas inhabit the same forests in several parts of Central and West Africa. It would be interesting to determine if such species compete for food, space, and the like, or if they are ecologically separated from each other. Work on gorillas and chimpanzees provides suggestive data that an ecological separation may indeed exist. Mountain gorillas in the rain forests of the Congo basin and in the Kayonza Forest of Uganda are primarily herbivorous, with fruits furnishing only a minor part of their diet (Schaller 1963). In a similar forest environment the bulk of the chimpanzee's diet consisted of fruits (Reynolds and Reynolds, Chap. 11, this volume), suggesting that when the two apes occupy the same forest there is little competition for food.

One of the most conspicuous behavioral differences between the apes lies in their group organization, and such prevalent statements in the literature as "Man's closest kin, the three great apes, live in simple harems" (Coon 1962) have tended to obscure this important and striking fact. As shown in Table 13–1, the Asiatic apes live in very small social units, each ranging from two to six individuals in size, while units of the African apes tend to be relatively large, numbering 25 or more animals on occasion. The gibbon and the gorilla have relatively stable and cohesive groups and many of these retain the same composition over a period of several months. However, the average gibbon group consists only of one male, one female, and several young, whereas the gorilla group may contain several members of each age and sex class. The orangutan and chimpanzee, on the other hand, are characterized by unstable social units with members parting and joining at frequent intervals. Encounters with orangutan groups consisting solely of a female and a young indicate that such groups join or are joined by a male on occasion. Large chimpanzee groups are so loosely organized that all members are rarely together.

These brief comments and the broad comparisons in Table 13–1 serve to illustrate the tremendous variation in the social structure and in other aspects of behavior of the four apes, but much more data are necessary before a detailed enumeration of similarities and differences is possible.

# PART III

## ◆ Comparative Studies

THE PRECEDING CHAPTERS of this book are devoted to studies of the ecology and behavior of primates in the field. From the very beginning of its discussions, however, the Center study group felt that some topics should be treated comparatively. Enough species have now been studied to allow tentative generalizations that embrace all of the monkeys and apes, and it is only through such generalizations that strategies in future field studies can be planned. In addition, some aspects of nonhuman primate behavior have been studied in laboratories for several decades, and the seven new Regional Primate Centers will enormously increase the amount of information derived from laboratories. Consistently our group discussions concerned the increasing possibilities for liaison between field and laboratory workers. Chapter 18 both offers strategies for future field studies and suggests some of the important implications these studies will have for problems that have traditionally been studied only in laboratories.

At the initial planning conference many topics were suggested as suitable for comparative treatment, but *all* attending agreed that three topics should certainly be treated: reproductive cycles, the social development of infants, and primate communication. One of the most striking conclusions to be drawn from field studies during the last decade is that, contrary to the widely held notion that the nonhuman primates engage in reproductive activities at all seasons, many monkey populations show marked seasonal differences in such behavior. In laboratory colonies, under relatively constant conditions of temperature, light, and diet, sexual activity and births occur at all times of the year, but this does not seem to be true of most monkeys in a natural habitat. Jane B. Lancaster and Richard B. Lee have brought together in Chapter 14 what is now known about the annual reproductive cycle in monkeys and apes and have related these reports to seasonal variations in the various habitat areas.

During the past decade one of the most prominent research problems in primate laboratories has been the intensive analysis of the maturation and socialization of infants. The effects of early social deprivation on the behavior of the adult monkey or ape have clear implications for the understanding of human psychiatric problems. A complete understanding of the maturation process must include careful observation of animals under natural conditions, but the field worker's ability to manipulate his subjects is severely limited, and many aspects of infant development can only be understood when the animals can be controlled in captive colonies. William A. Mason is primarily known for his studies of infant behavior in the laboratory, and it was for this reason that the group asked him to discuss their field data in the perspective of his laboratory experience. Chapter 15 is the result. It is gratifying to report that Dr. Mason is now in South America engaged in a monkey field study of his own.

One of the most frequent questions asked of a field worker is "Do monkeys and apes speak a language?", and through the years many attempts, all unsuccessful, have been made to teach nonhuman primates to speak. Speech is a prerequisite for human society, and communication is equally essential for the social life of monkeys and apes. The human infant learns to speak whatever language is spoken by the adults who rear it, and it has become increasingly apparent that learning in the context of a social group is essential for the normal maturation of the young monkey or ape. Yet the adult nonhuman primate communicates by means of a signalling system that appears to be essentially identical from one population to the next. That is, nonhuman primate communication is species-specific. It is puzzling that there should be so great a difference between human language and the signalling systems of the primates, which man so closely resembles in body and behavior, but it is clear that the techniques developed by zoologists to study animal signalling systems are more appropriate to the analysis of nonhuman primate communication than are the methods used by linguists to study human languages. In Chapter 16 Peter Marler, whose research in animal communication grew out of his studies on the development of bird song, has evaluated primate communication in its general zoological context. One result of his discussions with the Center group is that Professor Marler is now in Africa gathering data on the communication systems of monkeys in the wild.

Human speech is at the root of man's unique cultural qualities and any discussion of human evolution must eventually deal with the development of language. By the time language was reduced to writing, human speech was already as fully developed as any modern language, and it seems certain that no unequivocal evidence for the prehistoric development of language will ever be uncovered. The signalling systems of nonhuman primates, then, are our most important sources for the reconstruction of the earliest stages of human speech. Despite the fact that the scientific study of monkey and ape communication is only beginning, Jarvis R. Bastian was asked to discuss what we now know about the nonhuman primates in terms of contemporary linguistics. His treatment of this intriguing and difficult subject is presented in Chapter 17.

JANE B. LANCASTER and RICHARD B. LEE

# 14
# ◆ The Annual Reproductive Cycle in Monkeys and Apes

## INTRODUCTION

Perhaps the most persistent controversy running through the literature on primate behavior in the last 35 years concerns the question of a mating season. Zuckerman stated the case for the existence of an uninterrupted sexual life in monkeys and apes and emphasized that this characteristic set all the higher primates apart from other mammals (1931, 1932). Since then evidence to the contrary has been brought forward indicating that at least some monkeys show striking seasonal variations in reproductive activities (e.g., Hartman 1931; Carpenter 1942a; Haddow 1952; Imanishi 1960). However, as recently as 1961 one writer could assert:

> There remains to be considered the special question of the primates (the monkeys, apes and man), which are characterized by the unusual habit of breeding throughout the whole year. Most of them appear to experience a smooth and uninterrupted sexual life extending from puberty to old age (Bullough, 1961:16).

Such assertions of year-round sexuality in primates have led other writers to conclude that it must form the basis of primate social life:

> It was the development of the physiological capacity to mate during much of, if not throughout, the menstrual cycle, and at all seasons, that impelled the formation of year round heterosexual groups among monkeys and apes. Within the primate order, a new level of social integration emerges, one that surpasses

The co-authors, who contributed equally to this chapter, would like to thank the following workers for allowing them access to unpublished field data: Irven DeVore, Phyllis Jay, Carl B. Koford, Hans Kummer, Vernon Reynolds and Frances Reynolds, Suzanne Ripley, Donald S. Sade, George B. Schaller, Paul Simonds, and Sherwood L. Washburn. Special thanks are given to Hiroki Mizuhara for making available the birth data on the Japanese macaque.

that of other mammals whose mating periods, and hence heterosexual groupings, are very limited in duration and by season (Sahlins, 1959:56).

Evidence on reproductive cycles from laboratory and zoo colonies has always proved equivocal. In indoor laboratories infants are normally born throughout the year, whereas data from zoo colonies are usually highly variable and based on small numbers of animals. The resolution of this issue has awaited reliable observational data on the seasonal incidence of births and copulations in free-ranging primate populations. These data have become available only within the last five years and much of this material is presented here for the first time.

A comparative examination of the annual reproductive cycle in free-ranging primates is the task of this chapter. The data are drawn from the field studies of 14 primate populations. The emphasis is on demographic observations of breeding populations, but occasionally laboratory data are incorporated. Although a theoretical position is presented in the conclusion of this chapter, our primary purpose is to give as complete a summary as possible of the present state of knowledge on the subject.

## THE DETERMINANTS OF REPRODUCTIVE CYCLES IN BIRDS AND MAMMALS

According to Amoroso and Marshall (1960), research on reproductive cycles in mammals and birds indicates that birth seasons are the result of two different factors that interact to bring members of a breeding population into reproductive condition at the same time. First there is an internal physiological rhythm with an approximate periodicity of one or more years. It has been repeatedly demonstrated that this internal rhythm by itself cannot indefinitely maintain a regular periodicity of birth seasons but must be triggered and synchronized by stimuli external to the animals (Amoroso and Marshall 1960; Bullough 1961). These external stimuli, which determine the actual time of mating, are apparently some combination of environmental variables such as amount of sunlight or ultraviolet light, relative humidity, temperature, or other factors that exhibit a seasonal rhythm. It is not surprising then that, in an environment such as the laboratory in which there are no pronounced seasonal variations in these stimuli, mating seasons should be absent or greatly attenuated. Research on causative factors in primate reproductive cycles is just beginning (see Koford, Chap. 5, this volume). A preliminary attempt is made later in this chapter to find climatic correlates for the patterns exhibited by the populations of the present sample.

## DEFINITION OF TERMS

Contradictory meanings have often been applied to elementary concepts in the study of reproductive cycles. The term "breeding season," for ex-

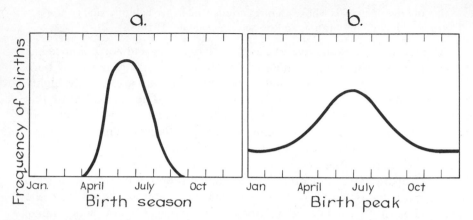

Fig. 14–1. A diagrammatic comparison of a *birth season*. a. *(Left)* The discrete period to which all births are confined. b. *(Right)* A *birth peak*, the period in which most births occur.

ample, may mean the season of copulation to one worker (e.g., Bullough 1961); it may mean the season of births to another (e.g., Zuckerman 1953); or it may be applied only to species in which both activities coincide in the same season (Moreau 1950). Below are listed our working definitions of four concepts important in a discussion of reproductive cycles in nonhuman primates:

*Annual reproductive cycle.* The seasonal distribution of copulations, conceptions, and births in a population.

*Mating season.* A distinct period of the year to which fertile copulations are confined. By definition, the result of a mating season is a birth season, but not all birth seasons need be caused by restricted periods of copulations (after Bullough 1961).

*Birth season.* A discrete period of the year to which all births are confined. There must be some months in which no births occur (see Fig. 14–1*a*).

*Birth peak.* The period of the year in which a high proportion of births but not all births are concentrated (see Fig. 14–1*b*).

## METHODOLOGICAL CONSIDERATIONS

Not enough attention has been paid to the actual evaluation of reproductive data collected by various means and under differing circumstances. For instance, the birth statistics from a monkey colony housed in a laboratory or zoo have little bearing on the problem of understanding the ecological relationships of a species of monkey or ape with the environment in which it has evolved. This is part of a general problem faced by workers in relating field to laboratory studies and is discussed in the introduction to this volume. In evaluating data on seasonality of births it is particularly crucial to keep this problem in mind. Any change in the relationship between an animal and its environment, such as removal from its natural habitat, change or supplement of its usual diet, or restriction of its movement may profoundly affect its normal rhythm, and reproductive data from such animals must therefore be regarded with caution.

In collecting field data on reproductive cycles there are two things to look for: (1) the seasonal distribution of copulations (and in some species, the associated changes in sexual skin), and (2) the seasonal distribution of births. The former are the more difficult data to collect, requiring continuous daily observations of groups and careful counting of the numbers of copulations. In addition, it is not always possible to distinguish true copulation with ejaculation from other forms of mounting behavior (Koford, personal communication). Censuses of newborn infants, on the other hand, are less subject to observational and sampling errors than are counts of copulations, and the dates of births of young infants may be established days or weeks after the event. Ideally, data on reproductive cycles should meet the following criteria:

1. The observations should be on free-ranging populations, in their natural habitat, subsisting on natural foods.

2. The observations should be long-term and continuous, covering at least a full year and preferably several years. In lieu of continuous observation, probably the most accurate data are derived from careful counts, made at different times of the year, of the relative numbers of females with young infants.

3. The estimated birth dates of young infants should be as accurate as possible, preferably within a few weeks of the date of birth. Because of a change in coat color that occurs in many species of monkey during the first year of life, it is relatively easy to distinguish younger from older infants. Such a color change occurs in bonnet macaques at the age of two months, in baboons between four and six months, and in the langurs between three and five months of age.

4. The larger the population observed the better, since the comparatively slow reproductive rate of primates in combination with a small sample can yield atypical distributions of births or fail to show significant seasonal differences where they may actually exist. The sample should be large enough to show the relative frequency of births throughout the entire year.

Evidence derived from the examination of the uteri of collected specimens, a technique commonly used in the past (Zuckerman 1931; Haddow 1952), should be regarded with extreme caution because of the possibility of sampling error in shooting. An adequate picture of the annual cycle requires collecting specimens throughout the year. Shooting causes a disruption of normal activities and a permanent alteration in the composition of the breeding population resulting from the removal of females. In addi-

**TABLE 14-1. RECENT PRIMATE FIELD STUDIES YIELDING REPRODUCTIVE INFORMATION**

| Species and Source | Location | Habitat | Forage | Sample Size | No. of Groups | Study Period | Accuracy of Dating |
|---|---|---|---|---|---|---|---|
| Japanese Macaque (Mizuhara) | Takasakiyama, Japan | natural | supplemented | 750 | 1 | 6 years 1956–1962 | ±5 days |
| Rhesus Macaque (Koford) | Cayo Santiago, Puerto Rico | artificial | supplemented | 426 | 5 | 3 years Jan. 1960 to Jan. 1963 | ±1 day (Diet and habitat not natural. Crowded.) |
| Rhesus Macaque (Southwick, Beg, and Siddiqi) | Uttar Pradesh, north-central India | natural but varied | natural and crops | 7000 | 400 | 9 months Sept. 1959 to June 1960 | ±30 days (Observations over wide geographic area in a population survey.) |
| Bonnet Macaque (Simonds) | Gundlupet Taluk, Mysore State, India | natural | natural and crops | 66 | 1 | 6 months Sept. 1961 to Jan. 1962. Apr., May 1962 | ±1 day in 2 cases ±30 days in rest |
| Indian Langur (Jay) | Abujhmar Hills, Madhya Pradesh, central India | natural | natural | 56 | 3 | 1 year Nov. 1958 to Nov. 1959 | ±30 days. (Observation conditions poor.) |
| | Raipur-Nagpur Road, Madhya Pradesh, central India | natural | natural and crops | 146 | 6 | | ±30 days (Counts made on trips in Nov. and Dec. 1959; Feb., Mar., April 1960.) |
| | Lucknow District, Uttar Pradesh, India | natural | natural and crops | 54 | 1 | 4 months Dec. 1959 to April 1960 | ±5 days |

| | | | | | | | | |
|---|---|---|---|---|---|---|---|---|
| Baboon (Kummer) | Ethiopia | natural | natural | 1350 | 6 | 9 months | Feb. 1961 to Nov. 1961 | ±30 days (Regular counts of females with dark infants.) |
| Kenya Baboon (DeVore) | Nairobi Park, Kenya | natural | natural | 140 | 4 | 10 months | March 1959 to Jan. 1960 | ±30 days (Direct observation of newborns and estimation of birthdates of young.) |
| (Washburn) | Amboseli Reserve, Kenya | natural | natural | 440 | 5 | 2 months | Sept. 1959 to Oct. 1959 | ±5 days (Regular counts of dark infants.) |
| Chacma Baboon (Hall) | Cape Peninsula, Union of South Africa | natural | natural | 135 | 3 | 1 year + | Apr. 1958 to Apr. 1959, Aug. 1960 & 1961 | ±30 days (Observation of dark-phase infants.) |
| Mountain Gorilla (Schaller) | Virunga Volcanoes, Eastern Congo | natural | natural | 190 | 3 | 13 months | Aug. 1959 to Sept. 1960 | ±30 days (Direct observation of newborns, estimate of birthdates of young animals.) |
| Chimpanzee (V. and F. Reynolds) | Budongo Forest, Uganda | natural | natural | c.200 | * | 9 months | Mar. 1962 to Nov. 1962 | |
| Chimpanzee (Goodall) | Gombe Stream Reserve, Tanganyika | natural | natural | c.60 –80 | * | 28 months | July 1960 to Dec. 1961; Aug. 1962 to Jan. 1963; April to Oct. 1963 | |

* Concept of group does not apply to chimpanzee.

tion, the collection of specimens is incompatible with successful behavioral observations of free-ranging primates (see Appendix on field procedures, this volume).

These strictures need emphasis because of the uncritical use that has been made in the past of fragmentary and anecdotal observations. Unfortunately there are no studies at this time satisfying all the criteria listed above. However, there are several field studies that approach these requirements, and these are summarized in Table 14–1. We have generally limited ourselves to data derived from these studies in our discussion of the annual reproductive cycle.

## THE SAMPLE POPULATIONS

The data that best satisfy these criteria come from a group of Japanese macaques living on the small, steep mountain of Takasakiyama on the northeast coast of Kyushu, Japan (Mizuhara, unpublished). Although Takasakiyama represents the natural habitat of these monkeys, their normal diet is supplemented by a variety of foods introduced by man. The birth dates of 545 infants born over a period of six years (1956–1962) have been recorded.

The only other set of long-term observations has been made on a colony of rhesus macaques on Cayo Santiago, an island off the southeast coast of Puerto Rico (Koford, Chap. 5, this volume). For the period January 1960 to January 1963, 237 births were recorded. Although this population is far from its natural habitat (northern India) and is maintained on artificial as well as natural foods, it has been established on the island for more than 25 years and the immediate causes of seasonal timing of reproductive behavior can be attributed to stimuli from the environment in which the animals are presently living.

Data on the rhesus macaque in India are derived from surveys of more than 400 groups in northern India by Southwick, Beg, and Siddiqi (1961b, Chap. 4, this volume), with supplementary data from Prakash (1958, 1960). Southwick and his co-workers counted more than 3000 adult females during the nine-month study period. A total of 144 of these were seen with infants judged to be less than one month old, and an additional 73 were counted with infants less than ten days old. Although this area represents part of the natural distribution of the rhesus, the groups observed were living in a wide variety of ecological settings, ranging from forests to railway stations and temples.

Simonds (Chap. 6, this volume) has studied another species of Indian macaque, the bonnet macaque, in Mysore State, India. His observations on one group of 66 animals covered a period from September 1961 to June 1962. He observed ten newborns in this group and supplemented these data by observations on neighboring groups. Most of the macaques that he studied were living along roads near cultivated fields and at least 40 percent of their diet came from crops.

Jay (Chap. 7, this volume) has collected birth data on langurs from three localities in central and northern India. She observed the presence of young infants in three groups of langurs in the Abujhmar Hills of Madhya Pradesh over a period of a year. During a series of trips from Raipur to Nagpur in central India, she noted seasonal variations in the number of young infants present in six langur groups along the roadside. Near Lucknow in Uttar Pradesh she recorded several births in four months of continuous observation of one group of 54 langurs and estimated the birth dates of all infants in the group from a careful analysis of physical and behavioral differences.

The African baboons have been studied by Kummer and Kurt near Erer-Gota, Ethiopia; by DeVore in Nairobi Park, Kenya; by Washburn in Amboseli Reserve, Kenya; and by Hall in the Cape of Good Hope Reserve, South Africa (Kummer, personal communication; DeVore and Hall, Chap. 2, this volume; Washburn, personal communication; Hall 1962b). The lengths of the study periods are shown in Table 14–1. Some births and newborns were recorded in all four localities, but no data are available for the total number of births in a specific population for a full year.

Data on African apes come from three recent field studies. In 13 months of continuous observations of a mountain gorilla population, Schaller (1963; Chap. 10, this volume) recorded 13 newborn infants for the period from August 1959 to April 1960, and estimated the birth dates of another 41 infants in his study area. V. Reynolds and F. Reynolds (Chap. 11, this volume) spent eight months in continuous observation of a population of more than 200 chimpanzees from March to November 1962 in the Budongo Forest of Uganda. Goodall (Chap. 12, this volume) studied the chimpanzee population of the Gombe Stream Reserve, Tanganyika, for more than 28 months between July 1960 and October 1963. The birth dates of individuals have not been reported in these chimpanzee studies.

New-World monkeys and prosimians are not considered in this review. For the one intensively studied species of New-World monkey, the howling monkeys of Barro Colorado Island (Carpenter, Chap. 9, this volume), there is abundant census material, but this was collected in a series of field studies covering periods of great population fluctuation. Therefore, seasonal differences in the presence of young infants have reflected population growth or loss in addition to that related to an annual cycle. Petter (1962) has completed a long-term investigation of prosimian reproductive cycles; however, the data are based largely on small samples of a number of species.

Our criteria are not completely satisfied by any of these recent field studies. With the exception of the Japanese macaques of Takasakiyama and the rhesus on Cayo Santiago, all the studies were made on free-ranging populations in their natural environment, subsisting on natural foods or natural foods supplemented by crops. However, the only long-term, continuous observations are on two artificially maintained colonies and on the

Tanganyika chimpanzee population where the sample size is small in view of the relatively slow reproductive rate of the great apes. The only other studies with large enough samples for any variations to have statistical significance (Southwick *et al.*, and Washburn) did not cover a whole year in the field. In view of these disparities the reader may generally place more confidence in the conclusions derived from the long-term and/or large sample studies, whereas conclusions from the remaining studies should be thought of only as indicating the most likely interpretation.

TABLE 14–2. SEASONAL INCIDENCE OF MATING AND BIRTHS
IN THE SAMPLE POPULATIONS*

| Species and Source | Number of Births and New-borns | Mating | Births |
|---|---|---|---|
| Japanese Macaque (Mizuhara) | 545 | Copulations restricted to season from Oct. to April. Peak frequency in Jan. and Feb. | 99% of births during May to Sept. 1% April and Oct. No births ever reported mid-Oct. to mid-April. |
| Rhesus Macaque (Koford) | 237 | Copulations restricted to distinct period beginning in July and ending in Jan. | Most births restricted to period from Jan. to June, 75% in March and April. No births Aug. to Jan. (1 on Dec. 29). |
| Rhesus Macaque (Southwick, Beg, and Siddiqi) | 217 | Copulations observed in all months of study except March. Greatest frequency of sexual behavior from Oct. to Dec. | Births and young observed March to June and a few in Sept. From Nov. to March observed 2092 females, none with newborn infants. |
| Bonnet Macaque (Simonds) | 10+ | Copulations observed throughout year. Peak observed in Oct. and Nov. Probably high in Sept. as well. | Births occur mainly from late Jan. to late April. A few in June and July. No dark-phase infants observed Sept. to mid-Jan. |
| Indian Langur (Jay) Abujhmar Hills | 6 | Copulations rarely observed. | No seasonal clustering of births noted. |
| Raipur-Nagpur Road | 33 | | A few births Jan. to March, many newborns in April. No newborns in Nov. or Dec. |
| Lucknow District | 10 | Copulations observed in all 4 months of study (Dec. to April). | Births and newborn infants observed in March and April. |

TABLE 14–2. SEASONAL INCIDENCE OF MATING AND BIRTHS
IN THE SAMPLE POPULATIONS—*Continued*

| Species and Source | Number of Births and New-borns | Mating | Births |
|---|---|---|---|
| Hamadryas Baboon (Kummer) | | Copulations observed throughout observation period (Feb. to Nov.). Sharp increase of swelling in females and of copulations in May, peak in June. | Births observed throughout study. Greatest number of dark infants from May to Aug. |
| Kenya Baboon (DeVore) | 11 | Copulations noted all months of study but fewer in Sept. to Dec. | Observed 1 birth from March to Sept. 10 births Sept. to Jan. |
| (Washburn) | 80 | A few copulations observed each day of study. | Counted twice as many newborn infants in Oct. as in Sept. |
| Chacma Baboon (Hall) | | Copulations noted all months of year. March and April frequency more than twice that of Sept. to Nov. | No clustering of births noted. |
| Mountain Gorilla (Schaller) | 54 | Copulation rarely observed. | Births observed throughout year. |
| Chimpanzee (V. Reynolds and F. Reynolds) | | Copulations rarely observed. | Mothers and young observed in all months of study. |
| Chimpanzee (Goodall) | | Copulations observed almost daily in Sept., Oct., and rarely in other months. Females with sexual swelling observed at all times of the year. | Small infants observed in April, June, Sept., and Oct. |

* See also Chap. 9, p. 311 — ed.

## THE ANNUAL REPRODUCTIVE CYCLE

The seasonal incidence of mating and birth in the 14 sample populations is summarized in Table 14–2. The data most satisfactory in reliability and clarity come from studies of the macaque: the two long-term observations of colonies, a population survey and three field studies in India, and also supplementary data from a laboratory colony (Hartman 1931). This material is drawn from three species of macaque (Japanese, rhesus, and bonnet) in a variety of ecological settings. Consequently the occurrence of a birth season in different macaque groups seems well documented.

This is the first publication of the birth data from Takasakiyama (Mizuhara, personal communication), and therefore we present this material

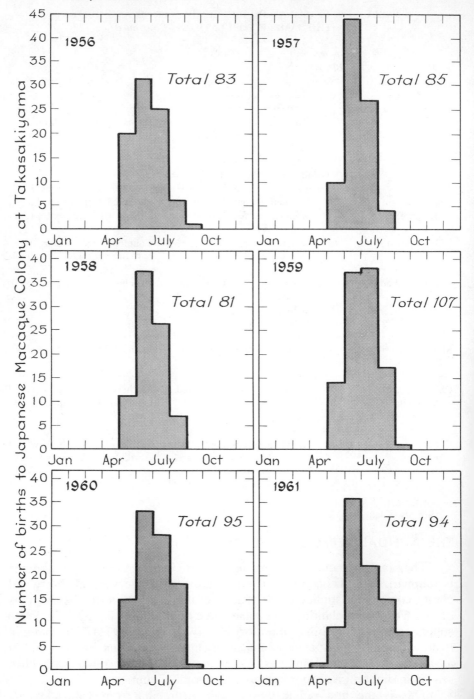

Fig. 14—2. The monthly distribution of live births to the Japanese macaques of Takasakiyama, 1956 to 1962 (Mizuhara, personal communication).

in some detail. The Japanese macaques of Takasakiyama have a discrete birth season, beginning in early May and ending in September, with the highest frequency of births in June and July (see Fig. 14–2). The actual totals by months for the period 1956–1961 are as follows: April, 1; May, 79; June, 218; July, 166; August, 67; September, 11; October, 3. No births have been recorded from mid-October to mid-April. The dates of the earliest and latest births and the lengths of the birth season by years are presented in the following table.

TABLE 14–3. TIMING AND DURATION OF BIRTH SEASON OF
JAPANESE MACAQUES AT TAKASAKIYAMA 1956–1961*

| Year | Date of First Birth | Date of Last Birth | Length of Birth Season in Days** | Total Number of Births |
|------|------------|-----------|-------------------|-------------|
| 1956 | May 7 | Sept. 8 | 123 | 83 |
| 1957 | May 10 | Aug. 14 | 95 | 85 |
| 1958 | May 11 | Aug. 15 | 95 | 81 |
| 1959 | May 5 | Sept. 13 | 130 | 107 |
| 1960 | May 3 | Sept. 14 | 133 | 95 |
| 1961 | April 20 | Oct. 14 | 176 | 94 |
| Total births | | | | 545 |

* After Mizuhara (personal communication).
** Average length of birth season, 125 days.

For the period 1956–1960 the onset of the birth season and date of the median birth showed a strikingly narrow range in time. The range for the former was May 3–May 11, and for the latter June 20–July 5. For the same period the mean length of the birth season was 115 days. This suggests that the last conception of the year would have occurred at least one month prior to the first birth, given a gestation period of 150–165 days, which has been reported for this species (Mizuhara, personal communication).

Matings are also restricted to a distinct season of the year. At Takasakiyama, Imanishi reports that the highest frequency of copulation occurs from November to March, with some copulations in October and April. He adds that during the birth season "males can never be found mounting females in Takasakiyama" (1960:395). The mating period is associated with a reddening of the face and genital regions of both males and females. Females that are neither pregnant nor lactating are reported to maintain a regular menstrual cycle throughout the year.

Kawai has assembled data from two to six years of birth seasons of eleven additional groups of Japanese macaques (Mizuhara, unpublished). Table 14–4 emphasizes the brevity and discreteness of the birth season in these monkey populations in a variety of habitats. The modal length of the birth season is three months, and throughout Japan births rarely occur between September and February. There are regional variations in timing; the groups on Honshu Island tend to have earlier birth seasons than the groups on Kyushu Island. There is also some suggestion that larger groups have longer birth seasons than small groups.

TABLE 14–4. THE BIRTH SEASONS IN 11 GROUPS OF
JAPANESE MACAQUES (AFTER KAWAI 1962)

| Troop Name and Location | Births (percent) | *Period of Year in Which More Than 95 Percent of Births Occur* Season | Length of Season (months) |
|---|---|---|---|
| Coastal Honshu and adjacent islands | | | |
| Takao-yama | 100 | March through June | 4 |
| Shodoshima K | 100 | March through June | 4 |
| Shodoshima T | 96 | March through May | 3 |
| Takago-yama | 100 | April through July | 4 |
| Okinoshima | 98 | April through June | 3 |
| Honshu: mountainous regions | | | |
| Taishakukyo | 97 | April through June | 3 |
| Arashi-yama | 96 | May through June | 2 |
| Kochi | 96 | May through July | 3 |
| Minoo A | 96 | May through June | 2 |
| Kyushu Island | | | |
| Toino-misaki | 97 | June through August | 3 |
| Koshima | 95 | June through August | 3 |

Koford's observations (Chap. 5, this volume) demonstrate the existence among rhesus macaques on Cayo Santiago of discrete mating and birth seasons. The birth period begins in January and extends through May, with the highest frequency of births in March and April. Occasional births have been reported in June and July (from 2 to 4 percent), but none for the period from August to late December. Koford reports that mountings with ejaculation also occur in a distinct season associated with reddening of sexual skin of males and females and that females do not come into estrus until the end of the birth season.

Observations on rhesus macaques in India by Southwick, Beg, and Siddiqi (1961b; Chap. 4, this volume) and by Prakash (1958, 1960) demonstrate that a birth season also occurs when rhesus are in their natural habitat. Southwick and his co-workers observed a total of 217 newborn in many different groups. Births were dated mainly to March, April, and May, with

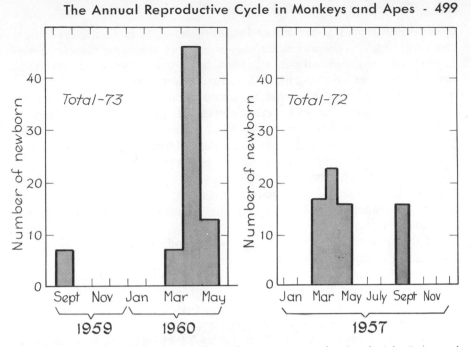

Fig. 14–3a. (*Left*) Observations of newborn macaques by Southwick, Beg, and Siddiqi in their survey of Uttar Pradesh, India, September 1959 to June 1960. b. (*Right*) The number of newborn macaques observed by Prakash in three groups in Rajasthan, India, from March through December 1957.

a few in September, but none in the remainder of the study period (see Fig. 14–3a). During the period from November to March 2092 adult females were counted and none had newborn infants. Southwick and Beg (1961) report that mounting behavior was seen in all months of the year except March but that consort associations and an increased frequency of copulations occurred from October to December.

Unfortunately the study period of the survey by Southwick and his co-workers did not extend into June, July, and August, so that the scattering of births in September might be interpreted as either a minor, but distinct, secondary birth season or the tail end of a birth season that extends from March to October. Observations by Prakash (1958, 1960) on three very large rhesus groups near Jaipur in Rajasthan suggest that two separate seasons may in fact occur in the rhesus of northern India (see Fig. 14–3b). Prakash noted a total of 72 newborn infants during a nine-month study period from March to December 1957. These births were concentrated in two periods—the first with 56 births from March to June and the second with 16 births around the beginning of October.

Simonds observed one group of 66 bonnet macaques in southern India from September 1961 to January 1962 and again later in the same year from April to June (Chap. 6, this volume). Ten young were born in this group in 1962: two at the end of January, and eight in February, March, and early April. This somewhat earlier start of the birth season in late January or early February in southern India has also been observed in bonnet macaques and langurs of Mysore State by members of the Japan Monkey Center (Jay, personal communication). No dark-phase infants (under two months of age) were observed in this or any other bonnet macaque group from September to mid-January. The young infants that Simonds noted when he first came to the field in September led him to believe that there may have been a few births in June and July. Simonds reported copulations throughout the study, but a higher frequency in the fall months from September through November. The bonnet macaque data are not incompatible with a discrete birth season but may reflect only a peak in births.

The data gathered on rhesus macaques in India by Southwick *et al.*, and by Prakash indicate a major birth season for several months just preceding the monsoon season as well as a possible secondary birth season for a few weeks immediately after the monsoons. Southwick's observations of more than 2000 females without young infants during the period from November to March conclusively demonstrate that the birth season for these macaques in their natural habitat is just as distinct as those observed in the colonies of Takasakiyama and Cayo Santiago (see Figs. 14–2 and 14–3*a* & *b*).

Supplementary evidence as to the possible cause of this infertile period comes from work done by Hartman (1931) on an outdoor laboratory colony of rhesus kept in Baltimore. Hartman noted that of 38 conceptions over a period of one year, only one occurred in the summer whereas more than 70 percent occurred between October and January, with the remainder scattered throughout the spring. Most females did not come into estrus and show reddening of the genital area during the summer months although their menstrual cycles were regular. Laparotomies demonstrated cessation of ovulation during the summer. Although some motile sperm were found in the males during the summer, Hartman noted a definite decrease in sexual activity.

Additional evidence suggestive of the physiological correlates for this reproductive cycle in rhesus has recently been gathered by Sade (in press). His observations on the seasonal cycle in size of testes in 86 rhesus males and in brightness of sexual skin in 43 males were made on Cayo Santiago during the period from August 1960 to June 1962. He found that "testes are large during the season in which copulations are observed, and are small during the season in which young are born." He suggests there is an increase in spermatogenesis correlated with a reddening of the sexual skin two months before mating begins and "the color of the sex skin of the males is brightest during the season of large testes." He concludes that "implicit assumptions that male monkeys are sexually receptive uniformly throughout the year should be re-examined." The Hartman and Sade data indicate that both male and female rhesus macaques may experience a long period of greatly lowered fertility that coincides with a period of sexual inactivity during the annual cycle.

Jay (Chap. 7, this volume) has collected data on births in groups of North Indian langurs. In the Lucknow district of Uttar Pradesh, the same general area in which Southwick *et al.* surveyed the rhesus macaque population, Jay observed one group of 54 langurs in December of 1959 and in the first three months of 1960. In December she judged the youngest animal in this group to be five months old on the basis of its size, coat color, and behavior. She saw copulations throughout the study period but births did not occur until March and April. Jay also surveyed six roadside groups of about 150 langurs during a series of trips along the Raipur-Nagpur road in Madhya Pradesh. No dark-phase infants were seen during trips in November and December; in February and March a few were observed; and, in April, 28 brown infants and 5 just beginning to turn light were counted.

In a third area of India, the forests of the Abujhmar Hills in Madhya Pradesh, Jay observed births in January and August in three groups of langurs. She also observed some two dozen newborn in neighboring langur groups but did not note any seasonal clustering of births. Jay's data indicate variation in the reproductive cycles between different populations of the Indian langur, ranging from no pronounced seasonal birth peak in one area (Abujhmar Hills) to a marked March-April peak in two others (Lucknow and the Raipur-Nagpur road). The data are not sufficient to say whether the observed clustering reflects a birth peak or a birth season, although a discrete season is suggested by the Raipur-Nagpur road observations. The close seasonal correspondence between the birth peak of North Indian langurs and that of macaques in the same area will be considered later in this chapter.

The African baboon is the only monkey other than the macaque and the langur on which pertinent field data have been gathered. The geographical distribution and range of habitats of the baboon are almost as extensive and varied as those of the macaque. The hamadryas baboons of Ethiopia were studied by Hans Kummer and Fred Kurt from February to November 1961. Although newborn infants were seen in all months of the study, the greatest number of dark-phase infants were observed from May to August (Kummer, personal communication). Copulations were also noted in all months; however, a sharp increase in the swelling of sexual skin in females and in the frequency of copulations began in May with a peak frequency in June.

Baboons in Kenya have been observed by DeVore for a period of ten months and by Washburn for six months. At Nairobi Park DeVore estimates that almost all births occurred between September and February (DeVore 1963). In four groups of 140 animals observed closely, DeVore counted only one birth between March and September (June 1) and ten births from September to January.

Washburn (personal communication), in a survey of 1203 baboons during September and October, counted 80 newborn infants. Five groups totaling 440 animals were counted several times, at least once in each month of the study. In September about 9 percent of the adult females in these groups had black infants. The same groups recounted in October showed 24 percent of the females with very small black infants. This increase in births is illustrated by one group of 171 which was recounted on five different occasions. Successive counts showed 4, 5, 9, 11, and 16 of the females with newborn infants. In other words, over 20 percent of the females in the group had given birth in this period of six weeks. Furthermore, Washburn noted many females in late pregnancy at the time the survey ended. Washburn has noted (personal communication) a high rate of infant mortality in the Amboseli groups observed, and it is probable that the actual birth rate during this period was higher than the percentages given above suggest.

Material gathered by Hall (1962b) on the chacma baboon at the southern tip of Africa indicates an even distribution of births throughout the year. He noted the presence of young infants in the Cape of Good Hope groups in all months, with no obvious clustering of births. He did observe over twice as many copulations per observation hour in March and April (0.8 per observation hour) as in the months from September to November (0.3 per observation hour).

This evidence from field studies of baboons in four different areas indicates a peak of births at two localities in Kenya and an apparent lack of birth clustering in the Cape of Good Hope. The hamadryas baboons in Ethiopia show a birth peak that coincides with a peak in frequency of copulations. All of the four field studies report the occurrence of mating in months when births were observed. Apparently there is no season during which almost all male and female baboons are unable to reproduce, and this is in contrast to the situation in the closely related macaque group.

Some evidence relating to birth seasons in the redtail monkey of Uganda (*Cercopithecus ascanius*) has been presented by Haddow (1952: 361–368). This is based on anatomical examinations of 52 female specimens. He found the greatest number of late-term fetuses in the specimens collected from May to August. The data underline the need for careful censuses and observations of undisturbed populations of the *Cercopithecus* group.

Three recent field studies of African apes indicate that births occur throughout the year in two populations but that in a third population a birth season may be present. Schaller (1963, Chap. 10, this volume) observed 13 newborn and estimated the birth dates of another 41 infants in a mountain gorilla population of 200 in the Virunga Volcanoes. His records show a slight increase in births during the second half of the year, but no months when births did not occur. Copulations were observed only twice.

The Budongo Forest chimpanzee population, studied by V. Reynolds and F. Reynolds (Chap. 11, this volume), showed a similar pattern. Although the birth dates of infants were not determined, the Reynoldses saw mothers with young throughout the study period and found no seasonal differences in observations of females who were pregnant or in estrus. Copulations were observed on four occasions (in March, April, June, and October).

Goodall's three-year study of chimpanzees in the Gombe Stream Reserve, Tanganyika, included only 16 adult females, too small a sample for data on seasonality of births to have statistical significance, especially since a female chimpanzee only gives birth every three years or so. Goodall has observed newborn infants in April, June, September, and October. She has seen estrous females throughout the year, which would indicate that some mating occurs in all months. However, during the first months of the rainy season (September-November) the chimpanzees collect in larger groups than usual and copulations are seen almost daily.

When compared with that of the Old-World monkeys, the reproduction of the African apes is characterized by a much slower birth rate. Field observations of copulations of apes and of arboreal monkeys have been few in comparison to such observations of terrestrial monkeys. These two factors, when combined with a small breeding population, make generalizations about seasonal differences in births or mating difficult. Aside from the copulation cluster observed among the Tanganyika chimpanzees, there is no evidence yet for a birth season in apes, although it is possible that birth peaks may occur in an attenuated form that would be difficult to observe.

## CLIMATIC CORRELATIONS

In the analysis of data on birth seasonality, the distinction between proximate and ultimate causation first suggested by Baker (1938) has proved useful. The proximate causes are the mechanisms by which a mating season is maintained, including the internal reproductive cycle and the stimuli from the environment that bring individuals into reproductive condition at the same time. The ultimate causes reflect the adaptive significance of birth seasonality to the species.

In studying the reproductive cycles of other animals, zoologists have sought a relationship between the timing of births in the annual cycle and the most favorable season for the survival of young. Natural selection is said to favor populations in which births occur in the optimum period and to act as a check on the reproductive success of individuals giving birth outside the optimum period. The precise evolutionary significance of a birth season to a primate population is not as immediately obvious as might be expected. Although it is predictable that a species will time its births to take advantage of optimum periods in the environment, exactly when this period will come in relation to the reproductive cycle is not so obvious. In monkeys and apes the length of gestation varies from five to eight months depending on the species. Lactation also varies from about six months in the Japanese macaque to well over a year in the baboon and great apes. If there is only one part of the year that is favorable, such as spring and early summer in the temperate climates, then each species must make an evolutionary choice, so to speak, as to which parts of the reproductive cycle — conception, gestation, birth, lactation, or weaning — must be protected and which can come in the less favorable times of the year. The rhesus and langur monkeys of northern India give birth during the time of the year when the temperatures are hottest and when wells and tanks are often dry. However, gestation and the later months of lactation come during the monsoon season when food and water are abundant. In contrast, the East African baboons give birth at the beginning of the small rains, and gestation and the later part of lactation occur during the six-month dry season. Whether any pattern of relationship will be found to hold true for other species of primates is still not clear. It may be that a wide variety of patterns have evolved depending on the lengths of gestation and lactation and the particular ecological complex in which each species or even subspecies lives.

The study of proximate causation can be based on firmer ground. Members of a population respond to a complex of environmental factors that bring them into reproductive condition at the same time. In species in which the birth season is well defined, such as the Japanese macaque, it is evident that the climatic conditions prevailing in the preceding months are important in the triggering of conceptions. If the timing and frequency of conceptions vary from year to year within the same population, it can be postulated that the differences are due to variations in stimuli from the immediate environment. If the timing of conceptions consistently varies from locality to locality within a single species, it can again be postulated that the differences are most likely caused by environmental variations, but the distinction between proximate and ultimate causation here is less clear. In the latter situation environmental stimuli may act directly on various subspecies and thus may be the proximate causes of the birth season or they may act only indirectly as the selective agents for slight genetic differences in threshold levels or sensitivity to environmental stimuli. These distinctions can be defined only under the controlled conditions of the laboratory, but the kinds of variations that occur under natural conditions are indicative of what may be the significant relationships between reproductive and climatic cycles.

The reproductive data on the Japanese macaque will illustrate the variations to be found between different groups of the same species. The climate of Japan is generally mild and precipitation is high. Winters are cool and November through February are the driest months of the year. April through October are the wettest months and the summer temperatures reach a peak in August (see Fig. 14–4). Within this general climatic pattern there is considerable variation both in precipitation and in temperature levels in different regions of Japan. The month in which conceptions begin in four populations of Japanese macaque is set out in the second column of

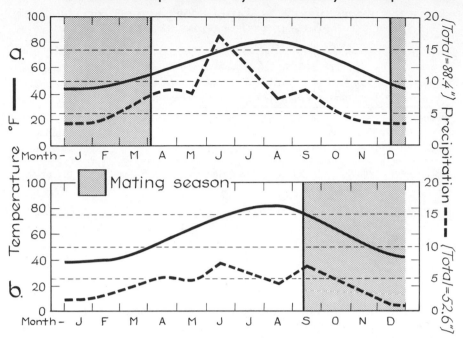

Fig. 14–4. The mating season in two populations of Japanese macaque in relation to average mean temperature and average monthly precipitation. *a.* Mating
season of Japanese macaques at Toino-misaki and Koshima (Kyushu) (1956–1961)
with climatic data from Kagoshima averages. *b.* Mating season of Japanese macaques of Shodoshima K and T (Honshu) (1958–1961) with climatic data from
Osaka averages.

Table 14–5. The last four columns show the trends in day length, temperature, rainfall, and food supply for the *two months preceding* the onset of
conceptions at each of the four localities. For instance, at Shodoshima,
where conceptions begin in mid-September, day length is decreasing; the
temperature is just dropping from the summer highs; the level of rainfall
is steady but high. At Takago-yama, where conceptions begin one month
later, the situation is similar except for a sharper drop in temperature and
slight increase in rainfall which comes with the very end of the rainy season.
At the more southerly localities, Takasakiyama and Koshima and Toino-
misaki, conceptions do not begin until mid-November and mid-December
respectively. These localities show similar trends in temperature and day
length (both decreasing), but differ from the more northerly areas in rainfall
(declining). The onset of conceptions in all four localities is associated with
the fall fruiting season, which is a period of abundant food supply. Itani
(1956) reports that at Takasakiyama food is most plentiful in the months
of May and June and again later in the year in September and October. The
summer months are hot and humid and the food supply is poor.

TABLE 14–5. ENVIRONMENTAL CONDITIONS FOR 2 MONTHS PRECEDING THE ONSET OF CONCEPTIONS IN 4 POPULATIONS OF JAPANESE MACAQUES

| Area | Date of Onset of Conceptions | Latitude | Trends in Day Length | Trends in Mean Temperature | Trends in Monthly Rainfall | Seasonal State of Food Supply |
|---|---|---|---|---|---|---|
| Shodoshima | mid-September | 34° N. | decreasing | down 5° F. | steady | beginning of fruiting season |
| Takago-yama | mid-October | 35° N. | decreasing | down 17° F. | up 2 in. | fruiting season |
| Takasakiyama | mid-November | 33° N. | decreasing | down 21° F. | down 5 in. | fruiting season |
| Koshima & Toino-misaki | mid-December | 31° N. | decreasing | down 21° F. | down 2 in. | end of fruiting season |

The features common to the period preceding the onset of conceptions are decreasing day length, falling temperature, and the timing of the onset at the end of the wettest half of the year, the time when food is abundant. Experimental manipulation of these variables may prove fruitful in isolating the threshold levels and triggering mechanisms of reproductive cycles in Japanese macaques. However, local differences in temperature and day length do not appear to be of sufficient magnitude to explain the fact that macaque populations on Honshu Island come into reproductive condition from two to four months earlier than do the populations on Kyushu (see

TABLE 14–6. ENVIRONMENTAL CONDITIONS FOR 2 MONTHS PRECEDING THE ONSET OF CONCEPTIONS IN MONKEY POPULATIONS IN 3 AREAS OF INDIA

| Area | Date of Onset of Conceptions | Latitude | Trends in Day Length | Trends in Mean Temperature | Trends in Monthly Rainfall | Seasonal State of Food Supply |
|---|---|---|---|---|---|---|
| NORTH INDIA (rhesus and langurs) | mid-September | 24°–31° N. | decreasing | down 8° F. | up 8 in. | growing season |
| CENTRAL INDIA (langurs) | August | 23° N. | decreasing | down 10° F. | up 15 in. | growing season |
| SOUTH INDIA (bonnet and langurs) | mid-July | 11° N. | decreasing | down 7° F. | up 4 in. | growing season |

Fig. 14–4). There are only four degrees difference in latitude between the most northerly (35° N.) and the most southerly (31° N.) population in the sample, and variation in day length is negligible. In the mating populations at Shodoshima, conceptions begin in September when mean monthly temperatures are high (75° F.), whereas in the south, at Takasakiyama, mating does not begin until the mean temperature has dropped to 50°F. Social factors such as group size and group structure may also play a part (see Koford, Chap. 5, this volume), but the influence of these and of genetic variables can only be determined through careful experimentation.

The climatic trends associated with the onset of conceptions in Indian macaques and langurs are shown in Table 14–6. In northern India conceptions begin in mid-September, during a period of decreasing day length, high rainfall, declining temperatures, and abundant food supply. In central and southern India conceptions begin about two months earlier, in mid-July; day length and temperature are decreasing, rainfall and food supply increasing (see Fig. 14–5). Like those in Japan, monkeys in India appear to conceive in the second half of the year during or after a peak in rainfall

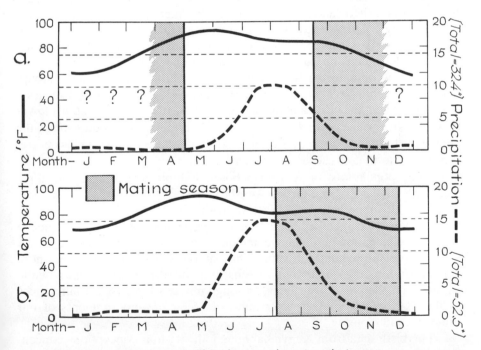

Fig. 14–5. The mating season of Indian monkeys in relation to average mean temperature and average monthly precipitation. *a*. The major mating season of rhesus macaques and Indian langurs in northern India (1960), with climatic data from Kanpur averages. *b*. The mating season of Indian langurs, Raipur-Nagpur Road, central India (1959), with climatic data from Raipur averages.

and during the annual decline in temperature. In India there is no single macaque or langur reproductive pattern but rather one pattern for each geographical region. In northern India, where the monsoon season begins later than in central and southern India, both macaque and langur groups begin to conceive about two months later than do similar groups to the south. This north-south difference in India is the reverse of the situation in Japan where northern groups mate *before* southern groups. Thus within a single genus, *Macaca*, there is no simple correlation of the onset of conceptions with latitude. Bonnet macaques at 11° N. conceive in July, rhesus macaques at 24°–31° N. conceive in September and October, Japanese macaques at 34°–35° N. conceive in September and October, and Japanese macaques at 31°–33° N. in November and December. The Indian situation is further complicated by the possibility of a secondary cluster of conceptions in March that coincides with increasing day length, high temperatures, and lack of precipitation.

The Cayo Santiago rhesus present an interesting case of a primate population in which the annual reproductive cycle has become adjusted to a new set of environmental variables. Judging by the birth dates, conceptions begin on the island in late July or early August during a period of decreasing day length, steady temperatures, high rainfall, and abundant food supply. Koford (Chap. 5, this volume) has suggested that food supply, which is dependent on sunlight and the abundance of rainfall, is a major factor in determining the time of mating. In 1961 rhesus mating activity began one month later than in 1959, 1960, or 1962, which Koford suggests may have been because rainfall in the first half of 1961 was a third lower than in other years. With respect to rainfall, latitude, and food supply, the annual reproductive cycle of the Cayo Santiago rhesus shows a close correspondence to that of rhesus in northern India.

Some populations of African baboons exhibit a birth peak, but none appear to have a discrete birth season. In contrast to macaque populations, in which all individuals come into reproductive condition roughly at the same time, some members of baboon populations may conceive outside the usual conception period and some entire baboon populations are known to conceive throughout the year. This suggests that there may be more variability in baboons in individual sensitivity or response to environmental stimuli than there is in macaques, although it may simply reflect differences in the clarity and intensity of stimuli between the environments of our sample populations.

The birth data from Kenya baboons indicate that conceptions concentrate in the months from March through June. Since these populations straddle the equator, differences in day length must play a negligible role in the timing of conceptions, and annual variation in temperature is also very slight—only about 7° F. The abundance of rainfall with its consequent effect on food supply may be important, since the March increase in conceptions does correspond in time to the height of the major rainy season.

It is worth noting that baboons on the equator have sharper seasonal differences in reproduction than do the baboons of the Cape of Good Hope Reserve at 34° S. Many species of mammals and birds show the opposite trend, with the most marked birth seasons exhibited by populations at the highest latitudes (Bullough 1961). The situation in baboons again emphasizes the general lack of fit between latitude and the timing of births in primate populations. The variations of a month or more in the onset of the mating seasons from year to year in a single population (Cayo Santiago and Takasakiyama) also indicate that relative day length, which is invariable, cannot be the sole determining factor.

Populations of the genus *Macaca* all display discrete seasons of conceptions of from two to seven months' duration, usually confined to the latter half of the year. Langur populations show a wider range of variation, with an apparent lack of a conception peak in groups in the Abujhmar Hills to a probable conception season in the latter half of the year in other Indian populations. Baboon groups also vary in reproductive timing, from a conception peak in Kenya to an apparent lack of seasonality in conceptions at the Cape of Good Hope. This contrast in the range of reproductive variation between the closely related macaque and baboon groups may illustrate a divergence within the primates or it may be partly a reflection of the environments in which the sample populations have been observed.

In general, the timing of conceptions in the annual cycle of all populations shows some association with decreasing day length, favorable diet, and high levels of precipitation.[1] Within species there are regional differences in the timing of conceptions (in Japan, India, and Africa), and these may be related to variations in food supply resulting from differences in climate. Any or all of the factors listed above may be critical, but since all are a part of a total ecological complex it is not possible to evaluate them from field data alone. Generalizations based on evidence from field studies must be tested and refined under the controlled conditions of the laboratory.

## THE TIMING OF REPRODUCTIVE EVENTS: AN OVERVIEW

We have been concerned with three kinds of reproductive events: copulations, conceptions, and births. The most reliable information on seasonal distributions comes from the data on births, and conception dates can be calculated by subtracting the mean period of gestation from these. Copulation data, as noted above, are the most difficult to collect, and our information is least reliable on this subject. Also, in the discussion to follow,

---

[1] An exception to this comes from recent data collected by S. Ripley on the gray langur and the toque macaque at Polonnaruwa, Ceylon, which indicate that conceptions there occur during August, September, and October—a hot, dry period which is several months before the beginning of the monsoon season.

it should be kept in mind that the most thorough observations have been made on the species that exhibit a discrete birth season. Species that appear to exhibit a birth peak or an even distribution of births have often been studied where observational conditions were poor or where observations do not cover a full year.

### Patterns of Birth

Nine of the 11 monkey populations in our sample display either a birth season or a birth peak. The Japanese macaque and the rhesus macaque on Cayo Santiago exhibit the former pattern, with all births falling into a two-to-seven-month period of the year. Within this season the frequency of births describes a unimodal distribution curve (see Fig. 14–2). The rhesus and bonnet macaques in India appear to have discrete seasons of birth. But here the situation is complicated by the appearance of a secondary minor clustering of births about five months after the major one. This may represent a discrete birth season of eight months duration, with a *bimodal* birth distribution curve, or two discrete birth seasons (see Figs. 14–3 and 14–4).

Three of the four sample populations of baboons exhibit a birth peak (Nairobi, Amboseli, Ethiopia) and a peak is present, as well, in two of the three populations of Indian langurs (Lucknow, Raipur-Nagpur). These facts make it unlikely that a birth peak is entirely absent in the two remaining populations, Cape baboons and Orcha langurs. Although it would be difficult to demonstrate, these collateral lines of evidence suggest that a birth peak may exist at the Cape and at Orcha, and that it appears to be absent in these populations because of insufficient sampling. It is clear that the timing and frequency of reproductive events may vary between populations of the same species living in different areas and it may be possible to correlate these variations with the timing and intensity of environmental stimuli. These climatic differences appear to account in part for the variation in length of the birth season in different populations of Japanese macaque.

Over most of its range the savanna baboon (of which the chacma is a race) experiences the sharp alternation of wet and dry seasons characteristic of inland eastern and southern Africa. In localities where this climatic cycle and its concomitant effect on food supply is absent, such as the maritime winter rainfall region of the Cape, one would expect seasonal differences in primate reproduction to appear in attenuated form. This lack of marked wet and dry seasons may influence seasonal differences in births in the Cape population of baboons and may also be responsible for the apparent lack of a discrete birth season noted by Zuckerman among the baboons near Grahamstown, Cape Province (1932). However, there are two lines of evidence that suggest seasonal differences in conceptions in the chacma baboon. Gilbert and Gillman (1951) recorded 14 births in their laboratory colony of chacma at Johannesburg. Twelve of 14 conceptions occurred in the period from December through June, and 5 of these fell in March. Hall's observations (1962b) on free-ranging chacma indicated no significant seasonal variations in the number of dark-phase infants. However, he noted twice as many copulations per hour of observation in March and April as in the remaining 10 months of the year (1962b:287–288). These observations point to a moderate peak of conceptions in the southern autumn (March-April), which agrees with the generalization that conceptions in monkeys are concentrated in the half of the year in which day length is decreasing.

The situation of the Orcha langurs is similar to that of the chacma baboons. In the Abujhmar Hills the climatic cycle of a hot, dry season followed by monsoons is present in an attenuated form. There is some rain and water in the streams in all months of the year, and new shoots, buds, and fruits are present in the langur diet throughout the year. One might expect the seasonal differences in langur births, which are so marked elsewhere, to be leveled out at Orcha. Further observations of these crucial cases are required to determine the intensity and the actual configuration of the birth curve.

It is suggested then that seasonal differences in births are characteristic of most and possibly of all the monkey populations in the present sample. In some species there is a *birth season* which is relatively easy to demonstrate observationally. In others there is a *birth peak*, which in its more striking forms is easy to observe, but which becomes increasingly difficult to discern when seasonal differences are slight and the sample is small.

Birth periodicity among the African apes remains an open question. Observations of the gorilla and the chimpanzee populations are limited to small samples, as are those of the Orcha langurs and Cape baboons. Given the situation in monkeys, it should not be assumed that apes give birth uniformly throughout the year. All ape populations in the sample inhabit tropical rain forests within 5 degrees of the equator, with moderate to high rainfall in all months of the year. It is to be expected that species living in this kind of habitat will not exhibit the well-defined birth peaks characteristic of the savanna forms. There is a particular need for further demographic observations on the great apes, since these species have the greatest relevance for problems in the evolution of human reproductive patterns.

**Patterns of Copulation**

The annual distribution of copulations shows a close but not exact correspondence with the distribution of births. Again the best documented examples are the Japanese and Cayo Santiago macaques. There is a cessation of female estrous periods and of copulations with ejaculation around the onset of the birth season and resumption some five months later. In the Indian macaques, rhesus and bonnet, there are some copulations during most of the year, even in some months of the birth season. Southwick *et al.* (Chap. 4, this volume) observed mounting in all months of the study except March, with a marked peak in copulations and associations of consort pairs from October through January, which corresponds to the season during which conceptions occur (see Southwick *et al.*, Table 4–11). Simonds' group of bonnet macaques were observed to copulate in all months of the study and to have a peak of copulations in October and November.

In two populations of baboons seasonal differences in copulation frequency were noted. Hall's observations on the Cape baboons have been mentioned. Kummer found an increase in the perineal swelling of female hamadryas baboons in May and June, and a peak of copulations during this period. In the remaining studies of baboons and in langurs, copulations were observed in all the months of the study periods, including the months of the birth peaks. The differential frequencies of copulations by seasons are not available.

In contrast to the observations in studies of ground-living monkeys, copulations were very rarely observed in the studies of African apes. V. Reynolds and F. Reynolds saw copulation on 4 occasions in 8 months of chimpanzee observations, and Schaller recorded only 2 in 13 months of study of the mountain gorilla. Goodall observed 32 copulations in her study of Tanganyika chimpanzees, but most were confined to a 3-month period when observation conditions were best. Copulations are rarely reported in studies of forest-living monkeys (*cf.* Haddow, red-tail monkey; Jay, Abujhmar Hills langur), which suggests that difficult observation conditions may account for these low frequencies.

## CONCLUSIONS

Contrary to the widely held notion that primate sexual life is not affected by the changing seasons, a number of populations of monkeys show marked seasonal differences in reproductive activities. All groups of macaques studied have a discrete birth season of from two to seven months' duration, and some groups exhibit a complete cessation of true copulation during a long period of the year. Langurs and baboons have not been studied as thoroughly as macaques, but the available evidence indicates either a peak or a season of births in populations of these species. The intensity of the birth concentration varies geographically within a species, and this probably relates to differences in environmental stimuli. For instance, the chacma baboon at the southern tip of Africa, which appears to lack a birth peak, represents a regional variant of a widely distributed species in which a birth peak is well defined. It is probable, in light of present evidence, that nonhuman primate species altogether lacking in seasonal differences in reproduction will prove to be rare.

It is clear that constant sexual attraction cannot be the basis for the persistent social groupings of primates. Despite the absence of primary sexual behavior in the Japanese macaque for a period of from four to nine months each year, stable group organization is maintained without interruption or change. Males remain within the social unit, and in some groups of Japanese monkeys they even participate in caring for the young of previous years (Itani 1959; Mizuhara, unpublished). In these populations of monkeys sexual attraction cannot be responsible for the maintenance of group cohesion. Whether copulations are restricted to a few months, as in macaques, or seem to occur all year long, as in the chacma baboon, there is no variation in the strength of the social bond.

The human pattern of reproduction does not resemble reproduction of any other primate. The human system is characterized by the absence of estrous cycles in the female and of the marked seasonal variations that appear to characterize reproduction in nonhuman primates. The reproductive systems of man and the monkeys and apes are closely related in respect to the evolutionary development of the one from the other—but they are qualitatively different in the behavior they produce. The important similarities in the social lives of higher primates, such as living in year-round bisexual groups, cannot be attributed to nonexistent similarities in mating systems.

WILLIAM A. MASON

15

◈ The Social Development
of Monkeys and Apes

## INTRODUCTION

Until recently information on the social development of nonhuman primates was based on observation of a few individuals, chiefly macaques and
chimpanzees, maintained in captivity. The present chapter could not have
been written a decade ago—Nissen's excellent review of primate social
behavior in 1951 devoted less than three pages to social development—
and at the present rate at which new data are appearing, from both naturalistic and experimental investigations, what is written now will probably
be out of date within a few years.

There are many sources of interest in the social development of monkeys and apes. It has always been apparent that much is learned during
human infancy and childhood that influences adult behavior. The importance of early social experience in the formation of adult personality characteristics was dramatically emphasized by Freud and his followers, and
recent years have seen the development of intensive clinical explorations
of the impact of adverse conditions during childhood on later psychological
development. Studies of the socialization process in nonhuman primates
may occasionally aid directly in clarifying problems of human adjustment.
The major contribution of these studies, however, will most probably be
indirect, by helping to describe trends that have been involved in primate
evolution.

One such trend, suggested by studies of physical growth, has important

The preparation of this chapter and work on unpublished experiments described herein were
supported by research grants (M–4100 and M–5636) from the National Institute of Mental
Health of the Public Health Service.

implications for the problem of social development (Schultz 1956:890): "In regard to all parts of postnatal life one can recognize a clear trend toward prolongation, beginning in monkeys, as compared with lemurs, more pronounced in gibbons, still more in all three great apes and by far the most marked in man." It follows from this that the period of postnatal dependency should change in similar fashion, thereby increasing the opportunity (and probably the necessity) for more intense, elaborate, and enduring social relationships than are found in most mammalian groups. For reasons that are not yet clear, associated with the tendency toward retardation of growth, there is a trend for instinctive behaviors to become more variable and diffuse, and consequently for individual experience to play a more subtle and intricate role in forming these responses into biologically effective patterns.

In man this process has reached a point where it is often difficult, if not impossible, to determine the primitive motivational (*instinctoid*, Maslow) bases of his social behavior, let alone describe the specific manner in which these tendencies interact with experience. Moreover, with the emergence of the human way of life many of these primitive behaviors (for example, clinging, to be discussed more fully below) have lost the obvious adaptive value which they possess for the nonhuman primates, while they may retain some of their original psychological force.

It is still too early, however, to say much about evolutionary trends in primate socialization, and the two main objectives of this chapter are to provide a generalized description of the normal socialization process in monkeys and apes, and to indicate how early experience may influence their psychological growth. Information will be drawn from naturalistic studies, including those described in earlier chapters of this volume, from descriptive studies of the development of captive animals, and from experimental investigations. Documentation, when not indicated in the text, will be found in the references listed below.

Naturalistic studies are the primary source of information on normal aspects of social development. The major focus of naturalistic studies is on the tempo and direction of development within the group, beginning with the infant-mother relationship and terminating when the individual assumes reproductive or other functions characteristic of adult members of the group. The special value of such studies is that the developing individual is viewed as part of an elaborate network of social relations occurring in a complex ecological setting. There are two major benefits resulting from this approach:

1. A clearer and more comprehensive picture of the adaptive value of behavior can be obtained in the field than under artificial conditions. For example, the tendency of young primates to approach another animal who is manipulating or mouthing some object and to engage in similar behavior (social facilitation) is frequently observed in laboratory-reared animals. One

might speculate that this tendency is involved in various aspects of adjustment under natural conditions (transition to solid foods, acquisition of new dietary habits, and so on), but its actual role must be established with the aid of studies conducted in the field.

2. A second important benefit of naturalistic investigations is that they are not limited to the analysis of simple dyadic social relationships, as between mother and young or between peers, but may take more complex possibilities into account. Field studies of Japanese monkeys, for example, suggest that the status of the mother within the group may have important consequences for the psychosocial development of her male infant. Low-status mothers are more often found at the periphery of the group than in the central portion with the dominant adult males. Imanishi (1957b) has suggested that the infant male of a low-status female acquires submissive attitudes from its mother and in addition has few opportunities for intimate contact and "identification" with the dominant males. These factors are said to reduce seriously the likelihood that the infant will later achieve high social status.

The naturalistic approach is indispensable in studies of primate socialization, but it is not without limitations. The field worker must take his chances on finding a sufficient number of animals of appropriate age and on being able to observe them long enough and closely enough to secure reliable data. Ordinarily, it is difficult under field conditions to complete a detailed analysis of a restricted phase of development (e. g., the neonatal period) or of a specific aspect of behavior (e. g., postural development, discriminative capacities, learning ability, emotional responsiveness). To obtain such information it is often necessary to observe the same individual repeatedly under relatively constant conditions. Frequently special testing procedures are required, and the animal must be maintained in a situation that permits close contact between the observer and the subject. These conditions, of course, are most readily met by the use of captive specimens.

Studies of captive animals may be principally concerned with describing normal development, that is, development as it occurs under natural conditions; or they may be designed within an experimental framework to investigate the effects of special conditions. Experimental investigations characteristically involve the systematic manipulation of one or more independent variables to study their effects upon some aspect of behavior (dependent variable). Other variables that might affect the behavior being measured are either randomized or controlled. The difference between normative and experimental studies of social development is one of degree only, and the two approaches are basically complementary. To illustrate: Field studies may establish that young primates spend much time playing with each other and that specific play patterns emerge at different stages of development. It might be hypothesized that the experience gained in play contributes to socialization and that the consequences of such experience will depend upon the developmental stage at which it occurs. Whether this is actually so can be completely established only by systematically varying the play opportunities of young animals and determining the effect of such variations on their social development. As experimental investigations proceed new problems emerge or earlier questions are stated more precisely, creating fresh opportunities for normative and experimental research.

### SOURCES OF NORMATIVE DATA

| *New-World Monkeys* | *Old-World Monkeys* | *Gibbons and Great Apes* |
|---|---|---|
| Altmann (1959) | Altmann (1962b) | Bingham (1927, 1928) |
| Carpenter (1934) | Bolwig (1959a) | Carpenter (1940) |
| Collias and Southwick | Carpenter (1942b) | Hayes (1951) |
| (1952) | DeVore (1963b) | Jacobsen, Jacobsen, and |
| Stellar (1960) | Foley (1934, 1935) | Yoshioka (1932) |
| | Hall and DeVore | Kellogg and Kellogg (1933) |
| | (Chap. 3, this volume) | Nissen (1931, 1956) |
| | Harlow (1962a, 1962b) | Riesen and Kinder (1952) |
| | Hines (1942) | Riess, Ross, Lyerly, and |
| | Jay (1963b, Chap. 7, | Birch (1949) |
| | this volume) | Schaller (Chap. 10, |
| | Lashley and Watson | this volume) |
| | (1913) | Yerkes and Yerkes (1929) |
| | Mason (1963) | |
| | Mowbray and Cadell | |
| | (1962) | |
| | van Wagenen (1950) | |
| | Zuckerman (1932) | |

## NORMATIVE ASPECTS OF SOCIAL DEVELOPMENT

### Social Responses of Infancy

#### Nature of Infantile Responses

In the beginning the relationship to the mother is, comparatively speaking, quite simple. Like other animals born immature and helpless the monkey or ape is equipped at birth with responses to aid it in adjusting to the mother. However, unlike many other mammals, who are left in a den or nest until they are able to accompany the mother under their own power, the infant monkey or ape must from the very beginning go everywhere with its mother and its survival is dependent upon maintaining the closest possible contact with her. This fact, perhaps more than any other, helps us to understand the behavior and motivations of infant monkeys and apes.

Among the first coordinated behavior patterns to appear postnatally are those that serve to maintain bodily contact with the mother and to make feeding possible. Initially these responses appear reflexlike in form. They are most sensitive to specific forms of stimuli or to stimulation of particular regions of the body, but they are also evoked or augmented by many events that seem to have little more in common than the characteristic of producing a rather abrupt increment in the general level of stimulation. Thus, sucking is elicited most readily by tactile stimulation in or around the mouth, but it may also occur in response to toe-pinching, hair-pulling, or loss of support. In the sections to follow changes induced in this way will be ascribed to an increment in arousal level, following the general approach developed by Bindra (1959), Duffy (1957), Hebb (1955), Malmo (1957), and others. At a minimum, this has the virtue of accommodating events that are physically heterogeneous (for example, loud sounds, pain, loss of support, visual size or complexity, tickling) and diverse behavioral outcomes (for example, withdrawal, aggression, screaming, sucking, clinging, play-fighting) within a single theoretical framework. A more systematic effort to apply this approach to primate social behavior is described elsewhere (Mason in press).

### Rooting, Sucking, and Clinging

Since primate mothers ordinarily do not help the infant to find the breast, it is necessary that the neonate be able to locate the nipple by its own efforts. An important factor in this achievement is the "rooting reflex" or head-turning response. This response has been studied most thoroughly in human infants (Prechtl 1958), but the findings are probably equally applicable to nonhuman primates. The head-turning response is elicited most readily by tactile stimulation around the mouth, but it may occur in hungry infants in the absence of such stimulation. Other factors besides hunger that influence the rooting response are the number, locus, and intensity of preceding stimulations and the degree of wakefulness. Head-turning functions to bring the stimulating object in contact with the lips and this is followed by oral grasping and by sucking movements.

Stimulation in and around the mouth is the most effective stimulus for sucking, although, like head-turning, sucking may occur in the absence of external stimulation. Sucking movements are present at birth in most infants, and their strength and efficiency generally improve with age.

The principal postural adjustment of infancy is grasping or clinging. The infant is generally given some support by its mother, but support is not continuous, and under natural conditions it is necessary that the baby be able to cling independently, particularly in situations that require the mother to run or climb. Systematic studies in this area have focussed mainly on assessing the strength of reflex grasping to stretch stimulation, measured by the length of time that the infant can suspend itself. The grasp reflex is usually present at birth in neonatal humans, chimpanzees, rhesus monkeys, and presumably in all Old- and New-World forms. Intra- and inter-species variations in strength of grasp is large, but the trend is toward decreasing grasp duration from rhesus monkey (recorded maximum, 33 minutes) to chimpanzee (5 minutes) to man (2 minutes) (Richter 1931, 1934; Riesen and Kinder 1952), and there is some suggestion of a complementary trend in the nature and amount of maternal assistance provided. The strength of reflex grasping characteristically reaches a peak several days after birth and then wanes. The grasp reflex is probably only one mechanism involved in the maintenance of contact and support (Halverson 1937; Hines 1942), and Seyffarth and Denny-Brown (1948) have proposed a distinction between the grasp reflex and the instinctive grasp reaction. In contrast to the grasp reflex (which is elicited by deep pressure on the palm and by stretching) the instinctive grasp reaction occurs to light tactile stimulation and is usually accompanied by pursuit movements. Both responses are believed to be present at birth in the human infant.

One aspect of the early grasping activities of monkeys and apes that has obvious adaptive value is a characteristic movement of the arms analogous to the head-turning response. If an infant chimpanzee is placed on its back, this response occurs in the form of a sweeping motion, performed with the hands open. When an object is contacted, it is grasped and drawn toward the belly. In the neonatal monkey reaching and grasping movements give rise to the righting reaction, which is suppressed if an object for clasping is placed on the ventral surface. Reaching and grasping are probably the forerunners of the clinging embrace shown by older infants, in which grasping and ventral contact almost invariably occur together.

### Functional Relationships

Although each of these early response patterns may be analyzed individually, they are functionally interrelated not only in infancy but throughout childhood. Thus the coordination of sucking and swallowing reflexes during feeding may be disrupted unless the infant monkey has its hands and feet firmly engaged. Grasping activities are intensified as nursing begins even when the infant is securely supported (Bieber 1940; Halverson 1938). The observation that young monkeys, chimpanzees, and children alternately open and close their hands or engage in various forms of finger play while sucking or drinking from a cup suggests that the association between sucking and grasping may persist in modified form at later stages of development (Foley 1934; Levy 1928), and this is consistent with the finding that infantile forms of sucking and grasping may reappear in human adults suffering neurological damage (Bieber 1940; Seyffarth and Denny-Brown 1948).

The factors that produce momentary increases in sucking and grasping activities have not been fully explored, but the available evidence indicates that there is a broad range of relevant variables, having in common the characteristic of augmenting arousal. Halverson (1938), in one of the few studies of correlated changes in sucking and grasping, found that in human infants the strength of sucking and grasping decreased during nursing and was intensified by thwarting of feeding activities. Jensen (1932) reported that many forms of intense stimulation, including sudden onset of light, loss of support, toe-pinching, and hair-pulling would reinstate sucking in human infants. Although concurrent changes in grasping were not examined, Halverson's data (1938) suggest that grasping would be similarly affected.

### Infantile Responses, Arousal, and Filial Attachment

The effect of infantile social responses, especially the clinging reaction, is to insure intimate and continuous contact with the mother, and in the absence of the mother, or a suitable substitute, the infant shows various signs of agitation or distress. One of the earliest accounts of clinging behavior is given by Alfred Russel Wallace. His observations of a baby orangutan clearly indicate the strength and tenacity of infantile social responses.

> For the first few days it clung desperately with all four hands to whatever it could lay hold of, and I had to be careful to keep my beard out of its way, as its fingers clutched hold of hair more tenaciously than anything else, and it was impossible to free myself without assistance. When restless, it would struggle about with its hands up in the air trying to find something to take hold of, and, when it had got a bit of stick or rag in two or three of its hands, seemed quite happy. For want of something else, it would often seize its own feet, and after a time it would constantly cross its arms and grasp with each hand the long hair that grew just below the opposite shoulder. . . . Finding it so fond of hair, I endeavoured to make an artificial mother, by wrapping up a piece of buffalo-skin into a bundle, and suspending it about a foot from the floor. At first this seemed to suit it admirably, as it could sprawl its legs about and always find some hair, which it grasped with the greatest tenacity. I was now in hopes that I had made the little orphan quite happy; and so it seemed for some time, till it began to remember its lost parent, and try to suck. It would pull itself up close to the skin, and try about everywhere for a likely place; but, as it only succeeded in getting mouthfuls of hair and wool, it would be greatly disgusted, and scream violently, and after two or three attempts, let go altogether (Wallace 1869).

Wallace's description emphasizes two aspects of infantile responsiveness that have been frequently noted by other investigators. First, in the very young primate grasping or clinging is relatively nonspecific in its relation to stimulus conditions and may be evoked by a wide range of materials. McCulloch (1939) believes that the degree to which the material resists grasping determines its effectiveness, and in support of this cites Halverson's (1937) finding that strength of grasping is related to the size (diameter) of the grasped object. Although this may be true for strength of grasping, measured as an isolated response, grasping is but one element in a more complex pattern in which the grasped object is drawn toward the ventral surface. This suggests that the development of preferences for various objects of grasping will be determined not only by their resistance characteristics but also by the nature and amount of cutaneous stimulation the objects provide (Mowbray and Cadell 1962).

A second feature of infant behavior that is clearly indicated in Wallace's account is the extreme agitation produced when clinging[1] is prevented, and, contrariwise, the reduction in distress when a suitable object is attained. The inhibitory effect of clinging on distress reactions has been demonstrated

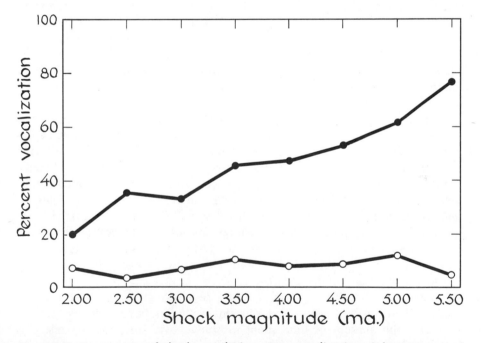

Fig. 15-1. Percentage of shocks producing stress vocalizations (whimpering and screaming) in neonatal chimpanzees while the subjects were held and while they were resting on a bare surface (from Mason and Berkson 1962).

[1] In the present discussion we shall refer to grasping accompanied by ventral contact with the object as *clinging*. Although later in development other forms of contact may acquire psychological effects similar to those produced by clinging, the clinging reaction is the modal pattern in the early relationship to the mother and it is the one most frequently observed at much later periods during moments of extreme excitement or distress.

by measuring vocal responses of infant chimpanzees to a painful stimulus (shock) administered when the infants rested on a bare surface and when they were held by the experimenter in a ventro-ventral position characteristic of the normal attitude of the infant on the mother (Mason and Berkson 1962). Figure 15–1 shows that even at the upper levels of shock crying occurred infrequently when the subject was held. If the shock was administered while the infant rested on a bare surface, however, the frequency of vocalizations increased progressively with increasing shock. Another experiment showed that hunger lowered the threshold for vocalization to shock, but, again, this effect was suppressed if the infant was held during testing (Mason and Berkson 1962). There is some indication that sucking may have inhibitory effects similar to those produced by clinging (Bridger 1962; Kessen and Mandler 1961).

CONTACT-SEEKING AND THE FORMATION OF FILIAL ATTACHMENTS. The strength and persistence of sucking and grasping activities and the distress occasioned when they are prevented have led several writers to conclude that contact-seeking and the seeking of bodily support are the principal drives of the newborn primate (Foley 1934; Tinklepaugh and Hartman 1932). The importance of contact-clinging in the development of filial attachments has been suggested by McCulloch (1939) and by Harlow and Zimmermann (1958). Harlow (1960), on the basis of data obtained with various types of artificial mothers, concludes that the two dominant systems in the formation of the infant rhesus monkey's tie to the mother are sucking and contact. In an experiment designed to provide a direct comparison of feeding experience and contact stimulation, infant monkeys were separated from their mothers at birth and placed in individual cages with access to a wire mesh cylinder from which they were fed and a cloth-covered cylinder which was the source of contact stimulation. Attachment was formed only to the cloth-covered cylinder. When infant monkeys were given two cloth cylinders identical except for color and were fed from only one of these, the cylinder which provided food was initially preferred, but this preference disappeared at about 100 days of age (Harlow 1962a; Harlow and Zimmermann 1958).

Attachment to an artificial mother develops gradually and may be measured in various ways. The Wisconsin studies have used as primary measures the amount of time spent in contact with the object while it is in the living cage, and its effectiveness in reducing emotional distress. In some tests the object has been used as an incentive for visual exploration, puzzle solution, and detour learning (Harlow and Zimmermann 1958). McCulloch (1939) used claspable objects as incentives for delayed response and discrimination learning by chimpanzees.

As would be expected, age is important in the formation of filial attachments. Rhesus monkeys who were given an artificial mother at 250 days came to spend considerable time on it, but they derived no security from its presence in a strange environment (Harlow 1962a). This effect may not be a general one, however, for rhesus monkeys raised from birth in individual cages show a definite reduction in emotional responses in an unfamiliar situation when another young monkey is present (Mason 1960a), and they remain capable of forming attachments to other monkeys at least through the first year of life. Monkeys paired for the first time at 11 months of age revealed definite preferences for the cagemate in paired-comparison tests and showed a sharp increase in distress vocalizations when the partner was removed from the living cage.

CLINGING AND AROUSAL: It is noteworthy that with the exception of measures obtained in the living cage strength of attachment to objects of clasping has been assessed in situations which seem to produce a high degree of arousal. The importance of such a factor has been emphasized by McCulloch (1939), who noted that claspable objects were maximally effective incentives for young chimpanzees only when the animals were highly excited or disturbed. He proposed that the effectiveness of clasping was dependent upon its inhibitory action:

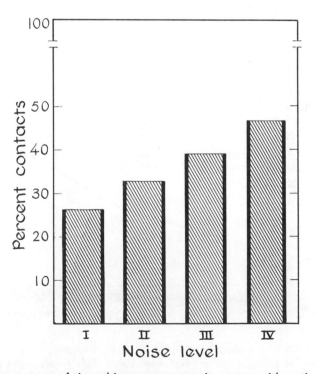

Fig. 15–2. Percentage of time chimpanzees were in contact with a stimulus-person who held them in relation to noise level in the room.

A common facilitating condition for the . . . [clasping] response in different species and in different levels of development of the same species is a stimulus situation which increases the state of excitement or disturbance. When clasping occurs, it tends to inhibit other responses of the organism. As a consequence of this inhibition, responses that closely precede clasping tend to become established as systematic responses or habits (McCulloch 1939:309).

A number of studies indicate that a high level of arousal increases the likelihood that clinging will occur. Figure 15-2 shows that contacts with an object of clinging by young chimpanzees increased progressively with conditions designed to produce increasing arousal. The relation of clinging to motivational factors can also be demonstrated by showing changes in the form of responses to the same object presented in different situations. Young chimpanzees given a claspable object (for example, rag mop) in their living cages responded to it playfully; in unfamiliar and presumably disturbing situations, however, play activities diminished and clinging became the dominant response. The same effect has been demonstrated by

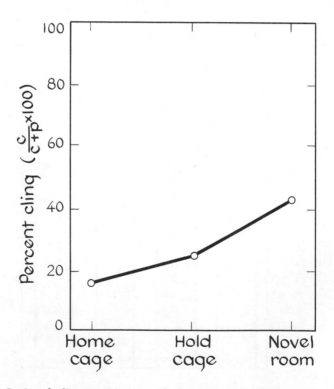

Fig. 15–3. Ratio of clinging (c) to total clinging and play responses (c and p) between pairs of young chimpanzees observed in their living cages (home cage), in an identical cage placed in a different location in the colony room (holding cage), or in a novel room.

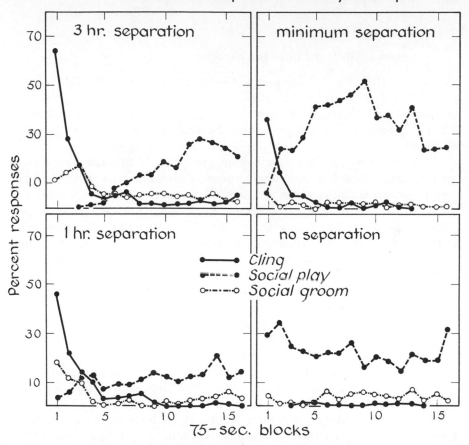

**Fig. 15-4.** Social behavior of pairs of young chimpanzee cage-mates following four conditions of separation. (*No separation* consisted of observing interactions in the absence of any experimental manipulation. *Minimum separation* consisted of separating and immediately reuniting the animals.)

recording the relative frequency of play and clinging in paired chimpanzees observed in familiar and in strange surroundings (Fig. 15-3) and by measuring the patterns of interaction between cagemates after they had been separated for intervals of as much as three hours (Fig. 15-4). Thus evidence consistently shows that a high level of arousal strengthens the tendency to cling. The corollary to this conclusion, namely, that clinging reduces arousal, is less firmly established but is supported by many nonsystematic observations and by some experimental data (Harlow and Zimmermann 1958; Mason and Berkson 1962). It is not yet clear whether reduction in arousal or distress constitutes a major factor in the development of attachments to the mother and to substitute objects, but the evidence now available indicates this is a reasonable conclusion.

## The Beginnings of Independence

### Changes in Mother-Infant Interactions

Long before the infant primate is nutritionally or emotionally independent of the mother, the early relationship with her based on the relatively simple clinging-rooting-sucking responses is complicated and enriched by a rapid growth in infant activity and the change this induces in maternal behavior.

Within a few days for monkeys or a few months for chimpanzees and gorillas, the infant forsakes its customary position on the mother's belly and begins to crawl about on her body. Particular interest is shown in her face, probably for the same reasons that the infant is attracted to any bright, distinctive object. Eventually these excursions take the infant short distances into the region surrounding the mother. The factors involved in this transition probably include, on the positive side, a growth in sensorimotor capabilities and increasing attraction to the relatively novel physical environment and to other animals; and on the negative side, a reaction against physical restraint. The chimpanzee at one month may be held for half an hour without showing signs of restlessness; at six months it rarely can be kept in the same position for more than a few minutes without a struggle.

The direction and tempo of infant development are largely determined by intrinsic changes, but the specific details in the transition from total dependence to limited independence are influenced by the mother. Mothers vary considerably in diligence and skill. Some, especially the young and inexperienced, forcibly reject their infants at birth or appear to be indifferent, or even bewildered or frightened by them (for example, Fox 1929). The importance of experience in the development of adequate patterns of maternal care is shown in recent studies of rhesus monkey mothers raised in the laboratory and deprived of normal socialization experiences (Harlow and Harlow 1962). These animals were deficient in their maternal behavior, showing abnormalities ranging from indifference to active rejection of their young. All mothers failed to nurse effectively and the infants required hand feeding. Such reactions are exceptional under natural conditions, however, and most mothers are strongly attracted to their infants and effectively perform the basic mammalian maternal activities of nursing, grooming, protection, and transportation. Within this framework there are impressive differences in maternal care and temperament, and it has been suggested that these may contribute to broad and persistent differences in infant behavior (Jay 1962; Tinklepaugh and Hartman 1932; Tomilin and Yerkes 1935).

Species differences in maternal behavior are pronounced. For example, baboon and macaque mothers are in continuous contact with their infants for about the first month after birth and vigorously resist any attempts at separation, whereas langur mothers permit other females to hold and carry their infants within hours after birth. The olive colobus monkey is distinguished by the unusual custom of carrying very young infants in the mother's mouth, a phenomenon that has not been observed in the black or red colobus (Booth 1957). Gorillas and chimpanzees show more subtle and varied patterns of maternal care than do monkeys, at least in captivity. Captive chimpanzees actively exercise and play with their babies and the ". . . infant is inhibited, curbed, directed, driven, or encouraged in multitudinous ways by maternal attentions" (Tomilin and Yerkes 1935:335). Similar behavior has not been observed among chimpanzees in the field, and it is possible that some aspects of maternal behavior are exaggerated in captivity. The caged mother is freed from the usual pressures of food-getting and protection, and the infant may provide a potent stimulus for activity in an otherwise monotonous and unstimulating environment.

In all species as the infant grows older there is some relaxation in maternal solicitude and restraint. Control by coercion is gradually supplemented by a more elaborate system of control based on subtle vocal and gestural cues, and the infant must learn to detect slight variations in the mother's posture or facial expressions that signal her mood or intent.

### Relations with Other Members of the Group

For most Old- and New-World monkeys and probably for the larger primates as well, the birth of a baby is an event of general interest, particularly for the juvenile and adult females in the group. These may crowd around the mother, inspecting the neonate and seeking to touch it or to hold it. Although the mother is usually reluctant at first to permit such liberties, she becomes increasingly tolerant of the attentions shown her infant by other animals, eventually permitting them to groom it and even to carry it short distances away from her. The peculiar attraction that the infant holds for young and old alike persists for some time after it has taken its first steps away from the mother and it may become the object of attentions that are neither solicited nor welcome. The mother is usually at hand, however, and retrieves her baby at the first signs of distress.

The reaction of adult males to infants is variable, but present evidence indicates that they are more often attentive and protective than hostile. Males have been observed to play with young animals, to retrieve them in emergency situations, and to transport and otherwise assist them during progressions (Bingham 1927; Bolwig 1959a; Carpenter 1934; Collias and Southwick 1952; DeVore 1962; Nissen 1931). Several observers have reported isolated instances of relatively stable associations between an adult male and a younger animal in which the adult served in some ways as mother substitute (Bolwig 1959a; Carpenter 1934; DeVore 1962; Haddow 1952; Imanishi 1957a). The male marmoset is reported to carry the infant at all times except when it is being nursed or cleaned by the mother

(Stellar 1960). The most remarkable instance of "paternal" behavior observed thus far in Old-World monkeys occurs in some groups of Japanese macaques (Itani 1959). In three of the 18 groups of Japanese monkeys surveyed it was found that during the birth season adult males of high social rank adopted yearling infants, clutched them, carried them, protected them, and, except for suckling, behaved in general as a mother does toward her offspring.

## Social Play

ONSET OF PLAY: Contacts with adults other than the mother probably facilitate socialization and help to integrate the young animal into the group, but for most species such contacts are infrequent compared to activities with other immature animals in juvenile play groups. Laboratory studies indicate that social play is exhibited near the end of the first month by rhesus monkeys and at about six months in chimpanzees. With advancing age play increases in frequency and complexity. With the onset of play the focus of infant behavior shifts progressively away from the mother and toward other young animals, but the infant continues to be emotionally dependent on the mother. Her presence in an unfamiliar situation probably facilitates the emergence of exploratory activities and play, and she continues to be sought when the young animal is frightened or distressed.

FORMS AND CONDITIONS OF PLAY: Rosenblum (1961) has classified the major play activities of rhesus monkeys into three broad categories: (a) rough-and-tumble play, (b) approach-withdrawal play, and (c) activity play. A similar classification would apply to the behavior of many mammals (Groos 1898), and the characteristics differentiating the play of the various genera of primates from each other and from other mammals will be found in comparative analyses of the form, the variety, and the complexity of response sequences and patterns (Welker 1961; Yerkes and Yerkes 1929). Such studies have not been completed and the following discussion is based mainly on observations of rhesus monkeys and chimpanzees.

The most frequent social activity among young chimpanzees and monkeys is play-fighting. Play-fighting in chimpanzees varies in intensity from gentle tapping, pulling, squeezing, tickling, and nudging to vigorous bouts of slapping and wrestling. By comparison the play-fighting of rhesus monkeys seems stereotyped and gross. Mounting occurs frequently in the playful interactions of monkeys and even very young animals may display a nearly perfect replica of the adult mating pattern. Among chimpanzees, gorillas, and gibbons, sex play is relatively less frequent and more loosely organized and diffuse. There have been no detailed studies of the importance of play in the socialization process, but field workers have expressed the conviction that experience gained in play facilitates the development of communicative skills and forms the foundation of adult social relationships. Recent laboratory findings are consistent with this view.

The distinction between social and nonsocial play is not a fundamental one. Characteristics that affect responses to inanimate objects, such as complexity, size, or mobility of the stimulus, also influence reactions to social stimuli. An important variable that is not yet clearly understood is the effect of previous experience. Investigations with young chimpanzees indicate that their initial response to an object of a new "class" is characterized by extreme caution. With successive exposures to comparable objects a generalized adaptation occurs and new objects of the same general type are contacted freely (Menzel 1963; Menzel, Davenport, and Rogers 1961). Moreover, when this point has been reached the moderately novel stimulus generally elicits more contacts than the familiar one (Menzel, Davenport, and Rogers 1961; Welker 1956). The situation seems to be very similar with regard to social stimuli. The home-reared chimpanzee Viki preferred strangers over familiar persons as playmates (Hayes and Hayes 1951). Laboratory chimpanzees of comparable age whose contacts with humans are limited show marked timidity in the presence of strangers, which is only gradually overcome (Hebb and Riesen 1943; Mason, Hollis, and Sharpe 1962). Similarly, young monkeys raised in isolation from adult animals showed a definite increase in affective responses when placed in an unfamiliar situation with a caged adult monkey as compared to their responses when another young monkey was present (Mason 1960a). In general, extreme departures from the familiar tend to depress play, whereas moderate degrees of novelty tend to enhance it. These results may be explained if it is assumed that play is facilitated by moderate levels of arousal and in turn augments existing levels. Thus, in situations in which the level of arousal is low or moderate, young animals are disposed to play (Mason, Hollis, and Sharpe 1962), whereas in situations in which arousal is already high, play is avoided. In view of the earlier discussion of the relationship between clinging and arousal level, it is not surprising that under the latter condition there occurs a pronounced increase in the tendency to cling.

An examination of the patterns of behavior directed toward inanimate objects supports the thesis that social and nonsocial forms of play are not fundamentally different. Threats, wrestling, grooming, and sexual behavior may sometimes occur with objects; some of these responses, for example, wrestling, may even be observed on occasion in the absence of an external stimulus, as a kind of reaction *in vacuo* (Bernstein 1962; Bernstein and Mason 1962; Foley 1934; Menzel 1963; Schiller 1957). Moreover, many activities such as climbing, swinging, and jumping that are often incorporated into social "games" of chasing, dodging, and wrestling are sometimes performed for their own sake, even when playmates are present. Hence, the term *social response* is equivocal unless the nature of the stimulus is specified. We must recognize, of course, that social stimuli possess certain features which distinguish them in degree, if not in kind, from inanimate objects. The appearance of a social stimulus is more variable from moment-to-moment than that of a physical object and such variation probably enhances the attractiveness of social stimuli (Butler 1954). Of greater importance is the fact that social stimuli, in contrast to physical objects, are not passive recipients of contacts, but may reciprocate, repel, or withdraw from the activities of another animal. Such reactions, repeated and modified by experience, provide for the development of subtle and elaborate social cue functions and for the integration of specific responses into broader sequences and patterns.

In spite of the difficulties in arriving at an acceptable and comprehensive definition of play, the fact remains that observers show considerable agreement in judging "playful behavior." Most probably such judgments are based on relatively simple behavioral cues, although knowledge of the situation is certainly a contributing factor. The problem of a comprehensive definition is more serious in theory than in practice. Certainly the responses that are judged "playful" are a normal and conspicuous feature of the heightened responsiveness of youth. This is illustrated by a comparison of the behavior of pairs of young and adult chimpanzees observed in their living cages. The young animals made more than 16 times as many social contacts as the adults, most of them during social play, and their scores for locomotion and contacts with the physical environment were also substantially higher; the only major activities in which the adults surpassed the young animals were self-manipulation and grooming. Field studies are consistent with these findings and indicate that young monkeys may spend as much as four or five hours a day in play groups (Jay 1963a). Playfulness, therefore, is rightly regarded as a useful index of the physical and psychological well-being of the young primate. Its prolonged absence raises the suspicion of retardation, illness, or distress.

## Normative Aspects: Overview

### Infantile Responses

In discussing social development it has been convenient to distinguish the responses present at birth or within a few hours of birth from social responses that appear somewhat later in ontogeny. To the extent that psychological development is a continuous process in which the effects of experience are cumulative, this division is artificial. In defense of this procedure one might argue that in their original form the first social responses should be termed *proto-social*. They are reflexlike in character and their elicitation and development are dependent not so much upon the interaction between two individuals as upon the presence of certain relatively simple physical characteristics—which ordinarily are embodied in the mother. Perhaps the major psychological significance of these neonatal responses is that they are the source of powerful motivations and predispositions which underlie much of the normal social behavior of infancy. They form the basis of the infantile attachment to the mother, which is probably the most intense social bond in the life of a primate. We are not yet in a position to judge the full significance of this attachment. Among other possibilities, it may provide the infant with the emotional security to venture away from the mother, while predisposing it to remain within the radius of maternal surveillance and protection. Throughout childhood and probably beyond, seeking social contact remains a characteristic reaction to stress, and it is reasonable to suppose that this tendency has its roots in the primitive responses of infancy.

### Maternal Behavior

By providing a source of support, nourishment, and protection the mother makes survival possible. Beyond this her interactions with the infant may be presumed to prepare it for later social adjustments. The nature of maternal care depends on the experience of the mother, the characteristics of the immediate situation, and the developmental status of the infant. Generally speaking the relationship between maternal behavior and infant capabilities is complementary. The helpless chimpanzee infant receives more elaborate maternal attentions than the precocious infant macaque. In all species the interactions between mother and young become more subtle and complex as development proceeds, and before the infant has achieved his independence he experiences succor, punishment, rejection, and restraint in a variety of degrees and forms. The endless process of social adjustment begins with the mother, whose behavior is, in many ways, representative of the larger group. From her the infant learns to perceive the meaning of a gesture or a glance, discovers that food may not be taken with impunity from a larger animal, and finds that bites and slaps will be returned in kind.

### Other Social Contacts

Early in development the young primate's experience is enlarged by opportunities to observe and to participate in social interactions with adults of both sexes and with other young animals whose activities and motivations are congruent with its own. Such experiences presumably carry forward the process of socialization which began with the mother.

## EFFECTS OF SOCIAL DEPRIVATION

### Methodological Considerations

Social development within a free-ranging group consists of an orderly progression, through time, from almost complete helplessness and dependence on the mother toward increasing self-sufficiency and orientation toward the group as a whole. In the natural habitat development always occurs in a complex socio-ecological setting in which many factors may contribute to the final behavioral result. Assessing the relative importance of these factors is a difficult and time-consuming task, and it cannot be accomplished without experimental intervention and control.

In the following sections we will consider some of the ways in which development is influenced by variations in conditions of rearing. The broad purpose of research on this question is to establish correlations (functional relationships) between single rearing variables, or combinations of variables, and specific behavioral outcomes. In the early stages of research (as in the present case), the definition of the independent variable is usually provisional and relatively gross, and is then refined as further studies indicate. For example, one might begin an investigation of the effects of maternal care on behavioral development by comparing two groups of animals, resembling each other in all important respects, except that one of them has no experience with a natural mother. If reliable differences between groups are found, one might then ask which of the many variables involved in maternal behavior account for the obtained effects. It would also be important to know whether all the important effects have been detected. The consequences of the rearing variable may be subtle, or they may assume forms that the experimenter does not expect. Isolating the developing organism from normal social contacts may not only prevent or retard the development of some behaviors, it may also create a situation in which other responses, never seen in the natural state, are likely to appear.

Thus far primate research on social deprivation has dealt mainly with gross variations in rearing conditions. Analysis of the consequences of such variations has been completed in considerable detail, however, and information is available on the effects of social deprivation on physical growth and mortality, on the development of infantile social responses (that is, those involved in feeding and the maintenance of contact with the mother), and on the ability to make effective social adjustments in adolescence and maturity.

### Growth, Mortality, and Social Stimulation

For some mammals maternal stimulation is required for adequate biological functioning of the neonate. In puppies and kittens elimination is facilitated by maternal stimulation (for example, licking) and such stimulation must be provided artificially to isolation-reared animals if they are to be maintained in good health. It has been suggested that a similar situation exists in respect to the human infant. Ribble (1943), in one of the more radical versions of this thesis, has stated that human infants receiving inadequate maternal stimulation show a syndrome of behavioral and physiological debility (marasmus) which may have fatal consequences. Data on rhesus monkeys and chimpanzees raised in social isolation cast serious doubt on the hypothesis that social stimulation plays a significant part in physical growth and viability in these primates (Davenport, Menzel, and Rogers 1961; Mason 1961c). Davenport *et al.* (1961) compared weight gain and mortality rates between mother-reared chimpanzees and animals removed from the mother at birth and raised in a laboratory nursery. Nursery-reared infants, even those reared in small enclosed cubicles, showed no higher mortality rates than chimpanzees left with their mothers, and they were substantially heavier than the mother-reared animals. Although physical growth in primates is not directly affected by social factors, there is a growing body of evidence that many aspects of psychological development are dependent upon social experience. As would be expected, the consequences of social deprivation vary with the age and developmental status of the organism at the time that deprivation occurs.

## Social Deprivation and Responses of Early Infancy

Infantile "contact seeking" behaviors show extraordinary strength and persistence and they may be elicited by a variety of stimulus objects. It would not be surprising, therefore, to find that these behaviors will be expressed in substitute activities when normal outlets are barred.

### Sucking and Self-clasping

Digit sucking appears to be one such substitute activity; it is seen in a large number of monkeys and chimpanzees raised in the laboratory and is rarely, if ever, observed in wild-born animals (Gillman 1941; Mason and Green 1962; Nissen 1944). Benjamin (1961a) found that nonnutritive sucking appeared within the first ten days of life in infant rhesus monkeys and was more frequent in animals that were bottle-fed than in those receiving their nourishment from a cup. In the latter group, however, nonsucking oral behavior (biting, licking) was relatively frequent. Differences between groups reached a maximum at from 40 to 60 days of age and then diminished, owing mainly to the decrease in nonnutritive sucking by bottle-fed monkeys. In both groups sucking persisted at substantial levels until the end of testing at 180 days of age. Another response frequently seen in primates reared apart from the mother that has an obvious parallel in normal filial behavior is self-clasping.

### Repetitive Movements

A conspicuous feature of the behavior of laboratory-reared primates is some form of individually stereotyped repetitive movement, commonly rocking or swaying (Davenport and Menzel 1963; Mason and Green 1962;

Nissen 1956). The form of these responses bears no obvious resemblance to normal social responses, and it has been suggested that they should be regarded as an attempt to compensate for low levels of environmental stimulation or for restriction of movement, rather than as a specific reaction to social deprivation (Casler 1961; Levy 1944). Although nonsocial factors may influence the level of repetitive stereotyped movements in animals that habitually display such behaviors (see below), early social experience is rather clearly implicated in the origin of these responses in nonhuman primates. That the general level of environmental stimulation is relatively unimportant in the development of repetitive stereotyped movements is suggested by the finding that animals reared in the laboratory with the mother do not rock or sway (Jensen and Tolman 1962), whereas those reared apart from the mother almost invariably do (Davenport and Menzel 1963; Hines 1942; Foley 1934; Mason and Green 1962; Nissen 1956; Riesen and Kinder 1952). Even the varied stimulation afforded the animal reared in a human household does not prevent the development of repetitive movements (Hayes and Hayes 1951; Jacobsen, Jacobsen, and Yoshioka 1932). Spatial restriction on movement is also an unlikely primary etiological factor inasmuch as repetitive movements characteristically appear before the animal has attained full locomotor capabilities for the exploitation of the available space; furthermore, it was found that severe restriction of tactual, kinesthetic, and manipulatory experience of a chimpanzee during infancy resulted in less, rather than more, stereotyped rocking, as compared to ordinary conditions of laboratory rearing (Nissen, Chow, and Semmes 1951).

### Role of Maternal Factors

The presence of the mother may operate in two ways to prevent the development of stereotyped self-clasping, thumb-sucking, and repetitive movements: First, the hands of the infant are constantly occupied in holding on to the fur and skin of the mother, thus preventing their use in self-clasping and thumb-sucking, and probably this factor also militates against the development of exaggerated repetitive movements. There is some suggestion that for the nursery-reared chimpanzee the onset of swaying in the prone position may be related to initial attempts to crawl. In the mother-reared infant, however, this stage of locomotor development occurs while the infant is still in constant contact with the mother and it is manifested in climbing about on the mother's body. The contours of the mother's physique, the frequent variations in maternal postures and activities, and the requirement that the infant adjust to these while maintaining contact, probably act as deterrents to the development of swaying or rocking as habitual responses. A second way in which the mother may prevent the development of stereotyped activities is by providing adequate outlets for the underlying response tendencies or stimulation needs that such activities presumably reflect.

*Functional Relationships*

Once stereotyped activities have become established in an animal's repertoire, they show variation in amplitude, frequency, and form as a function of both internal and external factors. A better understanding of the factors producing momentary changes in stereotyped activities can provide important clues to the functions that these behaviors serve for the laboratory-reared primate. Sufficient data exist to suggest that thumb-sucking, self-clasping, and repetitive movements differ in their specific relationships to eliciting conditions (Bernstein and Mason 1962; Smith 1960). Generally speaking, however, these behaviors retain the broad relationship to stimulus conditions that is characteristic of infantile responses. Situations that appear to create high levels of arousal augment substitute behaviors. Among the factors that have been shown to produce an increase in one or more of these responses are hunger (Benjamin and Mason 1963), frustration (Benjamin 1961b; Finch 1942), novel objects or surroundings (Berkson, Mason, and Saxon 1963; Foley 1934; Hines 1942; McCulloch and Haselrud 1939), and intense auditory stimulation (Smith 1960).

It has been suggested that boredom, that is, the absence of varied stimulation, may also influence the level of stereotyped movements once they have become habitual modes of responding (Hayes 1951; Nissen 1944, 1956; Levy 1944). Levy (1944) reports that the incidence of stereotyped movements in institutionalized children was reduced when toys were provided, and Menzel (1963) has shown that repetitive stereotyped movements diminished in chimpanzees in periods of active manipulation of objects and then increased as a reduction in contacts occurred. Possibly, additional work will show that stereotyped activities serve a homeostatic or regulatory function, coming into play whenever the over-all level of stimulation falls above or below a certain critical range.

*Significance of Stereotyped Behaviors*

Several considerations suggest that stereotyped behaviors are a potentially significant source of information on the interrelationships among innate tendencies, age, and experience in primate development:

1. There is convincing evidence that the development of these behaviors is related to rearing conditions. Although the specific etiological factors have not yet been demonstrated, the absence of a normal association with the natural mother seems to be an important predisposing condition. The age of onset for these behaviors can be specified and their emergence can probably be related to normal developmental changes.

2. There seems to be a critical period for the development of stereotyped behaviors in the sense that an animal that has passed beyond a certain age without acquiring such responses can be permanently placed in a situation identical to that which produced them in a younger animal and they will

not emerge (Davenport and Menzel 1963; Mason and Green 1962). (This is one characteristic by which they may be differentiated from the "cage stereotypes" of pacing and so on, commonly seen in some zoo animals [Hediger 1955; Levy 1944]). Moreover, stereotyped responses show only limited reversibility and may persist indefinitely, although the specific form of the response may change as the animal grows older. Thus, rhesus monkeys frequently begin sucking the true thumb, but most of those that become persistent nonnutritive suckers eventually shift to the big toe. Similarly, repetitive movements may begin in the chimpanzee as head-rolling or swaying in a prone or supine posture; later, similar movements may be made while the animal is sitting or standing bipedally. Some individuals alternate between two patterns, for example, rocking to-and-fro while sitting, and swaying from side-to-side while standing. Although the frequency of stereotyped responses tends to decrease with age, they may be observed on occasion in fully mature animals, particularly during moments of excitement.

3. There is a fundamental similarity in the form of these behaviors as they are seen in the nonhuman primates and in certain human groups, including blind (Keeler 1958) and schizophrenic children (Bender and Freedman 1952) and the severely retarded (Berkson and Davenport 1962; Gesell and Amatruda 1941). As would be expected, phylogenetic differences exist in the number and complexity of these responses and their postural concomitants. Only apes and man sway while standing erect; and even untestable human retardates may display a richness of stereotyped patterns that exceeds the most elaborate behaviors shown by monkeys and chimpanzees.

4. Because stereotyped behaviors become persistent modes of responding, they may substitute for or interfere with the development of responses which are more adaptive or appropriate, thus indirectly retarding psychological growth.

## Social Behavior and Social Deprivation

### Responsiveness

A necessary but obviously insufficient condition for effective social interchange is that the organisms involved approach rather than avoid one another. There seems to be a period early in primate infancy when the dominant tendency is approach, but as development proceeds fear responses emerge and with this there occur a differentiation and a refinement of reactions to novel objects (Bernstein and Mason 1962). These changes are determined in part by maturation, but whether a specific social stimulus will elicit approach or avoidance is also dependent upon prior experience (Hebb and Riesen 1943). Animals that have been reared in isolation from their kind but in an otherwise stimulating social environment may show no signs of fear when first confronted with a member of their own species. In fact, there is some indication that such animals are bolder than ordinary laboratory subjects (Foley 1934, 1935; Hayes 1951; Jacobsen, Jacobsen, and Yoshioka 1932; Kellogg and Kellogg 1933). In contrast with these findings, the animal reared in complete social isolation may show a persistent avoidance of social contact. In one experiment (unpublished) two rhesus monkeys were raised in total isolation from birth until they were 18 months of age. They were then placed together in a large observation cage for a total of fifteen 45-minute sessions and during this time were scored with only 25 social approaches, most of which occurred as the animals came into proximity while passing from one end of the cage to the other. Many common rhesus monkey social responses were never observed, and the animals spent much of the time crouched at opposite ends of the cage, clutching themselves and rocking. The reactions of these monkeys to each other and to the test situation suggest the excessive arousal effects shown by visually deprived animals upon being placed in normal visual surroundings (Riesen 1961). A comparison group in this experiment was provided by two monkeys individually housed from birth in wire mesh cages within a room containing other monkeys. In contrast to the isolates, these monkeys made over 500 social approaches and exhibited play, grooming, aggression, and some sexual behavior. Subsequently, the experimental animals were permanently removed from isolation and were paired continuously for successive two-week periods with each other and with the monkeys of the comparison group. Throughout these pairings their behavior showed no important change.

*Social Interaction*

Although monkeys raised in semi-isolation in the ordinary laboratory environment may be highly responsive to social stimuli, their development is retarded in many respects by the lack of social experience. This has been demonstrated by comparing the behavior of two groups of adolescent rhesus monkeys, one group born and raised in the wild for the first 12 to 18 months, and the other, born in the laboratory and housed from infancy in individual cages (Mason 1960b, 1961a, 1961b). In test situations the laboratory-reared subjects showed less social grooming, as compared to the feral animals, and had more frequent and severe fights. The stability of social relations, determined by competitive tests with food, was much greater in the feral group, and these animals were also more highly motivated to engage in social interaction with other members of their group, as measured by the number of times they released a group member from confinement. Similar tests were conducted in which both feral and socially deprived male monkeys were given an opportunity to interact with feral females. Under these conditions the laboratory-reared subjects showed a definite increase in gregariousness. When the procedure was reversed, however, and the experienced females were permitted to choose between wild-born and laboratory-reared males, their preference for the feral animals was unequivocal.

One of the most striking deficiencies observed in the socially deprived subjects was in sexual relations. Abnormalities in sexual performance were apparent in both sexes, but they were particularly pronounced in males. Socially deprived males were evidently sexually aroused, but their mating attempts were poorly integrated and body orientation toward the partner was frequently inappropriate. These deficiencies were apparent whether the animals were tested with naive or sophisticated females (see Fig. 15–5). Thus far, all efforts to establish effective sexual performance at maturity in socially deprived male rhesus monkeys have been unsuccessful (Harlow 1962b).

The evidence is conclusive that normal development of primate social behavior is dependent upon experience (Harlow 1962b; Nissen 1953; Yerkes and Elder 1936), but the specific factors involved have not been determined. Male mating behavior probably does not develop as a unitary pattern; rather the various constituents seem to appear at different stages in ontogeny and are differentially related to experience and to eliciting conditions. Penile erection and thrusting are present in infancy in both monkeys and chimpanzees and they occur in many situations in which the general level of excitement is high, for example, upon rejoining a companion after brief separation, at feeding time, when strangers are present, or in response to physical restraint (Bingham 1928; Hamilton 1914). The integration of these responses into the adult mating pattern occurs much earlier in monkeys than in chimpanzees, but it means little to say that experience is more important for one species than for another. If the male monkey is provided adequate social contacts, it develops the sexual pattern characteristic of the adult well in advance of puberty, whereas under similar conditions the chimpanzee apparently does not (Bingham 1928; Nissen 1953; Yerkes and Elder 1936). On the other hand, the male monkey that has not achieved the adult pattern by adolescence is unlikely to do so later, whereas the chimpanzee is capable of such learning. This contrast may be related in part to differences in the sexual patterns of the two groups and in part to differences in behavioral flexibility. Unless the male rhesus monkey succeeds in grasping the female's hind legs during mounting, intromission is impossible, and until this stage has been achieved even a highly experienced female can provide little assistance to the male. The male monkey whose opportunities for social learning have been curtailed until adolescence is probably handicapped in his sexual adjustment by the presence of strong playful and aggressive tendencies. In chimpanzee sexual relations the roles are not so sharply differentiated as is the case with monkeys and baboons. The male may approach the female, or he may solicit approach from her by sitting with legs drawn apart, displaying the erect penis (Yerkes and Elder 1936). With some cooperation from the male an experienced female may

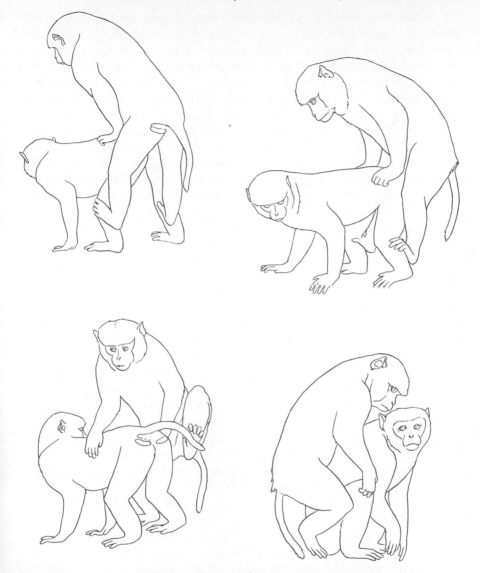

Fig. 15–5. Sexual behavior of wild-born and socially deprived rhesus monkeys with socially experienced female partners. (*Top left*) Rear view of wild-born male in typical copulatory position. (*Top right*) Side view of wild-born male in typical copulatory position. (*Bottom left*) Socially deprived male attempting to mount from the side. (*Bottom right*) Sexual behavior of socially deprived male (from Mason 1960b).

guide the penis or adjust her posture so as to compensate to some extent for deficiencies in her partner. Thus, there is a strong possibility that early social deprivation may have more severe and lasting consequences for masculine sexual development in the monkey than in the chimpanzee.

A series of experiments summarized by Harlow and Harlow (1962) provides significant information on the relative importance of mother-infant and infant-infant relations in the social development of rhesus monkeys. The results indicate that development is essentially normal if infants are raised by their mothers and given daily opportunities to interact with age-mates. Infants raised apart from the mother and given frequent contact with peers are initially somewhat retarded in their social development, but eventually attain normal social patterns, whereas infants whose only social contacts to the age of seven months were with their mothers are more retarded than either of the other two groups. Although additional data are required before a firm conclusion is warranted, this evidence suggests that the relationship with the mother is not essential to social development, although it may facilitate it, whereas contacts with peers must occur if development is to follow a normal course.

### Contribution of Experience

A consideration of the consequences of social deprivation offers some suggestion as to the various ways in which experience may contribute to normal social development.

1. *Responsiveness.* Perhaps the single most important motivational determinant of primate social responsiveness, particularly in the young, is the general level of behavioral arousal. Level of arousal is dependent upon a complex relationship between experience and the characteristics of the social stimulus and of the physical situation. Generally speaking, the older the animal and the more marked the contrast between the rearing environment and the test situation, the more extreme and persistent its reaction will be. Precise relationships between level of arousal and behavior have not yet been determined, but sufficient data exist to suggest that higher levels will be associated with withdrawal or aggression, either of which is inimical to effective social adjustment (Mason, in press).

2. *Response integration.* The importance of response integration is most clearly illustrated by the sexual performance of male rhesus monkeys, but response integration may also be a factor in the formation of other complex social patterns, for example, maternal behavior. Although most of the constituents of male reproductive behavior were present in socially deprived monkeys, these were not combined into an orderly pattern and appropriately applied to social stimuli. Fundamentally this appears to be a form of sensori-motor learning, analogous to that involved in the integration of isolated motor units into the complex patterns and sequences required in effective use of tools (Birch 1945; Schiller 1952). We may expect that for social responses, as for tool-using, significant maturational gradients will be found (Schiller 1952).

3. *Communication.* Communication may involve the discrimination of extremely subtle individualized cues indicating the mood or intent of a

particular companion, as well as differential responses to species-characteristic gestures, vocalizations, and postures (Carpenter 1942b). The basic form of many of these responses and their general relations to arousal level or affective state are almost certainly unlearned (Bernstein and Mason 1962; Jacobsen, Jacobsen, and Yoshioka 1932). On the other hand, their connection with specific stimuli and their effectiveness in controlling and coordinating social activity is probably heavily dependent upon the experience of both sender and receiver. Many illustrations could be given of the essential part played by communicative acts in all phases of social intercourse (Hebb and Thompson 1954). We limit ourselves here to a discussion of the contrasts between feral and socially deprived monkeys. Among sophisticated monkeys a dominant male rarely employs force to attain its goals, but instead uses less direct means, such as staring and threat gestures and vocalizations. If the sender's messages are to be effective, they must, of course, be received by one who knows their meaning, that is, responds to them as signals. The orderly progression of social interaction requires this kind of reciprocity between sender and receiver. Thus, when an experienced male rhesus monkey lightly touches a sophisticated female at the waist she responds by rising, bracing herself, and presenting in the typical female posture. If she does not rise, the male ordinarily will not attempt to mount. Among socially deprived monkeys the picture is entirely different. The male does not always touch the female lightly or in a specific region; instead the vigor and locus of his initial responses may vary considerably, leading to a variable outcome, even with experienced partners. And the male may continue his attempts at coition, even when the female does not assume a receptive posture (Fig. 15–5).

## CONCLUSION

Primate social development passes through various stages or levels that can be loosely characterized in terms of the dominant forms of activity and the social objects toward which these activities are directed. At a descriptive level it is apparent that the normal trend of development is away from the mother and toward more frequent, varied, and prolonged intercourse with other animals and with the physical environment.

The basis for the initial adjustment to the mother is essentially present at birth in monkeys and apes and this is as it must be if the infant is to survive. Infantile responses initially display a reflexlike quality. Many stimuli are adequate to elicit these responses, and stimulus effectiveness seems to be principally determined by physical characteristics. In nature, of course, these characteristics are embodied in the mother, but the evidence shows that inanimate objects may serve as substitute mothers during infancy. The social responses of infancy are highly motivated as evidenced by their persistence and by the various signs of agitation or distress that appear when suitable objects are not available. In the absence of the natural mother or an appropriate substitute the infant often develops self-clasping, thumb-sucking, and repetitive stereotyped movements as habitual modes of responding.

Ordinarily the focus of infant behavior is the mother. She is sought when the infant is hungry, fatigued, or frightened. The quality of maternal care is surprisingly unimportant in giving the mother her status as a refuge and a source of emotional security, and similar functions may be acquired by inanimate objects that are consistently associated with the performance of infantile social responses. When filial responses have become organized around a specific object or class of objects, we may speak of the formation of an attachment.

Experimental investigations using artificial mothers suggest that contact stimulation is more important than feeding experience in the formation of social attachments, but the mechanism involved in the development of attachments is not yet known. We have suggested in this chapter that arousal level may provide a useful conceptual tool for dealing with the problems of social motivation and social rewards, particularly in the young primate. The evidence indicates that many events which seem to have in common the characteristic of raising the level of arousal increase the likelihood that clinging will occur. Clinging appears to raise the threshold of arousal, and it may therefore serve to reinforce the infant's tie to the mother. The adaptive value of the relationship between clinging and arousal level is clear: Any sudden change in the environment (for example, the appearance of a predator) will cause the infant to seek its mother, who affords protection and is far better equipped than he to cope with the threatening situation.

With the formation of an attachment to the mother, favorable conditions are created for social learning. The primate's highly developed abilities for discrimination learning and other complex intellectual activities are exercised in social relations as well as in adjustments to the physical environment. The occasions for social learning are multiplied as the growing individual moves away from the mother and encounters other animals. Thus far, experimental investigations have given relatively little attention to the task of specifying the manner in which experience contributes to normal development. It is evident, however, that social learning begins with the mother and we must assume that one of the primary functions of contacts with other animals is to sharpen, strengthen, or generalize learned behaviors that originate in mother-infant interactions.

The task of bringing the behavior of man and the nonhuman primates into meaningful relationship within a comparative-evolutionary framework has scarcely begun. Broadly viewed, the social development of monkey, ape, and child follows the same basic pattern. For each the mother is the primary source of nourishment, protection, and emotional security, but the details of psychological growth and of the relationship between mother and infant vary systematically in primate phylogeny. Consider mother-infant relations during feeding in man, chimpanzee, and macaque. Human babies must be helped to find the nipple and supported while they nurse. The chimpanzee infant makes fewer demands on the mother but seems to require substantially more help than does the infant macaque, who can nurse virtually unassisted within a few days after birth. A similar pattern can be seen in other aspects of development, suggesting a trend in which the rate of ontogenetic development, the strength and efficiency of infantile responses, and the nature of maternal care change in complementary fashion. As the period of childhood dependency increases, there is a corresponding change in the need for varied forms of maternal care, and in the ability of the mother to provide such care. These changes may originate in common from an evolutionary process that has culminated in the extreme behavioral plasticity so characteristic of man.

PETER MARLER

# 16
## ◈ Communication in Monkeys and Apes

## INTRODUCTION

In animals, as in man, an act of communication is one of the most refined and intricate events in the behavioral repertoire. Initiated by one animal, which produces the communicatory signal, mediated by the environment through which the signal is transmitted, and culminating in the response evoked by the signal in a recipient, it spans both space and time. When it takes place in its proper context, which is the natural environment of the species, the communicative act cannot be isolated from the circumstances in which the signaler and the recipient find themselves at the time they are participating in the exchange. Insofar as the surroundings and concomitant behavior of the signaler are perceptible to the recipient they also may contribute something to the response that it gives to a signal. The events preceding emission of a signal that have contributed to its production may be either external to the animal, or within it, or most likely a combination of both. By the same token, the internal state and external environment of the recipient may affect the nature of its response to a given signal.

An attempt to unravel all the threads in this complex web of interacting events must necessarily begin at the place where the system is complete in all of its parts, in nature. The undertaking is an enormously difficult one, and it must be admitted at the outset that we have no more than an inkling of

This article originated from a series of discussions between the writer and some of the contributors to this book, particularly J. R. Bastian, I. DeVore, K. R. L. Hall, P. Jay, V. Reynolds, and G. B. Schaller. Without their knowledge of primate behavior and their generosity in making their thoughts and observations available it would not have been written. The author is also grateful for ideas and criticisms from John Eisenberg, John Kaufmann, Carl B. Koford, and Robert Kuehn, all of whom read the manuscript and made available unpublished work on primate behavior. Suzanne Chevalier, Paul Simonds, and others loaned photographs from which drawings were made, and Stuart Altmann, Robert Hinde, and Thelma Rowell kindly gave permission to reproduce illustrations from their papers.

how communication systems actually work in any but the most simple kinds of organisms. With animals whose structure, psychology, and social organization are as complex as that of the primates, the obstacles to a complete understanding of mechanisms of social communication are particularly great, to say nothing of the inaccessibility of the tropical jungle habitats where many of them live. In spite of these difficulties there have been some remarkable advances in our knowledge of these animals in recent years, and it is the aim of this chapter to review the pictures of social communication systems that are emerging and to compare them with what is known of other animals, particularly birds, which have been the object of the writer's own research in the past.

## THE ELEMENTS OF AN "IDEAL" INVESTIGATION

It may be instructive to start by considering in a general way what the ideal investigation of an act of communication might comprise. It must begin, as do all scientific ventures, with description, conducted either by the investigator or by someone who has gone before him. This most crucial phase is fraught with more difficulties in behavioral studies than is often appreciated by workers in other more mature branches of science. They have long-established traditions to guide them in the selection of the elements of a situation that provide an appropriate descriptive background to each kind of problem. Lacking these guide lines the animal behaviorist must make his own selection from the infinite number of parameters by which any situation may be described. The ultimate success of the investigation will be largely dependent upon the skill with which this initial choice is made. It must be done on an inductive basis, beginning with as few preconceptions as possible beyond the framework dictated by the initial aim, which in this case is an understanding of the processes of social communication.

The physical and mental processes by which an investigator exposes himself to an animal in its natural state and allows the salient characteristics of its behavior and the correlations between them to emerge gradually in his mind has been admirably described by Darling (1937) in his book on the behavior of the red deer (see also Schneirla 1950). Once delineated, the characteristics that seem to relate to the particular problem in hand become the focus of special attention. The description begins to take form. By careful quantitative analysis the investigator may then build up a convincing case that certain acts in the natural behavior of a species occur primarily for the purpose of communicating with other individuals. He may also be able to suggest what response is normally evoked in others that perceive the act of communication or its consequence. And if he is exceptionally industrious, or perceptive, or lucky, he may have some picture of the other variables—environmental, physiological, psychological—that also contribute to the production of a signal in one animal and to the response it evokes in another.

Up to this point the method is one of description and classification, assisted in varying degree by artificial aids—cameras, tape recorders, sound spectrographs, computers, and so on. The case upon which any conclusions are based rests on inductive reasoning and cannot be regarded as strictly proven until it is subjected to experimental testing (e.g., Falls 1963). None of the work upon social communication in nonhuman primates has reached this stage, and even the descriptive material is scant and concerns only a handful of the better-studied species. Furthermore, the descriptions are mainly concerned with signaling behavior and little attention has been given to responses the signals evoke. In such circumstances the judgment about what actually constitutes signaling behavior is a subjective one and may need revision in the future. Thus much of what follows is speculative and should perhaps be taken as a guide to the kinds of data we would like to have rather than as a review of what has already been accomplished.

## A "TYPOLOGICAL" APPROACH

For the most part the nature of the data forces the adoption of an approach that can be defined as "typological" or "syntactical" (Cherry 1957; Marler 1961). Such an approach is concerned primarily with describing and classifying signals and attempting to extrapolate to predictions about the potential properties of the signal system when used in actual communication. The complementary "pragmatic" approach seeks an understanding of the processes by which signals transmit information from one animal to another and requires detailed knowledge of the responses evoked by signals, knowledge we have only in a few species. This approach also requires information on all factors, environmental and otherwise, contributing to the process of communication, and, with animals whose sensory environment is as rich as that of higher primates, such information is laborious to collect and difficult to interpret.

"Syntactical" treatment is less demanding and is a logical way to begin investigations. It is worth noting that the study of captive animals can be of great value in syntactical studies, provided the captive environment is close enough to the natural one to avoid gross distortion of the signals and rich enough to elicit a sufficiently wide variety of them (e.g., Hinde and Rowell 1962; Rowell and Hinde 1962). Only when one proceeds to a pragmatic analysis is it absolutely essential to refer to the behavior in the natural state.

## RELATIVE DOMINANCE OF THE DIFFERENT SENSORY MODES

Communication by the senses of touch and taste, requiring physical contact by the communicants, is little affected by the medium in which animals are living. Vision, on the other hand, may be strongly affected. This is most obvious in nocturnal animals, like many of the lemurs, lorises, and tarsiers (e.g., J. Petter 1962a, Chap. 9, this volume), which, in spite of their many adaptations for improved vision at night, are nevertheless driven to use other senses for distance communication. Even diurnal animals may be subject to some restriction here if they live where vision over long distances is impeded, as in dense forest. Audition provides one alternative means of communication over short or long distances. In the prosimians olfaction is also frequently exploited, presumably in compensation for the restriction of vision, but in the monkeys and apes that are to be our main concern olfaction plays a much more limited role in communication. These animals are mainly diurnal, and exploit vision and audition for distance communication, with the addition of the sense of touch in communication at close range.

The exploitation of different sensory modalities for purposes of communication may profoundly affect the kinds of information that can be transmitted, particularly in communication over distances. A valuable function of many distance signals is to enable recipients to locate the signaler in space. Such localization is most readily achieved with visual signals. Except for the rare case of a reflected signal, a vertebrate eye cannot detect a visual signal without, at the same time, determining rather precisely the direction from which it has come. By comparison the localization of auditory signals under natural conditions is more difficult and less precise, relying mainly, as it does in vertebrates, upon the comparison of different properties of the sound signals in the two ears of the recipient. Still more difficult is the precise localization of the source of olfactory signals, particularly in still air (see discussions in Marler 1959). Thus when the mode of life and environment permit it an animal is likely to select vision as the medium for communication where precise localization over distances is important.

The status of a species within its biological community may have some bearing here. If it is liable to predation, visual signals may increase vulnerability. Such animals often need to seek some kind of compromise between conspicuousness of morphology and behavior for intraspecific communication and crypticity for purposes of concealment. Also the need for distance signals will vary according to the system of social organization, and, within the persistent group or subgroup that is characteristic of so many primates, signals for close range communication are most commonly in demand. These same circumstances also permit the maximum exploitation of multiple signals so that visual, auditory, tactile, and olfactory stimuli may all combine to communicate information to others, a development particularly characteristic of many primate groups.

## OLFACTORY SIGNALS

The paucity of studies on the structure of the chemical signals used by animals and the protracted biochemical methods required to identify them (e.g., Karlson and Butenandt 1959) leave behaviorists little choice but to describe what they judge to be signals in terms of the behavior associated with their emission or deposition. By this criterion there are several behavior patterns in prosimians that are reasonably interpreted in this way. Tree shrews have throat and chest glands that are used for marking (Sprankel 1961, 1962; Kaufmann unpublished). J. Petter (1962a) has described how several species of lemurs rub branches with the secretions of specialized glands located on forearms and in the armpit. Sifakas have glands under the chin that they rub on the trunks of trees.

Montagna has demonstrated the structure of a number of these glands, and has also shown in a series of papers (e.g., 1962) that in prosimians the skin, particularly on the face, feet, and in the ano-genital region, is richly supplied with sweat and sebaceous glands (see Fig. 16–1). One of their many functions may be olfactory communication.

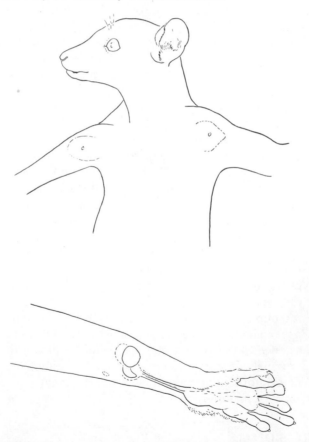

Fig. 16–1. Location of the brachial and antebrachial skin glands in the brown lemur. Secretions from them are rubbed on branches in the home area (*after Montagna 1962*). (*Courtesy of The New York Academy of Sciences*)

Like many mammals the prosimians have a number of behavior patterns associated with urination and defecation that appear to serve some communicatory end. Tree shrews have methods of spreading urine over their surroundings (Sprankel 1961, 1962). *Loris, Microcebus,* and *Galago* will moisten their paws with urine and distribute it over themselves and their environment. *Cheirogaleus* species smear feces directly upon branches (Eibl-Eibesfeldt 1953; Ilse 1955; J. Petter 1962). Although the evidence that this marking of the body and living area serves to communicate to neighboring individuals is slight and circumstantial, the impression that this is the case has repeatedly been noted, and the existence of clearly defined and distinctive "marking" behavior patterns is well established.

The contrast between the prosimians and the apes and monkeys in this respect is striking. Specialized skin glands in apes and monkeys are rare and so are associated behavior patterns for marking with them, though Eisenberg and Kuehn (unpublished) have evidence of throat glands in spider monkeys that seem to have a communicatory function. There is also a lack of stylized behavior associated with defecation and urination. Howlers defecate and urinate on people and strange objects, but this seems to function for repulsion rather than intraspecific communication (Carpenter 1934; Conaway and Koford in press). There are no localized latrine areas such as are so widespread in other mammals (Bourlière 1960). Although there may be an accumulation of feces around sleeping places, as in baboons (Hall 1962a), there is no evidence that these serve as foci for social interaction, as in various carnivores and ungulates (e.g., Hediger 1950; Heimburger 1959; Koford 1957; Leyhausen 1959). Olfactory communication appears to play little role in distance communication in the monkey and ape. It arises most clearly in females at the onset of estrus when the urine seems to convey information about their condition to males in the group. The odor of a female toque macaque in estrus is detectable to a human observer (Jay in press), and the males of many species sniff at the genitalia of estrous females. Olfactory signals may be particularly important in species that lack the visual signs of estrus characterizing female chimpanzees, macaques, and baboons.

This shift away from olfaction as a dominant means of communication, and perhaps as a means of environmental exploration as well, is not without its anatomical correlates both in the structure of the nasal passages and in the olfactory lobes, which are large in the prosimian brain and are progressively pre-empted in higher forms by the cerebral cortex. Zoologists have speculated that the precedence of primates by ancestors in which extensive brain areas were devoted to olfaction, rather than to vision as was the case with birds, may have been decisive in permitting the great development of the neopallium in this group.

The great increase of individual mobility in monkeys and apes as compared with the prosimians, stemming in part perhaps from the shift to a more predominantly diurnal habit, probably reduces the value of olfactory marking of the environment. A unique property of olfactory markers is their persistence during the absence of the signaling animal, and for species that range over a limited area this undoubtedly has advantages. This method of "remote" or "delayed" communication does not require the precise position of the signaler at any one moment to be revealed, thus perhaps hindering a potential predator from making use of the signals.

Monkeys and apes may make more use of olfaction than is at present appreciated. Individual recognition by olfaction is a possibility, known to occur in many animals, particularly perhaps in the relationship between mother and young. The frequent passing of wind noted for example in langurs and gorillas might be more than just a side effect of digestion or indigestion. They undoubtedly make some use of olfaction in exploring their environment and identifying food (e.g., rhesus, Altmann 1962a; baboons, Kummer 1957), and in receiving stimulation from estrous females. The strong odor of the semen of male rhesus may serve some sexual function (Altmann 1962a; Conaway and Koford in press). However, olfaction is clearly less preeminent as a sense in monkeys and apes than in the prosimians.

## TACTILE COMMUNICATION

Almost as little is known about the tactile worlds of animals as about their chemical worlds, though for different reasons. The impoverished olfactory sense of humans prevents us from empathizing with the olfactory experiences of other organisms. Our tactile sense, on the other hand, is highly developed and plays a crucial role in courtship behavior and in the relationship between parent and offspring. Yet, being unable to place ourselves in the appropriate position as recipients of the tactile signals of animals, as we can readily do with visual and auditory signals, we can hardly begin to describe them in terms that are really applicable to their function as signals. Thus we must once more substitute by describing them in terms of the behavior patterns employed and the parts of the body on the recipient to which tactile stimuli are directed.

The hand is the most common part of the body used by primates to initiate physical contact, thus contrasting with the characteristic naso-nasal or naso-anal contacts of most mammals (e.g., Schloeth 1956–1957), and correlating with the improved manual dexterity of the primates and the increasingly extensive representation of the hands in the sensory and motor areas of the cerebral cortex (e.g., Woolsey 1958; Bishop 1962). The teeth, lips, tongue, and nose may be used in some circumstances; the tail, when it is prehensile (Eisenberg and Kuehn, n.d.); as well as the general body surface; and also the pelvic area and penis.

The most widespread and characteristic behavior pattern involving tactile stimulation is grooming, in which one animal manipulates and mouths the fur of another. Tree shrews use the teeth and tongue for grooming (Kaufmann unpublished), and in lemurs the teeth and tongue regularly accompany the hands in combing the fur (Andrew 1963). The hands are typically used in monkeys and apes, the mouth being applied when a foreign object is located. Almost any part of the recipient's body may be groomed, although there is a tendency to concentrate on the head, neck, and back, which are inaccessible to self-grooming, and on the ano-genital area. In addition to extended manual exploration of the fur, the same effectors may be used in briefly touching different parts of the recipient's body. It would be difficult to overestimate the importance of such tactile signals in maintaining peace and cohesion in primate societies (e.g., Hall and DeVore, Chap. 3, and Jay, Chap. 7, this volume; Kummer 1957; Altmann 1962a). Grooming is particularly prominent in species in which dominance relations play a significant role, such as rhesus monkeys and baboons, and involves interactions between adults as well as between parent and young—females commonly taking the active role in both contexts (see Fig. 16–2). By comparison, mutual grooming is much less frequent between adult gorillas (Schaller 1963; Chap. 10, this volume), and it is tempting to see a correlation with the subtler and more peaceful dominance relations in this species. The contrast does not end here, for tactile sexual signals involving mounting and pelvic thrusting, which in free-living gorillas are restricted to true copulation, occur in macaques and baboons not only in copulatory behavior but also to resolve or reinforce dominance relations.

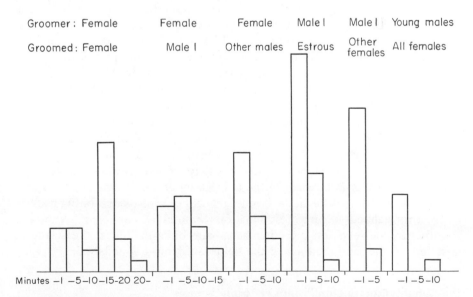

Fig. 16–2. Histograms of the time spent grooming by the different members of a troop of chacma baboons. Male 1 was the dominant member of the group (*after Hall 1962b*).

TABLE 16–1. AN ANALYSIS OF THE OCCURRENCE OF VARIOUS BEHAVIORAL
COMPONENTS, MOST OF THEM GENERATING TACTILE STIMULI, WHEN A
STRANGE MALE (MALE V) WAS GREETED BY THE VARIOUS MEMBERS
OF A GROUP OF BABOONS (AFTER HALL 1962b).

| Behavior-Component | By Females | By V to Females | By Males | By V to Males |
|---|---|---|---|---|
| Presenting | 7 | 0 | 0 | 3 |
| Mounting | 0 | 0 | 1 | 2 |
| Grooming | 8 | 1 | 6 | 4 |
| Lip smacking (ear flattening) | 17 | 8 | 34 | 20 |
| Standing on hindlegs | 1 | 1 | 5 | 5 |
| Embracing | 6 | 2 | 23 | 17 |
| Genital/stomach nuzzling | 10 | 0 | 10 | 3 |
| Rump nuzzling | 0 | 4 | 6 | 3 |
| Mouth/head kissing | 9 | 6 | 6 | 1 |
| Back-fur nuzzling | 2 | 1 | 1 | 0 |
| Rump fingering | 0 | 3 | 0 | 0 |
| Touch with hand | 0 | 3 | 4 | 0 |
| Totals | 60 | 29 | 96 | 58 |

In some species these various grooming and sexual contacts intermingle
to produce an extraordinarily rich repertoire of tactile signals used in "greetings behavior." As a remarkable illustration of this range of signals, Table
16–1 (from Hall 1962b) shows the greetings given during a period of eight
days by the different members of a group of chacma baboons to a tame male
that was released into the group. It will be noted that, of the 12 behavior
patterns observed, all but one involve contact with some part of the recipient's body or are preludes to such contact. In addition to these interactions
involving positive aggregative tendencies, tactile stimuli may also contribute
to negative, dispersive tendencies by eliciting pain and trauma. The hands
and feet may be used in striking opponents and pulling fur (e.g., tree shrews,
Kaufmann unpublished; rhesus, Koford in press), and of course the teeth are
used in biting. Once more the stimuli may be directed at certain parts of the
recipient's body, as in baboons where bites are commonly aimed at the thick
hair on the neck or at the base of the tail (Kummer 1957; Hall and DeVore,
Chap. 3, this volume), or in the bonnet macaque, where neck-biting has become a formalized gesture of domination (Simonds, Chap. 6, this volume).
Fighting tree shrews, on the other hand, aim bites mainly at the scrotum,
hind legs, rump, and the base of the tail (Kaufmann unpublished).

### The Communicatory Significance of Tactile Signals

As a first step in classification tactile signals have been characterized
by the effectors used in signaling and by the locus of stimulation of the

recipient. These two variables alone suffice to provide a wide variety of signal types, many of them with clearly different functions. If these are regarded as the "qualitative" properties of tactile stimuli, it is important not to overlook their "quantitative" properties, particularly the intensity and completeness of the signal, and the temporal pattern of delivery. To take a simple example, biting in an aggressive encounter between adult baboons is more violent, more rapid, and more complete than when a male bites a juvenile in play and is different again from the biting of the female by the male that sometimes precedes mounting (Hall 1962b). By the same token, grooming may take a number of different forms. Hall (1962b) has shown that the duration of grooming interactions differs strikingly in different types of pair contact (Fig. 16–2), leading him to conclude that "fine differences seem to have a more important bearing on the social significance of various types of grooming even than do mere frequency differences." It may be presumed that subtle variations in the manner and intensity of manipulation of the recipient's fur are likely to occur as well. Similarly, there is a whole spectrum of tactile signals of varying intensity and completeness associated with mounting, which also seem to have somewhat distinct communicatory functions.

This survey of the syntactics of tactile signals, incomplete though it is, indicates their rich variety, with significant variations in the effectors used and in the spatio-temporal aspects of the signals generated. What inferences can be drawn about the function these signals serve? Some may not even be "signals" in the proper sense of the word. Acts of grooming, for example, may serve the prime function of cleansing the partner's fur, and the concentration of grooming acts upon parts of the recipient that are inaccessible to self-grooming perhaps reflects this possibility. Schaller (Chap. 10, this volume) feels that most grooming in the gorilla can be explained in this way. On the other hand, all who have worked with baboons and rhesus monkeys agree that grooming is such a prominent part of social activity that some additional explanation is called for (DeVore 1963a).

Given, then, that a signal has a communicatory function, how can one set about defining the nature of this function more precisely? There are several ways of approaching this problem, all using as their point of departure the responses evoked in other animals when the signal is perceived. As indicated in the introduction, evidence on this point is not easy to obtain, particularly when the signals are as difficult to identify as those involving the sense of touch. Nevertheless there are indications of several quite different functions for tactile signals.

The tactile signals generated by the feet and teeth that inflict pain and trauma generally elicit either a like reaction, or withdrawal, or submission, and clearly function to repel or overcome the recipient. When the signals are used in a hierarchically organized group, they serve to assert or maintain status (e.g., the baboons, Hall and DeVore, Chap. 3, this volume). Used within a territorial society, they may serve to repel intruders from the territory (e.g., some of the lemurs, J. Petter 1962a). The set of responses evoked is clearly defined. The function of grooming and related tactile stimuli is much more subtle and elusive. All investigators are agreed that it serves, at least in part, to pacify relationships between the communicants; this correlates with its most common use in species in which aggression plays a prominent part in group organization and, in rhesus monkeys and baboons, with its more frequent initiation by females, which rank below males in the hierarchy most of the time. In bonnet macaques males also initiate grooming, and it is perhaps significant that dominance relationships are less prominent than in other macaques (Simonds, Chap. 6, this volume). The commonest response to the initiation of grooming is a general relaxation of tension and the adoption by the recipient of postures that invite further grooming. In one sense it can be regarded as a means of establishing a bond between the signaler and the recipient, for the tactile stimuli show every sign of serving as a reward to the animal which is groomed as seems to be the case in rodents (Eibl-Eibesfeldt 1958; Eisenberg 1962). In another sense it may also indirectly favor a bond by diverting the recipient to an activity — invitation to further grooming — that is incompatible with agonistic behavior, hence perhaps its occurrence in potentially aggressive situations. The use of mounting behavior in nonsexual situations, again in situations that are potentially aggressive, may be interpreted in a similar way but with the roles reversed. The potential aggressor is the donor rather than the recipient of the tactile stimuli, evoked by the visual invitation to mount presented by the opponent. The mounting male often has an erection, and once more this act may have enough in common with normal copulation for the "aggressor" to be rewarded by tactile sensory feedback associated with mounting and thus diverted from overt aggression, even though intromission does not seem to occur. For the recipient the further response evoked by mounting will depend upon its sex and physiological state.

In addition to actual mounting there is a whole spectrum of tactile signals with a sexual connotation that also occur in "friendly behavior." Acts such as embracing in langurs, baboons, gibbons, and chimpanzees often involve contact with the recipient's genitalia and signs of sexual arousal. Hall (1962b) draws attention to Köhler's (1925) remarks about a chimpanzee's placing a hand between a companion's thighs as a form of greeting or taking the companion's hand and placing it on its own groin. Goodall (Chap. 12, this volume) has recorded very similar behavior in wild chimpanzees.

It will be obvious, even from this oversimplified discussion, that the functions of tactile communication are exceedingly complex. The true significance of the communicatory function of some of these tactile signals may lie not so much in increasing the probability of a certain response in the recipient as in decreasing the probability of some other response that might otherwise be expected to occur. In this respect they resemble certain submissive or appeasement signals of other animals (Marler 1961), and they share the characteristic of being difficult to analyze by simple observation for this very reason. Only with the most careful statistical data on the sequence patterning of the behavior that precedes and follows these signals, such as Altmann (1962a) has collected in rhesus monkeys on Cayo Santiago, is there any hope of attaining a complete understanding of the information that these tactile signals actually communicate.

## AUDITORY COMMUNICATION

Once the technical difficulties of recording and analyzing sound signals are overcome, auditory signals lend themselves to study much more readily than signals perceived by the other sensory modes. The main advantage lies in the ease of isolating the significant elements from the background of other stimuli generated by the behavior of the signaling animal. The salient characters of visual signals are especially difficult to isolate, even in an experimental situation, and in describing them it is hard to know where to begin. In describing auditory signals one knows at least enough to concentrate on transmitted sound, preferably as received by a microphone and amplifiers with somewhat the same characteristics as the hearing equipment of the species being studied. Of course the problem still remains to determine whether all the properties of a signal are required in a particular communicatory situation, or whether some are redundant and this is especially difficult with the kinds of sound signals that many primates use.

### Nonvocal Sound

The main concern is with sounds generated by specialized vocal organs and their associated resonating structures — sounds that may be spoken of as vocalizations. Animals also generate sound in a host of different ways in simple locomotion and other activities by colliding with objects in their environment and by striking their own bodies. Here too there is evidence of specialization toward a communicatory function, yet it should not be forgotten that even the most incidental and commonplace sound can often serve the important function of informing nearby companions of the presence and position of the one making the noise and even something of what it is doing. Furthermore, in active animals the very ubiquity of such sounds can endow not only their production but also their cessation with a dramatic signal quality. The sudden checking of all sound emission, vocal and otherwise, is probably the most widespread means of disseminating alarm in animal groups. Simple respiration can, of course, readily generate sound and the sudden intake and holding of the breath in alarm that occurs in man is perhaps a relic of this arresting of sound production. This very effective means of communication also eliminates clues that might betray position to an enemy. It has the unique advantage that the "signal" is created by actually withholding energy from sound-producing structures.

Many monkeys and apes shake branches in the course of aggressive display (e.g., red spider monkeys, Carpenter 1934; gorillas, Schaller 1963, this volume; baboons, Hall 1962b, Hall and DeVore this volume; chimpanzees, Goodall, Reynolds this volume; rhesus, Hinde and Rowell 1962, Conaway and Koford in press), generating noise that may communicate something to the opponent. Several species produce less generalized sounds by striking the ground or the bases of trees with the palm of the hand or foot. In the chimpanzee these slaps are sometimes organized into "drumming," consisting of 2 to 13 rapid blows upon the buttresses of certain kinds of trees. Gorillas make a somewhat similar sound in a quite different way, by beating the chest with partially cupped hands. Schaller's careful study has shown that the sound produced varies with the age, size, and sex of the animal. Large males are the most distinctive and sound like a gourd being tapped, apparently because of the air sacs on the chest, which are inflated just prior to beating. Air sacs of various types are common in primates (review in Andrew 1963), but only in the gorilla are they known to be used as a drum.

There can be no doubt that these trains of sound pulses, with a fairly consistent rate and duration, serve as signals to communicate with other members of the species over considerable distances (Schaller 1963, this volume; Reynolds this volume). In view of their highly organized structure they will arbitrarily be considered together with vocalizations in the following discussion, while the less specific sounds made by single slaps, branch-shaking, and other activities will be excluded.

**Vocalizations**

Primates are equipped with ample means for generating vocalizations of a wide variety of types and degrees of loudness. One approach to vocalizations would be in terms of the mechanism by which each one is produced. Here the problem will be attacked differently, from a syntactical point of view, by reference to the structure of the sounds produced, as heard by the human ear and revealed by the sound spectrograph. The method must initially be an inductive one. As suggested in the introduction, the observer must expose himself to the vocal behavior of the species in as many different situations and seasons as possible. At first the impression will be a confused one, and it will be impossible to decide whether two different calls should be placed in separate categories or whether they are variations within the same category. Gradually some of the gaps are filled while others remain, with the result that the more or less variable sounds are grouped around a series of "modes" with gaps between them. Intermediate forms are uncommon or absent, either because they are outside the animal's vocal compass or because the circumstances associated with them are uncommon. Thus a typological series of categories is set up. Some signals will be stereo-typed, varying little from one rendering to another; others will be highly variable. The first concern will be the number of vocal signal types represented, irrespective of the degree to which each can vary.

Attention will mainly be focused on the repertoire of adult animals of both sexes. It is perhaps useful to be reminded of the need to take account of age classes in setting up the initial typological classification. It is known that many animal sounds develop gradually with growth, and longitudinal samples encompassing several developmental stages would undoubtedly blur many of the categories that can be seen in one age class. In practice it is probably easier to work back to the developmental aspects after the adult categories have been set up. It may also be noted that the question of function is excluded from this initial description and classification. In practice investigators can never exclude considerations of function completely, even in the very first observations made. Nevertheless, in dealing with communication signals the explicit consideration of function should probably be postponed until the basic typological categories are set up, to avoid the dangers of circular reasoning. By the same token, the terms used as labels of the signals should be descriptive of the signal or its physical structure and not of its function.

### Size of the Repertoire

Suppose then that one surveys the data on the vocal signals of the various primates upon which data are available, how many of these signal "modes" are generally found in the repertoire of adult animals? It will be clear from the outset that the available data do not permit accurate judgments on this and most reliance must be placed upon the results of investigators working under field or semifield conditions (e.g., Hinde and Rowell 1962). Given reasonably intensive study over an appreciable time, the most serious source of error is likely to arise by the subdivision of one continuously variable mode into discrete categories. This is particularly likely to occur with highly variable signals, such as are common in primates, if only because continuously varying data are easier to take down if divided into discrete classes. Bearing this in mind as a source of error, a survey of the data reveals a spectrum of repertoire sizes in the various species ranging from estimates of 7 in the brown lemur to 25 in the Japanese macaque. Probably neither of these extreme values is strictly comparable with the other estimates. Andrew's (1963) data on *Lemur fulvus* come from captive animals. J. Petter's field work (1962a) on the lemurs suggests a rich repertoire, although he was unable to get complete descriptions of all of the sounds. Thus there is probably no reason to think that the vocal repertoire of prosimians is smaller than that of other primates. In the Japanese macaque a number of gradations of the same basic type are listed separately and probably should be considered together for the present purpose. The same may be true in the howler. In the rhesus, for which the best data are available (Rowell and Hinde 1962; Altmann 1962), several of the calls listed separately are known to grade into each other (e.g., Rowell 1962).

It begins to appear that a repertoire of from about 10 to about 15 basic sound-signal types is rather characteristic of nonhuman primates as a whole. In some it may prove to be smaller or larger, but it is doubtful if the limits will be exceeded by very much. Perhaps the largest repertoires will be found in the prosimians or in some of the forest-dwelling monkeys, rather than in the higher apes, when these forms are studied as intensively as the rhesus monkey has been. Comparison with other highly vocal groups of vertebrates that have been closely examined reveals an approximately similar repertoire size (Table 16–2). Viewed in this way there seems to be nothing clear-cut to distinguish primates from other comparable animal groups.

TABLE 16–2. NUMBERS OF SOUND SIGNALS IN THE REPERTOIRE OF PRIMATES, SOME OTHER MAMMALS, AND ONE BIRD

| Species | Authority | Number | Comments |
|---|---|---|---|
| Gorilla | Schaller | 11 | Includes chest beating. These are the basic sounds. Schaller lists 22 altogether, some only heard once. |
| Chimpanzee | Reynolds | 13 | Including drumming. |
| Baboon | DeVore, Hall | 10 | Including tooth grinding. |
| Rhesus | Rowell and Hinde | 17 | Semicaptive animals. Altmann (1962a) records a total of 17, including juveniles, from field data. |
| Japanese macaque | Mizuhara | 25 | In 5 basic groups. Some are probably gradations of one type. |
| Langur | Jay | 9 | Includes tooth grinding. |
| Howler | Carpenter | c. 20 | Similar totals from Collias and Southwick (1952), Altmann (1959). |
| Brown lemur | Andrew | 7 | Petter (1962) and Andrew (1963) have valuable data on many prosimians, though the totals are not exhaustive. |
| Tree shrew (Tupaia) | Sprankel, Kaufmann | 5–8 | |
| Coati | Kaufmann | 7 | |
| Prairie dog | King | 10 | |
| Chaffinch | Marler | 12 | |

## Discrete and Graded Signals

When the degree of variation within the various categories of sound signal is considered, the situation is very different. In most birds studied so far the range of variation within each mode is fairly limited, to the extent that one is tempted to call them *discrete* types. In the chaffinch, which the author has studied, there are 12 basic vocal types in the adult, only three of which show a significant degree of variability. As Rowell and Hinde (1962) have pointed out, study of some of the more highly social bird species may reveal more variable signals, but the majority even of these will probably prove to be discrete.

Information on prosimians and lower simians is sparse, but what there is suggests that here too a significant proportion at least of the vocal repertoire consists of relatively discrete types. Andrew's (1963) survey of the vocalizations of captive brown lemurs shows a number of clearly demarcated categories. Although some are undoubtedly graded, such as the "squeaks" and "shrieks" and perhaps the "coughs" and the "click-grunts," the author was evidently able to set up separate categories without too much trouble. The few species of *Cercopithecus* and *Colobus* that have been studied in the field all seem to have at least some relatively stereotyped calls (Haddow 1952; Hill and Booth 1957; Ullrich 1961), although intensive study will undoubtedly reveal variability. As an exception to the generalization, the red colobus may be of special interest in view of Hill and Booth's (1957) suggestion that, unlike the other species they studied, most of its vocalizations are variations on one basic pattern.

Andrew (1963) makes special mention of the high degree of variability of some of the sounds emitted by some of the marmosets. Langurs have at least two clearly described graded systems, the "grunt-bark" continuum and the "squeal-scream" continuum. Other sound signals vary in some degree although the categories are distinct (Jay, Chap. 7, this volume). The situation in the gibbon is probably rather similar (Carpenter 1940). In baboons it is more complicated, with a number of intergrading systems. Of the various adult sounds (Hall and DeVore, Chap. 3, this volume, Table 3–5) the two kinds of grunting (Nos. 13 and 14) grade into each other and perhaps into roaring (No. 3) (*cf.* Bolwig 1959a). The three types of bark (Nos. 1, 8, and 12) also grade into each other, and so do screeching and yakking. Investigators of baboons repeatedly emphasize the difficulty of classifying the sounds into separate categories.

It will be clear that several of the estimates in Table 16–2 of the size of the repertoire of sound types defined as suggested are too large. Nowhere is this more evident than in the vocal behavior of the rhesus monkey, which has been studied more closely than that of any other species (Altmann 1962a; Rowell 1962; Rowell and Hinde 1962; Andrew 1963). "One of its most striking features is the possibility of an almost infinite range of intermediates between the main sounds" (Rowell and Hinde 1962) (see Fig. 16–3). Rowell (1962) has given a beautiful example of such a graded system used by rhesus monkeys in agonistic situations. A set of nine sounds is listed (see Fig. 16–3b) and described by Rowell as follows:

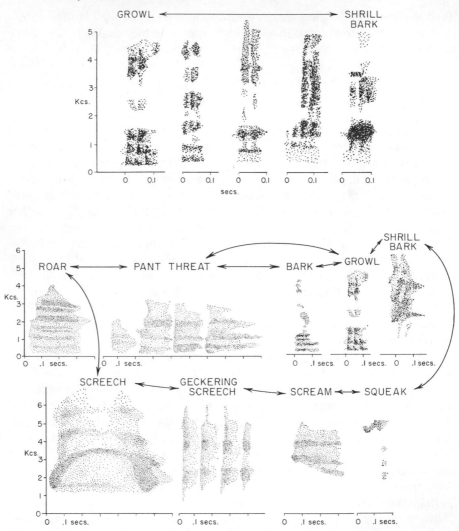

Fig. 16–3a. A graded series of rhesus monkey sounds from the growl to the shrill bark (*after Rowell and Hinde 1962*). b. A more extensive graded series of rhesus sounds encompassing nine calls. Note the complex relationship between the pant-threat, the bark, and the growl (*after Rowell 1962*).

*Roar:* loud, fairly long noise made by a very confident animal, when threatening another of inferior rank, or when protected by the cage from actual contact with the other. *Pant-threat:* a similar noise to the roar but broken up into short "syllables," made by a less confident animal wanting the support of the rest of the group in its attack. *Bark:* rather like a single bark of a dog, given by a threatening animal insufficiently aggressive to move towards the other. *Growl:* Differentiated from a bark in being quieter and rather shriller, and broken up with very short sound units, like a rolled 'r,' given by a mildly alarmed animal. *Shrill-bark:* the alarm call of the species, probably given to predators in the wild. *Screech:* typically has an abrupt pitch change up and then down. Made when threatening a higher ranking animal and when excited and slightly alarmed generally. *Geckering screech:* A similar noise to the previous one, but broken into syllables. Made by an animal being threatened by another. *Scream:* Shorter than the screech and without the pronounced rise and fall. Made by a losing monkey in a fight while being bitten. *Squeaks:* short, very high pitched noises made by a defeated and exhausted monkey at the end of a fight (pages 93–94).

Rowell (1962) has been able to show that these nine sounds actually constitute one system, linked by a continuous series of intermediates. Moreover there is one example of multidimensional variation, the pant-threat grading independently into three other calls (Fig. 16–3b). Here, then, is an extraordinarily rich system of connected variations encompassing a large part of the adult vocal repertoire, manifesting the greatest complexity that has yet been described in the vocal system of any animal. Rowell's descriptions also demonstrate correlations with a continuously varying set of social and environmental situations, a point which will be discussed later.

In the course of their field studies of chimpanzees the Reynoldses (Chap. 11, this volume) were able to make recordings of some of the chimpanzee's sounds. They are highly vocal, much more so than gorillas (Schaller, Chap. 10, this volume), and the Reynoldses were able to distinguish a considerable number of distinct sounds (Reynolds and Reynolds, Table 11–6, this volume). Preliminary analyses of some of the sounds suggest that here too there is continuous gradation between some of them (see Figs. 16–4 and 16–5). Again it seems that this gradation can involve several dimensions independently, so that a "long hoot" may be shortened to a "panting hoot," and still further shortened to become a "shrill bark." Alternatively it may undergo a change in spectral composition to become a "scream" or "squeal." It is conceivable that further study might show that the entire vocal repertoire of adult chimpanzees is actually one continuously varying system, with whatever signal modes that are to be found determined by the frequency with which appropriate conditions are encountered. Schaller's work (Chap. 10, this volume) suggests a similar possibility in the gorilla.

It appears then that some of the higher monkeys and apes have a vocal system in which stereotyped or discrete signals are rare. Signals that can very in structure, in several dimensions, account for a major proportion of the repertoire. This issue will be returned to later. First the variability of characteristics other than signal form will be considered. Many of the signals can vary in loudness in accordance with the context in which they are used, as Jay has described with the grunts of langurs. More significant

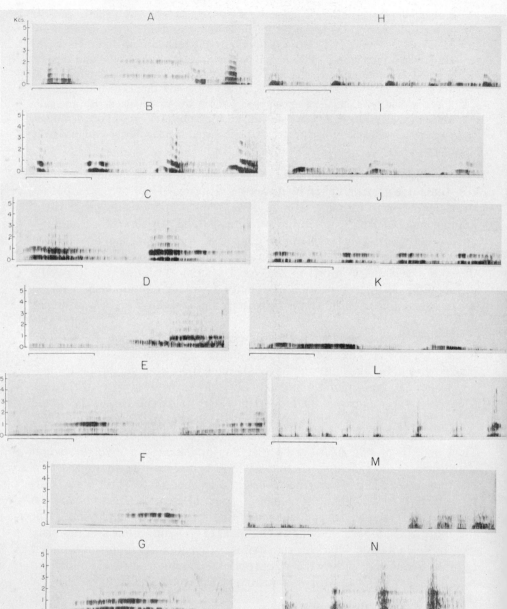

Fig. 16–4. Chimpanzee sounds recorded by Reynolds in the field, selected to illustrate their graded nature. A–G: A series of calls of increasing length but similar spectral structure. The shorter calls have a barklike quality (A). The longer ones sound more like howls (E–G). H–K: Another series of calls of increasing duration with emphasis upon the lower frequencies. They have a less strident tone than the previous series, ranging from a bark to a moan. L–N: Three series of barks, some short, some long. These have a harsh, grating, almost like grunting, quality

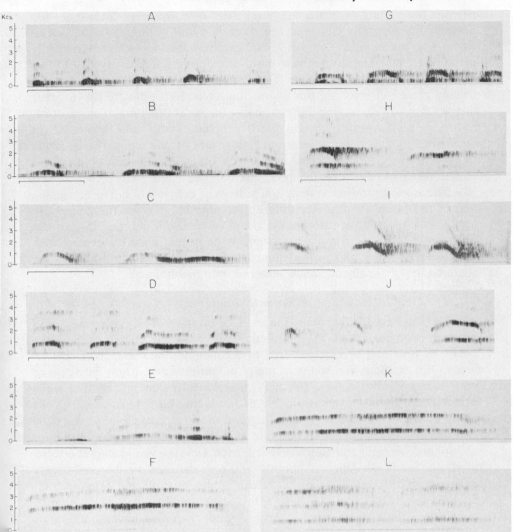

associated with a wide range of frequencies and a somewhat broken structure. Preliminary study suggests that the three types of spectral structure represented here can be imposed on calls with widely varying temporal characteristics.

Fig. 16—5. A selection of calls from Reynolds' data. A–D: A series of hooting sounds ranging from short barklike calls (A, B) to longer sounds that fluctuate in pitch. E–L: These are selected to illustrate the inclusion of a screaming quality in sounds of a different type. E is a fairly musical sound. F and K are screams with rather different harmonic emphasis. G and J are hooting sounds with a tremulous squealing quality. H and I are squeals that trail off into screams. Once more the data suggest a continuously graded system.

perhaps are variations in the temporal pattern of delivery. Once more the descriptions are sadly deficient, but there is a hint of some striking variations. For example, the "shrill bark" of the baboon is characteristically given just once. The "two-phase bark" is often repeated every two to five seconds, over a minute or more. The "doglike bark," on the other hand, is usually given in bursts of from two to four calls. In addition to these rather distinct ways of delivering different calls, the actual rate may vary according to the circumstances, as in the "two-phase bark" and, above all, in "grunting," which may range from a slow rate of one every two seconds to an extremely rapid sequence, in which other animals may join in as a chorus (Hall and DeVore, Chap. 3, this volume, Table 3–5.).

These variations in the temporal pattern of delivery of different signals, and of the same signal under different conditions, may be fundamentally related to the kinds of information they can convey and therefore to the function they can perform. Again there is an urgent need for descriptions of these properties, and as in defining variation in form, large samples are required if statistically adequate material is to be obtained.

### The General Structure of Primate Sounds

To a person familiar with the calls of birds most of the sounds used by such primates as the rhesus monkey are strikingly coarse, lacking the purity of tone and precise patterns of frequency modulation that characterize, for example, the songs of many passerine birds. Many birds do of course make harsh noises. Further reflection also reminds us that some primates are by no means incapable of producing birdlike sounds (see the many examples in Andrew 1963). Many of the sounds of *Colobus* and *Cercopithecus* species appear to be quite as long and as complex in structure as bird sounds (Hill and Booth 1957; Ulrich 1961). Even in the repertoire of rhesus monkeys, langurs, gibbons, and chimpanzees there are relatively pure drawn-out sounds (rhesus, "clear" calls, Rowell and Hinde 1962; langurs, the "whoop," Jay, Chap. 7, this volume; gibbons, type 1 "hoots," Carpenter 1940; chimpanzees, "howls" and "moaning hoots," Reynolds and Reynolds, Chap. 11, this volume). Primate vocal systems, then, are evidently capable of producing sounds that are musical in tone.

Nevertheless, in the higher forms there seems to be a predominance of sounds that have a relatively wide frequency spectrum, with most of the energy in relatively low frequencies (below four or five kilocycles per second), without much intricate changing of frequency; the changes in pitch that do occur are slow and are often blurred by the "noise" that is also created.

It may already have occurred to the reader that most of the purer sounds produced are also the ones that are loud and serve for communication over distance to maintain group spacing. Coincidentally the drumming and chest beating of chimpanzees and gorillas, also among the more highly structured sounds produced by apes, are distance signals. This might be related in part simply to the efficiency of transmission over distances. But if this were the only correlation, why should many of the close-range signals of prosimians and monkeys be structured, as they seem to be, rather than bursts of poorly structured "noise"? It seems likely that the problem of species identification also enters in here and that the degree of structuring of sound signals relates, at least in part, to the requirements of species specificity.

### Species Specificity in Primate Sound Signals

When animals are communicating under natural conditions, there is always a danger that alien sounds will intrude into the system and cause confusion. There are two situations in which the danger will be minimal: when a species is living out of earshot of any organisms similar in size and structure, and when sounds are used at sufficiently close range that visual cues can confirm the identity of the signaling animal. Both these conditions are satisfied in many of the higher primates considered here. In rhesus monkeys, baboons, gorillas, and chimpanzees the social unit is a more-or-less compact group, permitting almost constant reference to visual cues during intragroup communication. Furthermore, at least the last three are relatively isolated from close relatives of a similar size.

The contrast that is being sought here is with the condition in, say, some of the *Cercopithecus* species, which, in forests of the southwest Gold Coast, may be within hearing range of as many as six other species of monkey, either other *Cercopithecus*, or species of *Colobus* and *Cercocebus* (Booth 1956). It is true that these species occupy different levels in the forest much of the time, and if they were consistent in this, confusion would only be likely to arise between loud signals, used for distance communication. However, Haddow (1952) and Booth (1956) have shown that they frequently mingle in mixed groups when taking certain foods. *Cercopithecus petaurista*, for example, has been seen in mixed feeding parties with *Cercopithecus aethiops*, *C. campbelli*, and *C. mona*. In such circumstances the possibility of interspecific confusion is greatly increased and, correspondingly, the limited evidence available on the sound signals of such forms suggests that they are more highly structured and that this structuring is used at least in part to maintain species specificity in a major proportion of the vocal repertoire. As a result an experienced observer can distinguish between these many cohabiting, forest-dwelling monkeys by their sound signals (e.g., Haddow 1952). This is also the situation obtaining in most species of birds, which also mingle with large numbers of more or less similarly sized and structured species much of the time, and here again we find that many of the sound signals are specifically distinct (e.g., Thorpe 1962).

The argument being advanced is that the close-knit, terrestrial, or semiterrestrial social grouping and the relative isolation from numbers of cohabiting species of similar size and structure correlates significantly with the relatively ill-defined structure of most of the sound signals of the rhesus monkey, baboons, chimpanzees, and gorillas. By thus escaping from the demands of a high degree of species specificity, which calls both for structured sounds and for a relatively low degree of variability, they have been permitted to exploit an alternative type of sound system, which is noisier and simpler, in the sense of the basic structure of the sounds that are used, and yet much more complex in the development of these subtle continuous and multidimensional variations of the sound signals.

### The Communicatory Significance of Sound Signals

Without the most detailed knowledge of the responses evoked by sound signals, it is very difficult to specify the information that they transmit from one individual to another, particularly when they are cooperating with visual signals much of the time. In the pragmatic terminology of Morris (1946; cf. Marler 1961) identifiors, appraisors, prescriptors, and designators are all represented in primate sound signals. "Identifiors," disposing the recipient to direct his responses to a certain spatio-temporal region, are clearly present. In the opinion of many investigators a large part of the function of close-range sounds in such animals as baboons is to attract the gaze of the recipient who may then receive further information from visual signals that are emitted simultaneously. "Appraisors," disposing the recipient to respond preferentially to certain objects rather than to others, thus embodying a quantitative type of information, are probably represented particularly in the temporal pattern of delivery of some of the sounds. A high rate of grunting in baboons, for example, may be more likely to compete with other stimuli in controlling the behavior of a recipient than a lower rate. In contrast to this type of coding of appraisive information, "prescriptors" that dispose the recipient to make a particular class of responses rely more upon qualitatively different signals to specify different types of response. Thus different calls are used in asserting dominance over a rival and in alerting the group to the presence of a predator. "Designators," closely related to "prescriptors," dispose the receiver toward response sequences associated with particular objects, animate or inanimate, and the cry of a lost juvenile would convey this kind of information. In primates, as in birds, several types of designative information can be discerned.

As a rough comparison, in birds species-specific and sometimes group-specific (dialect) information is prominent, whereas in the higher monkeys and apes it is not. Sex-specific information occurs to some extent in both, particularly in distance sounds. Individual information has been commented upon in certain signals. Rowell and Hinde (1962) note that the clear calls of their captive rhesus monkeys were often individually identifiable, and Jay (Chap. 7, this volume) makes the same comment about the "belch" of langurs. Whether the individuality would persist in all situations or whether it is determined by status in the dominance hierarchy at the time is uncertain, but in either case it would suffice for individual recognition as long as dominance relationships are stable.

Of the other types of designative information thought to be transmitted by bird sound signals, environmental information concerning physical objects such as food or predators is probably found less often in primates. The range of alarm calls is generally limited. There are no sounds specifically to bring companions to food or water, such as there are in birds (e.g., Konishi 1963), and in honey bees (von Frisch 1954), although information about resting places may be conveyed, for example, as one of the functions of the grunting chorus of baboons (Hall and DeVore, Chap. 3, this volume). Certainly there is no evidence of a particularly rich content of environmental information. Motivational information on the other hand is abundantly represented, conveying the subtle changes in mood of the members of the group and providing for coordination of its various social activities, particularly those associated with the dominance hierarchy. It is here that the continuously varying structure of many of the signals permits a subtlety of portrayal of slight shifts in motivation that would be impossible with more stereotyped signals. The same expressiveness can be seen in visual signals, both in primates and in other animals, but there is no other recorded example of sound signals that can match the representation of varying levels of motivation seen in the primates. As a further point, it has been suggested that appraisive information is conveyed by the temporal pattern of delivery, but it may be that qualitative gradations in the signals also convey such information, if, for example, certain tonal qualities obtain higher priority in evoking responses than others. It is admittedly difficult to specify the information content of these highly graded signals, but it has at least been established that there is a type of system in apes, baboons, and macaques developed on a scale not matched by any other animal group that has been described.

*Sound Signal Structure in Relation to Function*

When most of the available data consist of verbal descriptions of sounds it is very difficult to determine what parallels exist in the structure of sounds used in similar situations by the various species. Nevertheless, some correspondence can be discerned. Barks, often shrill ones, are widely used to signal alarm by gorillas, chimpanzees, baboons, rhesus monkeys, and langurs. It is noticeable that none of these have developed the high-pitched thin whistle used by many birds when strongly alarmed, perhaps because its ventriloquial property would be of little value to large species, which, with ample means of defense, are so much less vulnerable to sudden attack by predators. This interpretation is reinforced by Andrew's (1963) evidence that some prosimians have developed this type of whistle as an alarm call.

As another parallel, screeching and screaming sounds are a widespread sign of distress with an almost universal significance. Growling, consisting of a rapid repetition of fairly soft, short, low-frequency sounds, is widely used in association with agonistic behavior by gorillas (annoyed grunts), chimpanzees (gruff bark?), rhesus monkeys (growl), bonnet macaques (growl?), langurs (belch). There are several records of soft grunts used by groups of animals as they move along, apparently as a means of maintaining contact with each other; these sounds occur in gorillas (soft grunt), chimpanzees (grunt), baboons (grunt), and langurs (grunt). Finally, although we have been concerned in this discussion with adult sounds, we may note that clicking and chittering sounds are used by many, though not all of the animals discussed here, as well as by many other lower primates, insectivores, and carnivores (Kaufmann 1962; Andrew 1963).

In a general way functional significance can be assigned to some of the characteristics of the sounds used in these different situations. The clicking sounds of the juveniles of some species, with rapidly repeated clicklike pulses having a wide frequency spectrum, are among the easiest sounds to locate in space accurately and quickly, and are less likely to be masked by environmental sounds than pure tones might be — all factors consistent with the function of alerting and guiding the parent to a lost or endangered infant (Andrew 1963). The grunting sound is soft and needs to travel only short distances. It is low pitched and brief, demanding a minimum of disruption of other ongoing activities such as searching for food or eating. Unless other factors interfere, these considerations would be likely to affect any species that forages in a close-knit group, hence perhaps the general similarity of the sounds used. They are unlikely to be affected by demands for a high degree of species specificity.

Growling sounds seem to recur very widely in aggressive situations in animals, even birds, that use the mouth as a weapon in fighting, and they are less evident in, say, ungulates, whose feet and horns may be more important. This particular type of sound may occur partly because it can be produced with the mouth closed or open in varying degree. Perhaps, also, the ease with which its intensity can be varied and the speed with which a change in rate of the separate pulses can be perceived by the recipient make it particularly suited to convey information about rapid changes in the motivation of participants in an agonistic encounter.

Intense screaming is used by many animals in similar situations. It is commonly associated with the combination of open mouth (the grimace, see Andrew 1963), violent expiration, and constriction of some parts of the vocal tract under the influence of strong activity of the sympathetic portion of the autonomic nervous system that occurs in fearful situations.

The alarm bark is a loud sound with a relatively wide frequency spectrum and with a sharp beginning and end, all aiding its locatability. It is probably as brief as it can be without a loss of energy and conveys its message as rapidly and as far as possible. Finally, it has been suggested that in many of the lower primates the requirements of species specificity modify the structure of many of the signals, especially those used over distances to maintain the spacing of groups. To achieve species specificity a larger range of sound properties must be exploited than in close-range communication, hence the extended and more highly structured nature and purer tone of many of these sounds. In higher primates only a minimum of the sound signals are so affected, but species specificity may prove to be an influence on much of the vocal repertoire of some lower forms living with numbers of closely related species.

Most of these speculations are poorly substantiated, even by observations, and it will be many years before they can be subjected to the critical test of experimentation. Only by synthesizing sound signals that are modified in various ways, and presenting them to animals, is it possible to show which of the properties of sounds are required to evoke the appropriate response and which are unnecessary. A given property may be significant in some communicatory situations and not in others. Even when signals are relatively stereotyped such experiments are exceedingly difficult and time-consuming (e.g., the white-throated sparrow, Falls 1963). It will be particularly challenging to work with the extensively graded signals we have been discussing, not only because of the problems of synthesizing the signals, but also because of the difficulty of discovering the situations in which their function is properly realized, arising in part from their extensive involvement with visual signals, under natural conditions.

## VISUAL COMMUNICATION

The close-knit social grouping of the higher primates, with the individual members in direct view of each other much of the time, sets the stage for the development of the extraordinarily subtle and elaborate systems of visual communication revealed in every new study made. Little can be indicated here beyond some broad generalizations with implications for our consideration of communication systems as a whole. In the description of visual signals it is difficult to separate the signal from its background. It is hard enough to describe colors, postures, and movements in terms corresponding to the stimulus pattern actually transmitted to the recipient, and this is only a beginning. Primates are relatively long-lived, and in many social groups all individuals are known to each other and have a more or less predictable relationship to each other depending on their relative dominance status. There is ample evidence that the effect of a signal is determined not only by its intrinsic properties, but also by which individual in the group gives it. Thus a complete description should include both the posture and movement and also the characters that permit individual identification of the signaling animal. As if this were not complex enough, there is also evidence that the identity of animals standing close to the signaler and the behavior of other members of the audience may drastically influence the response evoked in a particular recipient (e.g., in rhesus monkeys, Altmann 1962a; baboons, Hall and DeVore, Chap. 3, this volume), requiring that a complete definition of the visual signal include information on position and identity of other members of the group. By these standards the highly simplified discussion that follows, based on the parts of the body used in various types of visual signals, is hardly more than a point of departure for more sophisticated analysis.

### Parts of the Body Involved in Signaling

The very fact that the whole external aspect of an animal is visible to its companions makes any part of its body a potential signal. Perhaps the easiest place to start is with the entire silhouette, which undoubtedly plays a major role in species recognition. Haddow (1952) has pointed out the distinctive features of some of the East African species of *Cercopithecus* and also comments on the distinctive appearance of *Colobus* monkeys (see also Ullrich 1961). These same characters presumably contribute to the process of identification by the monkeys themselves. At a finer level the prevalent postures of different members of a group of one species often correlate with status in the dominance hierarchy, thus providing a means of individual recognition (e.g., rhesus monkeys, Hinde and Rowell 1962). External morphology is not static, but changes with time, and there are many species in which separate age classes are distinguished by other characters in addition to size. The silver back clearly identifies fully mature male gorillas (Schaller, Chap. 10, this volume), and the long mane characterizes adult male baboons. Again, juveniles often have a distinctive appearance that has clear communicatory significance. "The coat color of the newborn infant of all species of Old-World monkeys for which information is available is different from that of an adult of the same species" (Jay 1962). In langurs the infant coat is dark; as it starts to change to white at two or three months of age the previously intense interest of females of all ages wanes. Booth (1962) describes a similar situation in various *Cercopithecus* monkeys and presents evidence that a moving natal skin in the hands of an experimenter is particularly potent in eliciting approach and stance threat from adults of the same species. There may also be short-term changes in external morphology. The brightly colored, swollen sexual skin of estrous females of most macaques, mangabeys (Zuckerman 1932), baboons, and chimpanzees must surely serve as a visual signal to males, presumably reinforcing the olfactory signals also likely to be involved.

### *Facial Expressions*

While the whole animal is often involved in the rapid movements of muscles providing the repertoire of dynamic visual signals, there are certain parts of the body that seem to assume a particularly significant role. If one were pressed to name the most important parts concerned with visual communication within the group in the higher monkeys and apes, the face would certainly be selected (van Hooff 1962), but it would be difficult to choose between the eyes and the mouth. Perhaps the most widely shared aspect of threat behavior in the species studied is the direct gaze, often sufficient in itself for a dominant to displace a subordinate, in gorillas (Schaller, Chap. 10, this volume), baboons (Hall and DeVore, Chap. 3, this volume), rhesus and bonnet macaques (Altmann 1962a; Hinde and Rowell 1962; Simonds, Chap. 6, this volume), and langurs (Jay, Chap. 7, this volume). Conversely, the same authors note that looking away, or rather looking anywhere except toward the opponent, is a widespread sign of submission, being carried as far in the gorilla as shaking the head from side to side (Schaller). In the macaques and baboons this prominent use of the eyes as signals is further embellished by eyelid fluttering in which raising of the brows and lowering of the lids serves to expose the pale colored lids against the darker background of the face in a readily perceived signal. The conspicuous coloring around the eyes and on the brows of many mangabeys, guenons, and guerezas (e.g., Sanderson 1957) is also notable, although according to van Hooff (1962) there is relatively little movement of these parts, at least in the two latter groups. There may also be distinctive head positions as in langurs (Jay, Chap. 7, this volume) in which glaring at another individual is accompanied by tilting back of the head and lowering of the eyelids.

The mouth may take a number of different shapes, which have been intensively analyzed from a comparative point of view by Andrew (1963) and van Hooff (1962). There seem to be three main conditions. In the "open-mouth threat" (rhesus, Hinde and Rowell 1962) the corners of the mouth are drawn forward and the lips pressed tightly against the teeth, which are not exposed (Fig. 16–6). By contrast, in the "grimace" or "frightened grin" (Hinde and Rowell 1962) the corners of the mouth are drawn back, exposing the teeth (Fig. 16–7). There is a wide range of intermediates between these extremes, including a varying degree of opening of jaws, lip retraction, and so on. As a further pattern, in more neutral or pacificatory situations, the mouth may be involved in "lip smacking," (Fig. 16–8) in which the mouth corners are brought forward and the lips make kissing movements without the teeth coming together (Fig. 16–9b), this sequence and the rather similar "teeth chattering" expression having much in common with use of the mouth in grooming the fur of another animal (van Hooff 1962). Some other species use a rapid in-and-out movement of the tongue instead (e.g., langurs, Jay, Chap. 7, this volume; howlers, Carpenter, Chap. 8, this volume). In addition to those basic patterns, some species seem to use yawning as a visual signal (Fig. 16–9a, see also Hall and DeVore, Chap. 3, this volume). Also pouting of the lips occurs in certain situations, with an extreme development in the "flehmen" expression of the pig-tailed macaque when he smells the genital region of a female in estrus (van Hooff 1962).

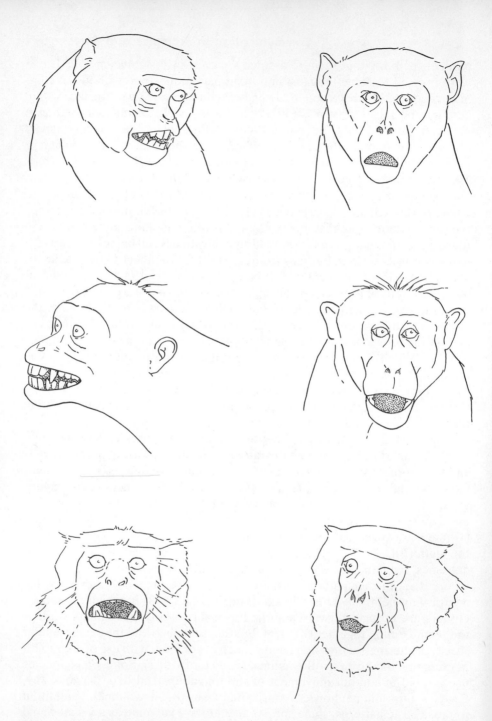

Fig. 16–6. Equivalent expressions of the "grimace" (*left*) and the "open-mouthed threat" (*right*) in rhesus monkeys (*top*), bonnet macaques (*middle*), langurs (*bottom*). Note the visibility of the teeth in the grimace (*after Hinde and Rowell 1962, and photographs by Dr. Paul Simonds and Dr. Phyllis Jay*).

572

Fig. 16–7. Facial expressions of captive crab-eating macaques. (*Top*) "Open-mouth threat." (*Bottom*) The subordinate animal on the right is showing a typical "grimace." (*Photographs by Suzanne Chevalier*)

Fig. 16–8. Two pictures of crab-eating macaques illustrating the difference in the muzzle of a mildly threatening animal (*top center*), with eyelids exposed, and an animal showing lip-smacking (*bottom*). (*Photographs by Suzanne Chevalier*)

The ears may also be moved. In many agonistic and pacificatory situations they are drawn back onto the head. In most of the higher primates this and an erect position seem to exhaust the possibilities, but the more labile pinnae of some of the prosimians are capable of a wider range of movements. Also the hair on the neck and back may be raised, serving as background for the face (Fig. 16–9a).

The sum total of this wide variety of facial expressions, combined with the elaborate adornment of the face in many species, is an exceptionally rich repertoire of visual signals, many of which are graded. Furthermore, in addition to variation in qualitative structure, some of them can vary in their temporal pattern of delivery, particularly the movements of the eyes, lids, and brows, adding a further dimension of signal properties. Finally, the elements of facial expressions can sometimes be recombined in different ways, thus creating the possibility of still more, distinct, composite signals. For example, van Hooff (1962) points out that some of the mouth positions can occur either with a direct gaze or while avoiding looking at the recipient, the choice of one alternative presumably modifying the significance of the over-all expression. Kohts (1935) also draws attention to the composite nature of some facial expressions in the study of the behavior of captive chimpanzees.

### Tail, Body, and Limbs

In many mammals the tail is of special significance in communication (Bopp 1954) and primates are no exception, although the movements vary greatly from one species to another. Thus, placing the tail between the legs seems to be characteristic of subordinate rhesus monkeys that are attacked by a dominant, but is more typical of the dominant animal among baboons

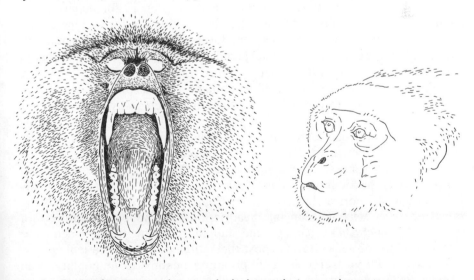

Fig. 16–9a. (Left) Yawning by a male baboon during an harrassment sequence. b. (Right) The lip-smacking expression in a rhesus monkey (after Hinde and Rowell 1962 and a photograph by Dr. Irven DeVore).

(Hinde and Rowell 1962; Hall and DeVore, Chap. 3, this volume). Conversely, a raised tail in rhesus monkeys often signifies a dominant animal (Altmann 1962a), and Itani (1954) has made a detailed correlation between tail position and status in the dominance hierarchy in Japanese macaques, although here too there is a great deal of variation. There may be still less consistency in some other monkeys (e.g., langurs, Jay, Chap. 7, this volume), perhaps partly because the tail of arboreal species must also serve a variety of important locomotor functions. Tail movements upward or to the side are also associated with "presenting" of the anogenital region which occurs as a pacificatory gesture and an invitation to mount (e.g., rhesus monkeys, Altmann 1962a; Hinde and Rowell 1962). In langurs, on the other hand, a lowered tail is part of the female's invitation to mounting (Jay, Chap. 7, this volume). Prosimians have a variety of complex tail movements (e.g., tree shrews, Sprankel 1962; Kaufmann unpublished).

The positions of the body and limbs also contribute to the over-all visual signal. There are various static postures, such as the "presentation for mounting" just described, in which a subordinate animal exposes the anogenital region toward the recipient, although a dynamic element may enter if the signaling animal backs toward the other and glances back over its shoulder (see Fig. 16–10b; also Hall and DeVore, Chap. 3, this volume). Over-all posture may also vary with the situation and dominance status of the individual (e.g., rhesus monkeys, Altmann 1962a; Hinde and Rowell 1962). There are also elaborate postures by which one animal invites another to groom it (Fig. 16–10a). As a special case of a postural signal, the leader of a gorilla group sometimes gets the others to prepare for departure by facing in the chosen direction and standing motionless for as long as ten seconds, with front and hind legs spread farther from each other than usual, although the same effect may be achieved simply by walking off steadily in one direction (Schaller 1963; Chap. 10, this volume).

There is also a wide variety of dynamic postural displays. The mode of carriage often seems to vary with the situation in such a way as to serve as a visual signal, the "strutting walk" of gorillas (Schaller 1963; Chap. 10, this volume) being only one such example. In agonistic encounters such postural displays are particularly prominent. A comparison between the detailed descriptions of aggressive behavior in rhesus (Altmann 1962a; Hinde and Rowell 1962), baboons (Kummer 1957; Hall and DeVore, Chap. 3, this volume) and the gorilla (Schaller 1963; Chap. 10, this volume) reveals the same recurring elements: lunging, head jerking and bobbing, feinting with the hands, branch shaking and ground slapping, charging the opponent. The victim of violent attack shows almost the antithesis of these violent aggressive movements in a crouching or prostrate posture of immobility. Van Hooff (1962) gives further examples and also points out that many static postural elements can be classified according to whether they prepare the animal for advancing toward the opponent, as is common in the dominant animal in an interaction, or whether they are preludes to a retreat as is more

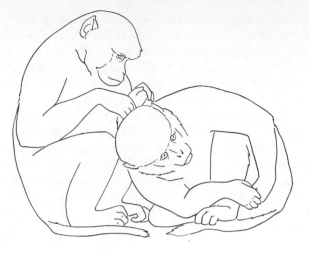

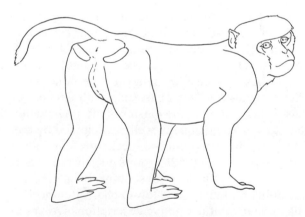

Fig. 16–10a. (*Top*) Grooming of one rhesus monkey by another. *b.* (*Bottom*) Presentation for mounting (*after Altmann 1962a*).

common in the subordinate, if it does not assume a position of crouched immobility.

### Visual Signals as Constellations

In the account of auditory signals we discussed the intermingling of independently varying sound properties, which by this process of recombination served to create new, composite signals. With visual signals the capacity for thus combining several elements is so widespread as to be virtually the rule rather than the exception. This is true, at least in animals like the higher primates, in which so many different parts of the body contribute to the over-all signal. By their nature such signals consist of both spatial and temporal constellations of stimuli, and the total number of elements making up such a constellation may be remarkably large. Consider, for example, the gestures exchanged during an aggressive encounter between two baboons. The eyes, lids, and brows, the lips and teeth, the ears, the limbs and the tail, the trunk and the hair on the shoulders all take on distinctive properties, not only intrinsically but also in their positions relative to each other. These properties may also have dynamic components, changing with time. Added to this there are the qualities identifying the signaler as a particular individual baboon, and thus having an important bearing on the response that the signal will elicit. Finally, the position and behavior of certain other members of the group at the time of emitting the signal may also impinge upon the communicatory process and influence the outcome. Imposed upon all of this there is always the possible addition of sound signals and even olfactory and tactile signals to the total combination.

Of special interest is the extent to which the elements of the constellation can vary independently, since this will affect the total number of constellations that are possible. It is clear that many of the elements are far from independent of each other, for they occur in regular groups, which might be thought of as spatio-temporal clusters of certain elements, from which the elements of other clusters tend to be excluded. Thus when an observer speaks of "threat behavior" he is identifying such a cluster. When he distinguishes "submissive behavior" he denotes another cluster and also implies a significant lack of overlap with clusters of other types. Although, as with this example, the cluster is often characterized by functional characteristics, it could equally well be identified by the constellation of signaling elements that are produced, occurring simultaneously or close together in time. As Altmann (1962a) points out, there are good reasons for preferring the second approach in describing behavior. However, such descriptions are difficult to make, and few explicit attempts have been made, although it is likely that careful intuitive description involves much the same kind of process.

These "clusters" of visual signal elements correspond to the several "modes" that we tried to delineate in our consideration of sound signals, and here, as there, we can make an estimate of the number of distinct groupings that exist. A survey of the literature suggests the following as a very rough representative list, characterized by the functional aspects of the situation in which they are used: (1) alerting (to danger, and so on), (2) attack (assertion of dominance, repulsion of rivals, enemies), (3) withdrawal, (4) pacifying (overlaps with next two), (5) grooming, (6) inviting to groom, (7) inviting to mount, (8) mounting (with or without intromission, and so on),

(9) coordination of group movement (feeding, drinking, and preparing to sleep), and (10) care of young.

This subdivision of the various groupings of visual signaling elements is obviously crude and incomplete, but it will serve the purposes of discussion. Most of them (items 1 to 8 above) are at least at times involved with agonistic relationships. The clusters also tend to include different auditory signals, and as a further parallel they also show a high degree of intergradation, so it is hard to say, for example, where the "attack" group ends and the "withdrawal" group begins. Agonistic and mounting behavior may merge in some circumstances. Inviting to mount, grooming and pacifying behavior also tend to form a continuum. Here then, as in vocal signals used in agonistic or potentially agonistic situations, there is a very complex system of graded signals. In spite of this great variability it is still possible to speak of the clustering of certain elements at certain points on a continuum. To look at it another way, there are certain combinations of elements that never occur. For example the "open-mouthed threat" is accompanied by a direct gaze at the opponent, and never by "looking away" (van Hooff 1962). As a more extreme example, the eyebrow raising in baboons never occurs when the body is crouched in submission after an attack (Hall and DeVore, Chap. 3, this volume).

Having established the reality of the clusters, it can now be acknowledged that there are some signal elements that can occur in several different groupings. Flattening of the ears in baboons, for example, can be present or absent both in threat behavior (attack) and in friendly behavior (pacifying). The direct gaze may be present or absent in a wide variety of facial expressions, associated with attack, withdrawal, and pacification. The "grimace" or "grin" can occur both in withdrawal and in sexual situations (Hall and DeVore, Chap. 3, this volume). No doubt, further detailed descriptions will yield more additions to the repertoire of signal complexes by the incorporation of elements from one cluster into another. In addition, there are certain elements that inevitably accompany all the groupings, such as those that identify the species and individual and, perhaps, its status in the dominance hierarchy. There is also the possibility of combining auditory and other signals with the visual ones. Thus not only is there a capacity to create a very wide range of subtly graded signals, each one made up of a constellation of several different elements, but there is also at least a limited ability to recombine some of the same elements in more than one way, thus further enlarging the total number of signals that can be created.

### Redundancy in Close-Range and Distance Signals

The fact that numbers of signal elements generally occur together as a unit implies a high degree of redundancy, perhaps aiding in the reliability of the process of communicating the subtly changing nuances of mood, which underlie the integration of group behavior in monkeys and apes. The different elements sometimes have slightly different thresholds so the presence or absence of some of them from the total complex may permit communication of the *intensity* as well as of the *nature* and *complexity* of the motivation of the signaling animal. The physical complexity of the signal system is such that although it is possible for one to conceive of effective communication taking place at close range it would be less efficient over longer distances. Most of the visual signals, like the auditory signals, serve for communication within the group and only need to be transmitted over short distances. However, there are some visual signals, closely associated with their auditory counterparts, that serve more for exchange between groups. These are more stereotyped signals, clearly adapted to the efficient conveying over considerable distances of simpler information than is communicated by the graded signals. Schaller (1963, Chap. 10, this volume) has described the extended and elaborate chest-beating sequence of gorillas, which serves as a distance visual signal as well as an auditory one. Chimpanzees have an analogous "hoot-drumming" sequence in which they also jump wildly around creating a combined visual and auditory signal (Reynolds and Reynolds, Chap. 11, this volume), and something similar is recorded in gibbons, siamangs, and langurs (Jay, Chap. 7, this volume). It is significant that Schaller (1963) proposes the gorilla chest-beating sequence as an illustration of "one of the most complex ritualized displays of mammals." Perhaps the relative rarity of such elaborate and more-or-less stereotyped signals in higher primates is related to the limited number of circumstances that call for communication over distances.

### The Communicatory Significance of Visual Signals

With visual signals, as with auditory signals, by far the greater number seem to mediate agonistic and pacificatory exchanges within the group, with a smaller number serving reproductive purposes and care of the young. Within the classes of designative information, motivational information looms far larger than any other type. The vast array of graded and recombining constellations of elements provides a truly remarkable medium for communicating slight changes in intensity and nature of mood from one animal to another.

Once again species-specific information is communicated and is particularly evident in the superficial facial adornments of the forest-living monkeys. Visual signals have the unusual quality that, at least at close range, any signal emitted must include the specific characteristics of the signaler's external morphology, so that the signals are freed from the need for any further constraints. It may be partly for this reason that the dynamic elements of visual signals are often similar in many different primates and other mammals (Andrew 1963). By the same token individual information is included also. In birds parts of the face and head are often involved, and there is some evidence that these areas also show more individual variability within a population than other parts of the body. The same may be true in primates, where the face is again the most variable part of the body in many species (Schultz 1947). Schaller (1963) found that the shape and markings of the nose were especially valuable in enabling him to identify individual gorillas. Haddow (1952) commented that some of the facial characters and the tail are especially variable in the red-tailed monkey. Perhaps they can be regarded as candidates for mediating individual recognition in this species.

Sexual information is present in varying degrees, not so much in posture, movements, or expression as in external morphology. In baboons, macaques, and gorillas males are conspicuously larger than females and have larger canines, while females have distinctively-colored sexual skin when in estrus, except in the gorilla. In most other monkeys sexual dimorphism is largely confined to superficial adornments or the external genitalia. Sexual differences in body and tooth size are much less striking. DeVore (1963) has convincingly argued for a correlation of sexual dimorphism with the ground-living habits of the baboon groups, which exposes them to more predators and places more of a premium on the defensive propensities of the male as compared with more arboreal species. Some of the elements involved, such as the long, ornamental mane of male baboons, are less obviously involved in defense. Perhaps an element of sexual selection may be involved here, for these are also the groups in which dominant males have the prerogative of mating with most or all of the estrous females, a condition that is not so characteristic of some of the less sexually dimorphic species such as the gibbon (Carpenter 1942a). A survey of the animal kingdom certainly suggests some correlation between polygyny and extreme sexual dimorphism (Huxley 1942).

As a final point there is an unusual involvement of reproductive behavior patterns, of mounting, and the invitation to mount in purely agonistic situations. These are only two of a rich array of signals, particularly visual and tactile, that seem to serve a pacifying function, primarily by eliciting some response that is incompatible with fighting behavior and thus indirectly inhibiting to it. However, there is another element, which is most clearly seen in the crouching, prostrate posture of a defeated animal, that seems to inhibit directly further attack (e.g., in rhesus monkeys, Altmann 1962a). In this case the effect is achieved, not by maximizing signals that elicit a response incompatible with attack, but by minimizing the signals that might provoke an attack. Thus, in Darwin's terms (1872), the prone posture is the antithesis of that of a threatening animal in every possible respect, except for the continued presence of the animal. Once alerted to this phenomenon, similar elements can perhaps be seen in the turning away of a subordinate to present its rear end to a dominant animal, contrasting with the frontal display in threat or in showing the neck, involving a turning away of the face as an invitation by a subordinate rhesus monkey for a dominant to groom it; perhaps even "looking away" reduces the probability of attack by a dominant below what it would be with a "direct gaze." As in birds, the effect of such behavior is quite different from actual flight, which provokes further attack (DeVore, unpublished thesis). Once more this is oversimplifying a very complicated situation, and much remains to be learned about how pacificatory communication signals operate (see the discussions of lip smacking and presenting in rhesus monkeys by Hinde and Rowell [1962]). Here, as in so many cases, the greatest need is for more detailed descriptions, and Altmann's (1962a) work in particular indicates the kind of approach to the sequence patterning of behavior that is likely to illuminate problems about visual communication in the future.

## INTERSPECIFIC COMMUNICATION

The main concern in this discussion has been with processes of intra-specific communication. The relationships between different species have been considered only as they bear on the need to *avoid* interspecific communication in some situations. It is important to remember that this requirement that the process of communication be restricted to animals of the same species does not apply equally to all types of signals. Indeed there are situations in which the facilitation of communication between different species living in the same area may be of positive value. The most obvious case involves danger signals. Whenever two cohabiting species are alike enough to be endangered by the same kinds of predators, each can gain advantage from being alerted by danger signals of the other. A signal that functions in such a context has little need to be species specific and may improve in efficiency if it actually resembles the signals with a similar function of other species.

There is abundant evidence that some monkeys and apes engage freely in such interspecific communication where circumstances permit it. Chimpanzees respond to the alarm calls of baboons, other species of monkey, bushbuck, several species of bird — by becoming more alert and even by moving away if the calls are persistent enough (Goodall, Chap. 12, this volume). Baboons engage in two-way communication with impala and bushback by means of warning barks and clearly gain considerable mutual advantage from this (Washburn and DeVore 1961b). The olive colobus profits greatly by responding to the alarm cries of the guenons, with which it often mingles (Booth 1957). Booth (1962) records a young, orphaned blue monkey that responded with alarm to its first experience of the warning calls of a vervet.

It seems probable that visual signals are also involved in this interspecific communication of danger. Certainly the involvement of sound signals is widespread. It is interesting to note how often the term "bark" is used in describing such signals, whether, in Kenya for example, it is a primate or an ungulate being discussed (e.g., Washburn and DeVore 1961b). One wonders whether the similarity in signal structure that is implied is just an accident or whether there may not have been some degree of evolutionary convergence on a common type, as is known to occur with the alarm call of certain birds. In contrast to such interspecific cooperation, where strife between species is frequent enough a species may find an advantage in repulsive signals that are not too divergent from those of the opponent. This perhaps explains in part the relative lack of species specificity in the aggressive signals of many species; the visual signals often involve the mouth and teeth, for example, and the auditory signals often have a growling quality. It is worth noting that relationships of this type can be sought only in the field with the breadth of the study expanded to include the whole community within which a given species is living.

## CONCLUSIONS

Perhaps the most striking generalization that can be advanced from this survey of the communication signals of monkeys and apes is the overwhelming importance of composite signals. In most situations it is not a single signal that passes from one animal to another but a whole complex of them, visual, auditory, tactile, and sometimes olfactory. There can be little doubt that the structure of individual signals is very much affected by this incorporation in a whole matrix of other signals. We have seen that these composite systems are a special feature of close-range communication, transmitting information between different members of the group. For communication over larger distances, such as occurs between groups, more stereotyped, patterned signals are used, visual or auditory. These are less obviously composite, and it may be assumed that many of the subtle properties of the very complicated multiple signals would be lost if perceived from a distance. At close range, however, the combination of multiple signals and the highly graded nature of many of the elements in the complex prepare the way for transmission of information about the slightest changes in the nature and intensity of moods in the signaling animal. If it is right to assume that they serve this function, then the development of these composite signals become easier to understand, for efficient communication of such subtle changes would require a high degree of redundancy. Moreover, as has been shown, there are at least some examples of independent recombinations of the constituent elements, raising the possibility of further addition to the types of information that can be conveyed.

The potential for some degree of independent reassortment of signal elements is one of the basic characteristics of human language, and it is intriguing to find it in animals, even though only in primordial form. Monkeys and apes put this capacity to rather narrow use, different only in degree from what we find in other animals. By far the greatest part of the whole system of communication seems to be devoted to the organization of social behavior of the group, to dominance and subordination, the maintenance of peace and cohesion of the group, reproduction, and care for the young. Interindividual relationships are complex enough in monkeys and apes to require a communication system of this high order of complexity. But there is little application of the communication system to events outside the group, beyond the existence of signals signifying potential danger. There are no calls associated with, say, water or food, such as are known in some birds (e.g., Konishi 1963). Environmental information, present or past, figures very little in the communication systems of these animals, and a major revolution in information content is still required before the development of a variety of signals signifying certain objects in the environment and a system of grammar to discourse about them can be visualized.

However, in the vocal systems of higher monkeys and apes, there is one sense in which perhaps the stage is being set for the development of the type of sound system used in human speech. Human children begin with an ability to produce a very wide range of sounds of somewhat the same type as are heard in macaques, baboons, and apes. Under the influence of the particular tradition to which they are exposed, they learn to break up this continuously varying system into phonemes, exploiting the ability of the enlarged postlaryngeal part of the vocal tract to filter the sound, introduce fricatives, and impose breaks in the sound output. There is no evidence that any nonhuman primate has a significant ability for vocal learning. However, reflection upon the kind of sound signals from which human speech might have developed suggests that it is much more likely to have stemmed from a richly graded system such as has been found in rhesus monkeys, and perhaps in chimpanzees and gorillas, rather than from a repertoire of discrete signals such as seem to be more common in the lower primates. One might even speculate that it was necessary to proceed from a genetically inherited system of discrete signals to an inherited system of graded signals before the further step was possible to a system of discrete signals that is completely learned.

The ability to produce new sounds is not unknown in animals (e.g., Thorpe 1962), and it seems reasonable to suppose that it could have developed in nonhuman primates if natural selection had favored it. Within their present social and ecological framework it is not easy to visualize how monkeys and apes could exploit the advantages that might evolve from the introduction of vocal learning. The major problem is thus not to explain how vocal learning started, in terms of neurophysiological mechanisms, but rather why such learning was first favored by natural selection. Only by the study of primate social systems in the natural state, still exposed to the kinds of selective forces that shaped the early history of man, can one hope to discover why this all-important change first came about from genetic control of vocal behavior to transmission by a learned tradition.

JARVIS BASTIAN

# 17

# ◈ Primate Signaling Systems and Human Languages

## INTRODUCTION

Any account of human origins must face at some point the problem of the development of languages. There are good grounds for expecting comparisons between the signaling systems of monkeys and apes and the languages of humans to illuminate this problem. However, these expectations have for the most part been disappointed. Lack of relevant information about nonhuman primates has not been the only reason the comparisons have largely failed to yield better understanding of this part of human evolution. On the human side of the comparison, although we know immeasurably more about human language than about primate signaling systems, we have not reached any clear understanding of its biological significance. And unless we understand the contributions to specifically human modes of adaptation made by the common features of men's languages, we cannot establish biologically pertinent bases for comparisons with the other primates.

Paradoxically, our rich knowledge of human languages is the source of a related difficulty. The long history of linguistic study has yielded some convincing and important characterizations of the internal logic or structure of our natural languages. But these relate primarily to languages as the products of cultural evolution and are of little direct help in our efforts to understand the biological adaptations associated with this evolution. Such an understanding requires that we direct our attention downward to the level of man's linguistic actions themselves and to the underlying behavioral

A large part of the thinking presented here was begun during the author's fellowship in 1961–1962 at the Center for Advanced Study in the Behavioral Sciences, and much of its early growth was stimulated and nurtured by the associations and facilities the Center provided. Most of the writing was done in the Department of Psychology, University of California, Santa Barbara.

585

capacities that permit the development of these logical features and their incorporation into his vocal acts. We are much more likely to realize the promise held by comparative analysis when we push the levels of comparison closer to the interface between particular behavioral acts and the social and ecological circumstances of their occurrence. Only as we approach this interface can we hope to find the common denominators required for biological comparisons and cues to the critical changes in homonid behavioral capacities, as well as suggestions of the kinds of selective forces fostering these changes.

In considering animal behavior in general we have customarily distinguished communicative acts from other social behavior. In this we have been prompted perhaps by the ease with which man's linguistic actions can be separated from the rest of his behavior and by the easy characterization of human languages as a means by which matters that otherwise are private, or limited to a few, may be made common. However, if we impose on the notion of communication these features of human languages, its nonhuman application is largely inappropriate and misleading, and if we do not impose them, then we have no basis for restricting communicative actions to anything less than the whole of social behavior. Can either communication or social behavior be considered as anything other than the partial and often reciprocal determination of the actions of one or more individuals by the actions of one or more others?

We can, nonetheless, distinguish in the flow of social behavior those actions of one individual by which the behavior of others is altered. In most of the discussion to come the stimulus patterns produced by such actions will be called signals. This is a commonly used term in this sense and has the further advantage of being relatively unprejudicial with respect to the many difficult problems to be encountered in the analysis of the semantic properties of these actions. The following discussion will be concerned with those signals whose occurrences have some kind of regularity within a population, and thus it is appropriate to say that they form a signaling system. With these designations made, this chapter can be described as an examination of the general properties of the linguistic and nonlinguistic signaling systems of man and certain other primates and the lines of continuity and divergence between them. Its scope is restricted to the macaques, baboons, and African apes, which, either because of their biological affinities to man or because of the similarities between their ecological circumstances and man's, are the most pertinent primate groups for such comparisons. This discussion is further limited to just the visual and auditory signaling systems of these animals. It attempts to take full advantage of the most illuminating comparisons and generalizations of the preceding chapter and of the information assembled in earlier parts of this volume concerning the specific features of social interaction within these nonhuman groups. However, this investigation is directed toward only those general properties of these nonhuman signaling systems having the most direct relevance to man's visual and auditory signaling systems. The major aims here are to describe and compare the operating characteristics of the different signaling systems and the behavioral processes on which they are based and to assess the bearing of each characteristic on the others in the over-all operation of these systems in the different modes of social adaptations of man and these other primates.

The discussion will begin with an examination of the differences in the physical natures and means of generation of the signals and in the problems associated with their effective reception. It will then proceed to an examination of the internal organization, or grammar, of the different signaling systems, an organization important to both the production and the perception of the exceedingly complex signals of man's linguistic interactions. The processes by which the individual becomes a competent member of a linguistic community will then be briefly treated as these, together with their grammatical features, underlie the semantic openness of linguistic signaling systems. It is this semantic openness, the potential for the effective production and reception of new signals without limits on what the signals may be about, that most decisively distinguishes the adaptive consequences of linguistic from nonlinguistic signaling systems. The particular goal of this discussion is to further the understanding of this potential for semantic openness by examining the various closely interrelated behavioral operating characteristics from which it derives. The discussion will close with an abbreviated investigation of the paramount role the openness of man's languages plays in his distinctively cultural mode of adaptation.

## THE NATURE AND PRODUCTION OF PRIMATE SIGNALS

It is appropriate to begin with an analysis of the physical nature of the signals themselves for this has too often been regarded as having little real bearing on their function. This appraisal has been particularly evident in the many discussions of human languages setting forth the view that in essence languages are symbolic codes and thus that there is nothing relevant to the functioning of the code in the nature of the signals or of the signaling apparatus. But the signaling actions of primates, human or otherwise, are integral parts of adaptive complexes, and the interrelations among the components have been shaped by evolutionary pressures acting on all parts together. We have every reason to suppose that the distinctive properties of human languages and of other primate signaling systems are intricately bound up with the very nature of the signals and of the processes by which they are produced and perceived.

Although a great deal remains to be learned about the signals produced by the ground-dwelling monkeys and African apes, the evidence examined by Marler in the preceding chapter clearly indicates some significant contrasts and similarities in the physical characteristics of these signals and of man's. First, simply with respect to the predominant physical mode, humans appear to be by far the most persistently noisy in their social interactions. In the other ground-dwellers auditory signals frequently occur, often at high intensities, but usually as concomitants of visual signals, a situation that for humans is largely reversed. The primary importance of visual signals in the face-to-face social processes of these nonhuman primates appears to be well established. In the evolution of the higher primates the anatomical changes toward increased and finely controlled mobility, especially of the muzzle area, seem significant, providing as they do a richer potential for visual signaling. The degree to which this potential has been realized is somewhat difficult to judge, for the continuous intergradation and blending of signals very much complicates the establishment of a determinate visual signaling inventory for each group solely in terms of the physical characteristics of the signals themselves. The basic types of visual signals for a given population can only be recognized if the context of their occurrences is taken into consideration. Though the sizes of the inventories may vary somewhat from species to species, it is quite certain, on the basis of evidence reviewed in the preceding chapter, that these signaling systems are closed; that is, there is a finite — and actually a rather small — number of basic types. To the extent, then, that there has been specialization of visual signaling in the higher primates related to changes in their facial and limb anatomy, it has not effected any considerable modification of a quite widespread mammalian adaptation for social interaction. Rather, what has been achieved by such anatomical changes can properly be called an interstitial openness in which there is increased intergradation and intermodulation between the types of basic signals.

In regard to the continuous nature of signal variability there seem to be very good reasons for considering the visual signals of humans as basically similar to those of the higher primates (Woodworth and Schlosberg 1954, Chap. 5). Though the question has been much debated through the years since Darwin's work, the correspondence may extend to some of the signaling patterns themselves, although it is abundantly clear that most of the human patterns are products of extensive and often quite divergent lines of cultural evolution within the species. Even so, it is not certain that humans have a greater repertory of visual signals, for though some, like winking, have been added, others, like piloerection, have been effectively lost. But whatever their nature and number, the visual signals of humans display at least an equivalent degree of continuous intergradation between patterns, except for those signaling systems, such as the finger-spelling systems of the deaf, that are of very recent origin and based on natural languages.

There is a problem of particular importance associated with the interstitial openness of the visual signaling system of man and these other primates. Though the increased richness of visual signaling possibilities may enhance the finer control of social interaction, there are definite perceptual-motor limits that curtail this signaling potential. The effectiveness of signals in mediating social action is limited to the degree that different signals are confusable, and confusability is heightened when the signals continuously intergrade and blend with each other. This is borne out by the difficulties humans have in identifying each other's facial expressions, even within the same communities (Woodworth and Schlosberg 1954, Chap. 5) and by the difficulties human observers have in cataloguing the basic patterns of the signaling systems of these nonhuman primates. The responses evoked in others by visual signals are very much dependent upon the total context in which the signals are embedded, and the signals are effective and typologically classifiable only because the set of context types is closed.

The auditory signals of humans and other primates also have a basic resemblance in their operating characteristics, in part owing to the similarity in the phonatory apparatus. As in other mammals, an air column is forced through the vocal tract by the bellowslike action of the respiratory muscles, but in the higher primates the neuromuscular changes in the muzzle region that are so important for visual signaling contribute also to an enlargement of the auditory signaling potential. The increased mobility of parts of the vocal tract above the larynx permits the formation of complex resonant systems through which the air column may be filtered and makes possible changes in the shape or coupling of the parts of the tract to generate a wider range of sounds with distinctive timbres.

Auditory and spectrographic assessment of the vocal signals of macaques, baboons, and the African apes indicates that during signal emission the acoustic power spectra tend to be steady, even though there may often be considerable variation in pitch and intensity. This in turn indicates that the disposition of the parts of the upper vocal tract that determine the configuration of the filtering system remains rather stable during signal emission. In addition, many signals of these primates are produced with open as well as steady filter configurations, the sounds so produced having prominent resonances and high over-all acoustic power. Most of the departures from the relatively stable and open configurations occur at the beginnings of the signals and appear to be most often due to the involvement of mobile parts at the very front (the lips) or the very back (tongue base and pharyngeal walls) of the upper tract. But though there is a wide range in the different types of signals determined by changes in the relatively fixed upper tract configurations, by far the largest part of the variation between and within signal types results from laryngeal and sublaryngeal changes. Even with the disposition of the upper tract apparently remaining quite constant, there are conspicuous differences in the direction of air flow, in the presence or absence of glottal pulsations, in the abruptness of onset and the frequency and intensity of glottal pulsations, and in the often repetitive cycles of activation. The laryngeal and sublaryngeal actions producing such changes are closely tied to the autonomic nervous system, and the relation of these signals to the emotional or arousal state of the signaler will be considered in a later section. For the present the important point to note is that these actions of both the upper and lower vocal tracts tend to be continuously variable, and thus the signals generated by these actions tend to intergrade.

There are also many human auditory signaling actions that have comparable simplicity and steadiness of upper tract configuration and predominant variation in laryngeal and sublaryngeal adjustments. These are signals of the sort that may be loosely termed expletives, such as laughs, moans, shrieks, cheers, and the utterances of infants. Such signals also have properties similar to human visual signals, with which in fact they are often closely linked, just as they are in the nonhuman primates. Though some of the basic types of signaling actions may be inherited, the diverse processes of cultural evolution and assimilation have clearly influenced the form and functions of most. And, like man's visual signals, as well as the visual and auditory signals of the other primates considered, these signals tend to intergrade and blend so their effects on the actions of others are highly dependent on the contexts of their emission. And just as in the signaling systems of these other primates, the nonlinguistic auditory signals of man constitute closed, though again interstitially open, sets. The actions by which these signals are generated are less complexly organized than the actions producing linguistic signals, which suggests that they may be integrated at lower levels within the central nervous system. However, the most important reason for not considering these signals part of linguistic signaling systems is that they have no grammatical status in those systems.

But leaving aside this important question of grammatical status, and considering the nonlinguistic auditory signals of man only in the light of their social significance, that is, in terms of their functional contribution to the government of social interactions, it is not easy to draw the line between these signals and linguistic signals proper. Furthermore, the predominant acoustic features of these nonlinguistic signals, which are governed primarily by the lower vocal tract, are also attributes of all linguistic signals. In fact, variations governed by glottal and subglottal actions, such as pitch, timing, and intensity, are often critically important in linguistic signals. For example, two signals with different linguistic status may differ only in the duration of a single portion, as in Zuni "mulà" (parrot) and "mu:la" (mule), where the only difference is in the length of the medial vowel; or, again, the difference may be associated with a combination of changes in pitch, intensity, or timing, as in English "You're an ice man?" and "You're a nice man!" But such variations, which, in connection with linguistic events, are often called prosodic variations, are physically continuous, and the critical prosodic features tend to intergrade from one occurrence to another within a linguistic community. The result is that the linguistic status of such signals is usually not determinable by prosodic features alone and can only be decided in the contexts of their occurrence. In the Zuni example, for instance, it may be necessary for the listener to consider the tempo at which the signals are produced, for the "long" vowel in rapid speech may have the same physical duration as the "short" vowel in slow, deliberate speech. The limitations on the communicatory effectiveness of signal variation of this type are well illustrated by the so-called drum-and-whistle "languages" (Stern 1957). These signaling systems employ prosodic variation almost exclusively, the signals transmitted usually being modeled after the prosodic patterns distinguishing certain linguistic signals, and so signal assessment becomes very much a relative matter. In order to minimize signal confusion these systems must resort to repetition and other redundant expedients so that they tend to be inflexible and closed.

Now although prosodic features are attributes of all linguistic signals, very little of the prosodic variation occurring is linguistically significant, in the sense of distinguishing different grammatical or lexical events, even for linguistic systems that use these modes of distinction most extensively. But though the bulk of such variation is not linguistically significant, much of it has considerable social significance, for often the effect of a linguistic signal on the actions of others may be widely altered by linguistically irrelevant variations in the prosodic features of the signal. Some years ago a comedy skit was commercially recorded involving only two actors, a female and male, each repeating over and over "John" and "Marcia," respectively. Though nothing except these two linguistic signals was uttered, each repetition contained different prosodic features which, however irrelevant linguistically, portrayed a complex and extended social interaction that, to some ears at least, was downright salacious. Such socially, but not linguistically, significant features of linguistic signals are similar to the nonlinguistic signals of men and the other primates in their close association with visual signals, their analogous production and acoustical properties, and their variable interpretation and consequent limitation in communicative effectiveness when received out of context.

There are, then, definite lines of continuity relating man's linguistic signals to his nonlinguistic auditory and visual signals, and hence to the auditory and visual signals of other primates. But certain marked differences of immense consequence between linguistic and nonlinguistic signals are also clearly evident; whereas nonlinguistic auditory signals are produced by relatively stable vocal tract configurations, man's linguistic signals are generated by extremely rapid concurrent alterations of the different mobile parts of the upper vocal tract between more-or-less closed and more-or-less open configurations in close coordination with equally rapid and relatively independent alterations of the lower vocal tract. In the rapidity, precision, and integration of these movements humans routinely display a truly astounding virtuosity. The anatomical changes in the muzzle region so prominent in primate evolution are nowhere more evident than in this capacity and the necessary control that has become superimposed on the separate mechanisms of the vocal tract associated with deglutition, respiration, and emotionality.

Within the acoustic flux produced by the generation of linguistic signals, relatively steady acoustic states such as those occurring in nonlinguistic vocal signaling seldom occur. Instead the foremost feature of linguistic signals is their transience. The resonance patterns rapidly fluctuate and are continually interrupted by brief intervals of friction noises and of more-or-less complete silence. These acoustic changes reflect the swift changes at varying places in the upper vocal tract in configuration toward and away from relatively complete occlusions and changes in glottal action. In the course of these changes the shifting resonant patterns may momentarily pass through "vowel" configurations similar to the steady and open resonances of most nonlinguistic signals. However, the signaling potential of the fleeting presence of these vowels is enormously supplemented and to a very considerable extent subordinated by the transitory acoustic consequences of articulatory processes.

The evolutionary development of man's articulatory capabilities increases the possible acoustical complexity of signaling far beyond that of nonlinguistic auditory signals and more than offsets the loss in acoustic power resulting from the incessant occlusions of the vocal tract. The open-to-closed and closed-to-open articulatory actions may occur at various places in the upper vocal tract; they may be partial or complete; they may or may not be accompanied by concurrent glottal action; and, most important, they may be readily combined in many different sequences. The acoustic output at any given time is determined by the total configuration of the tract at that time, and in sequential combinations these rapid articulatory actions overlap in time. Thus the acoustic products of any one of these actions is substantially altered by adjustments in other parts of the tract that are residual from preceding actions or preparatory to subsequent actions, and therefore automatically vary with the different sequential combinations in which the movement occurs.

But this enrichment of the acoustic complexity of linguistic signals, resulting from evolutionary changes in the signaling apparatus, has as its corollary the very perplexing problem of the efficient perception of those signals. This problem arises because man is impressively limited in his capacity to recognize effectively auditory signals much less complex than his linguistic signals (see House, Stevens, Sandel, and Arnold 1962 and references cited therein), and in this regard he does not appear to be appreciably different from other primates. This being so, it might well seem that linguistic signaling systems suffer from an embarrassment of acoustic riches. It is important to seek an understanding of how the efficient perception of linguistic signals has been effected within these operational restrictions, for this achievement is closely tied to the contribution of man's linguistic systems to his peculiar modes of adaptation.

## THE PERCEPTION AND STRUCTURAL ORGANIZATION OF LINGUISTIC SIGNALS

There is no end to the human possibilities for quickly and rather freely combining the relatively small number of basic articulatory actions into extended sequences, each resulting in different acoustic wave forms. However, in order that the social potential of this openness of signaling possibilities be realized, the different signals must each be recognizable. Now if each signal were a complete and indivisible whole, the full utilization of all signals would require man to retain knowledge of the whole set at all times, and man's finite retentive capabilities would necessarily restrict the size of the signal inventory. Man's linguistic signaling systems maintain their potential openness despite his limitations because the linguistic signals of humans do not have this structural integrity. Instead they are concatenations of signaling elements that we know as words, but which are perhaps better called lexical items, to be more specific. Within any linguistic system there are different classes of lexical items, and the concatenation of lexical items into formations having status within the system, or the transformation of such well-formed formations into others, is governed by restrictions that we traditionally call the grammar of that system. Because, then, of the grammaticalness of our linguistic signals, we are not required to establish a separate and integral signal that can be effectively produced and received for each socially important aspect of our commerce with our environments. This would be impossible for even the most impoverished and static human communities. We have instead the far less demanding task of retaining a fixed vocabulary and a fixed set of formation and transformation restrictions, and by grammatical operations on these fixed sets of components we may generate infinitely many signals.

It seems most reasonable to suppose that the grammatical organization of linguistic signals has consequences of equal importance to the sender and to the receiver. The perception of these signals in ordinary circumstances may be regarded as a series of decision processes organized hierarchically so that decisions as to the lexical identities assigned to one stage of the received wave train may depend upon decisions reached at different levels and relating to different stages of the signal. This means that it is not necessary to process the wave train on an instant-to-instant basis in such a way as to identify directly all the lexical items comprising the signal. Instead it is suggested that our appreciation of what is said to us derives at least in part from the same processes that we bring into play in generating linguistic signals when we ourselves are acting as speakers. If the lexical identities of some parts of the signal we receive can be established, we can synthesize a replication of the whole signal, or a sufficiently good match to it, largely because in doing so we operate within the same set of restrictions obtaining in the emission of the original signal.

By positing that effective listening is usually a matter of the listener's own contribution, we are better able to understand why the listener's reactions may often be only remotely related to the acoustic signals he receives. All of us are aware that our understanding of what is said to us depends upon a great deal more than the passive quivering of our eardrums, and, in the extreme case, we may observe schizophrenics in earnest conversation with fairly quiet steam radiators. This conceptualization of the perception of linguistic signals presumes a competence in linguistic synthesis on the part of the listener, and in evaluating its plausibility consideration must therefore be given to the perception of linguistic signals by those without this competence. Nonhumans living in close contact with humans may come to react differentially to an impressive number of linguistic signals or parts thereof, and this is also true of human children before they become skillful speakers. Such reactions may often depend at first upon the non-auditory contexts in which the signals occur or upon linguistically insignificant attributes of the signals, particularly their characteristic prosodic features. However, with sufficiently favorable conditioning, a large number of signals or lexical parts may come to be discriminated in a fairly wide range of speakers and settings when conditions of reception are favorable. But however many separate and indivisible speech-sound patterns a dog or a chimpanzee may be brought to recognize in this way, its performance in recognizing such patterns is contingent on just the acoustic energies received and so its performance is in constant jeopardy because the received signals are not only exceedingly complex and evanescent, but also are routinely generated at very rapid rates against a variable background of ambient noise. There is an additional problem for listeners lacking competence in linguistic synthesis. In any linguistic system different lexical items, and thus different well-formed combinations of them, are very often as much alike acoustically as repetitions of the same lexical items can be. Homophony of lexical items, even in its most restricted sense, tends to increase the more frequently they occur within the linguistic community (Zipf 1945). The appropriate reactions of the listener therefore must often derive from more than just well-developed auditory discriminations, as Lashley illustrated cleverly in the following: "The mill-wright on my right thinks it right that some conventional rite should symbolize the right of every man to write as he pleases" (Lashley 1951).

Now it does not appear that man is markedly different from the other primates in his capacity for evaluating auditory events. However, the competent human listener in most circumstances of listening does not, need not, nor is it likely that he even can, instantaneously assess the lexical identities associated with all parts of the received wave train. In the present view, he fixes the identities of lexical items only to the extent required to generate a well-formed replica of the signal that matches the time stretches of the wave train identified in the original signal. Under more adverse listening conditions he may have to listen more intently, identifying more lexica items, or narrowing the margin of matching error in his replications. But though his perception of what is said may be in part his own invention, his vast knowledge of the way his language works, his knowledge of his present circumstances, and the accumulated indirect confirmations of his syntheses of preceding signals, all usually serve to make his replicas appropriate.

However, the conditions of listening may sometimes be so unfavorable that the listener cannot recognize a sufficient number of lexical identities in the received wave train to synthesize a well-formed signal. And such conditions may arise from other things than adverse signal-to-noise ratios. The potential openness of linguistic signaling systems is far more gravely affected by the problems besetting the listener because of the wide differences in probabilities of occurrence of possible lexical items in linguistic signals. For most people most of the time the conduct of daily life involves linguistic interactions using a fairly stable vocabulary of lexical items. These items occur with sufficient frequency so that for human listeners, just as for the nonhuman listeners previously considered, their various acoustic-time complexes are well-established identities, easily recognizable under optimal conditions. But the most informative linguistic signals, at least in the information-theoretic sense, are those containing relatively rare and hence unfamiliar lexical items. Under such conditions the listener's competence as a speaker may again serve to circumvent his limitations of memory and of available time by enabling him to assign a provisional, nonlexical identity to the unfamiliar parts of the signal until their lexical status can be decided.

This nonlexical possibility of identifying linguistic signals is called phonemic identification. It is related to the notion that linguistic signals are identifiable by the "sounds" of a language, and it is fundamental to alphabetic transcriptions of linguistic signals. This notion most often assumes that linguistic signals are generated by the stringing together of a series of discrete phonatory events, as a sequence of notes is struck on a keyboard instrument. The separate chunks of acoustic energies thus produced are then thought to come floating in the stream of time to the listener's ears, whereupon he recognizes each as a given "speech sound" or "phoneme" in his language by its own distinctive and invariant ring against his eardrums. Now the keyboard analogy may fit the circumstances of production quite well, especially if hierarchically organized multicomponent "chords" are envisaged instead of simple chains of single notes (MacNeilage 1963), but the correspondence does not extend to the acoustic nature of the signal or to the processes by which it is phonemically identified. There are almost no segments of the essentially continuous wave forms of linguistic signals that are exclusively associated with any single phoneme. It has already been pointed out that the acoustic output of the vocal tract at any point of time is determined by its over-all configuration and by the nature of the energies filtered through it. Because the rapid actions of the mobile parts of the tract that govern its continually changing configuration regularly overlap in time, the wave form depends not only on the actions associated with pronouncing a given phoneme but also on the immediately preceding and succeeding actions. Therefore, the acoustic features associated with "p," for instance, vary considerably with the context in which it occurs, so that the acoustical products of the actions of closing and opening the lips to form the p's are each quite different in, let us say, "Post Pleistocene Primates." In addition to the acoustic variation resulting from the nature of such automatic interactions, additional variation is introduced by the conventional practices of the linguistic community. For example, in general American English the results of the "p"actions in saying "spit" are considerably different from those in saying "pit," because in this community it is the practice to adjust the larynx so that glottal pulsations begin almost immediately after the lips are parted in the former, but are delayed by 50 to 60 milliseconds in the latter. And beyond the variability associated with changing phonetic contexts, further acoustic variation arises from differences in the productions of the same linguistic signal, not only by different speakers but also by the same speaker, and from changes in the conditions of signal transmission and reception.

In the face of the essential continuity of the wave form of linguistic signals and the enormous variability in the acoustical consequences of any particular set of articulatory actions, such as those involved in "p"-productions, how is it possible that we can isolate a "p"-segment in the received signal and assign a fixed identity to it that we transcribe as the letter p? The complexities and transience of acoustic events and our limitations in auditory recognition and memory make it inconceivable that we reach our phonemic decisions by determining the goodness-of-fit of features of a particular time stretch in the received signal, or some transformation of it, with our memory of every one of the immense variety of acoustic patterns that may be associated with each phonemic possibility. A much more cogent conceptualization of the processes of phonemic identification, one that provides a basis for the perceptual segmentation and constancy of phonemes, has been develped in the research of the Haskins Laboratories (Cooper, Liberman, Harris, and Grubb 1958; and Liberman, Cooper, Harris, and MacNeilage in press) and has recently been importantly extended to the design of phonemic recognition devices in the work of the Electronic Research Laboratories at the Massachusetts Institute of Technology (Stevens 1960). The central idea of this conceptualization is that the phonemic identification of a linguistic signal is decided by the listener in terms of the articulatory controls by which he would repeat the signal when acting as a speaker.

In contrast to linguistic mimicries, repetitions require the replication of only the linguistically significant acoustic features of signals, and because these are an extremely small part of the total, the signals and their repetitions will otherwise be very different. Any member of a linguistic community is capable of repeating any utterance in that language, even though he may recognize none of the component lexical identities. In the course of a child's assimilation into a linguistic community, he soon develops a set of quite rigidly stabilized articulatory actions that is shared by all competent members of the community. The number of the basic articulatory actions involved in this set is very small compared to the enormous range of different acoustic effects that may be produced by them, and most often these actions involve distinctly different muscle groups adducting discontinuous articulatory surfaces that are very richly supplied with sensory nerve endings. As we have noted, in their many possible sequential combinations the temporal overlapping of these actions and the ballistics and inertias of the mobile parts involved in them result in acoustic interactions that greatly modify the acoustical consequences of any one of them. The actions themselves, however, appear to be quite invariable, with little intergradation between them (MacNeilage 1963).

The small number of these common basic muscle gestures, their constancy, and the categorical differences between them enable the articulatory reference conceptualization of phonemic identification to account for the perceptual constancy of phonemes and for the associated segmentation of acoustically continuous signals into combinations of a small number of discrete phonemic identities. It is interesting that this account appeals to the receiver's competence as an emitter of linguistic signals in much the same way as was posited for the perception of lexical identities of signals. One of the implications of this account is that so far as linguistically significant features of signals are produced by motor gestures that vary continuously from one significant pattern to another, as the prosodic features do, then the less determinate the phonemic identities referred to such gestures will be. Since the constancy and discreteness of phonemic identities is supposed to derive from the constancy and discreteness of the underlying motor gestures, the most decisively determinate phonemic identities should be the various consonants of a phonemic system, followed in decreasing order by liquids, semi-vowels, diphthongs, vowels, and prosodies.

It is significant in this regard that no linguistic systems are known that use only variations in open (vowel) configurations and prosodies. It also seems that phonemic writing systems, both presently and in their historical development, have been more consistent and decisive in rendering consonants than they have been in rendering linguistically significant vowel and prosodic features. The phonemic identifiability of linguistic signals is immensely important in the development of efficient and easily mastered writing systems, and therefore is significant in enhancing the cultural impact of literacy. The most important consequence of this performance capacity, however, is its contribution to the effective perception of linguistic signals when lexical identification is difficult or impossible, especially in the assimilation of new lexical items.

## THE SEMANTIC SCOPE OF PRIMATE SIGNALING SYSTEMS AND MAN'S LANGUAGES

Combinations of signals occur in the nonlinguistic signaling systems of humans and other primates as well as in man's linguistic systems. The frequent concurrence of visual and nonlinguistic auditory signals has already been noted, and the effect of such combined signals on the action of others may well be different from those of either mode by itself. A similar possibility may exist for sequential combinations of signals, and a claim for grammatical structure in nonlinguistic signaling systems could be supported on this ground if there were constraints on "permissible" sequences. It is clear, however, that the semantic scope of these systems, whatever the sense in which they may be said to be grammatical, are still severely restricted in comparison with linguistic systems.

These restrictions are especially apparent in the signaling systems of the nonhuman primates, in which all signals appear to be clearly related to the immediate emotional states of the signaling individuals and their levels of arousal. The information transmitted to the receiver refers primarily to the current emotional disposition of the signaler. The consequences of effective reception are largely modifications of the emotional dispositions of the receivers. There is often additional information of considerable biological significance carried by the signals, such as the location, age, sex, social status, or species of the signaler, but in terms of the conditions governing signaling actions this transmission appears to be adventitious. It is also of interest that much of the signal variation in these systems that was discussed above seems to be primarily related to differing levels of arousal in the signaler. Many of the signal combinations, especially those involving both visual and auditory signals, are referable to changes in arousal levels. Thus, if there is any basis for attributing grammatical features to these nonlinguistic signaling systems, then such features would appear to be concerned with the grammatical operations of intensification. The intergradation and blending of nonlinguistic auditory signals that has been described as interstitial openness may thus be due to continuous changes in levels of arousal mediating changes in the predominant laryngeal and sublaryngeal components of signaling action. But the reason for characterizing these systems as semantically closed, though interstitially open, is that, however many finely graded variations between basic signal types there may be, they all relate to the emotional states of the signaler.

For humans the semantic scope of nonlinguistic signals may be much less restricted, though many signals of this type are much like those of the nonhuman primates in the directness of their reference to the emotional states of the signaler. Since signals that are not so directly linked to emotional dispositions exhibit considerably more cultural diversity, it seems likely that they are products of different ontogenetic processes. This does not mean that the signals referring to emotional states are necessarily genetically determined either in man or other primates, but only that if they are shaped by learning they are evidently the products of a different kind of learning from that resulting in signaling actions less closely tied to emotional dispositions.

The conditions of the learning of some human nonlinguistic signals that presumably contribute to freeing them from emotional reference are not at all well understood, but some general suggestions of their nature have been offered (Skinner 1957). It was pointed out above that the consequences of receiving emotionally determined signals are primarily emotional also, and thus the effect of such signals on the actions of others often may be directly and immediately advantageous to the signaler. The instrumental effects of such signaling actions would be sufficient to account for their acquisition by an individual. On the other hand, the consequences of the less emotion-bound signals on the actions of others may not be advantageous, at least in any direct way, to the signaler himself, but his actions may be very advantageous to the community at large. For this reason the community as a whole may devote considerable effort to fostering the individual's tendency to perform socially advantageous signaling actions in appropriate circumstances, even to the extent of direct tutelage. The relatively prolonged period of infantile and juvenile dependency in humans and the capacity and inclination for imitation so conspicuous in humans during these developmental stages are of immense importance in this connection. But by whatever means some nonlinguistic signals may attain freedom from reference to the emotional states of signaler and receiver, their semantic scope is still restricted in other ways because of the physical nature of the signals and the related perceptual limitations that have been discussed above. In order for many different nonlinguistic signals to be secure against the possibilities of misinterpretation, so many redundant and time-consuming features must be incorporated that the size and combinational possibilities of the signal ensemble are severely limited and the signals require optimum conditions of reception.

No doubt the same processes, whatever they may be, are involved in extending the semantic scope of linguistic signals beyond those having a direct personal advantage to the signaler. Here the contributions of linguistic imitation and vocal play seem to be even more strongly implicated, as well as those of relatively long dependency and a social organization permitting prolonged tuition. The evolution of these human characteristics appears to have been tightly interwoven with the development of the limitless semantic potential associated with the great signaling efficiency of human linguistic actions, for it will be seen that the semantic properties of linguistic signals rest heavily on the ontogenetic development of their uses within a linguistic community.

Since the remainder of the discussion will be primarily concerned with linguistic signaling systems, this is an appropriate point in the discussion to recognize the important distinction between linguistic meaning and reference (Quine 1953). The *reference* of any kind of signal is found in the features of the signaler's environment or of his internal conditions that contribute to his tendency to emit the signal. On the other hand, the *meaning* of a signal is found in its relation to other signals in the signaling practices of the community. The term *meaning* can be applied only weakly, if at all, to nonlinguistic signals because such signals are related only as different items in a list may be said to be related, except, as noted earlier, that intensification relations may obtain in some primate signaling systems. Through their grammatical organization and the conventions of the community, the signals of linguistic systems are closely interconnected in an extensive network of different kinds of relations on different planes. The relation having the most decisive bearing on the status within the network of a signal or of its parts is synonymity. In some sense, then, meaning for linguistic systems may be described as intralinguistic reference, whereas reference proper pertains to extralinguistic matters, relating linguistic to nonlinguistic events.

Perhaps the most important result of the development of the grammatical features required for conferring meanings on linguistic signals and on their constituent lexical items is that these features provide special modes of assimilating new members into linguistic communities. New lexical items may be added to the language learner's vocabulary through definition and explication that are not available in the processes of acquiring novel nonlinguistic signaling actions and reactions because nonlinguistic signaling systems lack the required syntactic features. The peculiar semantic features of linguistic signals result from this difference in the acquisition of new elements to the learner's signaling repertory. But in the initial stages of language learning the child's linguistic actions and his reactions to the linguistic signals of others are conditioned by the personal advantages accruing to him from them, which automatically fix their references (the appropriate circumstances of their occurrence). To whatever degree the signaling actions and reactions of nonhuman primates are determined by social learning, the processes of conditioning would appear to be much the same for the human child at the start of his linguistic acculturation, although these processes are undoubtedly facilitated by the child's propensity for vocal play and mimicry. Nevertheless, the firm establishment of these actions in the child's signaling repertory and of his understanding of the appropriate circumstances of their occurrence is not a passive affair, but very much depends on the social consequences of their emission.

However, very early in the course of language learning after the child has developed only a relatively small number of signals, each through its own history of conditioning, the possibility for phonemic repetition emerges, and the child is able to determinately identify new lexical items before any particular reference or meaning attaches to them. Furthermore, he quite rapidly acquires control over a sufficient number of grammatical operations to generate, and thus to understand, new formations and transformations of the lexical items he already knows. Once this stage has been reached, further enlargements of the learner's vocabulary may be achieved through definitional procedures, through learning the relations the new lexical items have to others in the practices of the linguistic community, and not through the direct conditioning required for the first items. That is, the meaning of these new items may be acquired by fixing their status in the network of linguistic interrelations in which they are embedded in the linguistic usages of the community. But though their meanings may be well developed in this manner, the establishment of the referential relations of such new lexical items to extralinguistic states of affairs is not thereby necessarily achieved, as it is for signals acquired through conditioning at the start of language learning. A new item may have references for the learner only indirectly through the other lexical items by which it has been defined and explicated, so that the learner's appropriate usage of the new item does not necessarily rest on any direct sensory commerce with the nonlinguistic environmental circumstances to which it may refer. But once their meanings are delineated, these lexical items with only indirect reference may be used in turn to define and explicate still further additions to the vocabulary, and the process may continue until a very large part of the vocabulary has only the most remote and tenuous connections with extra-linguistic states of affairs.

The crucial importance of this to the semantic nature of man's linguistic signals and to the part played by them in his mode of social adaptation is that lexical items may be developed that are not directly based on nonlinguistic sensory experience. Sensory appreciation of the references of lexical items, whether direct or indirect, is not required for their development and use in the linguistic interactions of the community. The concepts that may be said to be behavioristically associated with the use of lexical items or with grammatical formations of them need not, therefore, encompass the user's immediate environmental situation or his past history of experience outside the realm of his linguistic experience. The consequences of this may be illustrated by lexical items referring to personal kinship, such as "my uncle." The relational logic of the associated concept is not complex and is surely within the range of the conceptual attainments of some nonhuman primates. Yet the particular states of affairs to which this concept refers are outside the range of direct sensory experience, for it is in the nature of things that no one can attend the criterial obstetrical events. The concept is inconceivable without the possibilities of indirect reference provided by the meaning of the term in the practices of the linguistic community.

Thus, the acquisition of a great many items of vocabulary may be associated with the development of concepts that are very different in kind from those attainable by nonhuman primates. It is important to recognize along with this, however, that there is no discernible gap in the continuous distribution of capacities for conceptual attainment across the various primate groups (Harlow 1958). Indeed there are actually areas in which there is considerable overlapping of conceptual abilities between, for instance, macaques, chimpanzees, and human retardates (Hollis 1962). Though in general it may be that lexical items with specific references may relate to narrower or more rarefied aspects of immediate environmental circumstances than the scope of concepts formed by nonhuman primates in their free-ranging conditions, when nonhuman primates are subjected to stringent conditioning regimens comparable to those of humans they demonstrate conceptual attainments of a similar level of abstractness.

However, even lexical items whose incorporation into an individual's vocabulary involves the most direct sensory traffic with the extralinguistic environment, so that their reference is most clear and immediate, also have meanings that may very much color the nature of their associated concepts. The nature and scope of the concepts will be more fully determined by the linguistic interconnections of the associated lexical items to the extent that their references are mediate and remote from nonlinguistic sensory experience. It is interesting that the direction of this analysis leads to a kind of eversion of the Sapir-Whorf hypothesis (Whorf 1956) which maintains in effect that the concepts derived from direct sensory commerce with the extralinguistic environment are shaped by the linguistic practices of the community. Many, many human concepts of immense importance are developed and influenced by linguistic experience, but this is certainly not their only source. It is difficult to imagine, for example, that the concept associated with "the ripeness of fruit" for the speaker of English can be very much different from the concepts developed by either chimpanzees or speakers of Swahili from experience with fruit of varying ripeness. But to the extent that the meaning of the phrase hinges on, for instance, its relation to chemical, botanical, or agricultural statements that humans may utter, then the human concepts will diverge from that of the chimpanzees. The influence of linguistic processes on man's conceptualization of his world is greatest when the lexical items with which his concepts are derivatively associated have only indirect and distant reference to extralinguistic sensory conditions.

But many human concepts of the greatest social significance do arise from the development of lexical items of just this kind. Though indeed they permeate every nook and cranny of human modes of life, such lexical items may pass through their entire histories almost exclusively within the linguistic matrices in which they were constructed, with only the most fragile, indirect, and shifting connections to extralinguistic conditions. This is true not only of the very grammatical operators that form the structural basis for linguistic meaning, but also for such items as "$\sqrt{-1}$," "gene locus," and "holy ghost," whose conceptual associations are fundamentally elaborated within the structure these grammatical operators provide. The social significance of this kind of lexical item is so great that it would be far better to take items such as "which," "logarithm," or "sympathy" as type specimens of linguistic events rather than the usual darlings of the philosophers such as "table," "horse," or "red." Besides, though the references of the latter items may be a good deal more determinate, their cultural value in the community depend very much on their meanings, the things that can be said with and about them, as do indeed their changeable references in the various meanings they may assume. Such a shift in what is regarded as typical in man's linguistic actions would surely create additional difficulties for philosophical notions such as "protocol utterances" and "observational languages," but it might also better promote the understanding these ideas were designed to achieve.

It is clear that it is very difficult to arrive at uniformly acceptable ways of evaluating the extent to which linguistic utterances conform, if they conform at all, to extralinguistic states of affairs. But however much these difficulties may disturb philosophers, theologians, scientists, and others who are concerned with developing valid conceptualizations of the circumstances of life and advantageous means of coping with these circumstances, the very existence and cumulative growth of such enterprises rests upon the evolution of signaling systems with operational characteristics permitting meaning as well as reference. By enabling individuals to acquire new lexical items and to fix the linguistic and conceptual status of these new items by means other than the direct reference to the environment otherwise required, and by permitting the further elaboration of the status of all lexical items, however acquired, man's languages give him access to intelligence obtained and accumulated by others at different places and times that may be only remotely connected to his present personal circumstances.

Although this is not the occasion to explore the nature and consequences of man's accumulated intelligence, it may be fitting here to point to the biological relation between this intelligence and the psychological trait bearing the same name that is often presumed to separate man most definitely from the other primates. There is simply no reason to assume that the adaptive premium held by this supposed trait would substantially differ for any of the primate stock whose distribution, like man's and that of other more terrestrial forms, covers a wide range of environmental conditions and exigencies. What principally distinguishes man from other primates, and man from man, is not the *degree* of intelligence but the *kinds* of intelligence or knowledge they accumulate and share. Hayes (1962) has suggested that the most important source of human differences in this regard is the interaction between heritable differences in motivational interests and differing histories of environmental opportunities for pursuing those interests. This view of intelligence should surely be explored, for it may enable us to come to a better understanding of the relations between linguistic (cultural) histories and intelligence, and thus provide a firmer basis for comparing the intelligence of individuals from different species and from different places and times within our own species.

## SUMMARY AND CONCLUSIONS

In many aspects the preceding discussion can be regarded as an extension of the pioneering efforts of C. F. Hockett (1960) to analyze what he has called the "design features" of animal signaling systems. The main concern here has been to examine and compare the behavioral processes associated with the general operating characteristics of the signaling systems of man and of certain other primates. In these comparisons many similarities have been found between man's nonlinguistic signaling systems and those of the other primates considered, and some clear lines of continuity have been seen between nonlinguistic auditory signaling systems and human languages. Many of the points of differences that did appear in comparing linguistic signaling systems with the others were found to stem from the physical nature of the signals as determined by their mode of generation.

The essential contribution of the grammatical organization of man's linguistic signals to his effective perception of them, in the face of his limited perceptual capacities and the great acoustic complexity, fragility, and time demands imposed by this mode of signaling, was seen to be based on his double competence as listener and speaker. It was suggested that ordinarily the effective reception of linguistic signals involves the listener's synthesis of a well-formed signal incorporating lexical identities assigned to only parts of the received wave train. Combined competencies in production and perception were also seen to underlie the possibilities for phonemic repetition and production that contribute to effective perception under adverse conditions of reception, particularly when the conditions are unfavorable because of the occurrence of unfamiliar lexical items.

These grammatical and phonemic properties of linguistic signaling systems were also found to have important consequences for the semantic features of linguistic signals. The semantics of culturally transmitted signaling systems depend upon the conditions of signal learning, and it was observed that the processes by which humans are assimilated into linguistic communities are largely concerned with their learning to appreciate the manifold interrelations between linguistic signals and the parts thereof in the practices of the community. Because of the possibility of this mode of acquisition, lexical items may have linguistic meaning without any direct extralinguistic reference, so that concepts associated with lexical items may be developed without sensory experience of their references. There are thus no experiential limits to the semantic properties of linguistic signals, and this makes it possible for the sharing and social accumulation of intelligence attained by others in different places and times.

Perhaps the most impressive outcome of the line of analysis followed here is that the property of semantic openness (which for the history of cultures is the most critical part of the contribution man's languages make to his over-all mode of adaptation) depends upon the other operating characteristics of linguistic signaling systems acting together, and that these other properties are themselves interdependent. However, this does not necessarily mean that all parts of these systems have evolved together as a functional whole. First of all, though languages are the principal medium of cultural evolution, they are themselves products of cultural evolution. Secondly, aside from certain differences in rates of ontogenetic development that very likely have considerable importance for general social organization, there is but one clear-cut class of gross biological differences between man and the other primates presently known that may be directly relatable to the differences in their signaling systems. These are the differences associated with man's peculiar phonatory apparatus and the specialized development of his brain for the control of this apparatus, particularly notable in the cortical representation of the parts of the apparatus along the Rolandic strips, which may be presumed to be involved in the superb central neural control and integration of complex phonetic actions.

Now, if these were the only major biological changes involved in the evolution of linguistic systems, their only direct behavioral result would be an enlargement of vocal signaling potential. It is conceivable that the other operating characteristics of linguistic systems might have arisen as cultural innovations enabling man to exploit more fully the social advantages of this potential. The standardization of signaling patterns within a community suggested by Marler in the preceding chapter would by itself lead to the phonemic organization of the signals, which in turn could provide the basis, and add to the pressure, for the cultural evolution of grammatical organizations. And these changes, together with other changes in social organization, could set the stage for the increased development and social exploitation of the semantic openness of linguistic systems. These cultural accretions might therefore have involved somatic changes no more extensive than those subserving that other very important linguistic invention, writing. Literacy is not in itself contingent upon a specific line of biological evolution, but does depend upon a particular sequence of cultural development. Similarly, the other operating characteristics of linguistic signaling systems, regarded as means of effectively capitalizing man's biological capacities to make many different and distinctive noises, might be products of a lengthy history of cultural changes and their appearance in present form may have been relatively recent. (For thoughtful alternatives to this and some of the other views presented here, see Lenneberg 1960.)

As a final note, much of the foregoing discussion has sought to provide a basis for furthering the understanding of the part played by man's unique signaling systems in determining the differences in his general modes of life and those of the other primates, particularly in regard to the development and use of cultural intelligence. It is especially hoped that it may help to resolve the puzzle that so plagued Alfred Russell Wallace in his thinking about the way mankind might fit into the evolutionary scheme. The solution to the problem posed in his observation that "natural selection could only have endowed the savage with a brain a little superior to that of an ape, whereas he actually possesses one but very little inferior to that of the average member of our learned society" (quoted in Eiseley 1958) is very much tied up with the nature and uses of man's languages.

SHERWOOD L. WASHBURN
and DAVID A. HAMBURG

# 18

# ◈ The Implications of Primate Research

Substantial studies of free-ranging primates are comparatively new, and for a long time the incidental observations of hunters and travelers seemed an adequate source of fact and basis for generalization. Yerkes and Yerkes, *The Great Apes* (1929), summarize much of the material that had been gathered over the previous century. In spite of the large number of sources and the thoroughness of the coverage, it is remarkable how little reliable information this volume contains. Yerkes himself saw the problems of the data and was a leader in stimulating more comprehensive investigations. These remarks are in no sense critical of him, but it is necessary to understand the intellectual climate of the early field studies to see why present ones are so different. Zuckerman (1932, reprinted in Southwick, 1963) gives an excellent account of the anecdotal era, and it is hard to believe that tales of this kind were accepted as evidence. Yet it was the anecdotes that were incorporated into the thinking of the evolutionists and that still influence social science.

The unstated, underlying assumptions of the anecdotal era are two: (1) it is easy to observe animal behavior, and, (2) what is observed is simple, largely stereotyped, and easy to describe. If these assumptions are accepted, then it becomes probable that the occasional observations of native, hunter, or traveler will contain useful information, because even the most casual observation will contain a substantial element of truth.

The major conclusions of the recent studies are that: (1) the problems of observation and description of animal behavior are complex, and (2) local adaptation and learning are important in primate behavior. Not only are the adaptations of the different primate species complex and locally variable, but also the individual animals differ in temperament, experience, and the way they play their social roles. The result of these conclusions, or rather new attitudes, is that the requirements for field studies have changed

607

and are still changing rapidly. No one knows the dimensions of an excellent, definitive study, but it is clear that field investigations of the quantity and quality to build reliable theories of primate behavior have yet to be made.

The era of the modern field studies on the behavior of free-ranging primates started in the 1930s with the work of Carpenter (howler, gibbon, rhesus macaque), Bingham (gorilla), and Nissen (chimpanzee). These studies differed from the earlier ones in that the scientist went out to study behavior and spent at least some months in careful observation. However, owing to the difficulty of observation, only Carpenter was successful. His howler monograph (Carpenter 1934) still stands as a major contribution, and restudies have shown that the original observations were correct. Bingham's few observations (1932) and Nissen's account (1931) are now completely replaced by the work of Schaller and Goodall.

Zuckerman's *Social Life of Monkeys and Apes* (1932) belongs to the same era. In this influential book a few weeks of field observations were combined with physiological and other data from animals in the London Zoo. On the basis of these data it was proposed that primate society is due to the lack of a breeding season, and that continued sexual interest is the cohesive force. This theory has been very influential, and we will return to a discussion of it.

With the advent of the war field studies ceased, but after a delay of some years they started in several countries at approximately the same time. In marked contrast to the thirties, when there was little general interest and researchers were few, there are now more than 50 individuals from the fields of anthropology, psychology, and zoology engaged in such enterprises (DeVore and Lee 1963).

## FUTURE FIELD STUDIES

Up to the present field studies have been of a general nature. Usually one person has attempted to study ecology, social behavior, and all the ramifications of both. In the future three different kinds of studies are needed: preliminary, comprehensive, and those dealing with a special topic.

*Preliminary studies* are needed on many species, or genera, where there is little information at present. In picking groups for special attention the choice should be made for theoretical reasons and not solely because the group has not been investigated. For example, there has been a great deal of speculation on the problems that confront a species of monkey or ape that starts to become ground living. Baboons have yielded a wealth of information on this question. But patas monkeys (*Erythrocebus*), unlike baboons, have adapted to ground life by speed rather than by size and social organization. Hall is now supplementing his excellent studies of baboons by a study of patas. This should afford an excellent check on numerous suggestions that have lacked comparative controls. A preliminary study in this sense (basic ecology, elements of social organization) requires from six to eight months, after a good locality is discovered. This is considerably more than was thought necessary for a definitive study a few years ago.

*Comprehensive studies* attempt to gain a thorough understanding of the ecology and adaptive mechanisms of a species. They will require investigation in several localities, both where the species is well adapted and where it is living on the edge of its range. We estimate that at least three observers, two years, and 2000 hours of observation are necessary before a useful understanding of a species is obtained.

*Special topics* are often of the greatest interest and an adequately detailed study of mother-infant relations, dominance, predation, or home range (to mention only a few topics) cannot be undertaken at the same time one is observing all aspects of behavior. In a general observational study one tries to collect as many data as possible every day. In a special study one must adhere to one topic, even if much more interesting behavior of a different kind is taking place. Ideally, the special topic should be investigated under controlled conditions in the laboratory, under undisturbed circumstances in the field, and, whenever possible, by a combination of observational and experimental techniques in the field.

The reason for separating preliminary studies from comprehensive studies and studies of special topics, for stressing experimental work, and for emphasizing the interrelations of laboratory and field work is that an advance in science is very likely to carry with it the germs of its own decline. We know from the analogy with comparative anatomy and from the problems already arising in the field studies that comparison is likely to generate more comparison without regard to the solution of major theoretical problems. The comparative field studies will become specialized and relatively unrewarding if they lose touch with the main interests in anthropology, psychology, and zoology. Description and comparison are very weak tools scientifically, and, wherever possible, the suggestions from the field should be checked in the laboratory. Likewise, the understandings of the laboratory should be enriched by being seen in the context of the field study.

## SEX AND SOCIETY

These general points may be illustrated by a consideration of sexual behavior. It is now clear that there are restricted breeding seasons in some species of monkeys.

In the Japanese macaque of Takasakiyama mating is restricted to the winter months, with a peak frequency in January and February, and over 90 percent of births occur from May to September. (No birth has ever been reported from mid-October to mid-April). This is based on observations of

545 newborn over a six-year period, supported by many incidental observations over a much longer period (see Lancaster and Lee, Chap. 14, this volume).

In rhesus macaques on Cayo Santiago, off the coast of Puerto Rico, a three-year study by Koford (Chap. 5, this volume) shows mating restricted to a period beginning in July and ending in January. From January to the end of July there were 237 births, of which 75 percent occurred in March and April.

Southwick (Chap. 4, this volume) observed matings in Indian rhesus in all months, but with greatest frequency in October to December. Newborn were observed from March to June and a few in September. Of more than 2000 females seen between November and March, *none* had newborn infants.

There is no doubt that in Japanese macaques and rhesus macaques most mating occurs in a three-month period and births in a comparably restricted period six months later. The social group continues throughout the year, and there is no indication that seasonal mating affects the group's nonsexual activities. The notion that societies of monkeys are held together primarily by continued sexual interest is not supported by the data.

In chimpanzees matings and births probably occur throughout the year (Reynolds and Reynolds, Chap. 11; Goodall, Chap. 12, this volume). But in chimpanzees, of all monkeys and apes described so far, the local group is least well defined. The highly structured monkey society is compatible with restricted mating and birth seasons, and continuous receptivity may occur in a species in which the social organization is so loose that the local group defies definition.

Probably the commonest situation is one in which mating and births occur in all seasons, but in which there is a marked peak in a relatively restricted two- or three-month period. This appears to be true for at least some langurs, baboons, and vervets (Lancaster and Lee, Chap. 14, this volume).

The question of the existence of mating and birth seasons has been reviewed both because it has been a point of theoretical interest and because it shows the nature of the complexities that arise in field studies. Different species are not the same, and in widely distributed species such as baboons there may be a peak in one part of the range (Kenya, Rhodesia) and not in another (the Cape). Small samples of behavior in a few groups over a short period may be very misleading. One of the major reasons that the "sex causes society" theory could continue as it did is that adequate descriptive data have become available only in the last few years. Another reason is the uncritical use of data obtained in zoos and laboratories. Rhesus maintained indoors under constant conditions do not show annual reproductive cycles. Apparently, as with many other mammals, the cycles are due to external causes (light, diet, and so forth). When the National Primate

Center at Davis, California, begins raising rhesus monkeys—both indoors under constant conditions and outdoors—it will be interesting to note whether the monkeys living outdoors will show seasonality in their reproductive cycles and those indoors will not. With these groups as controls the physiologic basis of the cycles can be investigated experimentally.

This brings us back to the question of the kinds of field studies that are needed and their relation to controlled experiments. In a *preliminary* field study (one of six-to-eight-months duration after a good location has been found), it is possible to get an indication of what the breeding structure of the species is like. If conditions for observations are excellent and if the birth season is very discrete, the breeding structure may be clear at this point. But most of the studies available so far show that this is unlikely to be the case. If the matter seems of sufficient importance, the preliminary study might be followed by a *topical* study, focusing on the problems of reproduction and devised to remedy the problems and ambiguities of the preliminary study. Even after a study of this sort is successful, interpretation will require controlled laboratory investigation of the causes of what has been seen in the field. The adaptive value of the behavior can only be determined in the field, but a more definitive analysis of component factors can only be accomplished in the laboratory.

Before proceeding to a discussion of the social group, there are two more points that should be made relative to the general topic of sex and society. The first is the enormous range of differences in potency among adapted self-reproducing species, and the second is a comment on the frequency of sexual activity and the importance of estrus. In Schaller's excellent study (1963) on the mountain gorilla he saw only two copulations in a period of more than a year and in well over 400 hours of observations. Carpenter (1940) rarely saw mating between gibbons. Haddow (1952) reports so little sex behavior in the red-tail monkey (*Cercopithecus ascanius*) that he concluded it must occur at night. In contrast, 168 baboon matings were seen by a single observer in a two-month period of observation. More baboon matings were seen in almost any single morning in the Amboseli Reserve, Kenya, than in the combined gibbon and gorilla studies. There appear to be widely different patterns of sexual activity, all of which are compatible with keeping the females pregnant. Sexual activity is far from constant among different kinds of monkeys and apes. It certainly plays a much larger role in the social life of some groups than of others.

Estrus greatly changes the amount of sexual activity. In all the societies of monkeys and apes described so far, the females and young are the core of the social group. Yet a female spends most of her life either juvenile, or pregnant, or lactating. For most of her life she is neuter; she simply is not of sexual interest to the males. And yet she is social; she does not leave the group—and sexually active males are far more likely to be peripheral or separated from the group than are the inactive females.

## THE SOCIAL GROUP

All species of monkeys and apes live in social groups. The size of the usual group varies between about 10 and 50, but in gibbons the group is a pair of adults and their offspring, whereas it may be composed of some hundreds in macaques and baboons. The characteristics of the groups vary, and the degree of sociality, dominance, sexuality, and so forth is by no means the same. But all monkeys and apes spend the greater part of their lives in close association with other members of the same species. Even the solitary gorillas observed by Schaller joined one group and then another and each had lived in a group until adult. It is in a social group that the primate learns to express its biology and to adapt to its surroundings. Differences in primate societies depend on the biology of the species, on the circumstances in which the species is living, and on learning.

For example, Kummer and Kurt (1963) have described the hamadryas baboon as sleeping on rocky cliffs in large aggregations that may number more than 700. In the morning these aggregations divide into moderately sized groups that superficially seem comparable to the stable groups seen in other species of baboons. But these groups divide in turn into one-male groups, that is one male plus one or more females and their young. It is the one-male group that is stable, and, although close to many other groups in the sleeping places, the one-male group does not mix with the others. Kummer and Kurt interpret this social system as meeting two special, local adaptive problems: the lack of safe sleeping places and the difficulty of finding food in the near desert.

In areas where trees and food are more abundant, other species of baboons live in groups that are the long-term social units, and the one-male group does not occur. Kummer and Kurt's interpretation is supported by Hall's observations on a small island in the Zambesi River. The island was formed when the area behind the Kariba Dam was flooded. Many—too many—baboons took refuge on the island, and there was a shortage of food. The troops broke down and the animals foraged individually. These observations show the interrelations of the social structure and the food supply. Hamadryas baboons guard their females. Mating is confined to the members of the one-male group. In the other baboons studied so far, males do not guard females and an estrous female may mate with many different males. These species differences persist in zoos (at least to some degree), but in the restricted, artificial environment they appear to be merely facets of sexual behavior. In nature the different patterns of male and female behavior appear to be a feeding adaptation, an adjustment to the most extreme of desert conditions in which any monkey has learned to survive.

The behavior of the hamadryas baboons shows the function of social behavior as adaptation, the interrelations of ecology, troop size, and sexual behavior, and it suggests the importance of genetics, learning, and experience. From the zoo data the basis for some of the different behavior of the hamadryas appears to be inherited. But Kummer and Kurt introduced a female, which had been a captive, to a group of free-ranging hamadryas. She was adopted by a young male who had no females, but she had not learned to "follow," as a hamadryas female ordinarily does, and so the male stayed with her at the sleeping place. It is clear, then, that learning also plays a part in the adaptive social behavior of the hamadryas.

We have relied very heavily on Kummer and Kurt's excellent study, but it is a preliminary one. The experiment is based on a single animal. Obviously, to check the interesting interpretations data are needed on the behavior of nonhamadryas baboons under near-desert conditions. It would be very interesting to see if young chacmas could be introduced into a hamadryas troop so that a direct comparison could be made. Also it would be interesting to see if the behavior of hamadryas is modified in areas where the conditions are less severe. For example, in East and South Africa, although baboons sleep in trees in most places, they also sleep on cliffs (without any modification of their normal group structure).

Why does the group exist? Why does the animal not live alone, if not all year at least for much of it? There are many reasons but the principal one is *learning*. The group is the locus of knowledge and experience far exceeding that of the individual member. It is in the group that experience is pooled and the generations linked. The adaptive function of prolonged biological youth is that it gives the animal time to learn. During this period, while the animal learns from other members of the group, it is protected by them. Slow development in isolation would simply mean disaster for the individual and extinction for the species.

If we consider either basic ecology (problems of range, food, predation) or social structures (dominance, positive affect, or communication), social learning plays an important part in the development of behavior.

To emphasize the importance of learned behavior in no way minimizes the importance of biology. Indeed, learning can profitably be viewed in the adaptive context of evolutionary biology. The biology of a species expresses itself through behavior, and limits what can be learned. Evolution, through selection, has built the biological base so that many behaviors are easily, almost inevitably learned.

In field studies observations are primarily of the results of learning rather than of the process itself. Different groups of the same species living only a short distance apart behave differently. Infants are seen beside their mothers trying the foods the mother is eating. Imitation in the play group is constantly observed, but any detailed analysis of the importance of learned behavior requires experimental intervention.

Harlow's experiments (Mason, Chap. 15, this volume) have shown the importance of the mother-infant relationship and of the play group in the development of normal social behavior. Clearly, under natural conditions fundamental learnings take place inevitably. A monkey that did not learn to be social would be eliminated.

Adaptive behavior depends on the biology of the species, the local ecological situation, and the social traditions. For example, it would be useless for a male baboon to inherit the teeth and muscles enabling it to fight, unless it also inherited the necessary temperament and then learned to fight skillfully in the play group. Structure, emotion, and the capacity to learn are interrelated, and selection for adaptive behavior integrates the various aspects of the species-specific biology.

## THE CONTINUING SOCIAL GROUP

It is in the field that the social group may be seen functioning as an adaptive mechanism. Social adaptation has many functions, some of which we will discuss briefly, but learning is vitally important in each.

### Sleeping

All monkeys and apes sleep in groups, and usually in trees. They are active by day and sleep in protected locations, keeping out of the way of predators. A major reason that some monkeys and apes may become ground-living is that their pattern of activity keeps them away from the normal hunting of lions, leopards, and many other predators. Baboons may sleep on ledges, and gorillas usually nest on the ground. These are the major exceptions to the importance of sleeping trees for most species, and the distribution of suitable sleeping trees may limit the distribution of nonhuman primates. Apparently the gorilla has become so large that it can sleep on the ground. With more than twice the bulk of any other primate, gorillas frequently provide exceptions to generalizations that hold for the other monkeys and apes.

Evidence for learning in sleeping habits is given by choice of locations, the kind of location, and by nest building. Goodall speaks of a marked change in the frequency of nests in palm trees as "a fashion." In baboons the tree-sleeping habit is modified where trees are unsuitable or absent; even caves may be used and Brain (personal communication) describes the use, in cold weather only, of a cave near Pretoria, South Africa. Many Old-World monkeys sleep sitting on their ischial callosities, but will sleep lying on their sides when a comfortable shelf is provided in a zoo. A baboon, when resting during the day, will sleep on its side, provided other animals are nearby.

Sleeping nests are made by orangutans and gorillas (Schaller 1961, 1963). The young play at nest building. Goodall describes a chimpanzee approximately two years old still unable to bend limbs to make an adequate nest. In the light of Bernstein's findings (1962), we believe that nest building is learned. However, two persons at the Center doubted that the point was proven. Both thought that if the isolated young animals had opportunity to build nests, they would learn without copying adults. We think that it would be worthwhile to see how much locomotor skill and other manipulative ability would develop in a chimpanzee kept in isolation but in a rich arboreal environment. Our guess is that the elements of locomotor patterns would all be there but that skill would be deficient, that branches might be bent but that useful nests would not be made.

These alternative explanations of nest building illustrate points made earlier. In preliminary, general studies there will be little information on sleeping habits, although they are an important adaption and occupy half of an animal's time. As yet there is no special study of sleeping and sleeping patterns. In zoos New- and Old-World monkeys sleep quite differently, but just how they behave in nature remains for observation with infrared equipment. Even if such a study were made, the interpretation would still be in doubt until there had been experimental interventions to see what determines choice of tree, location in tree, posture in sleep, and the relation of built-in tendencies and learning in nest building.

**Range**

Range varies from much less than a square mile in gibbons and howler monkeys to some 15 square miles in gorillas and baboons (DeVore 1963a). In general the ranges of tree-living forms are smaller than those of ground-living ones, but "area" obviously means something quite different in a forest as opposed to an open savanna. The ranges of groups of primates commonly overlap, and as far as present evidence shows, there are no defended territories with clearly demarcated borders. However, tolerance for other groups or individuals of the same species varies widely. For example, gibbons and howler monkeys signal the location of groups by calls, and the core part of a range is occupied almost exclusively by one group which reacts noisily to the approach of another group when in its own core area. Gorillas appear to be at the other extreme with groups and individuals moving over the same range. Usually, groups of primates of the same species are spaced apart and tend to stay away from each other.

The ranges of different species may overlap completely, but when they do there is at least some ecological separation. For example, chimpanzees' diet is more than 80 percent fruit and most feeding is in the trees. Gorillas eat shoots, bark, pith, and the like and feed largely on the ground. The two species utilize almost completely different parts of the same environment. The olive colobus monkey does not come to the ground nor does it feed high in the trees, and this pattern of activity largely separates it from other species in the same area (A. H. Booth 1957). Haddow (1952) has pointed out that the degree of ecological separation is greater if competing species are present, as shown by the fact that black colobus was more restricted if the red colobus was present. Even when species are mixed and apparently eating the same foods, there may be differential use. Rhesus monkeys, living in the same group with langurs and eating close to them, ate grain, which the langurs did not eat (Jay 1963a).

However, ecological separation is by no means complete, and inter-specific competition does occur. Baboons may attempt to drive vervets (*Cercopithecus aethiops*) from fruit trees and certainly they displace them from the rich feeding areas around waterholes. Chimpanzees may drive off baboons, or vice versa (Goodall, Chap. 12, this volume). In preferred feeding locations a larger species may displace a smaller one without apparent aggressions, and this may have been an important fact in the evolution of large body size.

The function of a range is in part economic; it must be large enough to provide a group with foods its members can eat. But it is also an area of knowledge. A group's range is the area its members have learned to know and, from day to day, familiarity is the limiting factor, rather than avail-ability of food or method of locomotion. This may be shown by two experi-ments. Hall tried to drive a group of baboons beyond its usual range. As long as the animals were within the area they knew they were easily driven, but on reaching the edge of their range they turned back. When the Jap-anese (Miyadi, n.d.) tried to bait monkeys by putting out food in a long line, which finally extended well beyond the group's range, the animals would not follow the food beyond their usual range.

Obviously, in the long run ranges must change, but in the short run familiarity seems to be the major factor in limiting the group's activities. This is particularly striking in the case of arboreal monkeys. These are visual animals which cannot help but see the adjoining area, but normally do not venture into it. The range that is characteristic for a species is limited not only by its specific needs for food or water, but also by the amount and kind of its learning. Utilization of learning capacities in a given environment leads to familiarity (predictability, knowledge), and hence to greater utiliza-tion of environmental resources of food, water, shelter, and defense.

The adaptive advantages of living in a known area may be shown by the case of a baboon that changed groups. Both the groups involved had been studied prior to the change and the baboon was known as an adult male that had been living on the edge of one troop. There were five adult males that dominated him and drove him to the periphery of the group whenever he tried to enter it. He shifted to the next group and defeated the only adult male in it. Here, then, he was the number-one adult male in dominance, but in a new group. The group into which he had moved ranged in the park beside Victoria Falls. It was possibly the tamest troop in Africa and its members were completely used to human beings. The new dominant male was afraid of humans, hid behind bushes, and dared not take the food that the rest of the group was getting. As time went on he learned which humans to avoid, how to steal mangoes, and which paths to take. Six weeks later, when the study ended, this male was still learning the behavior appropriate to the group in which he was the most dominant animal.

Range is the economic base, but to exploit the range the group must learn the local conditions, the dangers and the opportunities. Although local adaptation through learning is emphasized here, it must be remembered that the kinds of learning are limited as much by the biology of the species as by local conditions and opportunity. Human hunting, for example, could not be carried on in the small range characteristic of all the nonhuman primates, but human gathering also covers wide areas and man may adjust to seasonal changes in a way found in no other primate. The significance of range can best be understood if relevant characteristics of the central nervous system are also taken into account.

### Group Composition

In gibbons and many monkeys the local group is constant, and repeated counts give the same number with little variation. The same individuals may be recognized time after time in the same group. In chimpanzees there is no clearly defined local group like that common in monkeys; the same animals are seen in the same area, but in many different combinations. Whether there is a society of animals which know each other or whether there are boundaries to a group is not known, but certainly there is no constant group which moves together. The fact that Goodall repeatedly recognized the same individuals suggests a local population, the members of which know each other. Since there were only from 60 to 80 chimpanzees in the area, the whole population is smaller than many groups of monkeys. In gorillas a group averaging 16, composed of one or more adult males, females, and young, is the norm (with other adult males separating and returning).

If females and young are considered the core of the group, then such individuals are always associated with at least one adult male, except in chimpanzees and orangutans (Schaller 1961). It is possible that these exceptions are due to lack of predation and to the fact that a large arboreal animal may escape from pressures that affect the ground-living gorillas or the smaller monkeys. Whether the local group is stable, shifting in membership, or only a population combining in various ways, it is in this setting that the individual monkey or ape is socialized by means of its relationship with the mother and the play group.

The close relationship with the mother continues for at least a year in monkeys and for from three to four years in chimpanzees and gorillas. The probable lack of mating between mother and son and the patterns of grooming (Sade, unpublished) show that this relationship continues to affect behavior among adult animals long after the juvenile has ceased to ride upon or to be close to its mother. Schultz (1956) has summarized the data showing how the length of infant and juvenile periods have increased from prosimian to monkey, ape, and man, with the resulting extension of the time available for learning and it is within the group that this learning takes place, under conditions that must be very different for gibbon, chimpanzee, baboon, and langur. The infant may start life with only a parental pair, or in a changing aggregation; it may be jealously guarded by the mother or passed from female to female. Much more detailed studies are needed before the implications of the biological and environmental differences in maturation can be understood, but some generalizations may be suggested.

### Play

Recent studies have shown the importance of an enriched environment in the development of intelligence (Krech, Rosenzweig, and Bennett 1962); yet what is called "enriched" in the laboratory is poor indeed compared to the normal habitat. Free-ranging primates live in complex social groups, and all the activities of the group are visible to the young. A wide variety of foods are eaten, and these must be located and appraised, and nonedible foods must be avoided. Enemies must be identified. The group's whole range offers a wide variety of opportunities and problems. The drives to play and explore bring about a diversified sampling of the environment that is probably of great importance in adaptation. The quantity of such activity in free-ranging monkeys compared to that in caged ones is one of the most striking differences between the laboratory and the field. The amount of play needs to be quantified in future studies so that accurate comparisons between species can be made, but it is our belief that the monkeys and apes will prove to be by far the most playful of mammals. This is inferred not only from the large amount of time devoted to play each day, but also from the continuation of play over more years. The importance of play may be seen negatively. Suppose a juvenile monkey did only what was necessary to feed itself and to stay near the adults. Most of the day it would simply be sitting. Juveniles spend very little time feeding. The inner drive to activity leads to the practice of all phases of adult behavior, and to constant development of the skills of running, climbing, chasing, wrestling. The rich social life and environmental exploration by the young monkey or ape are the results of its doing far more than it needs to do for immediate utilitarian purposes. Prolonged youth would have no advantage unless the inner drive to activity led to knowledge and skills. Merely to grow slowly would be a liability, unless in that time adults were developed that were more likely to survive. The individual animal's skillful utilization of the rich natural environment is made possible by its prior play.

The amount of play certainly differs from species to species, but it is difficult to make comparisons from existing accounts. The whole topic needs investigation in further, much more carefully planned field studies. But at the moment it appears that the chimpanzee may be one of the most playful primates and the gorilla one of the least. It is striking how often the gorilla seems to be exceptional. Gorillas are the largest and most ground-living primates; also they sleep the longest, sit the most, and groom, play, and copulate the least. The newborn baby must be supported by the mother for weeks, instead of holding on by itself. Clearly, field studies of the lowland gorilla and of mountain gorillas in other localities are necessary before these differences can be fully understood, but it appears that the great size of the gorilla permits a way of life very different from that of any other primate.

## Tradition and Adaptation

The adaptive variability of behavior within a primate species indicates that learning is important; it appears likely that the primate group passes on traditions that are effective in local adaptation. The biology of the species limits the kinds of learning, but there is a great deal of local adaptation within each species that has been well studied in various locales.

Extreme examples of this are the monkeys living in the cities of India. This not only involves adjustments to man but to new foods, other animals, new sleeping places, begging behavior, crowded conditions, and an amount of fighting unrecorded for any species in a less modified habitat. Southwick's excellent motion picture gives a vivid view of this highly modified monkey life.

Similarly, the spread of new food habits has been carefully studied by the workers at the Japan Monkey Center (Itani 1958; Kawamura 1959). It is easy to see learning in reactions to man or in the acquisition of new food habits, but the important point is that the diversity of habit in free-ranging groups suggests that these monkeys and apes make extensive local adaptation by learned behavior even in the absence of human intervention.

The importance of group knowledge may be illustrated by the reaction to danger. In the Nairobi Park there are many groups of baboons that are accustomed to cars. A parasitologist shot two of these baboons from a car and eight months later it was still impossible to approach the group in a car. It is most unlikely that even a majority of the animals saw what happened and the behavior of the group was based on the fear of a few individuals. *It is highly adaptive for animals to learn what to fear without having to experience events directly themselves.* Just as the young primate learns its first food habits from its mother, so it learns to avoid certain situations (probably motivationally reinforced by the experience of fear). Such initial learning is supplemented in the play group and by participation in the activities of the entire group. An example of this in baboons is the establishment of a behavioral tradition based initially on fear-avoidance under conditions of danger. Some groups of baboons flee up trees when threatened by carnivores (lions and others), but flee *down* from the trees if the danger comes from man. This difference persists even in groups protected in parks, and even though, for at least some, it is probably years since the group was shot at. The younger members of the group react with the appropriate behavior, although they quite probably have never participated in the situations that initiated the behavior.

## Prolonged Immaturity

Since the prolongation of preadult life is biologically expensive for the species, there must be major, compensatory advantages in the young's remaining relatively helpless for so long. If learning is the explanation, it must involve the development of a capacity for *complex* learning that can be employed adaptively in a variety of environmental contexts. Relatively prolonged helplessness imposes appreciable behavioral constraints on the group, especially on the mother. But the long period of infancy has selective advantage in spite of these behavioral constraints; we suggest that it is this that in the long run provides the species with the capacity to learn the behavioral requirements for adapting to a wide variety of environmental conditions. Bruner (1963) points out that highly skilled activity is composed of simpler acts that the less skilled can perform. "What higher skills require is that component operations be combined. Maturation consists of an orchestration of these components into an integrated sequence."

We believe that the prolongation of youth is related to the learning of complex skills. This belief is supported by the experiments showing that a monkey or ape mother does not know how to take care of her infant if she has been living in isolation, and by the observations of all field workers that older juvenile females play with the infants, carry them, and practice the skills of the role of mother before being sexually mature. The slower the growth, the longer the period in which these skills may be learned. Even with slow growth, monkey mothers who have had experience with infants of their own appear to be more efficient, as described by Jay (1963) for langurs. Prolonged youth is advantageous to the degree that behavior is determined by the traditions of the group and that learned skills are important for survival. In general, to be a skilled mother it appears that a monkey must have been in a play group, specifically she must have played the role of mother, and even so she must have had one baby before the role is played with full effectiveness.

In evaluating the importance of learning and skills in the behavior of free-ranging primates, it must be remembered that the criterion of success is survival in crises and not necessarily merely successful day-to-day behavior. Over a period of months the mother has only to make one mistake to kill the infant. When the play fighting of the older juvenile males changes to real fighting, skill means the difference between victory and a serious wound. It does not surprise us that athletes must practice constantly to be in top form, but it is easy to forget that the survival of animals under conditions of crisis may be just as demanding.

Haddow (1952) describes seeing a group of feeding *Colobus* monkeys when a monkey-eating eagle suddenly came around the tree. These eagles fly below the level of the tops of the trees and appear with no warning. All the monkeys dropped down out of the high branches, except for one adult male which climbed *up* at the eagle. The precipitous downward flight of frightened monkeys is dramatic, but the point that should be stressed is that in the brief duration of such a crisis infants are retrieved and carried down, and leaps are taken that are much longer than those used in normal locomotion. This sudden flight requires the highest skills of climbing, and any error results in injury or death. The high incidence of healed fractures in monkeys and apes gives clear evidence that the selection for skill is important (Schultz 1958), and such statistics are based on the animals which *survived*. The actual rates of injury must be higher, much higher in our opinion, but even so healed fractures are present in 50 percent of old gibbons. Many severe injuries do not result in fractures, so total injuries must far exceed this percentage. As Schultz points out, many of the injuries may be due to fighting. This is certainly true for baboons, and the anatomical evidence suggests strong selection pressures operating on the great apes (for example, the sexual dimorphism of the gorilla), factors which may be very difficult for the field worker to see. However that may be, our point here is that the criterion of successful learning through a prolonged youth is survival in crises and that such survival depends on knowledge and skill.

## CONCLUSION

The most fundamental reason for field studies is that monkeys and apes have evolved as a result of selection pressures under natural conditions. The field studies are essential to an understanding of the way the structure and behavior are adapted to various ways of life. Many topics can be investigated only in the field, for example, range, troop size, predation, diet, social structure, disease and many aspects of communication. The normal competitive relations with other species can be studied only in the field. But the full description of the natural behavior will raise many problems of interpretation that can be settled only by experiments. We think that the role of learning will increasingly be shown to be important, and that this can be proved by experiments designed to show the relation of the biological potential of the species to the behaviors actually performed.

Perhaps the most important conclusion of the field studies so far is that it is in fact possible to obtain quantities of reliable data. In marked contrast to the anecdotal era, the studies are now critical and cumulative; and the methods are being rapidly improved. It has been proved possible to obtain detailed, continuous observations. Individual animals can be recognized and the role of personality in the social structure described. The complex interrelations of different species can be observed.

It is with optimism that we look forward to the next edition of this book, with the assurance that the number of species studied will be increased and the quality of the data greatly improved. Each year is bringing forth new studies of free-ranging primates. May they be rich in observation, enriched by speculation, and grounded in experiments.

# APPENDIX

## FIELD PROCEDURES

The various authors of the field-study chapters in this volume have described the methods that they used in studying a particular species of monkey or ape. The purpose of this appendix is to summarize briefly, to comment on a few field techniques, and to discuss some of the problems an observer of primates may encounter. The purposes and scope of a primate field study, as well as the accompanying problems and techniques, are no different from those for the study of any other mammal. A good background for a primate study is a survey of the mammalian literature, including various monographs and articles in journals such as *Journal of Mammalogy, Journal of Wildlife Management, Ecological Monographs, Mammalia, Behaviour, Proceedings of the Zoological Society of London, Zeitschrift für Tierpsychologie, Zeitschrift für Saugetierkunde*, and others. Several papers in Scott (1950) provide useful information on field techniques and the role of experimental procedures in field studies.

Knowledge of any species logically proceeds from the general to the highly specific, and a scheme for studying a primate would ideally include the following three main categories:

1. An ecological survey of all or part of the primate's range with special emphasis on diversity of habitat, distribution and abundance of the species in various parts of its range, and similarities and differences between populations in group size, group composition, food habits, and the like.

2. Detailed observations into the social life of a selected group, groups, or population, concentrating on obtaining the species' repertoire of behavior with quantitative data.

3. Intensive studies into a particular aspect of behavior with concomitant experimental procedures, either in the field or the laboratory, to elucidate those points not readily clarified by observation alone.

The studies in this volume consist primarily of basic species descriptions with little or no intensive quantification or experimental work. The study of primates in the field is in its infancy, and improvements and refinements over our methods are sure to be many as more detailed problems are developed.

Prepared by George B. Schaller from suggestions made by participants in the conferences associated with the Primate Project, held in September 1962 and May 1963 at the Center for Advanced Study in the Behavioral Sciences.

623

The ideal program for the future study of animal behavior would involve the coordination of field and laboratory investigation. Each has its characteristic advantages. Field investigation offers an opportunity to work with the animal's full pattern of activities from various approaches, with a broad perspective, with the relevance and, to a great extent, the validity of laboratory findings in view. In the laboratory, one may focus on specialized problems such as sensory discrimination, motivation, learning, and higher processes, pursuing them in detail and under conditions involving refined controls (Schneirla 1950).

## SOME ECOLOGICAL CONSIDERATIONS

To census a species reliably over a large area is often difficult, for many primates are small, shy, and silent, and they may be hard to locate, especially when inhabiting forest and other dense vegetation types. Hence the most thorough censuses to date have been very local in nature, and all are based on long residence of the observer in a particular area. Carpenter (1934), for example, tallied all howler monkey groups on the six-square-mile Barro Colorado Island, often by first locating the animals by their vocalizations and then confirming their presence by sight. DeVore (Chaps. 2 and 3, this volume) became familiar with all baboon groups that frequented the forty-square-mile Nairobi National Park. Southwick et al. (1961a, b), in the most extensive survey made so far, censused rhesus monkey groups in villages, towns, temples, roadsides, canal banks, and forests of northern India by counting all animals in the vicinity of their route. Similar strip sample counts, a technique commonly employed to census ungulates (see Dasmann and Mossman 1962), can probably also be applied to other primate species living in habitats where visibility is adequate. Relative figures of population densities of primates that leave some recognizable spoor may be derived by counting nests, dung, food remnants, and other signs. Schaller (1963) censused the mountain gorilla in various parts of its range by traveling along compass lines through the forest and counting all nest sites; he used a similar technique to derive an estimate of population size for the orangutan in Sarawak (Schaller 1961). A good summary of the various censusing techniques commonly employed in wildlife management is presented by Mosby (1960).

A detailed description of the vegetation type in which the primate resides is one of the most important and one of the most commonly neglected ecological aspects of a study. Primates rarely, if ever, respond to specific physical and chemical aspects of the environment but rather to certain broad features of the habitat, like the physiognomy of the vegetation. Some species, like baboons, frequent several distinct vegetation types — savanna, open woodland, thick forest — and their behavior may differ considerably from one to another. The problem of adequately describing and measuring complex habitats has often plagued field workers, for many of the methods, like those described in Mosby (1960), National Academy of Sciences Publication 890 (1962), and others, tend to be fairly time consuming. Emlen (1956) presents a particularly useful scheme for measuring habitats directly with a minimum of effort. Some of the important measurable features mentioned by Emlen are the height of the canopy at the top and bottom, the screening effect of the various strata, the foliage and twig type, the percentage of coverage of a particular stratum as seen from above, and the dispersion of the plants. Other ecological measures include ground slope, ground water, soil type, various categories of surface water, barren areas, and human habitations.

## DETAILED OBSERVATIONS

The ease with which a species can be observed varies considerably and depends greatly on the vegetation type that it frequents. Baboons in the plains of Africa and rhesus monkeys and langurs in the fields, parks, and villages of India are far easier to watch than primates that restrict their activities to forest. Many monkeys, gibbons, and orangutans tend to remain in the canopy of the forest trees, sometimes 100 or more feet above ground, where they are frequently obscured by foliage, making accurate group counts and other behavioral observations difficult. However, a considerable amount of data can be obtained on forest-dwelling primates if the study techniques are adapted to the situation, as the work of Carpenter (1934, 1940) has shown. He studied howler monkeys by concealing himself in hides or blinds and behind trees, and by habituating one group to his presence in the course of remaining near it for one month. It should also be emphasized that many primates inhabit several vegetation or forest types. Although study possibilities may be poor in one type, they may very well be adequate in another, as noted by Jay (Chap. 7, this volume).

One of the main objectives in a primate study is to observe undisturbed animals for many consecutive hours throughout the day. However, the presence of an observer usually affects the behavior of the animals, often to such an extent that their regular routine is seriously affected. To neutralize the observer-animal interaction is one of the principal tasks of the investigator. Primates can frequently be watched from a distance or from the cover of a bush or tree and the observer thus remain undetected. If the activity of the animals is fairly localized and the visibility adequate, hides, as used by Hall in one study area on baboons (Chap. 3, this volume) and by Kortlandt (1962) on chimpanzees, may be of value.

Some of the most thorough studies of primates to date have been made near human habitations (langur, rhesus) and in nature reserves (baboon), where the monkeys have become habituated to the local inhabitants and to visitors through frequent contact. Although the behavior of such animals may be slightly atypical in some respects, they have great study advantages not only in that the observer can readily approach or even enter the group, but also because simple experimental procedures can easily be employed to clarify behavioral observations.

If visibility is adequate, the observer may also habituate groups to his presence by approaching the same animals day after day, and remaining quietly near them until he is accepted as an innocuous part of the surroundings. This method was used at least to some degree on most species described in this volume. In habituating relatively shy primates the following procedures were found to give the most rapid results: (1) The observer approached the animals slowly and alone, on foot or by car, without venturing close enough to cause excitement. (2) The observer refrained from staring at the animals, either with his eyes or with binoculars and cameras, to eliminate any gestures that could be interpreted as threatening. (3) The animals were not pursued once they had voluntarily moved out of range.

A method of habituation, used with considerable success by the personnel of the Japan Monkey Center, is to bait animals into a localized food supply. Fifteen groups of Japanese macaques now accept food daily at certain spots (Mizuhara, personal communication). However, the localized food source may skew some kinds of behavioral analyses by interrupting day-range patterns and by accentuating certain interactions such as aggression, while reducing others, such as grooming. To enter directly into the group life of a primate, either by feeding or by other means, in such a way that the behavior of the animals becomes oriented to the observer may be undesirable for certain types of observations.

The nature of the information that is to be recorded varies naturally with the training of the investigator and with the type of problem under consideration. This dictates the kinds of observations that will be collected, but it is worth bearing in mind that the guidelines used by the investigator are framed by the existing data, and it is equally important to uncover new problems by avoiding preconceptions that are so rigid as to hinder the recognition of new types of information. Perhaps the single most important point to be made about recording data is that qualitative judgments established during the initial phases of observation should be subjected to quantification whenever possible. Detailed comparisons between populations and species can be made only if the information is in numerical form. The tabulation of sexual behavior in baboons by Hall (1962b) is a good example of such quantification. The amount of quantification necessary to characterize a particular behavior pattern is related to its variability. The great plasticity of many primate patterns requires very large samples for statistically adequate description. Observations should also be recorded throughout the daily activity cycle of the animal, since the frequency of some behavior patterns, such as copulation, may vary with the time of day (Hall and DeVore, Chap. 3, this volume). To determine key questions such as possible qualitative and quantitative differences in reproductive behavior, food habits, and so forth, a study should encompass a full year in one location.

## INTENSIVE STUDIES AND EXPERIMENTAL PROCEDURES

All studies in this volume concentrated on obtaining the basic ecological and behavioral information on certain species without attempting extensive experimentation or focusing attention on one particular aspect of behavior. Intensive studies have an advantage in that a considerable amount of data on a certain topic can be collected in a brief period of time, as the work on the breeding behavior of rhesus monkeys on Cayo Santiago has shown (Koford, Chap. 5, this volume). Similar work on free-living primates in their natural habitat has not yet been done, but there are great opportunities to study intensively such aspects as mother-infant relations, dominance, and mating, in baboons, langurs, and others.

Simple experimental techniques can sometimes be employed to elucidate certain aspects of behavior without interfering extensively with the natural life of the animal. In general, experiments in the field have the following uses:

1. To reproduce a natural situation of rare occurrence. Hall (1962a), for example, presented baboons with a snake and scorpions, and observed the reaction of the monkeys to these potentially dangerous creatures. He also released single baboons from one area near groups in another area and recorded the integration of the stranger with the resident animals. Carpenter (1942) removed key animals in the group to determine the effect on the social organization; and DeVore (Chap. 3, this volume) threw pieces of food between two baboons as an aid in working out dominance relations.

2. To test hypotheses obtained from field observation. In order to determine how a new food habit is acquired by Japanese monkeys, a group was presented with such new items as peanuts and candy and the responses of the animals recorded (Imanishi 1957a).

3. To study the effect of man-made (or naturally occurring) disturbances on the environment. Observations on the responses of primates to modification of their habitat through destruction by fire, flood, timber-felling, and the like may yield interesting information on the adaptability of the species to new or rarely occurring situations.

## EQUIPMENT AND OTHER SPECIFICS

Basic field equipment includes such items as notebooks, binoculars (for example, 7 x 35, 8 x 30, 7 x 50), plant press, compass, and perhaps a spotting scope (20 or 30x). A plastic jar filled with alcohol or 10 percent formalin is highly useful for preserving fruits, tubers and other food items, insects, feces (for parasite and food analysis), stomach contents, small mammals, and so forth. Vocalizations of animals are notoriously difficult to describe verbally, and a tape recorder is useful for recording primate sounds for later spectrographic analysis. Since the majority of primate vocalizations are of low intensity, a parabola may be necessary. Another experimental use for sound recordings is in playing them back to the animal in the field. Some monkeys like *Aotus* (and many prosimians) are nocturnal, and the study of these primates in the field may require such specialized equipment as "sniperscopes" and infrared film (J. Petter 1962b).

Photography is usually not compatible with behavioral observations, being time consuming and so demanding of attention that considerable information may be lost. The type of camera equipment needed varies with the shyness of the animal and the habitat. For photographing habituated groups in open terrain with a 35 mm. still camera, a 135 mm. or even a 50 mm. lens is often sufficient. On the other hand, monkeys and apes in the forest canopy are very difficult to photograph not only because they are high above the ground and obscured by foliage, but also because their bodies tend to be mere black silhouettes against the bright sky. Movie photography can be of great value because it permits frame by frame analysis of complex actions, but it is suggested that intensive photography be attempted only when knowledge of the species helps in making efficient use of time and film.

Individual recognition of animals is essential in a detailed study of social behavior. Fortunately, monkeys and apes tend to show so much variation in their facial and other features that numerous individuals can be recognized. Marking has so far not been extensively employed primarily because it was not necessary, because studies were relatively short, or because the trapping and marking would have entailed much effort and perhaps disturbed the animals excessively. If, however, permanent marking is desirable for long-term work, tattooing or branding hold promise. Koford (personal communication) found that metal tags readily tear out of the ears of young rhesus monkeys, but that some adults retained tags for more than three years. Mosby (1960) describes many of the marking techniques commonly used on mammals. The shooting of a syringe filled with a sleep-inducing drug (Buechner *et al.* 1960; Jarvis and Morris 1960; Talbot and Lamprey 1961; Talbot and Talbot 1962) or the oral administration of such drugs as chloralose by concealing them in proferred food items deserve attention as techniques for capturing monkeys in the wild.

Notes should be taken at all times, regardless of weather, during or immediately after the event under observation, for to remember accurately a complex series of actions for later transcription is difficult and unreliable. It is often useful to augment the verbal picture with a crude outline sketch of the behavioral situation. A pocket tape recorder may aid the investigator in recording prolonged interactions between individuals, since the eyes need not be taken from the animals. Each day's notes should be reviewed, elaborated, and summarized the same evening. Some observers categorize the behavior and put it on punch cards for later rapid reference. Schneirla (1950), Emlen (1958), and Mosby (1960) discuss note-taking in detail.

# BIBLIOGRAPHY

Affolter, M., 1937, "Les Organes Cutanés Braciaux d'*Hapalemur griseus*," *Bull. Acad. Malgache*, 20:77–100.

Altmann, S. A., 1959, "Field Observations on a Howling Monkey Society," *J. Mammal.*, 40:317–330.

——, 1962(a), "A Field Study of the Sociobiology of Rhesus Monkeys, *Macaca mulatta*," *Ann. N. Y. Acad. Sci.*, 102(2):338–435.

——, 1962(b), "The Social Behavior of Anthropoid Primates: An Analysis of Some Recent Concepts," *The Roots of Behavior*, E. L. Bliss, ed. New York: Harper & Row, pp. 277–285.

Amoroso, E. C., and F. H. A. Marshall, 1960, "External Factors in Sexual Periodicity," *Marshall's Physiology of Reproduction*, 3d ed., A. S. Parkes, ed., Vol. 1: Part 2. London: Longmans, pp. 707–831.

Andrew, R. J., 1963, "The Origin and Evolution of the Calls and Facial Expressions of the Primates," *Behaviour*, 20:1–109.

Anonymous, 1962, "Basic Problems and Techniques in Range Research," *Natl. Acad. Sciences Publ.*, No. 890.

Archbold, R., 1932, "A New Lemur from Madagascar," *Amer. Mus. Novitates*, No. 518.

Asdell, S. A., 1946, *Patterns of Mammalian Reproduction*. Ithaca, N. Y.: Comstock Publishing Co. Inc.

Avis, V., 1962, "Brachiation: The Crucial Issue for Man's Ancestry," *Southwestern J. of Anthrop.*, 18:119–148.

Ayer, A. Ananthanarayana, 1948, *The Anatomy of Semnopitheus Entellus*. Madras, India: Indian Publishing House Ltd.

Baker, J. R., 1938, "The Evolution of Breeding Seasons," *Evolution*, G. R. deBeer, ed. Oxford: Clarendon Press, pp. 161–178.

Bastock, M., D. Morris, and M. Moynihan, 1953, "Some Comments on Conflict and Frustration in Animals," *Behaviour*, 6:66–84.

Beatty, H., 1951, "A Note on the Behaviour of the Chimpanzee," *J. Mammal.*, 32(1):118.

Beccari, O., 1904, *Wanderings in the Great Forests of Borneo*. London: Constable.

Beddard, D. E., 1884, "On Some Points in the Structure of Hapalemur griseus," *Proc. Zool. Soc. Lond.*, 1884:391–399.

——, 1902, "On the Carpal Organ in the Female *Hapalemur griseus*," *Proc. Zool. Soc. Lond.*, 2:158–163.

Bender, L., and A. Freedman, 1952, "A Study of the First Three Years in the Maturation of Schizophrenic Children," *Quart. J. Child Behav.*, 4:245.

Benjamin, L. S., 1961(a), "The Effect of Bottle and Cup Feeding on the Nonnutritive Sucking of the Infant Rhesus Monkey," *J. comp. physiol. Psychol.*, 54:230–237.

——, 1961(b), "The Effects of Frustration on the Nonnutritive Sucking of the Infant Rhesus Monkey," *J. comp. physiol. Psychol.*, 54:700–703.

——, and W. A. Mason, 1963, "The Effect of Hunger on Nonnutritive Sucking in Infant Rhesus Monkeys," *J. abnorm. soc. Psychol.*, 66(6):526–531.

Berkson, G., and R. K. Davenport, Jr., 1962, "Stereotyped Movements in Mental Defectives," *Amer. J. ment. Defic.*, 66:849–852.

630

———, W. A. Mason, and S. V. Saxon, 1963, "Situations and Stimulus Effects on Stereotyped Behaviors of Chimpanzees," *J. comp. physiol. Psychol.*, 56(4):786–792.

Bernstein, I. S., 1962, "Response to Nesting Materials of Wild Born and Captive Born Chimpanzees," *Anim. Behav.*, 10:1–6.

———, and W. A. Mason, 1962, "The Effects of Age and Stimulus Conditions on the Emotional Responses of Rhesus Monkeys: Responses to Complex Stimuli," *J. genet. Psychol.*, 101:279–298.

Bieber, I., 1940, "Grasping and Sucking," *J. nerv. ment. Dis.*, 91:31–36.

Bindra, D., 1959, *Motivation: A Systematic Reinterpretation.* New York: Ronald.

Bingham, H. C., 1927, "Parental Play of Chimpanzees," *J. Mammal.*, 8:77–89.

———, 1928, "Sex Development in Apes," *Comp. Psychol. Monogr.*, 5:1–161.

———, 1932, "Gorillas in a Native Habitat," *Carnegie Inst. Wash. Publ.*, 426:1–66.

Birch, H. G., 1945, "The Relation of Previous Experience to Insightful Problem-solving," *J. comp. Psychol.*, 38:367–383.

Bishop, A., 1962, "Control of the Hand in Lower Primates," *Ann. N. Y. Acad. Sci.*, 102:II:316–337.

Blanford, W. T., 1888–1891, *The Fauna of British India: Mammalia.* London: Taylor and Francis.

Bolwig, N., 1959(a), "A Study of the Behaviour of the Chacma Baboon, *Papio ursinus*," *Behaviour*, 14:136–163.

———, 1959(b), "A Study of the Nests Built by the Mountain Gorilla and Chimpanzee," *S. Afr. J. Sci.*, 55(11):286–291.

———, 1961, "An Intelligent Tool-using Baboon," *S. Afr. J. Sci.*, 57:147–152.

Booth, A. H., 1956, "The Distribution of Primates in the Gold Coast," *J. W. Afr. Sci. Ass.*, 2:122.

———, 1957, "Observations on the Natural History of the Olive Colobus Monkey, *Procolobus verus* (van Beneden)," *Proc. Zool. Soc. Lond.*, 129:421–431.

Booth, C., 1962, "Some Observations on Behaviour of Cercopithecus monkeys," *Ann. N. Y. Acad. Sci.*, 102:II:477–487.

Bopp, P., 1954, "Schwanzfunktionen bei Wirbeltieren," *Rev. Suisse de Zoologie*, 61(1):83–151.

Bourlière, F., 1960, *The Natural History of Mammals*, 2d ed., revised. New York: Knopf.

———, J. J. Petter, and A. Petter-Rousseaux, 1956(a), "Le Dimorphisme Sexuel de la Glande Sous Angulo-maxillaire d'*Avahi laniger* (Gmelin)," *Mém. Inst. Scient. Madagascar*, Sér. A, X:299–302.

———, ———, and ———, 1956(b), "Variabilité de la Température Centrale Chez les Lémuriens," *Mém. Inst. Scient. Madagascar*, Sér. A, X:303–304.

Brandes-Hall, 1909, "Zur Anatomie von *Lemur catta*," *Verh. Ges. d. Naturf. u. Arzte*, Cologne Zweiter Teil:196–197.

Bridger, W. H., 1962, "Ethological Concepts and Human Development," *Recent Adv. Biol. Psychiat.*, 4:95–107.

Bruner, J., 1963, "On Intellectual Growth," paper presented at the annual meeting of the American Psychological Association.

Buck, J. L., 1927, "The Chimpanzee Shaken out of His Nest," *Asia*, 27:308–313.

Buechner, H. A., A. Harthoorn, and J. Lock, 1960, "Recent Advances in Field Immobilization of Large Mammals with Drugs," *Trans. N. Amer. Wildl. Conf.*, 25:415–422.

Bullough, W. S., 1961, *Vertebrate Reproductive Cycles*, 2d ed. London: Methuen.

Burt, W. H., 1943, "Territoriality and Home Range Concepts as Applied to Mammals," *J. Mammal.*, 24:346–352.

Butler, R. A., 1954, "Incentive Conditions Which Influence Visual Exploration," *J. exp. Psychol.*, 48:19–23.

Calhoun, J. B., in press, "The Social Use of Space," *Physiological Mammalogy.* New York: Academic Press.

## 632 - Bibliography

Carpenter, C. R., 1934, "A Field Study of the Behavior and Social Relations of Howling Monkeys," *Comp. Psychol. Monogr.*, 10(48):1–168.

——, 1938, "A Survey of Wildlife Conditions in Atjeh, North Sumatra," *Netherlands Comm. Internat. Prot.*, No. 12, pp. 1–33.

——, 1940, "A Field Study in Siam of the Behavior and Social Relations of the Gibbon, *Hylobates lar*," *Comp. Psychol. Monogr.*, 16(5):1–212.

——, 1942(a), "Sexual Behavior of Free Ranging Rhesus Monkeys, *Macaca mulatta*," *J, comp. Psychol.*, 33:113–142.

——, 1942(b), "Societies of Monkeys and Apes," *Biol. Symp.*, 8:177–204.

——, 1953, "Grouping Behavior of Howling Monkeys," *Extrait des Archives Néerlandaises de Zoologie*, X(2):45–50.

——, 1958, "Soziologie und Verhalten Freilebender Nichtmenschlicher Primaten," *Handbuch der Zoologie*, Band 8, Teil 10(11):1–32.

——, 1960, "Howler Monkeys of Barro Colorado Island," (film), Pennsylvania State University Library.

——, 1962, "Field Studies of a Primate Population," *Roots of Behavior*, E. L. Bliss, ed. New York: Harper & Row, pp. 286–294.

Casler, L., 1961, "Maternal Deprivation: A Critical Review of the Literature," *Monogr. Soc. Res. Child. Develpm.*, 26(2):1–64.

Chakravarti, C., 1938, *The Common Indian Plants*. Calcutta.

Champion, F. W., 1934, *The Jungle in Sunlight and Shadow*. New York: Scribner.

Champion, H., 1936, "A Preliminary Survey of the Forest Types of India and Burma," *Indian Forest Records* (Silviculture Series), Vol. 1, No. 1.

Chapman, F. M., 1938, *Life in an Air Castle*. New York: Appleton.

Cherry, C., 1957, *On Human Communication*. New York: Technology Press and Wiley.

Christy, C. C., 1915, "The Habits of Chimpanzees in African Forests," *Proc. Zool. Soc. London*, p. 536.

Chu, E. H. Y., and M. A. Bender, 1962, "Cytogenetics and Evolution of Primates," *Ann. N. Y. Acad. Sci.*, 102(II):253–266.

Clark, Le Gros, 1936, "The Problem of the Claw in Primates," *Proc. Zool. Soc. Lond.*, 1936:1–24.

——, 1960, *The Antecedents of Man*. Chicago: Quadrangle Books.

Collias, N., and C. Southwick, 1952, "A Field Study of Population Density and Social Organization in Howling Monkeys," *Proc. Amer. phil. Soc.*, 96:143–156.

Conaway, C. H., and C. B. Koford, in press, *Estrous Cycles and Mating Behavior in a Free-ranging Band of Rhesus Monkeys*.

Coolidge, H., 1929, "A Revision of the Genus *Gorilla*," *Mem. Harvard Mus. Comp. Zool.*, 50:293–381.

Coon, C. S., 1962, *The Origin of Races*. New York: Knopf.

Cooper, F. S., A. M. Liberman, K. S. Harris, and P. M. Grubb, 1958, "Some Input-Output Relations Observed in Experiments in the Perception of Speech," *Proceedings of the Second International Congress on Cybernetics*, Namur, Belgium.

Cunningham, D. D., 1904, *Some Indian Friends and Acquaintances, A Study of the Ways of Birds and Other Animals Frequenting Indian Streets and Gardens*. New York: Dutton.

Darling, F., 1937, *A Herd of Red Deer*. New York: Oxford University Press.

Darwin, C., 1872, *The Expression of the Emotions in Man and Animals*. London: J. Murray.

Dasmann, R., and A. Mossman, 1962, "Population Studies of Impala in Southern Rhodesia," *J. Mammal.*, 43(3):375–395.

Dastur, J. F., 1951, *Useful Plants of India and Pakistan*. Bombay: D. B. Taraporevala and Sons.

Davenport, R. K., Jr., and E. W. Menzel, Jr., 1963, "Stereotyped Behavior of the Infant Chimpanzee," *Arch. gen. Psychiat.*, 8:99–104.

——, ——, and C. M. Rogers, 1961, "Maternal Care During Infancy: Its Effect on Weight

Gain and Mortality in the Chimpanzee," *Amer. J. Orthopsychiat.*, 31:803–809.

DeVore, I., 1962, "The Social Behavior and Organization of Baboon Troops," unpublished doctoral thesis, University of Chicago.

——, 1963(a), "Comparative Ecology and Behavior of Monkeys and Apes," *Classification and Human Evolution*, S. L. Washburn, ed., Viking Fund Publications in Anthropology, No. 37. New York: Wenner-Gren Foundation, pp. 301–319.

——, 1963(b), "Mother-Infant Relations in Free-ranging Baboons," *Maternal Behavior in Mammals*, Harriet L. Rheingold, ed. New York: Wiley, pp. 305–335.

——, and R. Lee, 1963, "Recent and Current Field Studies of Primates," *Folia Primatologica*, 1(1):66–72.

——, and S. L. Washburn, 1960, "Baboon Behavior," (16 mm. sound-color film.), Berkeley, Calif.: University Extension, University of California.

——, and ——, 1963, "Baboon Ecology and Human Evolution," *African Ecology and Human Evolution*, F. C. Howell and F. Bourlière, eds., Viking Fund Publications in Anthropology, No. 36. New York: Wenner-Gren Foundation, pp. 335–367.

Donisthorpe, J., 1958, "A Pilot Study of the Mountain Gorilla (*Gorilla gorilla beringei*) in South-west Uganda, February to September 1957," *S. Afr. J. Sci.*, 54(8):195–217.

Du Chaillu, P. B., 1861, *Explorations and Adventures in Equatorial Africa*. London: J. Murray.

Duffy, E. 1957, "The Psychological Significance of the Concept of 'Arousal' or 'Activation'," *Psychol. Rev.*, 64:265–275.

Eggeling, W. J., 1947, "Observations on the Ecology of the Budongo Rain-forest, Uganda," *J. Ecol.*, 34:20–87.

Eibl-Eibesfeldt, I., 1953, "Eine besondere Form des Duftmarkieren beim Riesen Galago, *Galago crassicaudatus* (E. Geoffroy 1812)," *Saugetierk. Mitt.*, 1:171–173.

——, 1958, "Das Verhalten der Nagetiere," *Handb. Zool. Berlin*, Kukenthal, ed., Band 8, Lieferung 12, 1–88.

Eiseley, L. C., 1958, *Darwin's Century; Evolution and the Men Who Discovered It*. New York: Doubleday.

Eisenberg, J., 1962, "Studies on the Behavior of *Peromyscus maniculatus gambeli* and *Peromyscus californicus parasiticus*," *Behaviour*, 19:177–207.

——, and R. Kuehn, (n.d.), "Studies on the Behavior of Spider Monkeys in Captivity," unpublished manuscript.

Elder, J. H., and R. M. Yerkes, 1936, "The Sexual Cycle of the Chimpanzee," *Anat. Rec.*, 67:119–143.

Elftman, H., 1944, "The Bipedal Walking of the Chimpanzee," *J. Mammal.*, 25:67–71.

Emlen, J. T., 1956, "A Method for Describing and Comparing Avian Habitats," *Ibis*, 98: 565–576.

——, 1958, "The Art of Making Field Notes," *Jack-pine Warbler*, 36:178–181.

——, and G. Schaller, 1960, "Distribution and Status of the Mountain Gorilla (*Gorilla gorilla beringei*) – 1959," *Zoologica*, 45(1):41–52.

Enders, R. K., 1935, "Mammalian Life Histories from Barro Colorado Island, Panama," *Bull. Mus. Comp. Zool.*, Harvard University, 78(4):385–502.

Erikson, G. E., 1963, "Brachiation in the New World Monkeys," *Symp. Zool. Soc. Lond.*, "The Primates," 10:135–164.

Falls, J. B., 1963, "Properties of Bird Song Eliciting Responses from Territorial Males," *Proc. 13th Int. Ornithol. Congress*, I:259–271.

Fiedler, W., 1956, "Übersicht über das System der Primates," *Primatologia*, Vol. 1, H. Hofer, A. H. Schultz, and D. Stark, eds. New York: S. Karger, pp. 1–266.

Finch, G., 1942, "Chimpanzee Frustration Responses," *Psychosom. Med.*, 4:233–251.

Fitzsimons, F. W., 1919, *The Natural History of South Africa*, Vol. 1. London: Longmans.

Foley, J. P., Jr., 1934, "First Year Development of a Rhesus Monkey (*Macaca mulatta*) Reared in Isolation," *J. genet. Psychol.*, 45:39–105.

——, 1935, "Second Year Development of a Rhesus Monkey (*Macaca mulatta*) Reared in

Isolation During the First Eighteen Months," *J. genet. Psychol.*, 47:73–97.

Fox, H., 1929, "The Birth of Two Anthropoid Apes," *J. Mammal.*, 10:37–51.

Frisch, J., 1959, "Research on Primate Behavior in Japan," *Am. Anthrop.*, 61:584–596.

Fry, T. B., 1925, "BNHS Mammal Survey of India, Burma and Ceylon, Report 37," *Jour. Bombay Nat. Hist. Soc.*, 30(3):525.

——, 1928, "BNHS Mammal Survey of India, Burma and Ceylon, Report 46," *Jour. Bombay Nat. Hist. Soc.*, 32(3):545.

Furuya, Y., 1957, "Grooming Behavior in the Wild Japanese Monkeys," *Primates*, 1(1): 47–68 (in Japanese).

——, 1960, "An Example of Fission of a Natural Troop of Japanese Monkeys at Gagyusan," *Primates*, 2(2):149–177.

Garner, R. L., 1896, *Gorillas and Chimpanzees*. London: Osgood, McIlvaine & Co.

——, 1918, "Troops of Chimpanzees on Open Plains," *Bull. N. Y. Zool. Soc.*, 21:1566–1567.

Gavan, J. A., 1953, "Growth and Development of the Chimpanzee: A Longitudinal and Comparative Study," *Human Biol.*, 25:93–143.

Gesell, A., and C. S. Amatruda, 1941, *Developmental Diagnosis*. New York: Hoeber.

Gilbert, C., and J. Gillman, 1951, "Pregnancy in the Baboon (*Papio ursinus*)," *S. Afr. J. Med. Sci.*, 16:115–124.

Gillman, J., 1941, "Toe-sucking in Baboons: A Consideration of Some of the Factors Responsible for This Habit," *J. Mammal.*, 22:395–402.

——, and C. Gilbert, 1946, "The Reproductive Cycle of the Chacma Baboon, *Papio ursinus* with Special Reference to the Problems of Menstrual Irregularities as Assessed by the Behaviour of the Sex Skin," *S. Afr. J. Med. Sci.*, 11 (Biological Supplement):1–54.

Goldman, E. A., 1920, "Mammals of Panama," *Smithsonian Misc. Coll.*, 69(5):309.

Goodall, J., 1962, "Nest Building Behavior in the Free Ranging Chimpanzee," *Ann. N. Y. Acad. Sci.*, 102(2):455–467.

——, 1963, "Feeding Behaviour of Wild Chimpanzees—A Preliminary Report," *Symp. Zool. Soc. Lond.*, No. 10, pp. 39–47.

Goodman, M., 1962, "Immunochemistry of the Primates and Primate Evolution," *Ann. N. Y. Acad. Sci.*, 102:219–234.

——, 1963, "Man's Place in the Phylogeny of the Primates as Reflected in Serum Proteins," *Classification and Human Evolution*, S. L. Washburn, ed., Viking Fund Publications in Anthropology, No. 37. New York: Wenner-Gren Foundation, pp. 204–234.

Gray, A. P., 1954, "Mammalian Hybrids: A Checklist with Bibliography," *Commonwealth Bureau Anim. Breed. Genet.*, Edinburgh, Tech. Comm. 10.

Gray, J. E., 1870, "On *Hapalemur simus*, a New Species Lately Living in the Gardens of the Society." *Proc. Zool. Soc. Lond.*, pp. 828–831.

Greene, J. C., 1959, *The Death of Adam*. Ames, Iowa: Iowa State University Press.

Groos, K., 1898, *The Play of Animals*. New York: Appleton.

Grzimek, B., 1953, "Beobachtungen an Schimpansen Pan Troglodytes (Blumenbach) in den Nembabergen," *Saugetierk. Mitt.*, Band 1:1–5.

Haddow, A. J., 1952–1953, "Field and Laboratory Studies on an African Monkey, *Cercopithecus ascanius schmidti Matschie*," *Proc. Zoo. Soc. Lond.*, 122(II):297–394.

——, 1958, "Uganda's Chimpanzees," *Uganda Wild Life and Sport*, Vol. 1, No. 3.

Hall, K. R. L., 1960, "Social Vigilance Behaviour in the Chacma Baboon, *Papio ursinus*," *Behaviour*, 16:261–294.

——, 1962(a), "Numerical Data, Maintenance Activities and Locomotion of the Wild Chacma Baboon, *Papio ursinus*," *Proc. Zool. Soc. Lond.*, 139(II):181–220.

——, 1962(b), "The Sexual, Agonistic and Derived Social Behaviour Patterns of the Wild Chacma Baboon, *Papio ursinus*," *Proc. Zool. Soc. Lond.*, 139(II):283–327.

——, 1963, "Variations in the Ecology of the Chacma Baboon, *Papio ursinus*," *Symp. Zool. Soc. Lond.*, No. 10.

Halverson, H. M., 1937, "Studies of the Grasping Responses of Early Infancy," *J. genet. Psychol.*, 51:371-392.

——, 1938, "Infant Sucking and Tensional Behavior," *J. genet. Psychol.*, 53:365-430.

Hamilton, G. V., 1914, "Sexual Tendencies of Monkeys and Baboons," *J. anim. Behav.*, 4:295-318.

Harlow, H. F., 1958, "The Evolution of Learning," *Behavior and Evolution*, A. Roe and G. G. Simpson, eds. New Haven, Conn.: Yale University Press, pp. 291-310.

——, 1960, "Primary Affectional Patterns in Primates," *Amer. J. Orthopsychiat.*, 30: 676-684.

——, 1962(a), "The Development of Affectional Patterns in Infant Monkeys," *Determinants of Infant Behavior*, B. M. Foss, ed. New York: Wiley, pp. 75-97.

——, 1962(b), "The Heterosexual Affectional System in Monkeys," *Amer. Psychologist*, 17:1-9.

——, and M. K. Harlow, 1962, "Social Deprivation in Monkeys," *Sci. Amer.*, 207:137-146.

——, and P. H. Settlage, 1934, "Comparative Behavior of Primates. VII. Capacity of Monkeys to Solve Patterned String Tests," *J. Comp. Psychol.*, 18:432-435.

——, and R. R. Zimmermann, 1958, "The Development of Affectional Responses in Infant Monkeys," *Amer. Phil. Soc.*, 5:501-509.

Harrisson, B., 1962, *Orang-utan*. London: Collins.

Hartman, G. G., 1931, "The Breeding Season in Monkeys with Special Reference to *Pithecus* (Macacus) *rhesus*," *J. Mammal.*, 12:129-142.

Hayama, S., and M. Kaji, 1962, "On the Examination of the Infectious Diseases in the Natural Troop of Japanese Monkeys at Takasakiyama," *Yaen*, No. 11 (in Japanese).

Hayes, C., 1951, *The Ape in Our House*. New York: Harper & Row.

Hayes, K. J., 1962, "Genes, Drives, and Intellect," *Psych. Reports*, Monograph Supplement 2, 10:299-342.

——, and C. Hayes, 1951, "The Intellectual Development of a Home-Raised Chimpanzee," *Proc. Amer. Phil. Soc.*, 95:105-109.

Hazama, N., 1954, *The Affectional Life of Monkeys*. Tokyo: Hosei University Press (in Japanese).

——, 1962, "On the Weight-measurement of Wild Japanese Monkeys at Arashi-yama," *Bull. Iwatayama Park*, No. 1 (in Japanese).

Heape, W., 1894, "The Menstruation of Semnopithecus entellus," *Phil. Trans. Roy. Soc. London*, B. Vol. 185:411-471.

Hebb, D. O., 1955, "Drives and the C.N.S. (conceptual nervous system)," *Psychol. Rev.*, 62: 243-254.

——, and A. H. Riesen, 1943, "The Genesis of Irrational Fears," *Bull. Canad. Psychol. Ass.*, 3:49-50.

——, and W. Thompson, 1954, "The Social Significance of Animal Studies," *Handbook of Social Psychology*, G. Lindzey, ed. Reading, Mass.: Addison-Wesley, pp. 532-561.

Hediger, H., 1950, *Wild Animals in Captivity*. (English edition of *Wildtiere in Gefangenschaft*, 1942). London: Butterworths Scientific Publ.

——, 1955, *Studies of the Psychology and Behaviour of Captive Animals in Zoos and Circuses*. New York: Criterion.

Heimburger, N., 1959, "Das Markierungsverhalten einiger Caniden," *Ztschrft für Tierpsychologie*, 16:104-113.

Hill, W. C. O., 1936, "Supplementary Observations on the Purple-faced Leaf Monkey (genus *Kasi*)," *Ceylon J. of Sci. B.*, 20(1):115-133.

——, 1937, "The Type of *Semnopithecus thersites*," *Ceylon J. Sci. B.*, 20(2):207-209.

——, 1939, "A Monograph on the Purple-faced Leaf Monkey (*Pithecus vetulus*)," *Ceylon J. Sci. B.*, 21(1):23-88.

——, 1953, *Primates, I. Strepsirhini*. Edinburgh: The University Press.

———, and A. H. Booth, 1957, "Voice and Larynx in African and Asiatic colobidae," *J. Bombay Nat. Hist. Soc.*, 54(II):309–321.

Hinde, R. A., and T. E. Rowell, 1962, "Communication by Postures and Facial Expressions in the Rhesus Monkey (*Macaca mulatta*)," *Proc. Zool. Soc. Lond.*, 138(I):1–21.

Hines, M., 1942, "The Development and Regression of Reflexes, Postures and Progression in the Young Macaque," *Contrib. Embryol.*, 30(196):153–209.

Hingston, R. W. G., 1920, *A Naturalist in Himalaya*. London: Witherby.

Hinton, M. A. C., and R. C. Wroughton, 1921, "On the Nomenclature of the South Indian Long-Tailed Macaques," *J. Bombay Nat. Hist. Soc.*, 27(4):813.

Hockett, C. F., 1960, "Logical Considerations in the Study of Animal Communication," *Animal Sounds and Communication*, W. E. Lanyon and W. N. Tavolga, eds. Washington, D. C.: American Institute of Biological Sciences, pp. 392–430.

Hollis, J. N., 1962, "Solution of Bent-Wire Problems by Severely Retarded Children," *Amer. J. Ment. Def.*, 67:463–472.

Hornaday, W. T., 1885, *Two Years in the Jungle*. London.

House, A. S., K. N. Stevens, T. T. Sandel, and J. B. Arnold, 1962, "On the Learning of Speechlike Vocabularies," *J. Verb. Learn. and V. Behavior*, 1:133–143.

Howells, W. W., 1959, *Mankind in the Making*. New York: Doubleday.

Humbert, H., 1954, "Les Territoires Phytogéographiques de Madagascar," *Leur Cartographie. Col. Intern. C.N.R.S.: Les Divisions Écologiques du Monde*, Paris, pp. 195–204.

Hurme, V. O., and G. van Wagenen, 1956, "Emergence of Permanent First Molars in the Monkey (*Macaca mulatta*). Association with Other Growth Phenomena," *Yale J. Biol. and Med.*, 28:538–567.

Hutton, T. H., 1867, "On the Geographical Range of *Semnopithecus entellus*," *Proc. Zool. Soc. Lond.*, pp. 944–952.

Huxley, J. S., 1942, *Evolution, the Modern Synthesis*. London: G. Allen.

Huxley, T. H., 1863, *Man's Place in Nature*. Reprinted 1959. Ann Arbor, Mich.: Ann Arbor Paperback Series.

Ilse, D. R., 1955, "Olfactory Marking of Territory in Two Young Male Loris, *Loris tardigradus lydekkerianus*," *Brit. J. anim. Behav.*, 3:118–120.

Imanishi, K., 1957(a), "Social Behavior in Japanese Monkeys, *Macaca fuscata*," *Psychologia*, 1:47–54.

———, 1957(b), "Identification: A Process of Enculturation in the Subhuman Society of *Macaca fuscata*," *Primates*, 1(1):1–29 (in Japanese).

———, 1960, "Social Organization of Subhuman Primates in their Natural Habitat," *Cur. Anthrop.*, 1(5–6):393–407.

Itani, J., 1954, "Japanese Monkeys at Takasakiyama," *Social Life of Animals in Japan*, K. Imanishi, ed. Tokyo: Kôbunsya (in Japanese).

———, 1955, "The Vocal Communication and the Social Life of the Japanese Monkey," *Gengo-Seikatu*, 1954(44):45–50 (in Japanese).

———, 1956, *Food Habits of the Wild Japanese Monkeys*. Primate Research Group Press (in Japanese).

———, 1958, "On the Acquisition and Propogation of a New Food Habit in the Natural Group of the Japanese Monkey at Takasakiyama," *Primates*, 1(2):84–98 (in Japanese).

———, 1959, "Paternal care in the Wild Japanese Monkey, *Macaca fuscata fuscata*," *Primates*, 2(1):61–93.

———, and K. Tokuda, 1954, "The Nomadic Life of the Wild Japanese Monkey, *Macaca fuscata fuscata*, in Takasakiyama," *Japanese J. Ecol.*, 4(1):1–7 (in Japanese).

Ito, Y., 1959, *Comparative Ecology*. Tokyo: Iwanami-syoten (in Japanese).

Jacobsen, C. F., M. M. Jacobsen, and J. G. Yoshioka, 1932, "Development of an Infant Chimpanzee During Her First Year," *Comp. Psychol. Monogr.*, 9(1):1–93.

Jarvis, C., and D. Morris, 1960, *The International Zoo Yearbook*, Vol. 2. London: Zoological Society of London.

Jay, P. C., 1962, "Aspects of Maternal Behavior Among Langurs," *Ann. N.Y. Acad. Sci.*, 102(II)468–476.

——, 1963(a), "The Ecology and Social Behavior of the Indian Langur Monkey," unpublished doctoral dissertation, University of Chicago.

——, 1963(b), "Mother-Infant Relations in Langurs," *Maternal Behavior in Mammals*, Harriet L. Rheingold, ed. New York: Wiley, pp. 282–304.

——, in press, "Field Studies of Monkeys and Apes," *Behavior of Nonhuman Primates*, A. M. Schrier and H. F. Harlow, eds. New York: Academic Press.

Jensen, K., 1932, "Differential Reactions to Taste and Temperature Stimuli in Newborn Infants," *Genet. Psychol. Monogr.*, 12:361–479.

Jensen, G. D., and C. W. Tolman, 1962, "Mother-Infant Relationship in the Monkey, *Macaca nemestrina*: The Effect of Brief Separation and Mother-Infant Specificity," *J. comp. physiol. Psychol.*, 55:131–136.

Jerdon, T. C., 1874, *The Mammals of India*. London: John Wheldon.

Jolly, C. J., 1963, "A Suggested Case of Evolution by Sexual Selection in Primates," *Man*, No. 221, pp. 177–178.

Karlson, P., and A. Butenandt, 1959, "Pheromones (Ectohormones) in Insects," *Ann. Rev. Ent.*, 4:39–58.

Kaudern, W., 1915, "Saugetiere aus Madagaskar," *Arkiv. f. Zool.*, 9(18):1.

Kaufmann, J. H., 1962, "Ecology and Social Behavior of the Coati, *Nasua narica* on Barro Colorado Island, Panama," *Univ. Calif. Pub. Zool.*, 60(3):95–222.

——, (n.d.), "Studies on the Behavior of Captive Tree Shrews (*Tupaia glis*)," unpublished manuscript.

Kawai, M., 1958, "On the Rank System in a Natural Group of Japanese Monkeys," *Primates*, 1(2):111–148. I. The basic and dependent rank. pp. 111–130, II. In what pattern does the ranking order appear on and near the test box? pp. 131–148. (in Japanese).

——, 1960, "A Field Experiment on the Process of Group Formation in the Japanese Monkey (*Macaca fuscata*), and the Releasing of the Group at Ôhirayama," *Primates*, 2(2): 181–253.

——, 1961, "On the Change of the Leader in Japanese Monkey Troops," *Yaen*, No. 9 (in Japanese).

——, 1962, "The Birth Season of the Japanese Monkey," *Yaen*, 11:9–12 (in Japanese).

——, and H. Mizuhara, 1959, "An Ecological Study on the Wild Mountain Gorilla (*Gorilla gorilla beringei*)," Primates, 2(1):1–42. (Published in 1962.)

Kawamura, S., 1958, "The Matriarchal Social Order in the Minoo-B Group," *Primates*, 1(2):149–156 (in Japanese).

——, 1959, "The Process of Sub-culture Propagation Among Japanese Macaques," *Primates*, 2(1):43–60.

——, and M. Kawai, 1956, "An Example of Social Organization in the Natural Group of Japanese Monkey, on the Minoo-B Group," *J. Japanese Ecolog. Soc.*, 6(2):45–50 (in Japanese).

Keeler, W. R., 1958, "Autistic Patterns and Defective Communication in Blind Children with Retrolental Fibroplasia," *Psychopathology of Communication*, P. H. Hoch and J. Zubin, eds. New York: Grune & Stratton.

Kellogg, W. N., and L. A. Kellogg, 1933, *The Ape and the Child*. New York: McGraw-Hill.

Kessen, W., and G. Mandler, 1961, "Anxiety, Pain, and the Inhibition of Distress," *Psychol. Rev.*, 68:396–403.

Klinger, H. P., J. L. Hamerton, D. Mutton, and E. M. Lang, 1963, "The Chromosomes of Hominoidea," *Classification and Human Evolution*, S. L. Washburn, ed., Viking Fund Publications in Anthropology, No. 37. New York: Wenner-Gren Foundation, pp. 235–242.

Koford, C. B., 1957, "The Vicuña and the Puna," *Ecol. Monogr.*, 27:153–219.

——, 1963(a), "Group Relations in an Island Colony of Rhesus Monkeys," *Primate Social*

*Behavior*, C. H. Southwick, ed. Princeton, N.J.: D. Van Nostrand Company, pp. 136–152.

——, 1963(b), "Rank of Mothers and Sons in Bands of Rhesus Monkeys," *Science*, 141:356–357.

Köhler, W., 1925, *The Mentality of Apes*. New York: Harcourt.

Kohts, N., 1935, "Infant Ape and Human Child," *Sci. Mem. Mus. Darwin Moscow*, 3:1–596 (in Russian).

Konishi, M., 1963, "The Role of Auditory Feedback in the Vocal Behavior of the Domestic Fowl," *Zeitschrift für Tierpsychologie*, 20:349–367.

Kortlandt, A., 1960, unpublished field notes.

——, 1962, "Chimpanzees in the Wild," *Scient. Am.*, 206(5):128–138.

Krech, D., M. R. Rosenzweig, and E. L. Bennett, 1962, "Relations Between Brain Chemistry and Problem-Solving Among Rats Raised in Enriched and Impoverished Environments," *J. comp. physiol. Psych.*, 55:801–807.

Kummer, H., 1956, "Rang-Kriterien bei Mantelpavianen," *Rev. Suiss. Zool.*, 63:288–297.

——, 1957, "Soziales Verhalten einer Mantelpavian-Gruppe," *Schweiz-Zeitsch. Psychol.*, No. 33.

——, and F. Kurt, 1963, "Social Units of a Free-Living Population of Hamadryas Baboons," *Folia Primat.*, 1:4–19.

Lashley, K. S., 1951, "The Problem of Serial Order in Behavior," *Cerebral Mechanisms in Behavior*, L. A. Jeffress, ed. New York: Wiley, pp. 112–146.

——, and J. B. Watson, 1913, "Notes on the Development of a Young Monkey," *J. anim. Behav.*, 3:114–139.

Leakey, L. S. B., 1963, "East African Fossil Hominoidea and the Classification Within This Super-Family," *Classification and Human Evolution*, S. L. Washburn, ed., Viking Fund Publications in Anthropology, No. 37. New York: Wenner-Gren Foundation, pp. 32–49.

Lenneberg, E. H., 1960, "Language, Evolution, and Purposive Behavior," *Culture in History*, S. Diamond, ed. New York: Columbia University Press, pp. 869–893.

Levy, D. M., 1928, "Fingersucking and Accessory Movements in Early Infancy," *Amer. J. Psychiat.*, 7:881–918.

——, 1944, "On the Problem of Movement Restraint," *Amer. J. Orthopsychiat.*, 14:644–671.

Leyhausen, P., 1959, "Das Revier einer Hauskatze," *Zeitschrift f. Tierpsychologie*, 16:66–70.

Liberman, A. M., F. S. Cooper, K. S. Harris, and P. F. MacNeilage, to be published, "A Motor Theory of Speech Perception," *Proceedings of the Speech Communication Seminar*, G. Fant, ed. Stockholm: Royal Institute of Technology.

Lydekker, R., 1893, *Mammals. The Royal Natural History*. Vol. 1. London: Frederick Warne and Co.

MacNeilage, P. F., 1963, "Electromyographic and Acoustic Study of the Production of Certain Final Clusters," *J. Acoustical Soc. Am.*, 35:461–463.

Malmo, R. B., 1957, "Anxiety and Behavioral Arousal," *Psychol. Rev.*, 64:276–287.

Marler, P., 1959, "Developments in the Study of Animal Communication," *Darwin's Biological Work*, P. Bell, ed. London: Cambridge University Press, pp. 150–206.

——, 1961, "The Logical Analysis of Animal Communication," *J. Theoret. Biol.*, 1:295–317.

Mason, W. A., 1960(a), "Socially Mediated Reduction in Emotional Responses of Young Rhesus Monkeys," *J. abnorm. soc. Psychol.*, 60:100–104.

——, 1960(b), "The Effects of Social Restriction on the Behavior of Rhesus Monkeys. I. Free Social Behavior," *J. comp. physiol. Psychol.*, 53:582–589.

——, 1961(a), "The Effects of Social Restriction on the Behavior of Rhesus Monkeys. II. Tests of Gregariousness," *J. comp. physiol. Psychol.*, 54:287–290.

——, 1961(b), "The Effects of Social Restriction on the Behavior of Rhesus Monkeys. III. Dominance Tests," *J. comp. physiol. Psychol.*, 54:694–699.

——, 1961(c), "Effects of Age and Stimulus Characteristics on Manipulatory Responsiveness of Monkeys Raised in a Restricted Environment," *J. genet. Psychol.*, 99:301–30.

——, 1963, "Social Development of Rhesus Monkeys With Restricted Social Experience," *Percept. mot. Skills*, 16:263–270.

———, in press, "Determinants of Social Behavior in Young Chimpanzees," *Behavior of Non-human Primates*, A. M. Schrier and H. F. Harlow, eds. New York: Academic Press.

———, and G. Berkson, 1962, "Conditions Influencing Vocal Responsiveness of Infant Chimpanzees," *Science*, 137:127–128.

———, and P. C. Green, 1962, "The Effects of Social Restriction on the Behavior of Rhesus Monkeys: IV. Responses to a Novel Environment and to an Alien Species," *J. comp. physiol. Psychol.*, 55:363–368.

———, J. H. Hollis, and L. G. Sharpe, 1962, "Differential Responses of Chimpanzees to Social Stimulation," *J. comp. physiol. Psychol.*, 55:1105–1110.

McCann, C., 1928, "Notes on the Common Indian Langur (*Pithecus entellus*)," *J. Bomb. Nat. Hist. Soc.*, 33:192–194.

———, 1933, "Observations on Some of the Indian Langurs," *J. Bomb. Nat. Hist. Soc.*, 36(3):618–628.

McCulloch, T. L., 1939, "The Role of Clasping Activity in Adaptive Behavior of the Infant Chimpanzee: III. The Mechanism of Reinforcement," *J. Psychol.*, 7:305–316.

———, and G. M. Haselrud, 1939, "Affective Responses of an Infant Chimpanzee Reared in Isolation from Its Kind," *J. comp. Psychol.*, 28:437–445.

Menzel, E. W., Jr., 1963, "The Effects of Cumulative Experiences on Responses to Novel Objects in Young Isolation-Reared Chimpanzees," *Behaviour*, XXI(1–2):1–12.

———, R. K. Davenport, Jr., and C. M. Rogers, 1961, "Some Aspects of Behavior Toward Novelty in Young Chimpanzees," *J. comp. physiol. Psychol.*, 54:16–19.

Merfield, F. G., and H. Miller, 1956, *Gorilla Hunter*. New York: Farrar, Straus.

Meteorological Office, Air Ministry, 1958, *Tables of Temperature, Relative Humidity and Precipitation for the World*. London: Her Majesty's Stationary Office.

Miller, R. A., 1945, "The Ischial Callosities of Primates," *Am. J. Anat.*, 76:67–87.

Miyadi, D., 1961, "Fission of Japanese Macaque Groups," *Tropical Ecology*, 2(1 & 2).

———, (n.d.), Paper presented at the annual meeting of the American Association for the Advancement of Science, Cleveland, 1963.

Mizuhara, H., 1957, *The Japanese Monkey, its Social Structure*. Kyoto: San-ichi-syobo (in Japanese).

Montagna, W., 1962, "The Skin of Lemurs," *Ann. N. Y. Acad. Sci.*, 102(II):190–209.

Moreau, R. E., 1950, "The Breeding Seasons of African Birds. 1. Land Birds," *Ibis*, 92:223–267.

Morris, C. W., 1946, *Signs, Language, and Behavior*. Englewood Cliffs, N.J.: Prentice-Hall.

Mosby, H., 1960, *Manual of Game Investigational Techniques*. Blacksburg, Va.: Virginia Coop. Wildlife Research Unit.

Mowbray, J. B., and T. E. Cadell, 1962, "Early Behavior Patterns in Rhesus Monkeys," *J. comp. physiol. Psychol.*, 55:350–357.

Napier, J., 1963, "The Locomotor Functions of Hominids," *Classification and Human Evolution*, S. L. Washburn, ed., Viking Fund Publications in Anthropology, No. 37. New York: Wenner-Gren Foundation, pp. 178–189.

Nissen, H. W., 1931, "A Field Study of the Chimpanzee," *Comp. Psychol. Monogr.*, 8(1):1–122.

———, 1944, "The Ape Colony in Florida," *Animal Kingdom*, 47(6):137–142.

———, 1951, "Social Behavior in Primates," *Comparative Psychology*, 3d ed., C. P. Stone, ed., Englewood Cliffs, N.J.: Prentice-Hall, pp. 423–457.

———, 1953, "Instinct as Seen by a Psychologist," "A Re-examination of the Concept of Instinct," W. C. Allee, H. W. Nissen, and M. F. Nimkoff, authors, *Psychol. Rev.*, 60:287–297.

———, 1954, "Development of Sexual Behavior in Chimpanzees," *Symposium on Genetic, Psychological and Maintenance of Patterns of Sexual Behavior in Mammals*. Unpublished Symposium, University of Kansas Library. Cited in *Sex and Internal Secretions*, W. C. Young, ed. Baltimore: Williams & Wilkins, pp. 1216–1217, Vol. II, 1961.

———, 1956, "Individuality in the Behavior of Chimpanzees," *Amer. Anthrop.*, 58:407–413.

———, K. L. Chow, and J. Semmes, 1951, "Effects of Restricted Opportunity for Tactual, Kinesthetic, and Manipulative Experience on the Behavior of a Chimpanzee," *Amer. J. Psychol.*, 64:485–507.

Noback, C. R., 1962, "Discussion of Elwyn Simon's Paper on 'Fossil Evidence Relating to the Early Evolution of Primate Behavior'," *Ann. N. Y. Acad. Sci.*, 102:294–295.

Nolte, A., 1955(a), "Field Observations on the Daily Routine and Social Behavior of Common Indian Monkeys, with Special Reference to the Bonnet Monkey (*Macaca radiata* Geoffroy)," *J. Bomb. Nat. Hist. Soc.*, 53:177–184.

———, 1955(b), "Friedlandbeobachtungen uber das Verhalten von *Macaca radiata* in *Südindien*," *Zeitschrift für Tierpsychol.*, 12:77–87.

Owen, R., 1859, *On the Classification and Geographical Distribution of the Mammalia.* London: G. W. Parker.

Perrier de la Bathie, H., 1921, "La végétation malgache," *Ann. Mus. Colonial Marseille*, 3ᵉ sér., IX:1–268.

———, 1931, "Les réserves naturelles de Madagascar," *La Terre et la Vie*, p. 247.

Petter, A., 1962, "Recherches sur la Biologie de la Reproduction des Primates Inférieurs," *Thèses Presentées a la Faculté des Sciences de l'Université de Paris, Mammalia Série A*, No. 3794; N d'Ordre: 4645.

Petter, J. J., 1960, "Remarques sur la Systématique du genre *Lepilemur*," *Mammalia*, XXIV(L):76–86.

———, 1962(a), "Ecological and Behavioral Studies of Madagascar Lemurs in the Field," *Ann. N. Y. Acad. Sci.*, 102(2):267–281.

———, 1962(b), "Recherches sur l'Écologie et l'Éthologie des Lémuriens Malgaches," *Mémoires du Muséum National d'Historie Naturelle, Série A* (Zoologie), XXVII(1):1–146.

———, and A. Petter-Rousseaux, 1956, "A Propos du Lémurien Malgache *Cheirogaleus trichotis*," *Mammalia*, XX(1):46–48.

Phillips, W. W. A., 1935, *Manual of the Mammals of Ceylon.* London: Dulan and Company.

Pitman, C. R. S., 1942, *A Game Warden Takes Stock.* London: J. Nisbet & Co.

Piveteau, Jean, 1957, *Traité de Paléontologie*, Tome VII (Primates, Paléontologie Humaine). Paris: Masson et Cⁱᵉ.

Pocock, R. I., 1928, "The Langurs or Leaf-Monkeys of British India, Part I," *J. Bomb. Nat. Hist. Soc.*, 32:472–504, 660–677.

———, 1929, *The Fauna of British India. Mammalia*, Vol. 1, *Primates and Carnivora.* London: Taylor and Francis.

———, 1931, "The Mammal Survey of the Eastern Ghats, Report on the Monkeys," *J. Bomb. Nat. Hist. Soc.*, 35(1):51–59.

———, 1934, "The Monkeys of the Genera *Pithecus* (*presbytis*) and *Pygathrix* Found to the East of the Bay of Bengal," *P. Z. S. Lond.*, 1934:895–961.

———, 1939, *Fauna of British India.* Mammals, 2d ed., Vol. 1. London: Taylor and Francis.

Prakash, I., 1958, "The Breeding Season of the Rhesus Monkey *Macaca mulatta* (Zimmerman) in Rajasthan," *J. Bomb. Nat. Hist. Soc.*, 55:154.

———, 1960, "Breeding of Mammals in the Rajasthan Desert," *J. Mammal.*, 41:386–389.

Prater, S. H., 1948, *The Book of Indian Mammals.* Bombay: The Bombay Natural History Society.

Prechtl, H. F. R., 1958, "The Directed Head Turning Response and Allied Movements of the Human Baby," *Behaviour*, 13:212–242.

Quince, W. V., 1953, *From a Logical Point of View.* Cambridge, Mass.: Harvard University Press.

Ravet, J., 1952, "Notice sur la Climatologie de Madagascar," *Mém. Inst. Scient. Madagascar*, IV:1–36.

Reichart, P., 1884, "Schimpanse am Tanganyika," *Archiv. für Naturgeschichte*, Band II, Vol. 50:120–124.

Reichenow, E., 1921, "Über die Lebensweise des Gorillas und des Schimpansen," *Die Naturwissenschaften*, Heft 5, Vol. 9:73–77.

Remane, A., 1956, "Palaontologie und Evolution der Primaten. Besonders der Nicht-Hominoiden," *Primatologia*, Vol. 1, H. Hofer, A. H. Schultz, and D. Starck, eds. Basel: S. Karger, pp. 268–378.

Ribble, M. A., 1943, *The Rights of Infants*. New York: Columbia University Press.

Richter, C. P., 1931, "The Grasping Reflex in the New-Born Monkey," *Arch. Neur. Psychiat.*, 26:784–790.

———, 1934, "The Grasp Reflex of the New-Born Infant," *Amer. J. Dis. Child.*, 48:327–332.

Riesen, A. H., 1961, "Excessive Arousal Effects of Stimulation After Early Sensory Deprivation," *Sensory Deprivation*, P. Solomon, P. E. Kubzansky, P. H. Leiderman, J. H. Mendelson, R. Trumbull, and D. Wexler, eds. Cambridge, Mass.: Harvard University Press, pp. 34–40.

———, and E. F. Kinder, 1952, *The Postural Development of Infant Chimpanzees*. New Haven, Conn.: Yale University Press.

Riess, B. F., S. Ross, S. B. Lyerly, and H. G. Birch, 1949, "The Behavior of Two Captive Specimens of the Lowland Gorilla, *Gorilla gorilla gorilla* (Savage and Wyman)," *Zoologica*, 34:111–118.

Riopelle, A. J., 1963, "Growth and Behavioral Changes in Chimpanzees," *Zeitsch. Morph. Anthropol.*, 53(1–2):53–61.

———, and O. J. Daumy, 1962, "Care of Chimpanzees for Radiation Studies," Proc. Internat. Symp. on Bone Marrow Therapy, and Chemical Protection in Irradiated Primates.

Rosenblum, L. A., 1961, "The Development of Social Behavior in the Rhesus Monkey," unpublished doctoral dissertation, University of Wisconsin.

Rowell, T. E., 1962, "Agonistic Noises of the Rhesus Monkey (*Macaca mulatta*)," *Symp. Zool. Soc. Lond.*, 8:91–96.

———, and R. A. Hinde, 1962, "Vocal Communication by the Rhesus Monkey (*Macaca mulatta*)," *Proc. Zool. Soc. Lond.*, 138:279–294.

Sabater Pi, G., 1960, "Beitrag zur Biologie des Flachland Gorillas," *Z. f. Säugetierkunde*, 25(3):133–141.

Sade, D. S., in press, "Seasonal Cycle in Size of Testes of Free Ranging *Macaca mulatta*," *Folia Primatologica*.

———, (n.d.), "Grooming Patterns and the Family in a Group of Free-Ranging Rhesus Monkeys," paper presented at the annual meeting of the American Anthropological Association, San Francisco, 1963.

Sahlins, M. D., 1959, "The Social Life of Monkeys, Apes and Primitive Man," *The Evolution of Man's Capacity for Culture*, J. N. Spuhler, ed. Detroit: Wayne State University Press, pp. 56.

Sanderson, I. T., 1957, *The Monkey Kingdom*. Garden City, N.Y.: Hanover House.

Sandwith, H., and R. Owen, 1866, "On the Aye-Aye," *Trans. Zool. Soc. Lond.*, 1866:33–101.

Sauer, E. G. Franz, and Eleonore M. Sauer, 1963, "The South West African Bush-Baby of the *Galago senegalensis* Group," Jour. S.W.A. Scientific Soc., 16:5–36.

Savage, T. S., and J. Wyman, 1844, "Observations of the External Characters and Habits of the Troglodytes Niger," *Bost. J. Nat. Hist.*, 4:382–386.

Schaller, G., 1961, "The Orang-utan in Sarawak," *Zoologica*, 46(2):73–82.

———, 1963, *The Mountain Gorilla: Ecology and Behavior*. Chicago: University Chicago Press.

Schiller, P. H., 1952, "Innate Constituents of Complex Responses in Primates," *Psychol. Rev.*, 59:177–191.

———, 1957, "Innate Motor Action as a Basis of Learning. Manipulative Patterns in the Chimpanzee," *Instinctive Behavior*, C. H. Schiller, ed. New York: International Universities Press, pp. 264–287.

Schloeth, R., 1956–57, "Zur Psychologie der Begegnung Zwischen Tieren," *Behaviour*, 10(1–2):1–80.

Schneirla, T. C., 1950, "The Relationship Between Observation and Experimentation in the Field Study of Behavior," *Ann. N. Y. Acad. Sci.*, 51(6):1022–1044.

Schultz, A., 1934, "Some Distinguishing Characters of the Mountain Gorilla," *J. Mammal.*, 15(1):51–61.

——, 1940, "Growth and Development of the Chimpanzee," *Contr. Embryol. Carnegie Inst.*, 29:1–63.

——, 1947, "Variability of the Face in Primates," *Am. J. phys. Anthrop.*, 5:1–14.

——, 1956, "Postembryonic Age Changes," *Primatologia*, Vol. 1, H. Hofer, A. H. Schultz, and D. Starck, eds. Basel: S. Karger, pp. 887–964.

——, 1958, "The Occurrence and Frequency of Pathological and Teratological Conditions and of Twinning Among Non-human Primates," *Primatologia*, Vol. 1, H. Hofer, A. H. Schultz, and D. Starck, eds. Basel: S. Karger, pp. 965–1014.

Schwarz, E., 1931, "A Revision of the Genera and Species of Madagascar Lemuridae," *Proc. Zool. Soc. Lond.*, 31:399–428.

——, 1936, "A Propos du *"Lemur macaco"* Linnaeus," *Mammalia* (1), pp. 25–26.

Schweinfurth, G. A., 1873, *The Heart of Africa*, Vol. 1. London: Low, Marston & Co., pp. 518–522.

Scott, J. P., ed., 1950, "Methodology and Techniques for the Study of Animal Societies," *Ann. N. Y. Acad. Sci.*, 51(6):1001–1122.

Seyffarth, H., and D. Denny-Brown, 1948, "The Grasp Reflex and the Instinctive Grasp Reaction," *Brain*, 71:109–183.

Simons, E. L., 1962, "Fossil Evidence Relating to the Early Evolution of Primate Behavior," *Ann. N. Y. Acad. Sci.*, 102:282–293.

Simpson, G. G., 1945, "The Principles of Classification and a Classification of Mammals," *Bull. Am. Museum Nat. His.*, 85:1–350.

——, 1949, *The Meaning of Evolution.* New Haven, Conn.: Yale University Press.

——, 1962, "Primate Taxonomy and Recent Studies of Nonhuman Primates," *Ann. N. Y. Acad. Sci.*, 102:497–514.

——, 1963, "The Meaning of Taxonomic Statements," *Classification and Human Evolution*, S. L. Washburn, ed., Viking Fund Publications in Anthropology, No. 37. New York: Wenner-Gren Foundation, pp. 1–31.

Skinner, B. F., 1957, *Verbal Behavior.* New York: Appleton.

Smith, L. J., 1960, "The Nonnutritive Sucking Behavior of the Infant Rhesus Monkey," unpublished doctoral dissertation, University of Wisconsin.

Southwick, C. H., 1962, "Patterns of Intergroup Social Behavior in Primates, With Special Reference to Rhesus and Howling Monkeys," *Ann. N. Y. Acad. Sci.*, 102(2):436–454.

——, ed., 1963, *Primate Social Behavior.* Princeton: Van Nostrand.

——, and M. A. Beg, 1961, "Note on Social Behavior of Rhesus Monkeys in a Temple Habitat in Northern India," *Am. Zoologist*, 1:262.

——, ——, and M. R. Siddiqi, 1961(a), "A Population Survey of Rhesus Monkeys in Villages, Towns, and Temples of Northern India," *Ecology*, 42:538–547.

——, ——, and ——, 1961(b), "A Population Survey of Rhesus Monkeys in Northern India: II. Transportation Routes and Forest Areas," *Ecology*, 42:698–710.

——, A. Ghosh, and C. D. Louch, (1964), "A Roadside Survey of Rhesus Monkeys in Bengal," *J. Mammalogy*, 45:443–448.

Sprankel, H., 1961, "Über Verhaltensweisen und Zucht von *Tupaia glis* (Diard 1820) in Getangenschaft," *Ztschrft. f. wiss. Zool.*, 165(1–2):186–220.

——, 1962, "Histologie und Biologische Bedeutung eines Jugulosternalen Duftdrüsenfeldes bei *Tupaia glis* (Diard 1820)," *Zool. Anz.*, 25 (Suppl.): 198–206.

Starck, D., and H. Frick, 1958, "Beobachtungen an äthiopischen Primaten," *Zool. Jahrb. Abt. Syst., DeKol. und Geogr. d. Tiere*, 86:41–70.

Stellar, E., 1960, "The Marmoset as a Laboratory Animal: Maintenance, General Observations of Behavior, and Simple Learning," *J. comp. physiol. Psychol.*, 53:1–10.

Stern, T., 1957, "Drum and Whistle 'Languages': An Analysis of Speech Surrogates," *Am. Anthrop.*, 59:487–506.

Stevens, K. N., 1960, "Toward a Model for Speech Recognition," *J. Acous. Soc. Am.*, 32:4? 55.

Stevenson-Hamilton, J., 1947, *Wild Life in South Africa*. London: Cassell.

Stott, K., and C. J. Silsar, 1961, "Observations of the Maroon Leaf Monkey in North Borneo," *Mammalia*, 25(20):184–189.

Straus, W. L., and G. B. Wislocki, 1932, "On Certain Similarities Between Sloths and Slow Lemurs," *Bull. Mus. Comp. Zool.*, 74:43–56.

Sugiyama, Y., 1960, "On the Division of a Natural Troop of Japanese Monkeys at Takasa-kiyama," *Primates*, 2(2):109–148.

Talbot, L., and H. Lamprey, 1961, "Immobilization of Free-ranging East African Ungulates with Succinylcholine Chloride," *J. Wildl. Mgmt.*, 25:303–310.

———, and M. Talbot, 1962, "Flaxedil and Other Drugs in Field Immobilization and Trans-location of Large Mammals in East Africa," *J. Mammal.*, 43:76–88.

Thorpe, W. H., 1962, *Birdsong: The Biology of Vocal Communication in Birds*. London: Cambridge University Press.

Tinklepaugh, O. L., and C. G. Hartman, 1932, "Behavior and Maternal Care of the Newborn Monkey (*M. mulatta, 'M. rhesus'*)," *J. genet. Psychol.*, 40:257–286.

Tomilin, M. I., and R. M. Yerkes, 1935, "Chimpanzee Twins: Behavioral Relations and De-velopment," *J. genet. Psychol.*, 46:239–263.

Ullrich, W., 1961, "Zur Biologie und Soziologie der Colobusaffen (*Colobus guereza caudasus* Thomas 1885)," *Der Zoologische Garten*, 25(6):305–368.

van Hooff, J. A. R., 1962, "Facial Expressions in Higher Primates," *Symp. Zool. Soc. Lond.*, 8:97–125.

van Wagenen, G., 1950, "The Monkey," *The Care and Breeding of Laboratory Animals*, E. J. Farris, ed. New York: Wiley, pp. 1–42.

von Frisch, K., 1954, *The Dancing Bees*. London: Methuen.

Wallace, A. R., 1869, *The Malay Archipelago*. London: Macmillan. (Reprinted, New York: Dover, 1962.)

Washburn, S. L., 1944, "The Genera of Malaysian Langurs," *J. Mammal.*, 25(3):289–294.

———, and I. DeVore, 1961(a), "Social Behavior of Baboons and Early Man," *Social Life of Early Man*, S. L. Washburn, ed., Viking Fund Publications in Anthropology, No. 31. New York: Wenner-Gren Foundation, pp. 91–105.

———, and ———, 1961(b), "The Social Life of Baboons," *Sci. Am.*, 204(6):62–71.

Watson, J. B., 1914, "Imitation in Monkeys," *Psychol. Bull.*, 5:169–178.

Welker, W. I., 1956, "Variability of Play and Exploratory Behavior in Chimpanzees," *J. comp. physiol. Psychol.*, 49:181–185.

———, 1961, "An Analysis of Exploratory and Play Behavior in Animals," *Functions of Varied Experience*, D. W. Fiske and S. R. Maddi, eds. Homewood, Ill.: Dorsey, pp. 175–226.

Whorf, B. L., 1956, *Language, Thought and Reality* (with an introduction by J. B. Carroll). Cambridge, Mass.: Technology Press.

Woodring, W. P., 1958, "Geology of Barro Colorado Island, Canal Zone," *Smithsonian Misc. Colls.*, 135(3).

Woodworth, R. S. and H. Schlosberg, 1954, *Experimental Psychology*. New York: Holt, Rinehart and Winston, Inc.

Woolsey, C. N., 1958, "Organization of Somatic, Sensory, and Motor Areas of the Cerebral Cortex," *Biological and Biochemical Bases of Behavior*, H. F. Harlow and C. N. Woolsey, eds. Madison: University of Wisconsin Press, pp. 63–82.

Wroughton, R. C., 1918, "Summary of Indian Mammal Survey," *J. Bomb. Nat. Hist. Soc.*, 25(4):551–563.

———, 1921, "Summary of the Results from the Indian Mammal Survey," *J. Bomb. Nat. Hist. Soc.* 27(3):520–521.

Yamada, M., 1957, "A Case of Acculturation in a Subhuman Society of Japanese Monkeys," *Primates*, 1(1):30–46 (in Japanese).

Yerkes, R. M., 1943, *Chimpanzees, a Laboratory Colony*. New Haven, Conn.: Yale University Press.

———, and J. H. Elder, 1936, "Oestrus, Receptivity, and Mating in Chimpanzee," *Comp. Psychol. Monogr.*, 13(5):1–39.

———, and M. I. Tomilin, 1935, "Mother-Infant Relations in Chimpanzee," *J. comp. Psychol.*, 20:321–359.

———, and A. W. Yerkes, 1929, *The Great Apes*. New Haven, Conn.: Yale University Press.

Young, W. C., and R. M. Yerkes, 1943, "Factors Influencing the Reproductive Cycle in Chimpanzees," *Endocrin*, 33:121–154.

Zipf, G. K., 1945, "The Meaning-Frequency Relationship of Words," *J. gen. Psych.*, 33:251–256.

Zuckerkandl, E., 1963, "Perspectives in Molecular Anthropology," *Classification and Human Evolution*, S. L. Washburn, ed., Viking Fund Publications in Anthropology, No. 37. New York: Wenner-Gren Foundation, pp. 243–272.

Zuckerman, S., 1931, "The Menstrual Cycle of the Primates. Part III. The Alleged Breeding Season of Primates, with Special Reference to the Chacma Baboon (*Papio porcarius*)," *Proc. Zool. Soc. Lond.*, 1931:325.

———, 1932, *The Social Life of Monkeys and Apes*. London: Routledge and Kegan Paul, Ltd.

———, 1953, "The Breeding Season of Mammals in Captivity," *Proc. Zool. Soc. Lond.*, 122:827–950.

———, and J. F. Fulton, 1934, "The Menstrual Cycle of the Primates. VII. The Sexual Skin of the Chimpanzee," *J. Anat.*, 69:38–46.

# NAME INDEX

# SUBJECT INDEX